Microbiology
with Applications to Nursing

Microbiology
with Applications to Nursing

CATHERINE JONES WITTON, M.A.

Associate Professor of Biology

Simmons College, Boston, Massachusetts

SECOND EDITION

1956

THE BLAKISTON DIVISION

McGraw-Hill Book Company, Inc.

New York   Toronto   London

THIS BOOK IS DEDICATED TO

Helen M. Wood, R.N., *Susie A. Watson,* R.N., *Caroline M. Holt,* PH.D.

AND TO THE MEMORY OF

Mary Marvin Wayland, R.N.

MY FRIENDS AND FORMER COLLEAGUES

AND LIFELONG TEACHERS OF NURSES

Editor's Foreword

Here is a book that describes one of the major underpinnings of health practices. Microbiology is a science whose initial discoveries opened doors to vast potentials in understanding the causes of disease in man, in animals, and in plants. On the foundation of that understanding has been built an intricate structure of therapy and prevention. So sound is the foundation that it continues to serve as the basis for new attacks on diseases that have resisted medical analysis for centuries.

This science gave a new slant to medical philosophy. Now we follow the pattern of thinking that calls upon us to find the cause of disease and its manifestations, and to attack it at its source rather than merely to treat its symptoms. It gives us opportunity to see the effect of the patient's environment on his health and shows us that not all illness arises from within the human body. And with the birth of microbiology came also the birth of preventive medicine, the process of intercepting the contact between pathogenic organism and human being.

Though a pure science, microbiology facilitates social sciences. Epidemiology, an outgrowth of microbiology that is defined as the study of the incidence and spread of disease, leads to the study of sociologic factors affecting control of disease. The concepts of epidemiology make more scientific also our methods of approach to social and psychologic problems of communities and nations. Epidemiology has produced systems of reporting disease that have become world-wide in scope and will promote better international health practices which will take into consideration social and psychologic factors as well as physical factors.

The nurse is a primary agent in managing the patient's environment in the hospital, home, school, and clinic, whether he be at work or at play, or sick in bed. Perhaps the most dramatic example of management of environment is seen in the operating room where extremely intricate techniques are used to prepare the complicated instruments of surgery. But in the control of occupational hazards and the simple instruction of mothers on the use of a safe milk supply we see other examples of control of environment. The nurse who, as a citizen, supports the cause of good housing and control of air pollution is also practicing the principles she has learned in microbiology, combining these with principles learned in social sciences to give her a philosophy of healthful living for herself and fellow citizens.

The student who receives satisfaction from the artistic orderliness of sciences will enjoy this book, which lays the science of microbiology before her in a systematic way that is easy to understand. She will learn more than the skeleton of this system as she studies "Microbiology with Applications to Nursing." The text makes a start on adding muscle, blood, and nerve to the skeleton of microbiologic principles and their applications.

As the student learns the other sciences related to nursing and puts them into operation daily, practicing the skills of nursing, she will see hundreds of additional ways in which this science is useful to her. The study of microbiology gives her tools for understanding the reasons for many of the nursing techniques she learns and as she increases in responsibility she will find that she can design new techniques soundly based on these principles, and that she can evaluate continuously the scientific soundness of her practices.

As is implied even in the name of this science the microscope is one of its keys. The nurse with imagination will be challenged also to use a figurative telescope to look toward the horizon of the development of health practices far beyond those which are given us today through the medical advances of which we are so proud. The nurse, who is a major contact point between people and medical sciences, will be challenged to understand ever more broadly and deeply the uses of this and the other sciences in making diagnoses and administering treatment as well as devising means of preventing illness in individuals and in groups of people.

Lucile Petry

Preface to the Second Edition

This book is designed as a text for students in schools of nursing and other medical arts. Microbiology is not an easy subject for the student because many of its facts and concepts are not closely related to her previous education and experience. No textbook worth study could make it a simple subject. But because it is of great practical importance in all medical fields and because it opens up exciting new fields of knowledge, the student who is diligent and imaginative will find it both profitable and enjoyable. This book attempts to bridge the gap between the student's past education and experience and the subject matter of microbiology, to arrange the material in such a fashion as to show her a clear path to this knowledge, and to provide all the minor aids such as good illustrations and study suggestions to help her on her way.

Microbiology overlaps so many other aspects of medical and related sciences that it is difficult to decide just what should be included and what should be omitted in a text. This text may be said to be *exclusive* in content because it does not include detailed discussions of preventive medicine, pathology, and technical procedures which are sometimes included in microbiology books. It is *inclusive* in that it aims to present all aspects of microbiology as completely as is possible within the limits of an elementary professional text. I fully realize the difficulties inherent in teaching microbiology in the time usually allotted to it in the professional school curriculum. But after thirty years of teaching students in a professional college, I am convinced that the student's needs are not met by a text that serves solely as a basis for her introductory course and as a preparation for state board or other professional examinations. It is my belief that the microbiology text should be continuously useful throughout her formal training and, as far as possible in this rapidly changing science, throughout her professional career.

In this text microbiology is presented as a tool for professional use. Detailed discussions of such subjects as public health and nursing techniques, which are taught in other courses, are omitted here, but the facts on which they are based are included. Discussions of therapy are limited to the use of biologicals and chemotherapeutic agents. No attempt is made to cover controversial subjects in detail, but references are made to those of special

importance, and oversimplification is avoided. Because of the increasing re-
alization of the importance of microorganisms other than bacteria, more
space is given to the viruses, rickettsiae, and pathogenic fungi than has been
customary. The chapter on pathogenic protozoa is not limited to consideration of the organisms of malaria and amebiasis, but also includes brief discussions of other important forms. A chapter on the worm parasites of man
is included because microbiology is the logical place for the study of these
important but generally neglected agents of human disease.

The chapter on the history of microbiology is placed near the middle of
the book following the sections dealing with the general nature of microorganisms. Developments during this century and the part played by American scientists are stressed.

A brief topical outline is placed at the beginning of each chapter. At the
end of each chapter are suggestions for study. These suggestions are not lists
of questions that can be answered by consulting the previous pages paragraph by paragraph. On the contrary they are aimed to show the student
the connections between the subject matter and her personal and hospital
experience, and to indicate ways in which she may study more effectively.
The reference material at the end of each chapter makes no pretense to exhaustive scholarship. The intention has been to limit it to usable, useful,
and generally available material. Appendix A lists useful books and journals.
It also summarizes for the student the process by which she may search the
literature for more information than is provided in the text.

The latest classification of the bacteria, rickettsiae, and viruses, as summarized from the sixth edition of *Bergey's Manual of Determinative Bacteriology,* is given in tabular form in Appendix B.

Each illustration has been selected as a definite aid in the comprehension
of the subject matter and should repay careful study. The drawings are simplified diagrams aimed to convey basic concepts of structure or function.
Many of the photographs and electron micrographs are portraits of pathogenic microorganisms. They have been included to serve as an extension of
laboratory experience.

Much of the material included in an appendix in the previous edition and
relating to laboratory experiments will appear in a new edition of the laboratory manual. However, the text itself now includes more general material
on laboratory methods. The chapters on bacterial morphology, the antibiotics, tuberculosis, and the nature of viruses have been practically rewritten
for this edition. Many other sections have been radically revised, including
those on bacterial genetics, antigens and antibodies, poliomyelitis, and toxoplasmosis. Discussions of the Coxsackie viruses and of blastomycosis have
been added. However, the general plan of the book has not been changed.
Over a quarter of the illustrations are new.

I am deeply grateful to those who have helped in the preparation of this and the previous edition. The sources of the illustrations so generously furnished by individual scientists and by business firms are acknowledged in the legends accompanying each figure. A considerable number are from the collection of the Committee for Visual Education in Microbiology, Society of American Bacteriologists. The chairman, Dr. Harry C. Morton, has been most helpful. Helen Witton helped in the preparation of the original drawings. The original photographs are the work of David Sokolov.

Many of my colleagues at Simmons College and affiliated hospitals contributed valuable suggestions and have read portions of the manuscript. I am particularly indebted to Professor Curtis M. Hilliard, Professor Evangeline H. Morris, Dr. Julian L. Solinger, Miss Elizabeth Hart, R.N., Miss Olive Nelson, R.N. (now Mrs. L. Lorbeer), and Miss Edith Chamberlain. Professor Mildred L. Coombs of Simmons College and Mrs. Marguerite B. Derry of the Massachusetts General Hospital School of Nursing, and Helen Witton of the laboratory of the Department of Tropical Public Health of the Harvard School of Public Health have read and reread the manuscript with extraordinary patience.

I am also most grateful to the many instructors who have sent me suggestions and constructive criticisms. They have been very valuable and stimulating. It is my sincere hope that this new edition of the text may be of additional help in making the study of microbiology an enjoyable and exciting experience for the student and for her teacher.

Catherine Jones Witton

Boston, Massachusetts

Contents

xiii

PART ONE

The Basic Structure and Activities
of Microorganisms

CHAPTER 1

The Scope and Usefulness of Microbiology

WHY MICROORGANISMS ARE IMPORTANT

Microorganisms are living things that are so small that they must be studied with high-powered microscopes. Their importance to mankind is all out of proportion to their size. It is essential that nurses know a great deal about them because

1. They cause all the communicable diseases. Measles, influenza, malaria, whooping cough, and all the other diseases that can be spread from person to person are the result of the invasion of the body by specific kinds of minute living organisms.

2. They are involved in many other disease conditions. The finger infection that develops from a splinter, the ulcerated wisdom tooth, the infection of the soldier's wound that keeps him so long in the hospital, all these conditions and many others are due to infections with disease-producing microorganisms. Disease-producing organisms are called *pathogens*. The great majority of sick persons are suffering from the attacks of pathogenic organisms or are in constant danger of acquiring organisms that may increase the severity of their illness. The nurse must have a complete and clear understanding of microbiology if she is to care for people who have infectious diseases and

3

if she is to protect her patients, herself, and others against harmful micro-organisms.

3. Our food is affected in innumerable ways by the activity of micro-organisms. Good crops are dependent on soil fertility, which in turn depends on the living organisms in the soil. A plant disease such as wheat rust may seriously curtail our supply of an essential food, and so may an animal epidemic of hog cholera. The spoilage of food is due mainly to microbial action. On the other hand, many foods, such as cheeses, are prepared with the aid of microorganisms.

4. Our clothing is affected by microorganisms. Textile fibers such as linen are prepared with the aid of microbial activity. Cloth and leather are spoiled by rotting and mildewing.

5. Many other materials of modern life are affected by microorganisms. Lumber is lost when white pines are attacked by the blister rust fungus. Alcohol and other chemicals used in laboratories and industries are prepared by the action of various microorganisms, and other microorganisms play an important part in the destruction of such materials as wood, rubber, and paper. Knowledge of all these processes will make the nurse more efficient in her work.

THE IMPORTANT KINDS OF MICROORGANISMS

There are literally thousands of kinds of microorganisms, but we will limit our study to those that are of considerable practical importance to the nursing profession. The ones that the nurse needs to study may be put into seven convenient groups. They are

The important microscopic animals:
  1. The worms
  2. The protozoa
The important microscopic plants:
  3. The yeasts
  4. The molds
  5. The bacteria
The ultramicroscopic forms of life:
  6. The rickettsiae
  7. The filtrable viruses

The Worms. Worms are not, strictly speaking, microscopic, since most of them can be seen quite well without the microscope. But they are studied with the truly microscopic forms for two reasons: (1) their presence is often discovered by the finding of their microscopic eggs; and (2) the

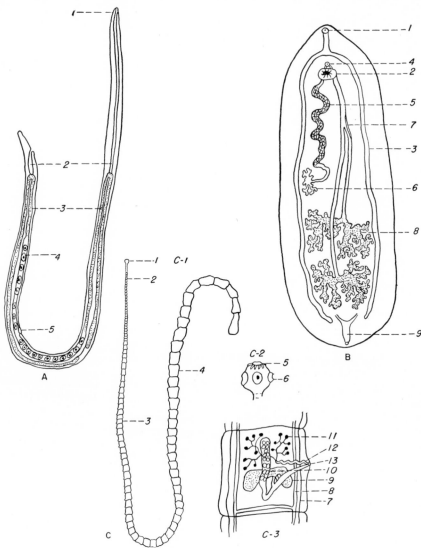

Fig. 1·1 Three worms parasitic for man. (*A*) Roundworm, *Strongyloides stercoralis* (female). ×80. (1) Mouth; (2) alimentary canal; (3) ovaries; (4) uterus; (5) genital opening. (*B*) Fluke, *Fasciolopsis buski*. ×4. (1) Mouth in anterior sucker; (2) posterior sucker; (3) alimentary canal; (4) genital opening; (5) uterus; (6) ovary; (7) spermatic duct; (8) testis; (9) excretory duct. (*C*) Tapeworm, *Taenia solium*. ×1/10. (*C*-1) Adult worm. (1) Head; (2) neck; (3) immature proglottid; (4) mature proglottid. (*C*-2) Head enlarged. ×10. (5) Hooks; (6) suckers. (*C*-3) Mature proglottid. ×5. (7) Nerve cord; (8) excretory duct; (9) ovary; (10) uterus; (11) testis; (12) spermatic duct; (13) genital opening.

pathogenic worms are controlled by methods similar to those used in the control of true microorganisms. All worms are multicellular animals. Although they have no skeletal system, they do have complicated nervous and reproductive systems. The anatomical structure of several representative worms is shown in Fig. 1·1. Other pictures of these animals can be found in Chap. 38.

The familiar segmented worms such as the common earthworms are not pathogenic. The disease-producing sorts belong to the groups listed below.

The Roundworms. These have elongated round bodies. Among those important to man are the hookworms, and the trichina worms from infected pork.

The Flukes. These are small, leaflike, flattened worms, which invade the alimentary canal, lungs, and blood of man and many other animals.

The Tapeworms. These are long and ribbonlike. The specialized head end attaches the worm to the lining of the alimentary canal. The rest of the worm consists of a variable number of segments containing highly developed sex organs.

The Protozoa. Each protozoan is a microscopic, single-celled animal. It feeds in an animallike manner by taking in solid food and digesting it within the cell. Many protozoa have very complicated structure. Some appear both in the usual active, or *vegetative,* form and in a less active, resistant form called a *cyst.* There are four principal groups. Each contains species that are pathogenic for man. The structure of representative pathogenic protozoa is illustrated in Fig. 1·2. In Chap. 37 there are photographs of important pathogenic species.

The Ameba Group. This consists of protozoa that are nucleated masses of protoplasm moving by the irregular extension of *pseudopodia* (literally, false feet). Several kinds live in the human mouth and intestine without doing harm, but a closely related species causes amebic dysentery.

The Ciliates. These are single cells covered with innumerable tiny hairlike processes that beat in unison and so propel the organisms through the liquid in which they live. These processes are called *cilia.* A large number of ciliates parasitize lower animals, but only one is known to invade man, causing ulceration of the colon.

The Flagellates. They are given this name because they move by means of *flagella* (literally, little whips). Each flagellum is a fine protoplasmic filament. It is often as long as, or longer than, the cell to which it is attached. Each flagellate has a definite number of flagella, usually one to five, attached to it in a definite arrangement, and each flagellum has an independent motion. Many flagellates are spread by insects. More than half a dozen types cause human diseases. An example is African sleeping sickness, which is spread by tsetse flies.

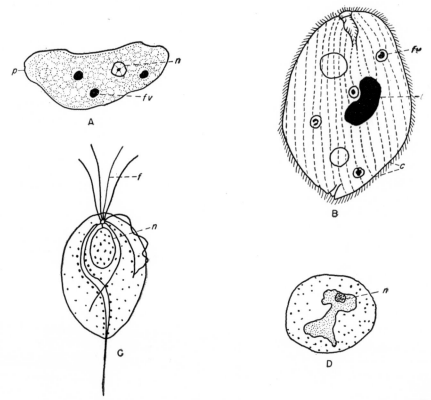

FIG. 1·2   Four representative parasitic protozoa. (*A*) *Endamoeba histolytica,* motile form. ×3,000. (*B*) *Balantidium coli.* ×1,500. (*C*) *Trichomonas vaginalis.* ×3,000. (*D*) *Plasmodium vivax* in human red blood cell. ×3,000. (*n*) nucleus; (*f*) flagellum; (*c*) cilia; (*fv*) food vacuole; (*p*) pseudopodium.

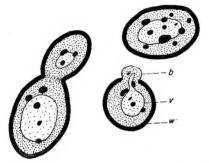

FIG. 1·3   A typical yeast, *Saccharomyces cerevisiae.* ×3,000. (*b*) bud; (*v*) vacuole; (*w*) cell wall.

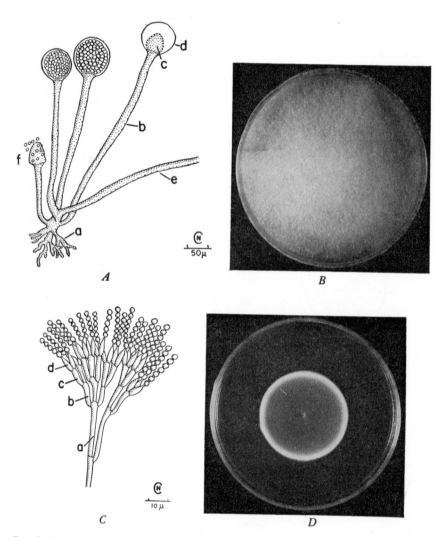

FIG. 1·4 Common molds. (*A*) *Rhizopus* sp. Rootlike hyphae (*a*) absorb nutriment. Nonseptate hyphae (*b*) bear spore-filled sporangia (*d*). When spores are mature, the wall of the sporangium ruptures, liberating spores (*f*). (*B*) *Rhizopus* colony. ×½. Coarse gray-white mycelium fills petri dish. Black pinhead sporangia are present. (*C*) *Penicillium* sp. Septate hyphae (*a, b, c*) bear special terminal cells (*d*) with terminal chains of spores. (*D*) *Penicillium* colony. ×½. Flat, velvety-white colony develops powdery blue-green surface.

[*Fig. 1·4 continued on following page.*

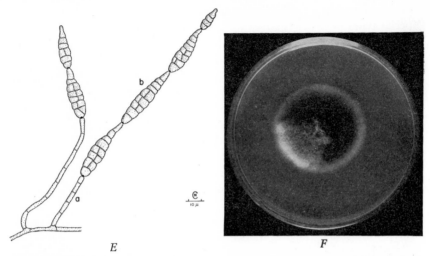

E   F

Fig. 1·4 (*Continued*) (*E*) *Alternaria* sp. Dark-colored septate hyphae (*a*) bear chains of multicellular spores (*b*). (*F*) *Alternaria* colony. ×½. Gray-green colony develops black powdery surface. Branching gray mycelium may overgrow sporulating surface. (*Courtesy of Dr. Norman F. Conant, from Conant et al., "Manual of Clinical Mycology," Saunders.*)

The Sporozoa. These have complicated life cycles including a sexual stage that produces many sporelike cells. These sporelike forms invade cells of the animal host and reproduce asexually there. Sporozoa parasitize many lower animals and cause one important human disease, malaria.

The Yeasts. Yeasts, molds, and bacteria all belong to the *fungi*. A fungus is a colorless plant with practically no differentiation of cell structure. It is called colorless because it lacks the green material, *chlorophyll*, which enables most plants to make their own food with the aid of sunlight. The yeasts are small single-celled forms that reproduce by the process of budding. Some of these yeasts can also reproduce by forming spores. These are the *true yeasts*. Others, which reproduce only by budding, are called *false yeasts*. Yeasts are important in the preparation of bread and alcohol. A few false yeasts cause diseases, usually of the skin or lungs. Figure 1·3 illustrates the structure of a typical yeast and its reproduction by budding. In Chap. 36 there are pictures of pathogenic types.

The Molds. Each mold plant is made up of branching threads of cells, so that mold growth is fuzzy in appearance. These threads are called *hyphae*. The mass of hyphal threads is called the *mycelium*. Part of the mycelium grows below the surface in the material from which the mold gets its food. The rest of the mycelium grows up into the air. This aerial growth is unusual among microorganisms. Molds produce spores for asexual reproduction in special structures on these aerial hyphae. In addition, many molds produce special types of sexual spores. Since these sexual spores are seldom seen in the laboratory and usually are absent among the pathogenic molds, only the asexual spores are illustrated in the diagrams in this chapter. Three common types of molds are illustrated in Fig. 1·4. Note that the mold may have *nonseptate* hyphae (hyphae lacking cross walls) and bear its spores in a spore case called a *sporangium,* or its hyphae may be *septate* and its spores be typically borne free on the ends of the aerial hyphae.

Molds injure plants and spoil foods and fabrics. Some add flavor to food, as in Roquefort cheese. Some cause diseases, usually of the skin. A well-known example is athlete's foot. The general name given to fungous infections is *mycoses* (sing. *mycosis*). Pathogenic molds are pictured in Chap. 36.

The Bacteria. Bacteria are single-celled fungi that reproduce by *fission,* which means that they reproduce by splitting in two. They are very tiny cells and must be studied with the highest power of the compound microscope. Those that are simplest in form are called the *simple* (or *true*) *bacteria.* Others that show more complicated structure are known as the *higher bacteria.* The typhoid bacillus is a simple bacterium. The tuberculosis bacillus is a higher bacterium. Figures 2·8 and 2·12 show some of the forms of bacteria. This group of microorganisms, because of its great importance, will be considered in detail in Chap. 2.

The Rickettsiae. These highly specialized microorganisms are named after the American scientist, Howard Ricketts. They are just barely visible with the highest power of the compound microscope. Each one is a tiny rod or sphere that lives within the cells of its host. They are parasites of certain insects such as fleas, ticks, and lice, and from them they sometimes spread

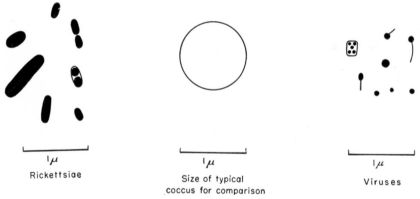

|⊢——— 1μ ———⊣| |⊢——— 1μ ———⊣| |⊢——— 1μ ———⊣|
Rickettsiae   **Size of typical coccus for comparison**   **Viruses**

FIG. 1·5 Morphology of rickettsiae and viruses. ×18,000.

to human beings. They cause the *typhus* (not the same as *typhoid*) group of diseases. Rickettsiae are illustrated in Fig. 1·5 and in Chap. 32.

The Filtrable Viruses. These viruses are even smaller than the rickettsiae. Some of them are scarcely larger than a molecule of hemoglobin. Neither they nor the rickettsiae can be grown in the laboratory by the simple means we use to grow the fungi. All known viruses are capable of disease production. They attack all forms of life from bacteria to man. Many cause diseases in plants and in lower animals. They live within the cells of their hosts. Some viruses are pictured in Chaps. 33 to 35 and in Fig. 1·5. Among the virus diseases of man are influenza, yellow fever, and measles.

STUDY SUGGESTIONS

Study both the text and the diagrams. Correlate both with your study of these forms in the laboratory.

Make a list of the new words used in this chapter. Can you define each one? Can you spell the new terms correctly?

What reasons or examples can you add to the discussion of the practical importance of microbiology?

Make a table with the title *Seven Important Types of Microorganisms* and the headings *Type; Important morphologic characteristics; Examples.* Fill in this table. Pick two types of microorganisms and state their essential differences: e.g., how do yeasts differ from molds?

Subdivisions of some of these groups were described in this chapter. Can you discuss the subgroups of the worms, protozoa, yeasts, and molds?

SUGGESTED READING

(See also Appendix A, page 571.)

Biological Background

Buchsbaum, R.: "Animals without Backbones." Rev. ed., University of Chicago Press, Chicago, 1948.

Rogers, J. S., T. H. Hubbell, and C. F. Byers: "Man and the Biological World." McGraw-Hill, New York, 1952.

Smith, G. M.: "Cryptogamic Botany. I. Algae and Fungi." 2d ed., McGraw-Hill, New York, 1955.

Villee, C. A.: "Biology." 2d ed., Saunders, Philadelphia, 1954.

Survey of Microorganisms

Frobisher, M., Jr.: "Fundamentals of Microbiology." 5th ed., Saunders, Philadelphia, 1953. Chaps. 2 through 8.

HENRICI, A. T. (rev. by E. J. Ordal): "Biology of Bacteria." Heath, Boston, 1948. Chaps. 1 through 7.

The Importance of Microorganisms

RAHN, O.: "Microbes of Merit." Ronald, New York, 1945.
SMITH, G.: "Plague on Us." Commonwealth Fund, New York, 1941.

The Worms and Protozoa (See also pages 569 and 597.)

BELDING, D. L.: "Textbook of Clinical Parasitology." 2d ed., Appleton-Century-Crofts, New York, 1952. Chaps. 7, 14, 24, 29.
JAHN, T. L., and F. F. JAHN: "How To Know the Protozoa." Brown, Dubuque, 1949.

The Fungi (See also page 530.)

ALEXOPOULOS, C. J.: "Introductory Mycology." Wiley, New York, 1952.
CHRISTENSEN, C. M.: "The Molds and Man." University of Minnesota Press, Minneapolis, 1951.

The Rickettsiae and the Viruses (See also pages 452 and 476.)

RHODES, A. J., and C. E. VAN ROOYEN: "Textbook of Virology." 2d ed., Williams & Wilkins, Baltimore, 1953.

The Morphology of the Bacteria

THE BACTERIUM

Each bacterium is an extremely small plant. Superficially studied, it seems to have very little specialized structure. However, special methods such as the use of selective stains and examination with the electron microscope have revealed details that are not usually visible. Many of the structures described in this chapter will not be seen by the student in the usual microscopic preparations.

Basic Shapes of Bacteria. Each bacterium has a definite shape. If the bacterium is spherical, it is called a *coccus* (pl. *cocci*); if it is a straight rod, a *bacillus* (pl. *bacilli*); if a spiral rod, a *spirillum* (pl. *spirilla*) (Fig. 2·8).

Size. Bacteria are much smaller than most plant and animal cells. They are measured by a microscopic unit called a *micron* (pl. *microns*). A micron is 1/1,000 mm., or about one twenty-five thousandth of an inch. Most cocci are slightly less than 1μ in diameter, while most bacilli are 1 to 3μ in length and $\frac{1}{2}$ to 1μ in diameter. Occasionally bacteria up to 50μ in length are found. Larger types may be detected under the lower powers of the com-

13

pound light microscope, but study with the highest-powered lenses is necessary in most cases. Even under the highest magnification of the usual laboratory microscope, which enlarges the bacteria nearly one thousand times, they appear very small.

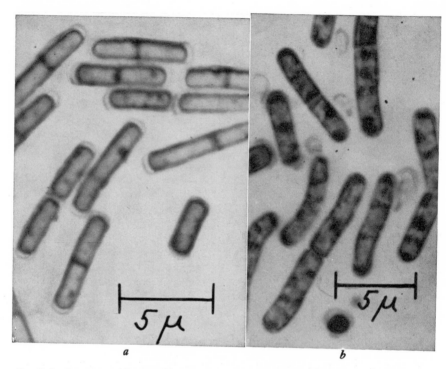

FIG. 2·1   Structure of bacilli. (*a*) Cell walls and retracted protoplasmic membranes of *Bacillus cereus.* Special cell-wall stain. (*b*) Cell contents of *B. megaterium.* Special stain to show cytoplasm. Nuclei and cell wall unstained. (*SAB prints 235 and 239, Courtesy of Dr. C. F. Robinow.*)

The Bacterial Wall. Each bacterium is completely enclosed by a thin, rigid cell wall. Its exact chemical structure is not known, but it is not the same in all kinds of bacteria. Cell walls as seen in a specially stained preparation are shown in Fig. 2·1; and Fig. 2·3 shows the cell wall of a dividing bacterium as seen by electron microscopy.

Nucleus. Each bacterium contains one or more nuclei. They can be made visible by special staining techniques which remove deeply staining material from the cytoplasm and color the chemical compound characteristic of nuclear matter (*desoxyribonucleic acid,* often referred to as DNA). A prep-

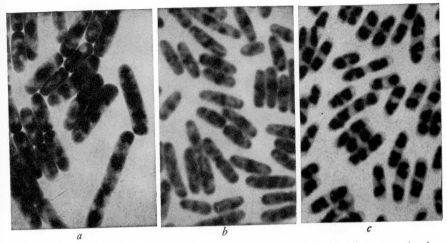

FIG. 2·2 Nuclei of a bacterium. Nuclei are light areas in (a) and (b) but are deeply stained in (c). (a) was taken with the electron microscope; (b) and (c) are photographs taken with the light microscope. (*SAB prints 238 and 239, from Hillier, Mudd, and Smith, J. Bact. 57:239.*)

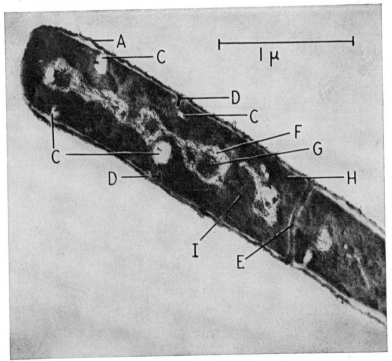

FIG. 2·3 Ultrathin section of a bacillus. Electron micrograph. ×37,000. (A) cell wall; (D, E) partial and complete cross cells; (F, G) nuclear areas; (C, H, I) structures of cytoplasm. (*SAB print 325, from Chapman and Hillier, J. Bact. 66:362.*)

aration of bacteria stained in this way is shown in Fig. 2·2c. The nucleus can also be seen in very thin slices of bacteria examined by an electron microscope (Fig. 2·3).

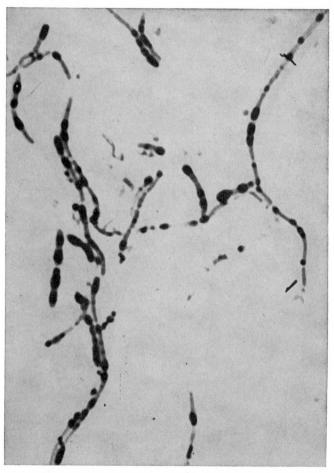

FIG. 2·4   Bacilli stained with Sudan black B to show fat droplets. ×2,000. (*Courtesy of Dr. K. F. Burdon, from J. Bact. 52:665.*)

The Internal Structure of the Bacterium. Although by common methods of staining the internal material of most bacteria appears practically structureless, special techniques of staining and special methods of microscopic examination have revealed great internal diversity of structures.

Just beneath the cell wall is a layer of dense material called the *cytoplasmic membrane* (Fig. 2·1b). *Granules* (masses of denser or more deeply staining material) are found in all cells. Large granules found commonly in some kinds of bacteria aid in their identification (see corynebacteria in Fig. 2·12). *Vacuoles* (droplets of liquid materials insoluble in the protoplasm) also occur. Fat droplets in bacilli are shown in Fig. 2·4. Such granules and vacuoles are masses of stored food or waste materials. In growing bacteria, granules that may be mitochondria have been described in "growing points" where the cell is elongating.

Slime Layer and Capsule. A layer of slimy material surrounds each bacterial cell. When it is thick enough to be readily seen, it is called a *capsule*. This

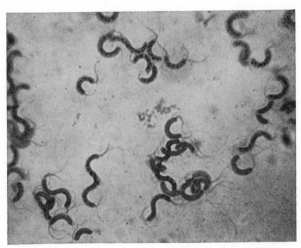

FIG. 2·5 Spirilla stained by special stain to show flagella. ×1,000. (*Courtesy of Dr. Jack Meyers.*)

material is outside the cell wall and is considered to be excreted, nonliving material. Many capsules contain *polysaccharides* (sugars of high molecular weight), and often the polysaccharide is specific for that particular bacterium. Capsules on pathogenic bacteria seem to make them more dangerous because they protect the cells against the defense mechanisms of the body. Capsulated bacteria in foods make the foods ropy or gummy.

Flagella. Bacteria never crawl on dry surfaces or fly through the air. Some species of bacteria are able to swim through the liquid in which they live. Spiral bacteria and some rod-shaped ones are motile; the cocci are nonmotile. Each motile bacterium has one or more very thin threadlike whips called *flagella* (sing. *flagellum*). They cannot be seen in the usual microscopic preparations. Special stains precipitate on the flagella making them thicker and therefore visible (Fig. 2·5). They can also be seen in electron micrographs (Fig. 2·6). Electron micrography also discloses the origin of the

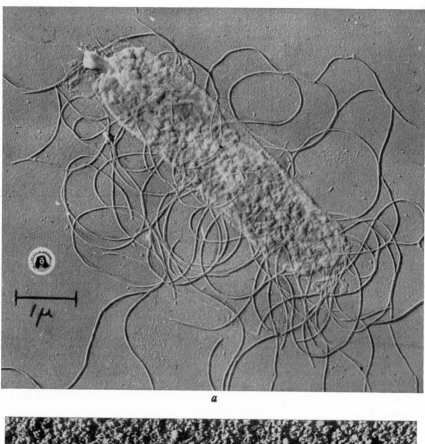

a

b

FIG. 2·6 Flagella as seen by electron micrography. (*a*) Electron micrograph of a motile bacterium that has been made partially transparent. Flagella appear to pass through the cell wall and originate from granules within the cell. ×18,000. (*SAB print 260, from Houwink and van Iterson, Biochem. et Biophys. Acta 5:10.*) (*b*) Highly magnified electron micrograph of a portion of a flagellum. ×110,000. (*SAB print 300, from Starr and Williams, J. Bact. 63:701.*)

flagellum within the cytoplasm of the bacterium (Fig. 2·6*a*) and the fine spiral structure of the flagellum, similar to the structure of contractile fibers of higher organisms (Fig. 2·6*b*).

The number and arrangement of the flagella are relatively fixed characteristics of each species of motile bacterium. Typical flagella arrangements and their terminology are illustrated in Fig. 2·7.

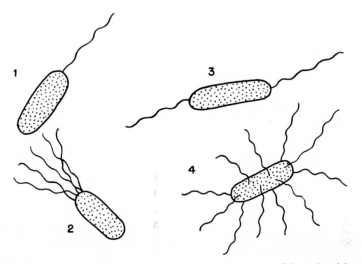

FIG. 2·7 Types of bacterial flagellation. (1) Monotrichate; (2) lophotrichate; (3) amphitrichate; (4) peritrichate.

Reproduction. When conditions are favorable and a bacterium has reached maturity, it splits transversely to form two new cells of the same kind. This type of asexual reproduction is called *fission*. It is such an important characteristic of the bacteria that the scientific name given to the group is *Schizomycetes*, which means "fission fungi." Division of the nuclear material by a process resembling the mitosis of animal and plant cells has been described in a few bacteria.

Characteristic cell groupings are formed by some types of bacteria because they tend to stick together after dividing. Rods and spirals always divide through the shortest axis, so they are found in short or long chains (Fig. 2·8*a*). The cocci show varied habits of cell division, resulting in pairs, chains, packets, and clumps (Fig. 2·8*b*).

Spore. Spores—resistant, single cells from which mature organisms may develop—are characteristic of all plants. But among the bacteria, only a limited number of the larger species of bacilli form spores. Smaller bacilli, cocci, and spirilla do not form spores. The bacterial spore is called an *endospore,* since it is formed within the cell. Each spore-forming rod develops one endospore, and the shape and position of the spore are often characteristic of the species. For example, one kind of bacillus may form a spherical endo-

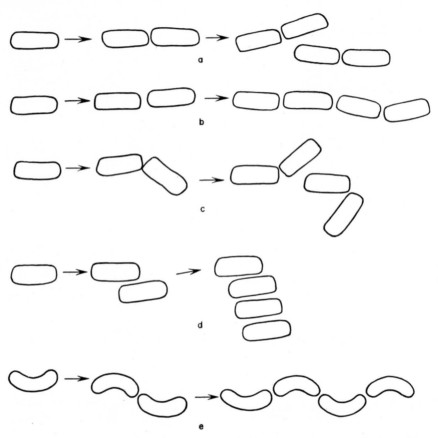

FIG. 2·8a   Development of typical bacillus and spirillum groupings. (*a*) Diplobacillus; (*b*) streptobacillus; (*c*) angular groupings; (*d*) parallel groupings; (*e*) chains of spiral cells.

spore at the center of its rod-shaped cell, while another may form an elliptical spore near the end of the rod. In some species the rod becomes swollen at the place where the spore is formed. (See Fig. 2·9.)

Spores are formed when conditions are not favorable for reproduction by the usual method of fission. It is important to remember that spores are not formed instantaneously. For example, spores cannot be formed when an object containing spore-forming bacilli is plunged into boiling water, but if

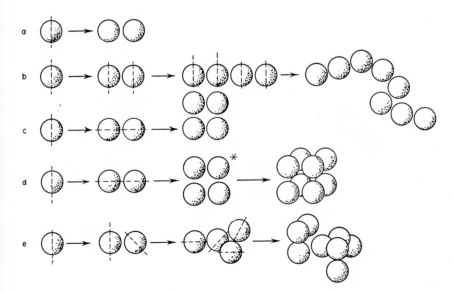

FIG. 2·8*b* Development of typical coccus groupings. (*a*) Diplococcus; (*b*) strepto-coccus; (*c*) tetracoccus; (*d*) sarcina; (*e*) micrococcus. Dotted lines indicate planes of division. * Plane of division here is parallel to page.

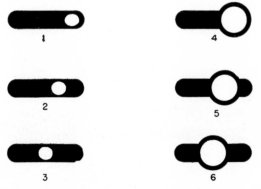

FIG. 2·9 Typical endospores of sporing bacilli. (1, 2, 3) cells not swollen; (4, 5, 6) cells swollen; (1 and 4) terminal spores; (2 and 5) subterminal spores; (3 and 6) central spores.

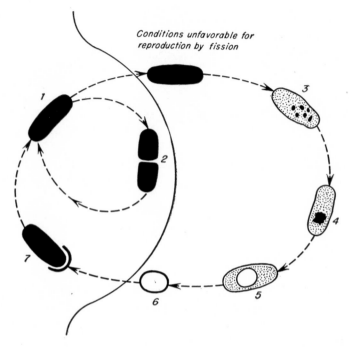

FIG. 2·10 Life cycle of sporing bacillus. (1) Vegetative cell; (2) reproduction by fission; (3) development of irregular staining; (4) development of prespore; (5) bacillus with endospore; (6) free spore; (7) germination of spore.

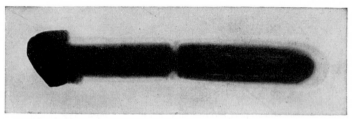

FIG. 2·11 Germination of a spore. Note also cell wall and division to form two new bacteria. (*From Hillier, J. Bact. 56;572.*)

spores are already present they will survive the boiling temperature for some time.

After the endospore is fully formed, the rest of the cell degenerates, leaving a *free spore*. This free spore can survive drying, exposure to light, boiling temperature, and other conditions which would kill the vegetative cell. When conditions again become favorable, the spore will germinate, forming a new vegetative rod capable of multiplying by fission or of forming an endospore (Figs. 2·10 and 2·11). Both free spores and endospores are resistant to the usual methods of staining and appear as uncolored, refractile bodies in most stained slides.

Fortunately only a few pathogenic bacteria are spore-forming. They are the bacilli causing anthrax, tetanus, the gas gangrene group of wound infections, and the food-borne disease known as botulism. The other pathogenic bacteria are nonsporing and therefore relatively easy to destroy.

THE BASIC FORMS OF THE SIMPLE BACTERIA

Common types of bacteria are given nonscientific names according to their shapes, cell groupings, ability to form spores, and reaction to some special stains. The most important of these special methods of staining is the Gram stain. It is a *differential stain,* since it colors some bacteria the original purple color and others the color of the counterstain, usually pink. Those that keep the purple stain are called *gram-positive* and those that take the counterstain are called *gram-negative.* For details of this method see page 51.

Here are the names in most common use. Note that these terms are not spelled with capital letters. These types are shown in Fig. 2·12.

coccus, pl. *cocci*—any spherical bacterium. The cocci are almost invariably nonmotile and nonsporing. With one exception, noted below, they are all gram-positive in young cultures. More definite names are given to certain of the cocci on the basis of their cell groupings.

diplococcus, pl. *diplococci*—paired, lance-shaped cocci.

neisseria, pl. *neisseriae*—paired, gram-negative, bean-shaped cocci. Many bacteriologists include them with the diplococci. Actually they differ in both staining and shape. When the gram-positive diplococci stay in groups they form chains like the streptococci, while the neisseriae may form packets but never chains.

streptococcus, pl. *streptococci*—cocci in chains.

tetracoccus, pl. *tetracocci*—cocci in fours.

sarcina, pl. *sarcinae*—cocci in regular cubical packets.

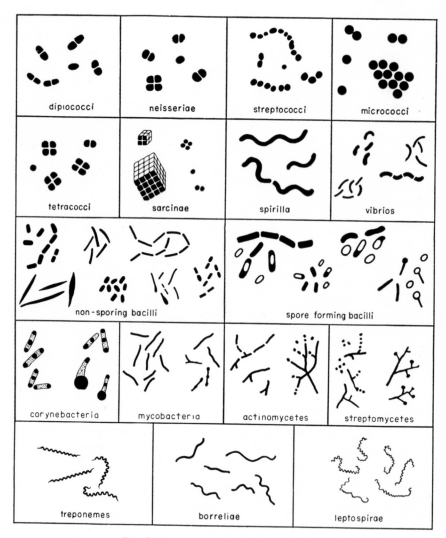

FIG. 2·12 Morphologic types of bacteria.

micrococcus, pl. *micrococci*—cocci in irregular grapelike masses. The term *staphylococcus* (pl. *staphylococci*) is a synonym.

spirillum, pl. *spirilla*—any spiral rod. Note that they are *helicoidal* (spring-like) rather than shaped like a series of waves. All are motile, but none has a spore. The term *spirillum* is used more specifically for the longer types, and the term *vibrio* (pl. *vibrios*) is given to the shorter cells.

bacillus, pl. *bacilli*—any straight rod. The bacilli may or may not have spores and may or may not be motile. Those that are spore-forming are usually gram-positive in the vegetative state. The most commonly found species of nonsporing bacilli are gram-negative. Because of the great variation in this group, the term *bacillus* should always be qualified by appropriate adjectives, e.g., a gram-positive, sporing bacillus; a gram-negative, nonmotile, nonsporing bacillus.

corynebacterium, pl. *corynebacteria*—gram-positive rods with granules or bars. The organism causing diphtheria belongs to this group. Others that have similar morphology are often called *diphtheroids.*

It is sometimes very difficult to assign an organism to a definite morphologic type. Short rods may easily be mistaken for cocci. In fact, some kinds have been called *coccobacilli.* Some bacteria exhibit *pleomorphism* (varied shapes) even when grown under the most ideal conditions, and many develop queer and unusual forms called *involution forms* when cultivated in unusual ways.

THE HIGHER BACTERIA IMPORTANT IN MEDICINE

In addition to the simpler forms of bacteria already described, there are many kinds that are more complicated. These are called the *higher bacteria.* They are bacteria because they are fission fungi, but they often show some resemblance to other forms of microorganisms. The higher bacteria are illustrated in Fig. 2·12. (See also Figs. 11·3 and 31·1.) Many of them are harmless soil and water bacteria, but there are two groups that include pathogenic organisms.

The *moldlike bacteria*—a group for which there is no common name. All these organisms are nonmotile and without endospores. They are considered moldlike because they tend to form filaments and some form bodies, called *conidia,* resembling the spores of septate molds. However, the filaments are much finer than any mold hyphae, and the sporelike bodies are not true spores. The three most important kinds are known as *actinomycete,* pl. *actinomycetes*—composed of fine, branching filaments fragmenting to short rods.

streptomycete, pl. *streptomycetes*—composed of fine, branching filaments bearing chains of conidia.

mycobacterium, pl. *mycobacteria*—acid-fast rods. Branching and conidia formation are rare. These organisms stain with great difficulty because of the waxy material in the cells, but once stained they cannot be readily decolorized with acid and so they are called *acid-fast.* (See page 413 for discussion of this staining technique.) The term *acid-fast bacillus* is also used.

spirochete, pl. *spirochetes*—motile spiral forms which differ from spirilla in being *flexuous* (nonrigid), more difficult to stain and cultivate, and more complicated in structure. Early microbiologists confused some of them with flagellated protozoa, and to this day many people associate them with protozoa. They are, however, true bacteria, for they are single-celled fungi that reproduce by fission. They may all be called spirochetes, or the more specific names given below may be used.

treponema, pl. *treponemata*—cells tightly coiled and regularly spiraled. Some bacteriologists use the term *treponeme* (pl. *treponemes*).

borrelia, pl. *borreliae*—cells loosely and irregularly spiraled.

leptospira, pl. *leptospirae*—finely coiled cells with one or both ends hooked.

THE SCIENTIFIC NAMING AND CLASSIFICATION OF BACTERIA

When a biologist refers to a specific organism, he calls it by its scientific name. This is a double name consisting of the name of the *genus* (pl. *genera*) or group to which it belongs and the name of the *species* (pl. *species*), the definite type to which it belongs. The genus name comes first and is spelled with a capital letter. The species name is spelled with a small letter. You are a specimen of *Homo sapiens;* the common mouse is *Mus musculus;* corn is *Zea mays.* These names often contain clues to the characteristics of the organism; e.g., *sapiens* means "wise"! The scientific names of bacteria may be descriptive of their morphology, activities, or other characteristics. Sometimes the name of a famous bacteriologist is made over into a generic name, e.g., *Pasteurella pestis.* A bacterium often found on the skin is *Micrococcus citreus.* The name *Micrococcus,* spelled here with a capital since it is a generic name, indicates that the organism is a coccus occurring in irregular bunches. We also know from the name that it is nonmotile, nonsporing, and gram-positive. The species name, *citreus,* indicates that this bacterium makes a lemon-yellow growth on culture media.

As with other forms of life, some of the commonly known bacteria have popular, everyday names. The bacterium causing tuberculosis has the scientific name *Mycobacterium tuberculosis,* but it is frequently referred to as the "TB bacillus." *Corynebacterium diphtheriae* is the cause of diphtheria. Because it was first investigated by bacteriologists named Klebs and Loeffler, it is sometimes called the Klebs-Loeffler bacillus, or even the K.L. bacillus.

Each genus consists of closely related species; similar genera are grouped into families; similar families are grouped into orders; and the orders of bacteria constitute the class *Schizomycetes.* Appendix B gives a modified form of the classification, covering bacteria, rickettsiae, and viruses, used by American bacteriologists and published as *Bergey's Manual of Determinative Bacteriology* (6th edition). It is not necessary for the student to learn this classification, but it should be studied carefully so that it is understood and used intelligently.

STUDY SUGGESTIONS

Check your knowledge of the new terms used in this chapter. Remember that the diagrams and micrographs deserve just as much study as the written text.

Can you describe a typical bacterial cell in detail? How does it differ from a yeast? from a protozoan?

Without consulting the text, list and draw the important morphologic types of simple bacteria and higher bacteria.

Can you suggest the probable nature of the following bacteria? What is the probable derivation of each name? Which of these organisms will form spores? Which will be motile? which gram-negative?

Spirillum undula	*Diplococcus pneumoniae*
Neisseria gonorrhoeae	*Borrelia vincentii*
Mycobacterium leprae	*Streptococcus pyogenes*

Look through Chaps. 23 to 32 and select six scientific names of bacteria. Analyze the names as well as you can, then consult Appendix B.

SUGGESTED READING

General References

BISSET, K. A.: The Morphology and Cytology of Bacteria, in "Annual Review of Microbiology." Vol. 5, Annual Reviews, Inc., Stanford, 1951.

BURROWS, W.: "Textbook of Microbiology." 16th ed., Saunders, Philadelphia, 1954. Chap. 3.

CHAPMAN, G. B., and J. HILLIER: Electron microscopy of ultrathin sections of bacteria. I. Cellular division of *B. cereus. J. Bact.* **66:**362 (1953).

DUBOS, R. J.: "The Bacterial Cell." Harvard University Press, Cambridge, Mass., 1945. Chaps. 1–4.

———, J. MONOD, and A. M. PAPPENHEIMER, JR.: The Morphology and Physiology of Bacteria, in R. J. Dubos's "Bacterial and Mycotic Infections of Man." 2d ed., Lippincott, Philadelphia, 1952.

KNAYSI, G.: "Elements of Bacterial Cytology." 2d ed., Comstock, Ithaca, 1951.

MUDD, S.: Cytology of Bacteria: The Bacterial Cell, in "Annual Review of Microbiology." Vol. 8, Annual Reviews, Inc., Stanford, 1954.

Special Cytology

DeLAMATER, E. D.: Cytology of Bacteria: The Bacterial Nucleus, in "Annual Review of Microbiology." Vol. 8, Annual Reviews, Inc., Stanford, 1954.

KNAYSI, G., and J. HILLIER: Preliminary observations on the germination of the endospore in *Bacillus megaterium* and the structure of the spore coat. *J. Bact.* **57:**23 (1949).

ROBINOW, C. F.: Spore structure as revealed by thin sections. *J. Bact.* **66:**300 (1953).

SCHMIDT, C. F.: Bacterial Spores, in "Annual Review of Microbiology." Vol. 9, Annual Reviews, Inc., Stanford, 1955.

STARR, M. P., and R. C. WILLIAMS: Hellicoidal structure of flagella of a motile diphtheroid. *J. Bact.* **63:**701 (1952).

WEIBULL, C.: Characteristics of the protoplasmic constituents of *Bacillus megaterium*. *J. Bact.* **66:**696 (1953).

Classification

BREED, R. S., *et al.:* "Bergey's Manual of Determinative Bacteriology." 6th ed., Williams & Wilkins, Baltimore, 1948. Introductory discussions, pp. 1–4 and 39–48; and listing of bacteria, pp. 66–1080.

BUCHANAN, R. E.: Taxonomy, in "Annual Review of Microbiology." Vol. 9, Annual Reviews, Inc., Stanford, 1955.

CHAPTER 3

How Microorganisms Live

LIFE PROCESSES OF ALL ORGANISMS

In the previous chapters the *morphology* (structure) of microorganisms has been discussed. This chapter and the next will be devoted to the *physiology* of microorganisms. Physiology is the study of functions or activities. Many of the same terms used in human physiology will be used here. These life processes involve chemical reactions. The student should, therefore, consult her physiology and chemistry texts. Microbiology, human physiology, and biochemistry are closely interrelated subjects even though we study them in separate courses.

The processes of life are essentially the same in all living organisms whether large or small. Every living thing must obtain food. This food is used in two ways. Part is used for the production of energy to carry on life processes, and part is built into new protoplasm for cell growth and reproduction. These processes constitute *metabolism*. Every organism also reacts constantly to its environment and reproduces more organisms of its own kind when conditions are right. Following a general discussion of these life processes, the variations found in the physiology of the different groups of microorganisms will be noted briefly. Here again, since the importance of the bacteria is so great, a separate chapter will be devoted to them.

The more the physiology of living cells is studied, the more extraordinary seem the almost unlimited chemical and physical changes that are involved in cell processes. Many of these reactions occur with great speed, and all are regulated and coordinated in truly amazing fashion. These activities of the cells are attributed mainly to two factors, the complex colloidal character of their protoplasm and their ability to form the organic catalysts known as *enzymes*.

The Nature and Activities of Protoplasm and the Protoplasmic Membrane. Water makes up the largest part of protoplasm. In the water, certain substances such as salts are present in solution. Dispersed through this solution are large molecules and aggregates of molecules of such size that they neither go into solution nor tend to settle out of their suspended state. The most important and numerous of these molecules are the cell proteins. The combination of aqueous matrix, dissolved substances, and suspended materials constitutes the colloidal state of the cell protoplasm. The surfaces of the colloidal particles adsorb water and other materials. These combinations give protoplasm its gelatinous nature and contribute to its stability. Moreover, it is at these surfaces that cell substances come together in increased concentrations and chemical changes favorable to the cell occur rapidly. The electric charges of the ions of dissolved salts and the charges at the surface of the colloidal particles are also of great importance in these *intracellular* processes (processes within the cell).

In every cell the outer surface of its protoplasm consists of a special layer, the cytoplasmic membrane. The interchange of materials between the cell substance and the surrounding medium must take place through this layer. The molecules of organic material in this layer—principally proteins and *lipoids* (fatlike substances)—are arranged in a very definite fashion. The membrane allows certain substances, usually in soluble state, to pass in or out of the cell. At the same time it keeps undesirable materials out and essential cell constituents inside the cell. In small organisms, such as the bacteria, the high ratio of the area of the cell surface to the volume of the cell contents may mean that the whole microorganism may act as a colloidal particle, adsorbing substances at its surface and so causing their interreactions there.

Enzymes. An *enzyme* is best defined as an organic catalyst formed by a living cell. Each enzyme is capable of hastening one type of chemical reaction. Some enzymes prepare materials for cell use. For instance, the *digestive enzymes* catalyze the hydrolysis of complicated food materials into smaller soluble and diffusible molecules. Other enzymes are called *respiratory enzymes* because they enable the cells to oxidize the absorbed food molecules, releasing energy for cell processes. Still others may be called *assimilative enzymes,* for they help the cell to build new substance from food so that the organism may grow and reproduce. Typical digestive enzymes are secreted through the cell membrane and act outside the cell. They may be spoken of as *extracellular*. Respiratory and assimilative enzymes remain and act within the cell, so they are intracellular. Enzymes are colloidal proteins.

The names given to enzymes indicate the specificity of their action. Usually the suffix *-ase* is added to the name of the substance acted upon. *Dextrase* is the enzyme that attacks the sugar dextrose; *urease* is the enzyme that causes the breakdown of the urea molecule. Sometimes the nature of the chemical reaction is indicated by the enzyme name. For example, intracellular enzymes that catalyze the oxidation of food to release energy are called *oxidases*.

Parasitism. Green plants are almost invariably free-living, since they can make their own food. Some smaller animals and many of the plants that lack chlorophyll have acquired the habit of living on or in some other animal or plant, known as the *host*. These dependent organisms are *parasites*. Often the host is not injured; in fact, in some instances the parasite and host may be mutually benefited. But many parasites do injure their host. Most disease-producing organisms are parasitic pathogens.

Parasites may become so accustomed to the temperature, food, and other conditions provided by the host that they are unable to grow anywhere else. Such organisms are called *obligate parasites*. There are all grades of parasitism between the completely free-living organisms and the obligate parasites. In the course of their evolution, obligate parasitic organisms may become definitely changed in structure and life habits because of their adaptation to life within a host.

NUTRITION OF MICROORGANISMS

Procurement and Digestion of Food. Foods are organic compounds that can be made over into cell substances or oxidized to liberate energy for cell processes. The principal food substances are the carbohydrates (sugars and starches), the fats, and the proteins.

Green plants make all these substances from the carbon dioxide of the air and the water and salts of the soil. The chlorophyll of the green plants enables them to do this. Energy from the sun is changed into latent chemical energy and incorporated into the food molecules. This process is *photosynthesis*. Naturally, some of the food made by a plant is used by the plant itself, but much of it may be used by any animal that feeds on the plant. We picture the development and use of food as a "food cycle" (Fig. 3·1).

Animals are not able to make food for themselves, so they have to feed on plants and on other animals. Animals *ingest* much of their food in solid form. It passes into their digestive systems, where it is decomposed by the digestive enzymes. The soluble end products of this process of hydrolysis are absorbed into the animals' tissues and used by the cells. Undigested food is discharged as solid waste (*egestion*). These processes of ingestion of solid food, digestion inside the animal's body, absorption of products of

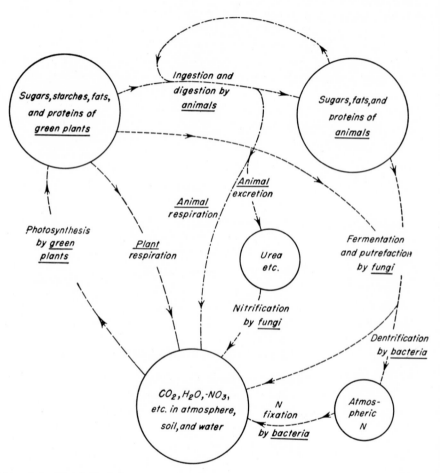

FIG. 3·1   The food cycle. ————— green plant action. ——·——·— animal action. --------- action of fungi including bacteria.

digestion, and egestion of solid wastes are characteristic of all animals from the ameba to man.

The colorless plants, including most bacteria, yeasts, and molds, are like animals in that they cannot make food. They, too, use food already made by plants or made over by animals. But they are unlike animals in having no digestive organs. Instead they secrete their digestive enzymes into the food materials in or on which they are living. Then they absorb the soluble products. Look again at Fig. 3·1 and note the part played by the fungi.

Use of Food by Microorganisms. All organisms use food in essentially the same ways. They store it, or assimilate it into new protoplasm and cell materials, or oxidize it to obtain energy.

Storage of Food. Many organisms store food in concentrated forms for future use. Granules and vacuoles in bacteria, yeasts, and molds are often stored food material. Strictly parasitic organisms usually do not store food. We have no evidence of food storage by rickettsiae or filtrable viruses. In all forms of life, any food that is stored is later used for assimilation or energy production unless some accident terminates the life of the organism.

Assimilation. All living things must form new protoplasm and other materials in order to grow, repair themselves, and eventually reproduce. The absorbed food substances provide this building material. This intracellular process is called *assimilation*.

Food for Energy. The latent or chemical energy put into the food molecule by the green plant is released when that molecule is oxidized inside a cell. In order to do this most organisms take in oxygen and excrete carbon dioxide. This exchange of gases is often called respiration. However, microbiologists prefer to use the word *respiration* to indicate any process within the cell that results in the production of energy for cell use. Organisms need this energy to carry on the processes of assimilation, to enable motile organisms to move, to develop heat, and for other essential activities. In higher animals most of the energy is used in the contraction of muscle; but in the rapidly growing microorganisms most of the food is used to provide materials for new cells and the energy to build these new materials. Just think how much food you would need if you were able to do as many bacteria do—grow twice your present size and divide in two every 20 minutes!

Excretion. Waste materials are eliminated from living cells. This is the process of *excretion*. Animals generally have special excretory apparatus to help discharge these soluble wastes. In green plants and fungi such apparatus is lacking and the wastes simply diffuse outward through the cytoplasmic membranes and cell walls.

CONSTANT REACTION TO ENVIRONMENT

If any organism is to grow and reproduce it must constantly adjust itself to outside conditions. Chemical and physical stimuli (such as light, sound, and heat) in their surroundings cause animals to react by contraction of muscles and by formation of secretions. The animals have nervous systems to coordinate and speed these reactions. The plants, both green and colorless, lack any definite nervous system, but they do react, though slowly, to stimuli. The morning glory opens in response to sunshine, and motile bacteria swim toward food material.

REPRODUCTION

When organisms have become mature by the assimilation of sufficient food, reproduction normally takes place. Varied forms of reproduction are found among the microorganisms, from the simple fission of the bacteria to the production of complicated fertilized eggs by some of the worms. Among the lower types reproduction is usually *asexual*. In these organisms sexually differentiated individuals are rare. Their reproduction may be of the very simplest vegetative type, accomplished by ordinary cell division, or they may reproduce by specialized spores. In the higher forms we find *sexual* reproduction, in which the new individual always develops from the union of two cells (*fertilization*), to be the usual method of reproduction.

LIFE PROCESSES IN THE SEVEN GROUPS OF MICROORGANISMS

The Worms. The physiologic processes of worms are very similar to those of human beings. The typical worm ingests solid food into an alimentary canal where it is digested. The digested products are absorbed and used as in any animal. The muscular, excretory, and nervous systems of worms are primitive, but they function in the same ways as do those of higher animals. Respiratory and circulatory systems are generally lacking. Some worms are *hermaphroditic;* i.e., each individual possesses both male and female reproductive systems. In other worms the sexes are separate. The fertilized *ova* (eggs) develop into larval forms before they become adults. The morphology, physiology, and life cycles of parasitic worms are markedly modified by their life within their hosts.

The Protozoa. In these one-celled animals all the life processes are carried on within the single cell. Most protozoa ingest food by taking in solid particles through an opening called a *gullet.* The food is held in a food vacuole while it is acted on by digestive enzymes. Then the digested food is absorbed to be assimilated or used as a source of energy. The indigestible material is egested from the cell. Soluble wastes are excreted through the cell membrane. Reproduction occurs by fission and also by sexual processes accompanied by mitotic division. Among the parasitic protozoa, the malaria organism shows great modification as the result of its parasitism. The others are not markedly different in structure from their free-living relatives.

The Yeasts. Since yeasts are fungi, they cannot build their own food. They live in moist material containing suitable plant or animal matter. Their favorite foods are the simpler sugars. In their processes of respiration the true yeasts oxidize this sugar to carbon dioxide and ethyl alcohol with the aid of enzymes known as *zymases*. The alcohol and carbon dioxide are wastes as far as the yeasts are concerned, but they are valuable to mankind (see Chap. 7). The true yeasts reproduce both asexually by budding and sexually by the fusion of two nuclei followed by the formation of special spores. The false yeasts do not form spores and do not produce alcohol from sugars.

The Molds. Molds are also colorless plants. Their vegetative hyphae absorb food material from the substances on which they grow. If these foods are in insoluble form, the mold secretes digestive enzymes to hydrolyze the foods to diffusible substances. The food is passed along the hyphae by diffusion from cell to cell. Molds utilize varied types of carbohydrates as food, including many of the organic acids. The ability of molds to reproduce both asexually and sexually was noted in Chap. 1.

The Bacteria. Since bacteria are also fungi, their physiologic processes resemble those of yeasts and mold but are much more varied. The physiology of bacteria will be considered in detail in the next chapter.

The Rickettsiae and the Viruses. Because of their small size and difficult cultivation, knowledge of the physiology of these organisms is very scanty. All of them are obligate parasites and apparently depend on their host cells to carry on most of their physiologic processes. The present-day concepts of their physiology are discussed in Chap. 33.

STUDY SUGGESTIONS

As you read this chapter, note down any terms or ideas that are not clear to you. Look them up in your other texts. If you cannot find satisfactory answers to your questions, bring them into class for discussion.

Can you state clearly the basic facts about the colloidal nature of protoplasm? enzymes? parasitism?

Study the diagram of the food cycle. To fix it in your mind copy it in your notebook, using green pencil for the activities of green plants, red for those of animals, and yellow for those of fungi. Make up some specific series of biologic events illustrating the food cycle; e.g., the manufacture of food by the grass in the pasture; the processes in the cow that eats the grass and produces milk; the bacteria and molds that decompose the milk into materials that other plants can use.

What happens to a piece of bread if it is swallowed by a worm? If mold grows on it? Use the terms *digestion, egestion, excretion, respiration, absorption, assimilation, extracellular enzyme, intracellular enzyme,* etc., correctly in your discussion.

Try to picture the life processes of a yeast cell and its descendants in a batch of bread dough set in a warm place to rise; the life of an intestinal fluke in the human duodenum.

SUGGESTED READING

(See also page 11.)

References for General Physiology

MITCHELL, P. H.: "A Textbook of General Physiology." 4th ed., McGraw-Hill, New York, 1948.

SCHEER, B. F.: "General Physiology." Wiley, New York, 1953.

CHAPTER 4

The Physiology of Bacteria

The physiologic processes characteristic of all living organisms have been discussed in Chap. 3. This chapter considers special aspects of bacterial physiology, including variation and mutation.

BASIC LIFE PROCESSES OF BACTERIA

Most bacteria act as typical fungi in their relation to food. Like the yeasts and the molds, they grow in watery environments in which food substances of plant or animal origin are present. The foods that are present in soluble diffusible form will pass through the slime layer, the cell wall, and the protoplasmic membrane into the bacterium. Thus, for example, a bacterium in the blood obtains water, salts, dextrose sugar, and amino acids for its use. When the foods in the surrounding material are in solid form or in colloidal suspension, the bacteria must secrete extracellular digestive enzymes to cause their hydrolysis to absorbable molecules. When butter becomes rancid, bacteria in it are secreting *lipase* to catalyze the hydrolysis of the nonsoluble fat to the more soluble fatty acids and glycerol which the cell can absorb. As a starchy pudding spoils it becomes more liquid, because the spoilage bacteria are secreting *diastase,* which splits the nonsoluble starch to soluble sugars. In much the same way, bacteria possessing *proteolytic* enzymes liquefy nitrogenous materials such as gelatin, blood clot, and milk protein, as these enzymes change the more solid proteins to soluble peptones and amino acids.

After the food is absorbed we may assume that it is used quickly, since there is little food storage in bacteria. One of two things will happen to the food molecule. First, it may be used as building material for new bacterial protoplasm, cell wall, or capsule, so that the cell can grow and reproduce. The amino acids and other nitrogen-containing compounds are particularly needed to construct protoplasm, and sugars to build capsular material. Second, the food may be used in respiration by its oxidation within the cell to release energy for cell use. The greatest part of this energy is needed to carry on the work of building protoplasm, but some of it goes into the formation of heat, some into flagella action. There are some bacteria that transform food energy into light (the *photogenic* or *luminescent* bacteria). In general, as in animals, the carbohydrates are the foods most readily used in this way. But in the bacteria as in animals, nitrogen-containing compounds, such as amino acids, may be oxidized after the nitrogenous part of the molecule is split off (the process of *deamination*). The nitrogen-containing portion, which is now a waste product of the cell, is most frequently in the form of ammonia. This ammonia and other waste substances formed by the intracellular metabolic processes are excreted. They are usually soluble and diffuse into the surrounding watery material.

THE UNUSUAL FEATURES OF BACTERIAL METABOLISM

Despite the statement at the beginning of this chapter that the processes of bacteria are essentially the same as those of other microorganisms, there are ways in which bacteria are notably different from most other living things. Yeasts and molds share these unusual aspects to some extent.

The Limited Enzymes of the Specific Bacterium. The digestive and respiratory enzymes of all human races seem to be alike. You may not think that you eat the same food as the Malayan or Eskimo. But their foods are made of the same chemical substances as yours and are digested and utilized by them with the help of exactly the same enzymes as are found in your body. Moreover, these enzymes are the same, broadly speaking, as those that are made and used by any bird, fish, worm, or other animal. All animals can use typical fats, starches, sugars, and proteins, and all do it in the same way.

This is not true of the bacteria. For example, the commonest bacillus of the intestine, *Escherichia coli,* has enzymes that can attack practically all common sugars except sucrose (cane sugar), but it cannot use starch as a food because it possesses no diastatic enzyme. Another bacterium that resembles it closely in appearance, *Salmonella typhosa,* the cause of typhoid fever, can attack only a very few sugars, since it lacks the necessary enzymes to attack others. One of the common sporing rods of the soil, *Bacillus subtilis,* can break down starch to sugars by an enzyme like the ptyalin of saliva, but it is unable to hydrolyze lactose (milk sugar), since it forms no lactase enzyme. The first unusual feature of bacterial metabolism may be stated in this way: *Each species of bacterium possesses the ability to make only a limited number of enzymes and therefore attacks only certain chemical substances.* This enzyme complex possessed by each species is generally regarded as fixed and definitely characteristic of that species; but there is considerable evidence that strains of bacteria may gain or lose the power to form a particular enzyme. For further discussion of this controversial subject see the references at the end of this chapter.

The Limited Analytic Activity of the Specific Bacterium. When an animal uses a molecule of fat or carbohydrate, we expect that it will be used completely. The processes of digestion and respiration normally result in the complete degradation of the material of the food molecule so that carbon dioxide and water are the excreted end products. Even in the breakdown of proteins, most of the molecule is completely oxidized. Only the deaminated nitrogenous portion, usually urea or ammonia, is capable of further oxidation when excreted. This complete breakdown does not occur when a specific bacterium acts on a complicated organic compound. A sporing rod may break starch down to the sugar maltose but then be unable to utilize the maltose. In the same environment there may be a nonsporing rod that can attack the maltose and form lactic acid from it. This acid may, in turn, be absorbed by the hyphae of a mold that can oxidize the acid completely to carbon dioxide and water. Other examples of this partial breakdown of materials will be discussed in Chap. 7. This second unique feature of bacterial metabolism may be summarized as follows: *A specific bacterium can often only partially decompose an organic compound.*

The Unlimited Ability of Bacteria to Attack Organic Materials. It is true, as has already been said, that a single species of bacterium possesses only a limited array of enzymes and can attack only a limited number of compounds in a limited number of ways. It is also true that if the bacteria are taken as a whole, it seems impossible to find any organic compound that cannot be attacked by some species. There are many compounds formed by plants and animals that animals cannot digest. The cellulose that forms the walls of plant cells, the lignin of wood, plant resins and waxes, and keratin of animal hair and hoofs are some of the substances that animals cannot use as food; but there are bacteria that attack each of these materials. Man has found ways of making over organic substances into new materials useful to him, such as rubber, paper, synthetic textiles, etc. These, too, are decomposed by certain bacteria. Some simple organic compounds that are not ordinarily used by animals as food are used by bacteria. Among these are the organic acids, ammonia, acetone, and alcohols. Some unusual bacteria of the soil are even capable of using such extraordinary foods as methane, carbon monoxide, paraffin, and even gasoline. So we may state the third unusual physiologic feature of bacteria in this way: *Bacteria are able to attack all forms of organic matter, including many that cannot be used by animals.*

Anaerobic Respiration. Animal and plant cells get energy from sugar molecules by oxidizing them to carbon dioxide and water. These are waste products, which the cells discard. It is the energy released from the sugar molecule that the cell uses. This is an extreme simplification of the process, for it actually takes place in several steps with the aid of several enzymes. But the fact remains that the food and the oxygen are taken into the cell, energy is released for cell use, and completely oxidized products, carbon dioxide and water, are excreted as the final products of the process. All higher plants and all animals require oxygen in free, uncombined form. Early microbiologists were surprised to find that bacteria and yeasts were often able to grow where there was no free oxygen. Such organisms are called *anaerobes* in contrast to those that use free oxygen, which are called *aerobes.*

Actually, anaerobic respiration is oxidation. Chemists consider that the process of oxidation is not limited to the combination of a material with free oxygen, but that other processes, such as the removal of hydrogen from a molecule, are also to be regarded as oxidative. The anaerobic bacteria obtain energy by such oxidative methods not involving the use of free oxygen. These processes result in partially oxidized end products and yield less energy than direct oxidation. For example, the English bacteriologist C. G. Anderson has reckoned that when a bacterial culture completely oxidizes glucose sugar to carbon dioxide, it obtains 674 Cal. of energy, and if it partially oxidizes the same amount of sugar with the aid of free oxygen to oxalic acid and water it will get 493 Cal. However, an anaerobe attacking this amount of sugar by anaerobic methods forming lactic acid will obtain only 22½ Cal. of energy.

Some species of bacteria will grow well only when the oxygen tension of their environment is that of the normal atmosphere. These are called *obligate aerobes.* On the other hand, there are *obligate anaerobes* that grow only when no free oxygen is present or when the environment contains strong reducing agents that use up oxygen. Most bacteria are *facultative aerobes* or *facultative anaerobes,* preferring anaerobic or aerobic environments but able to grow in a wide range of oxygen tensions. Some organisms seem to grow best when there is some free oxygen but not so much as in normal atmosphere. They are called *microaerophilic*. It is likely, however, that their real demand is for increased carbon dioxide rather than decreased free oxygen.

In summary, the fourth unusual feature of bacterial physiology may be stated thus: *All bacteria obtain energy by the intracellular oxidation of food, but this process may be one that does not involve the use of free oxygen.*

HETEROTROPHIC AND AUTOTROPHIC BACTERIA

Most fungi, including the bacteria, use organic materials for food and are therefore called *heterotrophic*. The organisms important in medicine all belong to this group. Among the bacteria of the soil and natural waters there are many that do not use preformed organic foods. These bacteria are called *autotrophic*. They make their own food. This food building is not done by photosynthesis, as in the green plants, but by the process of *chemosynthesis*. The autotrophic bacteria obtain energy by the oxidation of very simple substances such as ammonia, nitrates, and sulfur. This energy they utilize for the synthesis of protoplasm, which they build from carbon dioxide, water, and nitrate salts, or ammonia. Important members of the autotrophic bacteria will be discussed in Chap. 7 in the section on the microbiology of the soil.

PRACTICAL RESULTS OF BACTERIAL GROWTH

When microorganisms grow in a material, many changes are bound to take place. Some of these are familiar processes, although most people do not think of them as the results of microbial action.

1. The consistency of the material changes. Solid materials are likely to become softened because the higher organic compounds are hydrolyzed by the bacterial digestive enzymes to soluble materials of simpler composition. Liquids that were previously clear become cloudy and develop sediment and surface scum as the result of the accumulation of the bodies of millions of microorganisms.

2. If the material contains carbohydrates, bubbles of gas often develop as the organisms form carbon dioxide and hydrogen gases. It becomes sour as the result of acid formation by the respiratory enzymes of the bacteria, or alcoholic as the result of the action of yeast enzymes. This type of reaction is called *fermentation*.

3. When protein materials decompose, nauseous odors may be produced because of the formation of sulfur-containing compounds. The reaction becomes alkaline, rather than acid, because the proteolytic bacteria are utilizing

the amino acids as energy food and producing ammonia by deamination of these compounds. This type of change is referred to as *putrefaction*.

In decomposing organic materials, oxygen and complicated compounds tend to diminish, and waste products of microbial growth and the bodies of the organisms themselves tend to accumulate. The following examples will serve to illustrate these facts:

1. All market milk contains a great variety of microorganisms. If the milk is raw, certain types belonging to the genus *Lactobacillus,* the lactic acid-forming, nonsporing rods, grow rapidly. They break down the milk sugar to lactic acid, and the milk turns sour. The curdling of the sour milk is due to the coagulation of the milk casein by the acid. If milk has been pasteurized in the bottle, the lactobacilli will have been killed and the surviving bacteria will be of proteolytic types. Their enzymes will attack the milk proteins rather than the milk sugar. First the casein will become coagulated and then it will be hydrolyzed with the formation of ammonia and unpalatable nitrogenous decomposition products. The spoilage of raw milk is an example of fermentation, while the spoilage of pasteurized milk illustrates putrefaction.

2. Leaves and other plant debris collect continually on the surface of the soil and are continually disintegrated by the action of microorganisms. Some destruction is carried on by worms and other animals and some by the larger fungi such as mushrooms, but most decomposition is the result of microbial growth. The molds and bacteria that can digest the cellulose walls of plant cells grow abundantly in damp layers of leaves. The cellulose is softened as it changes to sugars. As it decomposes, microorganisms can penetrate through the plant cell walls and attack the proteins and sugars within the plant cells. By next fall, the leaves that fell this fall will have apparently vanished. Straw, wood, and other plant materials, the bodies of animals in soil and water, wastes such as garbage and sewage are disintegrated by similar microbial processes. These activities make microorganisms the most important *scavengers* (refuse removers) of the world. Equally important is the fact that the waste products of these bacterial decompositions provide the green plants with materials they need for growth.

3. Pathogenic organisms in the infected body live in essentially the same ways as any other organisms. They may use food that is already in soluble diffusible form, such as the dextrose sugar and the amino acids of the blood. Some pathogens do much harm by digesting body materials. The gas gangrene organisms form gas from muscle sugar and, as a result, the tissues where they grow become distended with gas bubbles. *Hemolytic* (blood-dissolving) streptococci make enzymes that can cause the dissolution of erythrocytes. Some bacteria form very poisonous waste products called *exotoxins.*

THE CHEMICAL COMPOSITION OF BACTERIA

Bacteria are made of protoplasm of the same general nature as the protoplasm of all living things. Its most important constituents are the proteins. In each bacterium there will be a number of different proteins—flagellar proteins, surface proteins, and *somatic* (body) proteins. In certain bacteria, notably those belonging to the acid-fast genus *Mycobacterium,* there is lipoid (fatlike) material in abundance. The presence of higher carbohydrates in capsular material has already been noted. Other complicated organic compounds that are found in bacteria include the enzymes, toxins, and pigments. Mineral elements are always present, as they are in all protoplasm. Phosphorus seems to be particularly important in bacteria. Sodium, magnesium, calcium, sulfur, and chlorine are always present.

BACTERIAL VARIATION

Variation is a universal characteristic of living organisms, and bacteria are no exception. Contrary to the impression given by many elementary discussions, no species of microorganisms is ever made up of absolutely identical individuals. Variations are due to the effect of environmental factors, to *mutations* (alterations in the mechanisms determining the hereditary make-up of the organisms), or to the results of new combinations of genetic material. All these forms of variation occur in nature and can also be studied in the laboratory. The variation of viruses is discussed in Chap. 33.

Temporary Modifications Caused by Environmental Conditions. We all take it for granted that food supply, temperature, and other conditions affect the growth of animals and plants. Crowded carrots in the garden row do not grow well; neither do crowded colonies of bacteria on an agar plate. *Bacillus subtilis* forms spores readily when it is grown on an agar slant. It forms relatively few in a broth culture. The nonsporing rod *Serratia marcescens* makes a bright-red pigment when it it grown at 27°C. Its growth at 37°C. is colorless. These changes are not permanent. *B. subtilis* transferred from the broth to another agar slant again forms plenty of spores. The colorless *S. marcescens* from the 37°C. culture will form red colonies if it is inoculated into fresh medium and incubated at lower temperature.

Mutation. All living organisms occasionally produce *mutants*. These are individuals definitely different from their ancestors and capable of passing on the difference to their offspring. Hereditary characteristics are determined by units of DNA called *genes*. In all higher plants and animals genes are found in definite arrangements within nuclear particles known as *chromosomes*. Mutations result from the loss of a gene, an alteration in a gene, or a rearrangement of genes within the chromosomes. Most mutations result in changes that make the mutants less able to survive or reproduce in the usual environment of the organism. Occasionally a mutant appears that is better adapted to its environment than its relatives. The term *selection* (or *natural selection*) is used for this process leading to the survival and multiplication of some mutants and the suppression of others.

Mutation of Bacteria. It is well established that bacteria contain DNA units that function as genes. There is also evidence that these units are arranged in chromosomes. The minute size of bacteria makes these structures extremely difficult to study. Mutations *appear* to occur very frequently in bacteria. This is because the bacteria multiply so rapidly. A mutation that occurs once in 50 generations would be found in man only once in every 1,000 years. A mutation occurring that frequently in a strain of bacteria would be found in a 24-hour culture started from a single bacterium. Radiations such as x-rays and ultraviolet rays and various chemicals such as mustard gas increase the incidence of mutations in all types of organisms including bacteria.

Two commonly observed types of mutations are described here. Examples of mutations that result in changes in virulence of pathogenic microorganisms and in the resistance of bacteria to antibacterial substances, such as antibiotics, will be discussed later in the text.

Variations in Colony Form. A strain of bacteria that normally has smooth, round colonies (*S colonies*) may give rise to colonies that are rough (*R colonies*), mucoid (*M colonies*), or dwarf (*D colonies*). Stained slides of these colonies show bacterial forms that are characteristic. The bacteria from S colonies are single and not markedly encapsulated. M-colony bacteria are heavily capsulated. Bacteria in R colonies are noncapsulated and are in chains or other aggregates. Most pathogens are in the S or M phase when isolated from their hosts. R mutants have often lost the ability to cause disease. Some flagellated bacteria form thin, spreading colonies on agar (*H colonies*), while nonflagellated mutants of these bacteria form solid colonies (*O colonies*) (Fig. 4·1).

Variations in Nutrition. A mutation may result in the loss or gain of the ability to utilize a particular compound. The intestinal bacterium *Escherichia coli* cannot ordinarily ferment cane sugar. When *E. coli* is placed in a medium containing this sugar but deficient in other sugars, it appears to acquire the ability to ferment this sugar. This does not mean, as is sometimes implied, that the bacterium has "become adapted to sucrose." What has happened is that a few mutant *E. coli* have been produced among the new cells in the growing culture. These mutants have an advantage over all the other cells because they can use the only sugar provided. So they grow rapidly while the others die off. In a short time their descendants constitute the bulk of the population.

In a similar fashion mutation may result in the gain (or loss) of the ability of a strain of bacteria to synthesize some substance, such as a protein or a "vitamin," that it needs to grow or reproduce. A pure strain of the mutant may then be able to grow in a simpler medium, or it may require a more complex one.

Sexuality of Bacteria. The usual method of bacterial reproduction is asexual. No one has directly observed any process of mating or sexual reproduction of bacteria. There are, however, several lines of experimental evidence which

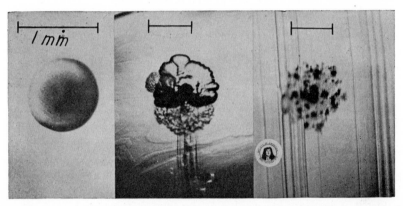

Fig. 4·1   Colony variations of hemolytic streptococci. (*SAB print 280, from Pomales-Lebron and Morales-Otero, Proc. Soc. Exper. Biol. & Med. 70:612.*)

indicate that some form of transfer of genetic material from one bacterial cell to another does occur.

Recombination of Bacterial Characteristics. In a study of great significance the American bacterial geneticist Lederberg has shown recombination of characteristics in the descendants of two mutant strains of *E. coli* grown together in broth. One strain was unable to synthesize three compounds needed for its growth but could synthesize two others. The second strain had just the opposite abilities. The first strain then was $T^-L^-B_1^-B^+M^+$; the second strain, $T^+L^+B_1^+B^-M^-$. (The letters stand for the specific compounds.) When the bacteria that had grown in the mixed broth culture were examined, it was found that approximately one out of every one hundred million cells could synthesize all the compounds. So a new strain, $T^+L^+B_1^+B^+M^+$, was produced. It was, therefore, a hybrid cell whose genes carried factors from two different "parent" cells. Although this hybrid bacterium was so rare, it could survive and grow in a medium deficient in all those compounds—a medium in which none of its relatives could survive.

Transformation and Transduction. Under certain conditions units of DNA may be transferred from one bacterium to another. This is *transformation*.

Noncapsulated (R) *Diplococcus pneumoniae* of the specific Type 2 will produce cocci that have Type 3 capsules when grown in a medium to which an extract of killed Type 3 diplococci has been added. Similarly, certain nonmotile strains of intestinal bacteria can be induced to produce motile offspring if they are grown in the presence of material from another strain that has been distintegrated by the action of a bacteriophage (a virus-attacking bacteria; see Chap. 33). In this and similar cases it is believed that the DNA is transported and introduced into the living cells by the infective bacterial virus. This process has been called *transduction.*

STUDY SUGGESTIONS

Are the biologic and chemical terms used in Chaps. 3 and 4 clear to you? Can you define them? Can you give illustrations? Consult your physiology and chemistry texts. Write down any questions that still puzzle you and bring them to class for discussion.

What observations have you made in the laboratory that indicate that processes of digestion, assimilation, excretion, and reproduction are going on in your cultures? What processes that you have observed there illustrate the unusual features of bacterial physiology?

Can you state and illustrate the four unusual features of bacterial physiology? Try to restate in your own words the processes of microbial decomposition of milk and leaves. Can you describe the possible life processes of a streptococcus invading the blood stream in a case of "blood poisoning"? Be sure you use the correct scientific terms in your description, and state the chemistry of the processes involved as completely as you can. What other examples of the results of microbial growth can you describe from your own experience?

To what factors are temporary (nontransmissible) variations in bacteria due? What is a mutation? How is a mutation brought about? What is the actual series of events that leads to what appears to be the changing of a bacterial culture into a culture that differs from the original in some measurable characteristic? Describe three forms of mutation that take place in bacteria. What is meant by *recombination?* by *transduction?* by *transformation?*

SUGGESTED READING

General References

ANDERSON, C. G.: "An Introduction to Bacteriological Chemistry." 2d ed., Williams & Wilkins, Baltimore, 1946.

LAMANNA, C., and M. F. MALLETTE: "Basic Bacteriology." Williams & Wilkins, Baltimore, 1953.

MOULDER, J. W.: Bacterial Physiology, in W. Burrow's "Textbook of Microbiology." 16th ed., Saunders, Philadelphia, 1954.

OGINSKY, E. L., and W. W. UMBREIT: "An Introduction to Bacterial Physiology." Freeman, San Francisco, 1954.

WERKMAN, C. H., and P. W. WILSON: "Bacterial Physiology." Academic Press, New York, 1951.

Summaries of Recent Research

ADELBERG, E. A.: The use of metabolically blocked organisms for the analysis of biosynthetic pathways. *Bact. Rev.* **17:**253.

COHEN, G. N.: Metabolism of Bacteria, in "Annual Review of Microbiology." Vol. 5, Annual Reviews, Inc., Stanford, 1951.

WOODS, D. D.: The integration of research on the nutrition of microorganisms. *J. Gen. Microbiol.* **9:**151 (1953).

Variation and Genetics

BRAUN, W.: "Bacterial Genetics." Saunders, Philadelphia, 1953.

CATCHSIDE, D. G.: "The Genetics of Microorganisms." Pitman, London, 1951.

COLD SPRING HARBOR SYMPOSIA, The Biological Laboratory: "Genes and Mutations." Vol. XVI, Cold Spring Harbor, N.Y., 1951.

LEDERBERG, J., and E. L. TATUM: Sex in bacteria: genetic studies, 1945–1952. *Science* **118:**169 (1953).

Techniques of Microbiology:
The Microscope, Culture Media

LABORATORY WORK IN MICROBIOLOGY

The scientist working in the microbiology laboratory strives to find the answers to both practical and theoretical questions such as What microorganisms are present in this material? How many are there? What are their morphologic and physiologic characteristics? What is their identity? If they are desirable types, what methods are effective in encouraging their growth? If they are undesirable, how can their growth be inhibited and how can they be killed? These questions are answered by the results of thousands of routine tests performed daily by technicians in hospital, public health, and industrial laboratories and by individually devised tests carried on by research scientists in special laboratories. Although such laboratory tests are seldom part of the duties of the nurse, she must understand them because she is usually the person responsible for the collection of materials for examination. In addition, the nursing care she gives must be based on intelligent interpretation of the reported results. Finally, since knowledge of the exact nature of microorganisms is based on their study by these methods, adequate education in microbiology must include understanding of its techniques.

Special Problems. Because of their extreme smallness, microorganisms have to be studied by the use of high-powered microscopes and special methods of microscopic preparation such as stained fixed smears. Since their physiology cannot be studied by observing the reactions of a single individual, pure cultures of specific kinds of microorganisms must be obtained and studied in special growth materials called culture media.

Presentation in This Text. In this chapter and the next, the nature and uses of the techniques and apparatus of microbiology will be discussed, the basic methods will be surveyed, and illustrations will be presented of applications of these methods to medical microbiology. In later chapters the special applications of laboratory technique to the various aspects of bacteriology will be discussed. For example, the standard methods for the sanitary bacteriologic examination of water and milk will be described in the chapters on the bacteriology of these substances. For formulas of media and stains and for special techniques, the student should consult the references given at the end of this chapter and at the end of Chap. 6.

VISUALIZATION OF MICROORGANISMS BY HIGH-POWER MICROSCOPES

The Compound Microscope. The microscope most commonly used in teaching microbiology and in practical laboratory work is the monocular compound microscope equipped with two interchangeable *oculars* (eyepieces) and three sets of *objectives* (Fig. 5·1). For most bacteriologic work we use the 10× ocular and the oil immersion objective which together give a magnification of almost 1,000 diameters. Lower-powered oculars and objectives are used for the study of yeasts, molds, and protozoa.

The mirror, the diaphragm shutter, and the glass condenser, which are all under the stage of the microscope, direct and regulate the light that passes through the object placed in the center of the stage. The image of the object then passes through the lenses in the objective, through the microscope tube, through the lenses of the eyepiece, and into the eye of the observer. Figure 5·1 shows diagrammatically how this light travels and how the image is enlarged. The large and small wheels on the side of the tube are the *coarse* and *fine adjustments,* which raise and lower the lenses to bring the object into exact focus.

The oil immersion objective is given that name because it is actually immersed in a drop of oil placed directly over the object. The oil is Shillaber oil, mineral oil, or cedar oil that has the same *optical index* as glass. This means that when light passes from glass into the oil or from the oil into glass its direction is not changed. The oil is used so that sufficient light will pass into the very tiny bottom lens of this highest-power objective.

The compound microscope is a delicate and expensive instrument. The type used for most microbiologic work costs several hundred dollars to replace. It must be handled with respect and care. If the student will take the

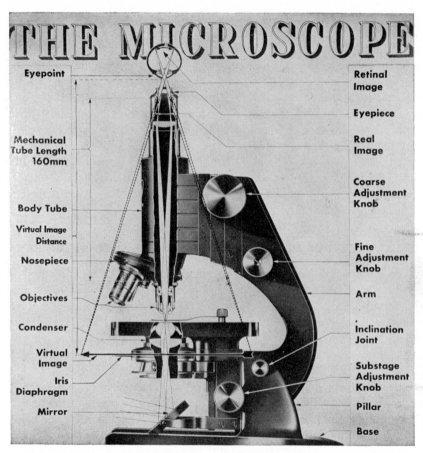

FIG. 5·1 Optical and mechanical features of the compound microscope. (*American Optical Company, Instrument Division.*)

trouble to keep it scrupulously clean and learn to use it properly, it will reveal marvelous and exciting things.

Methods of Microscopic Study. The most common method of studying bacterial morphology is by means of a fixed smear, stained with methylene blue or Gram's stain and examined under the oil immersion lens.

The Fixed Smear. A fixed smear is made by placing a small amount of the material to be examined on a clean glass slide. The inoculating needle

(Fig. 5·5*c*) is used for the transfer. If the material to be examined is thick, it is mixed on the slide with a loopful of distilled water. A thin smear is *fixed* (fastened) to the slide by thorough drying in air. To fix a thick smear, the slide is passed rapidly through a bunsen burner flame several times.

The Simple Stain. One or more drops of a solution of methylene blue are placed on the dried smear. After 30 to 60 seconds, the slide is thoroughly washed by holding it under a gently running tap or by agitating it in a container of clean tap water. The under side of the slide is wiped dry, and the upper surface is blotted dry with filter paper. A drop of immersion oil is placed over the dried, stained smear, and the smear is examined with the oil immersion lens. Other stains, such as dilute carbol fuchsin, safranin, and gentian violet, may be used in the same way.

The Gram Stain. The Gram stain is an example of a differential stain. Bacteria that retain the original dye even when treated with alcohol are gram-positive. Those that are decolorized by the alcohol and then take the counterstain are gram-negative. The technique and results of each step are summarized in Table 5·1. The reaction to the Gram stain reflects other important characteristics of the bacteria. For example, gram-positive bacteria are ordinarily much more susceptible to the effect of penicillin than are the gram-negative bacteria.

The common morphologic types can be readily identified in these stained preparations. Granules and vacuoles can be seen. Endospores appear as re-

Table 5·1

The Gram Stain *

Technical steps	Staining effect on	
	Gram-positive bacteria	Gram-negative bacteria
Stain fixed smear with ammonium oxalate crystal violet for 60 seconds		
Wash in water		
Cover with Gram's iodine solution for 60 seconds...	Purple	Purple
Wash in water		
Decolorize in 95 per cent alcohol for 30 seconds.....	Purple	Colorless
Dry in air		
Stain with safranin for 10 seconds................	Purple	Pink

* Hucker's modification. Slightly different chemicals and time intervals are used in other modifications.

fractile, unstained, round or oval bodies within the vegetative cells. Free spores are also unstained except for a fringe of dye around the periphery.

The Liquid Mount. Flagella are not visible by ordinary staining methods. The special methods needed are seldom successful in the hands of inexperi-

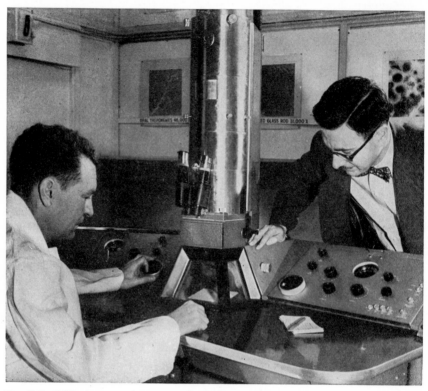

FIG. 5·2   RCA electron microscope. The large vertical structure is the vacuum column through which the electrons pass. Control dials are at the left and right. The image is viewed on the glassed-in area in front of the operator. If he wishes further magnification of that image, he can use the binocular viewer attached to the front of the vacuum column. (*Radio Corporation of America.*)

enced workers. However, motility can be demonstrated easily by the hanging drop technique. A loopful of a young culture of the organism is placed on a clean coverslip. The coverslip is inverted over the hollow of a special type of slide called a *hollow-ground* slide or *culture* slide. The small drop of liquid now hangs down into the hollow. The slide is examined with the high dry objective of the microscope. The light must be diminished so that the unstained bacteria can be distinguished. In this preparation all minute particles including bacteria exhibit a vibration caused by molecular motion. This is called *brownian movement*. Bacteria or other truly motile organisms will show true motility by progressing in definite directions.

Special stains are often useful for visualization of spores, capsules, some types of granules, and acid-fastness. Permanent mounts of stained preparations preserve them for future reexamination. Simple liquid mounts are used for the study of worm ova, protozoa, and yeasts. These may be unstained or stained with supravital stains. Liquid mounts of molds are best made with lactophenol solution as the mounting material.

Three special methods of examination with the light microscope are also useful in microbiology.

Dark-field Microscopy. Special substage condenser arrangements are used to prevent light from passing directly through the objects on the stage. Instead the light enters from the periphery of the field and illuminates the objects obliquely. As a result the objects appear bright against a black background. This method of microscopy is particularly useful in the study of the motion of spirochetes in a liquid mount.

Phase Microscopy. The usual light microscope can be adapted for phase microscopy by placing a special ring-form diaphragm in the condenser and diffraction plates in the objectives. By these means the light rays are altered and made to produce greater visible contrast between the finer structures in living microorganisms.

Fluorescent Microscopy. Microorganisms such as the bacterium of tuberculosis can be stained with special dyes (e.g., auramine) which make them luminous when ultraviolet light rather than the usual form of light is used for microscopic examination. This technique aids in finding and identifying the organisms. It does not show any details of morphology.

The Electron Microscope. Rickettsiae, filtrable viruses, and the finer structure of bacterial cells are best studied with the powerful new electron microscopes (Fig. 5·2). These very expensive instruments are not available in ordinary laboratories, but the excellent micrographs taken through them by experts are available for study. Many of the figures in this text are electron micrographs and therefore show details that the student will not see in her own laboratory experience.

The efficient magnification with the usual daylight microscope is seldom over 1,000 times. Photographs taken through it become blurred in outline and show little detail when the objects are magnified over 2,000 times. With the modern electron microscope, direct views of the object magnified up to 20,000 times are practicable, and the micrographs taken through it can be enlarged until a total magnification of 100,000 or more times is obtained (Fig. 5·3). Instead of rays of visible light, the electron microscope uses a stream of high-speed electrons with a wavelength only 1/100,000 that of visible light. These electrons pass through magnetic fields which redirect

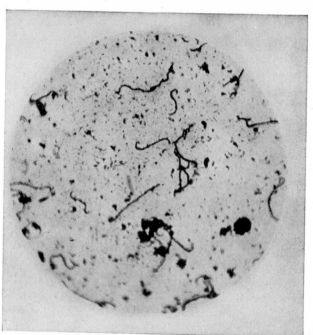

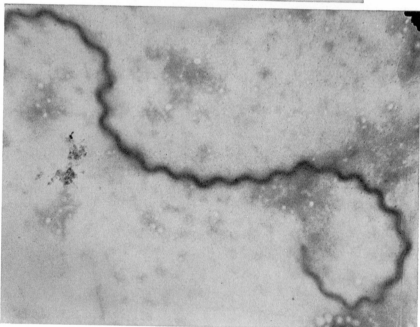

Fig. 5·3 Pictures of a spirochete, *Leptospira canicola*, taken with light microscope (×1,000) above; and taken with electron microscope (×10,000) below. (*Courtesy of Dr. Harry E. Morton, from J. Bact. 45:145*)

54

them in a manner analogous to the redirection of visible light by the condenser, objective, and eyepiece lenses of the light microscope.

Preparations for electron micrography are mounted on thin films of collodion rather than on glass slides. They are not "stained" in the usual sense of the word, but they may be treated with chemicals such as calcium chloride to increase the contrast between the background and the microbial structures. The microorganisms are also frequently treated with heavy metal such as gold or chromium. The special technique used, the *metal-shadowing method,* gives a very useful three-dimensional aspect to electron micrographs (Figs. 2·6*a* and 2·6*b*). Ultrathin sections of microorganisms or of parasitized cells of animals or plants show extraordinary detail when examined by the electron microscope. (See Fig. 2·3.)

The whole interior of the microscope, including the stage, must be maintained at a vacuum, for air would interfere with the motion of electrons. The image produced is not directly visible, since the human eye is not capable of receiving electrons, but a visible image is obtained on a fluorescent screen or photographic plate. (See Fig. 5·4.)

CULTURE MEDIA

Culture media (sing. *medium*) are the materials in which microorganisms are grown. The growth itself is called a *culture*. The general nature and use of media and the methods used in making cultures will be discussed here. Technical details of the preparation and formulas of media can be found in the books listed in the bibliography at the end of this chapter. Apparatus used in bacterial cultivation is shown in Fig. 5·5.

Characteristics of a Good Culture Medium. A satisfactory medium for the cultivation of bacteria must have the following characteristics:

1. It must be *sterile* (free from the presence of any living organisms) and be handled in such a manner as to prevent all *contamination* (entrance of undesired organisms).

2. It must be neutral in reaction rather than acid or alkaline. Or, to put it more scientifically, it must have a pH of approximately 7. (See later section in this chapter for discussion of pH.) In order to keep the medium from becoming excessively acid or alkaline as organisms grow in it, it contains buffer chemicals.

3. It must be free from any chemical that would hinder the growth of desired organisms.

4. It must contain, in proper amounts, all the ingredients that are needed for bacterial growth. These must be varied according to the nutritional requirements of the particular types for which the medium is designed. These ingredients will ordinarily include:

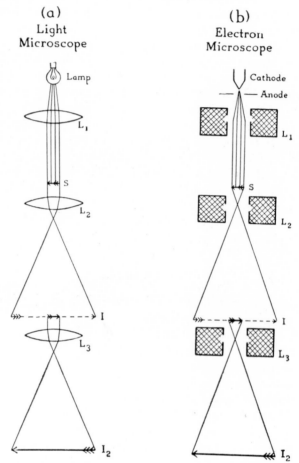

FIG. 5·4 The path of light through a light microscope (*a*), compared with the path of electrons through the electron microscope (*b*). A system of magnetic fields serves the same function in the electron microscope as the series of glass lenses in the light microscope. These fields and lenses are L_1, the condenser; L_2, the objectives; L_3, the oculars. S is the object to be magnified; I, the primary image; and I_2, the final image. (*SAB print 31.*)

a. Proteins, peptones, or other nitrogen-containing substances, which the organisms need to build protoplasm.

b. Energy foods such as sugar, starch, or protein, which the organisms can oxidize to provide energy.

c. Minerals in small amounts but in great variety.

d. A relatively large amount of water.

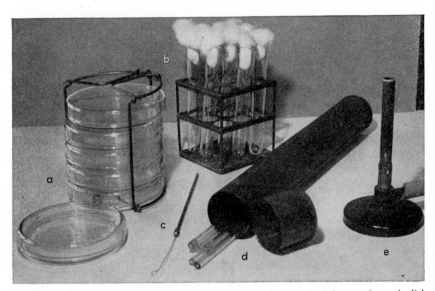

Fig. 5·5 Implements used by the microbiologist: (*a*) petri dishes and petri dish holder; (*b*) test tubes and test tube holder; (*c*) inoculating needle; (*d*) pipets in pipet box; (*e*) bunsen burner.

e. Accessory growth substances. These are specific, complicated organic compounds which the organisms may need but which they cannot manufacture for themselves. In animal nutrition such substances are called vitamins. Many of the vitamins of human nutrition are also accessory growth substances for bacteria. For example, many pathogenic bacteria cannot grow unless the culture medium contains minute amounts of vitamin B_1 (thiamine).

Commonly Used Types of Media. When a material that occurs in nature, such as milk, is used as a medium, it is called a *natural* medium. However, most of the commonly used media are *artificial* media—growth materials that are deliberately made to serve this purpose. If a medium is called *synthetic,* its exact chemical composition is known. It has to be made of exactly measured materials of known composition.

The media used by early bacteriologists were either *solid media* such as slices of carrot or *liquid media* such as dilute meat broths. In the early 1880s the German bacteriologist Robert Koch introduced the practice of adding gelatin or agar-agar to media to make them into jellies. Such media are called *liquefiable solid media*. They are in gel form at room temperature but can be melted by heat and then poured into culture plates (petri dishes) or made into slants in test tubes. On these media the bacteria, yeasts, and molds grow into visible spots of growth called *colonies*. Agar is more commonly used than gelatin. Gelatin melts at body temperature so that cultures kept in warm incubators become broths. Moreover, it is digested to liquid form by many bacteria. Agar remains in gel form at all temperatures used for incubation and is not digested by any common types of microorganisms.

Selective media are media to which substances have been added that encourage the growth of some desired type of organism or discourage the growth of undesired types, or both. Often they are so constituted that colonies of the desired organism develop characteristics by which they can be easily recognized. For example, Endo's agar is used to separate the common intestinal nonpathogen *Escherichia coli* from other bacteria. The lactose contained in the medium encourages *E. coli,* while the sodium sulfite and the fuchsin dye prevent the growth of most other kinds of organisms. Substances formed by *E. coli*'s growth make its colonies dark red with a green metallic surface luster so that they are readily identified (Fig. 24·2).

The Standard Culture Media. Nutrient broth and nutrient agar are the most commonly used of all culture media. The majority of other media may be regarded as modifications of these two. A consideration of these two media will illustrate the nature of media in general.

Nutrient broth consists of commercial beef extract, peptone, and water. The beef extract supplies the needed minerals and accessory growth substances. The peptone, a commercial preparation of partially hydrolyzed proteins, contains a mixture of peptones and other nitrogenous products and supplies the food for both assimilation and energy. *Nutrient agar* is made by adding 1.5 to 2 per cent dry agar-agar to the nutrient broth. The ingredients used are bought from drug companies and are so carefully manufactured that the resulting medium is free from any undesirable chemicals and has a pH very close to 7 (neutrality). The mixture is heated to thoroughly dissolve the ingredients, filtered to make it clear, put into suitable tubes or flasks, stoppered with nonabsorbent cotton to prevent air-borne contamination, and sterilized by steam under pressure.

Variants of Nutrient Broth and Agar. The most commonly used variants of these media are (1) the *infusion agars* and *broths* made with an infusion of fresh meat instead of commercial beef extract; (2) *gelatin media* made by adding gelatin instead of agar-agar to broth; (3) *sugar media* in which there is usually 1 per cent added specific carbohydrate; (4) *blood agar* and *blood broth* made by adding 10 per cent citrated whole blood to media containing

0.5 per cent sodium chloride. Frequently pH indicators are added to sugar media so that changes in hydrogen ion concentration will be evident. The name given a medium usually indicates its composition. For example, purple dextrose infusion agar contains brom cresol purple as an indicator, dextrose sugar, and meat infusion rather than meat extract. (We would assume that it also contains both water and peptone.) So-called chocolate agar does not contain chocolate. It is blood agar heated until the hemoglobin of the red blood cells has taken on a brown color.

Media are obtainable in dehydrated form. The required amount of the dry powder is added to water and the mixture is heated to dissolve, tubed, and sterilized. Many laboratories use these dehydrated products for the preparation of the more complicated types of media. They are convenient, time-saving, and inexpensive. Their use ensures that media used in different laboratories will be alike and results obtained with them will therefore be comparable.

HYDROGEN ION CONCENTRATION

The true acidity or alkalinity of a medium has great influence on the growth of microorganisms. The development of acid or base in cultures helps in the interpretation of the physiologic activities of microorganisms. For these reasons the terms hydrogen ion concentration, pH, and pH indicators are frequently used in any discussion of bacteriology and are explained here.

pH. The effective acidity or alkalinity of a solution is measured not by the total amount of acid or base present but by the concentration of free hydrogen ions and free hydroxyl ions liberated from the substances in solution. The term *pH* is a convenient arithmetical expression of this true acidity or alkalinity. Any material which has a pH of 7 is neutral. In it the hydrogen and hydroxyl ions present exactly balance each other. If a substance has a pH of more than 7, e.g., pH 8.5, there are more hydroxyl ions than hydrogen ions and the material is alkaline. If the pH is less than 7, e.g., 5.3, there is a predominance of hydrogen ions and the material is truly acid.

Hydrogen Ion Indicators. Certain dyes change color as the hydrogen ion concentration of the material in which they are dissolved is altered. Such dyes are called *indicators*. Each indicator has a *sensitive range,* a range of pH values over which it shows definite color changes. For example, the commonly used indicator brom cresol purple is purple at a pH of 6.8 and in all more alkaline solutions. If acid is added slowly, it gradually becomes red, orange, and then yellow. A bright definite yellow develops when the pH reaches 5.2 and persists at all more acid concentrations. This indicator, then, has a sensitive range of 5.2 to 6.8. The sensitive ranges and colors of the indicators most commonly used in microbiology are given in Table 5·2.

Table 5·2

Indicators Commonly Used in Microbiology

Indicator	Sensitive range	Full acid color	Full alkaline color
Phenol red............	6.8–8.4	Yellow	Red
Brom thymol blue *....	6.0–7.6	Yellow	Blue
Brom cresol purple.....	5.2–6.8	Yellow	Purple
Brom cresol green......	3.8–5.4	Yellow	Blue
Brom phenol blue......	3.0–4.6	Yellow	Blue

* Brom thymol blue has a distinctive grass-green color at the pH of 7 and so is very useful in determining neutrality.

Indicators have two chief uses in microbiology. First, they are used to determine and regulate the initial pH of a medium. When a culture medium is made up, the pH of which is in doubt, a few milliliters are removed and several drops of an indicator such as brom thymol blue added. If the grass-green color that indicates neutrality develops, nothing further needs to be done to the medium. If a blue color develops, it shows that the medium is alkaline; if a yellow color, that it is acid. In either case something must be done to make the medium neutral. Most frequently the mixture is found to be acid. Then measured amounts of dilute sodium hydroxide are added to the sample until the grass-green color is obtained. From the amount of alkali used to neutralize the small sample it is possible to compute the amount needed to neutralize the whole batch of medium.

The second common use of pH indicators is their incorporation in culture media, particularly those containing carbohydrates, so that changes in color indicating development of acid or alkali can be seen.

Fairly accurate determinations of pH can be made by these simple observations of color change or, in media that do not contain indicator, with the aid of paper strips saturated with indicator dyes. For more careful work, sets of standard colored solutions can be purchased and with them the pH can be determined to 0.2. For special research problems, electrometric measurement is done, using a potentiometer and the quinhydrone or glass electrode. For further discussion of these methods see the chapter references.

STUDY SUGGESTIONS

There is no substitute for actual laboratory experience. What apparatus described in this chapter have you used? What have you not used? Which techniques described here have you carried out or seen demonstrated? In later laboratory work in this course you will find it useful to recheck on material in this chapter and the next. The reference material in your laboratory manual should also be checked. You should not try to learn that material, but you should become familiar with its arrangement and content so that you can put it to practical use.

Describe the general plan of the compound microscope. How does the oil immersion lens work? What is the plan of the electron microscope? What are its advantages? Has it any disadvantages?

What are the characteristics of a good culture medium? What is a liquid medium? a liquefiable-solid medium? a selective medium? a synthetic medium? a natural medium? Give examples of media that you have used. List three media that are commonly used and state the chief source of energy food, the source of nitrogenous food for assimilation, the source of accessory growth substances in each.

What have you learned in high school and nursing school chemistry about acids and alkalies? Did you titrate any solution in the laboratory? Describe what you did in scientific terms. How did you adjust the reaction of the solution? How are these same methods used in the preparation of culture media? What pH indicators have you used in chemistry? in bacteriology? How and why did you use them?

SUGGESTED READING

Microscopes

Bausch and Lomb: "Student's Manual for the Compound Microscope." Rochester, N.Y., 1953.

Lonert, A. C.: "Turtox Microscopy Booklet." General Biological Supply House, Chicago, 1946.

Richards, O. W.: "Microscopy in Medicine." American Optical Company, Buffalo, 1937.

Rivers, T. M.: "Viral and Rickettsial Infections of Man." 2d ed., Lippincott, Philadelphia, 1952. Pages 43 to 50.

Culture Media

Baltimore Biological Laboratory, Inc.: "Culture Media, Materials and Apparatus for the Bacteriology Laboratory." 3d ed., Baltimore, 1951.

Difco Laboratories, Inc.: "Difco Manual of Dehydrated Culture Media and Reagents." 9th ed., Detroit, 1953.

Society of American Bacteriologists: Preparation of Culture Media, Leaflet II, in "Manual of Methods for the Pure Culture Study of Bacteria." Biotech, Geneva, N.Y., 1950.

————: Hydrogen Ion Concentration, Leaflet IX, in "Manual of Methods for the Pure Culture Study of Bacteria." Biotech, Geneva, N.Y., 1948.

CHAPTER 6

Techniques of Microbiology: Preparation and Study of Cultures

Bacteria can be discovered by direct microscopic examination of materials, but only when they are present in large numbers. Bacteria can be identified under the microscope only if they possess some unique combination of morphologic characteristics. Their physiologic processes cannot be studied under the microscope. No method of staining satisfactorily distinguishes between bacteria that are alive and those that are dead. For these reasons cultivation in artificial media is required to discover bacteria that are present in small numbers and to identify the majority of types. It is also required to determine whether they are aerobic or anaerobic, whether they are alive or dead, what foods they use, and many other facts about their physiology.

The greater part of this chapter will be devoted to methods used in the study of heterotrophic bacteria. Many of these methods are also used in the study of yeasts and molds. The techniques employed in the study of uncommon types of bacteria and of other microorganisms are summarized at the end of the chapter.

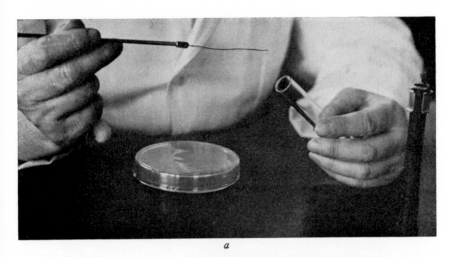

a

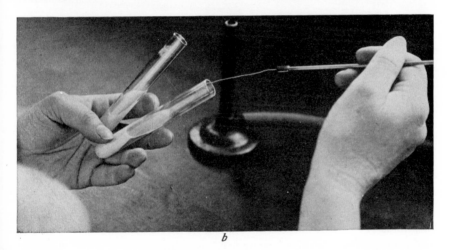

b

Fig. 6·1 Transfer techniques. (*a*) Transfer from tube to plate. Note the method of holding the plug. (*b*) Transfer from one tube culture to another. The two plugs are held by the hand that holds the needle—one in the curve of the little finger, the other between the fourth and fifth fingers.

TECHNIQUES OF CULTIVATION

Methods of Transfer. The handling of microorganisms requires special techniques because of their minute size and because cultures must be kept free from all unwanted microorganisms. In medical microbiology there is the additional need to prevent the escape of pathogenic organisms from cultures into the environment. Bacteria are usually handled with an inoculat-

FIG. 6·2 Fermentation of sugar broths by *Escherichia coli*. From left to right: dextrose broth, lactose broth, sucrose broth, maltose broth, xylose broth. Note gas formation in all except the sucrose broth. Bromcresol purple indicator is present in the broths. The sucrose broth is purple, therefore still neutral. The other broths, which look lighter in the photograph, are yellow, indicating the formation of acid.

ing needle, which may be used with a straight tip or as a loop for the transfer of liquids (Fig. 5·5). The needle is made of a type of metal wire that will withstand repeated sterilizations by flaming. It is flamed before use to destroy any organisms that may be on it and again after use to kill organisms from the culture that may still be present. This is a part of the *aseptic technique* that is required in handling cultures. The term implies the use of sterile materials and of methods of handling that avoid all contaminations. Figure 6·1 illustrates some steps in this technique. Sterile pipets and sterile swabs are also used for transferring microorganisms.

Incubation. *Incubation* provides suitable temperature for growth. In medical laboratories the incubator temperature is generally set at 37°C., since that is the optimum growth temperature for organisms that parasitize man. Saprophytic bacteria and yeasts and molds can be cultivated readily at warm room temperature. Open pans of water are placed in incubators to prevent drying out of cultures. The time and temperature of incubation are always recorded, as well as the type of medium used.

Types of Cultures. Broths are used in 5- to 10-ml. amounts in test tubes or small flasks. Sugar broths are placed in fermentation tubes so that gas formation may be readily detected (Fig. 6·2). Broths are inoculated by introducing a bit of solid matter or a loopful of liquid with an inoculating needle.

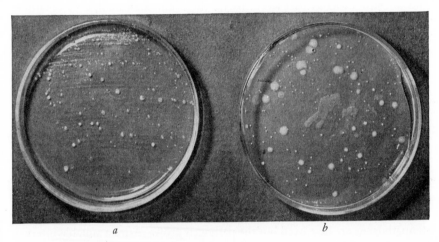

a   *b*

Fig. 6·3   Streak plate and pour plate of saliva on nutrient agar. (*a*) Streak plate. All colonies are on the surface of the plate. (*b*) Pour plate from 1:10,000 dilution of saliva. Since there are 215 colonies on this plate, the plate count of this specimen is 2,150,000 bacteria per milliliter. The large round colonies and some of the others are growing on the surface of the agar. Many of the smaller colonies are subsurface colonies. The filmlike growths are "bottom colonies" spreading between the agar and the glass.

Agar media are stored in flasks, or in test tubes containing 10 to 15 ml. Agar is most commonly used as a *plating medium,* by melting it and pouring it into petri dishes where it is allowed to harden. If the organisms are planted by streaking them over the already hardened agar, the culture is called a *streak plate.* A *pour plate* is made by mixing a bit of the material with a tube of melted and cooled agar and then pouring the mixture into the plate. In a streak plate the colonies grow in rows on the surface, while in a pour plate they are distributed all through the medium (Fig. 6·3). Agar media are also used as *slants.* The medium is allowed to solidify to form a slanted surface in the test tube. Slants are inoculated by stabbing the *butt* (solid bottom part of the agar) and then streaking the surface (Fig. 6·6).

Gelatin in a test tube may be stabbed with a straight needle to make a *stab culture*. It is also used as a plating medium. Since gelatin melts at 37°C., gelatin cultures are ordinarily incubated at temperatures of 20 to 25°C.

Crude Cultures. Materials that occur in nature, such as soil, water, foods, and animal excreta, contain mixtures of various sorts of microorganisms. When a culture is made of such material, many species of organisms develop and the culture is called a *crude* or *mixed culture*.

Pure Cultures. A *pure culture* contains just one species of organism. Such a culture is required for intensive study of an organism, for its identification, and for most experimental work. By far the commonest method of obtaining a pure culture is by the transfer of organisms from a single isolated colony on a crude plate culture to a tube of sterile medium. This is called fishing a colony. In practical laboratory work, the bacteriologist has some particular organism in mind that he wishes to isolate. He obtains a material that contains the desired type of organism and makes a crude streak culture plate using a suitable selective medium. When growth has developed, he searches for a colony typical of the organism that he wants. When one is found, he makes certain that it is well isolated from other colonies. He then makes a stained slide of it to be sure it is the type he is looking for. Finally he transfers it to a new medium, incubates it, and thus obtains a pure culture.

A pure culture of a pathogenic organism is sometimes obtained by animal inoculation. The material containing a mixture of organisms is inoculated into an animal. The animal acts as a selective medium. In its body the nonpathogens are destroyed but the pathogen grows. After a suitable interval, material from the animal can be transferred to a culture medium and a pure culture of the pathogen will result. A third method of isolation is required for special research problems where a single-cell strain of the organism must be used. A drop of liquid containing the organisms is mounted on the stage of a specially equipped microscope. By the manipulation of screws the bacteriologist directs a capillary pipet into the drop of liquid and picks up a single bacterium. The cell is transferred to a tube of sterile medium where it grows into a pure culture. This procedure involves the use of expensive equipment and the development of an expert technique.

APPLICATION OF MICROBIOLOGIC TECHNIQUES

The most common problems of bacteriologic laboratory work are (1) the investigation of types and numbers of organisms in a material; (2) the determination of the destruction or the survival of organisms subjected to unfavorable conditions; (3) the investigation of physiologic activities of microorganisms; and (4) the identification of specific bacteria. The basic methods used will be discussed here. When the student comes to the study of the laboratory methods for the testing of disinfectants, water, milk, food, etc., she will find that they are essentially applications of these methods to special instances of the same basic problems.

Investigation of Types and Numbers of Organisms. Two general techniques are employed to discover the types and numbers of organisms in any material. They are (1) direct microscope examination of the material, and (2) cultivation of the material in suitable culture media. Ideally both methods are employed since the information obtained from each alone is incomplete. Sometimes only one is used, either because the other method is impossible in that particular case or because only limited information is needed.

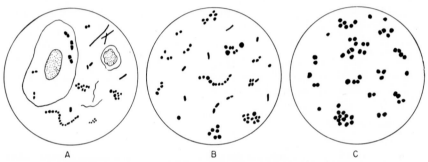

Fig. 6·4 Bacteria of saliva as seen on stained slides with oil immersion lens. (*A*) Direct smear of saliva showing two body cells and at least eight kinds of bacteria; (*B*) smear from broth culture of saliva—only three types of bacteria are seen; (*C*) smear of single colony from agar plate—only one type of bacterium.

Microscopic Study. Let us suppose that we are to examine a specimen of human saliva with the object of determining as completely as possible the types and numbers of organisms in it. If a fixed smear is made, stained with methylene blue, and examined, we will see a picture like that shown in Fig. 6·4*A*. From it we can determine that certain morphologic types of organism are present in the saliva. We can note their relative numbers. If the smear is made with a definite amount of saliva and examined with a calibrated microscope, we can determine the total number of bacteria per milliliter of the original material. This is called the *direct microscopic count.*

Study by Cultivation. Now suppose we make some cultures from this specimen. One loopful will be inoculated into a tube of infusion broth and another loopful will be streaked over a plate of blood agar. A pour plate of infusion agar will be made, using 1/10,000 ml. of the saliva. (The dilution is prepared by transferring 1 ml. of saliva to 99 ml. of sterile water. Then 1 ml. of this 1:100 dilution is transferred to another 99 ml. of sterile water, making a 1:10,000 dilution. This high dilution is used to avoid overcrowding of colonies on the pour plate.)

On removal from the incubator the broth will be cloudy. A stained slide made from it will show many bacteria (Fig. 6·4*B*), but it will not look like the slide of the original saliva. Fewer types of organisms will be seen, but they will be found in enormous numbers. They are the organisms favored by this particular medium and incubation temperature. Other organisms seen in the direct smear will not appear at all in the stain of the broth culture. They are the ones that were not favored by this method of cultivation.

The blood agar plate will show many colonies along the line where it was streaked. From the study of these colonies we will obtain some valuable information about certain important physiologic types of organism in the saliva. If some colonies are surrounded by clear areas in which the red blood cells have been dissolved, we will know that the saliva contained hemolytic bacteria. If other colonies are surrounded by greenish halos, we will know that the bacteria present include some that change hemoglobin to a green color. From this plate we may fish colonies for further study.

The colonies on the pour plate will be counted. Since each presumably grew from an organism planted there, the number of organisms in the 1/10,000 ml. of saliva must have been at least as many as this colony count. If this number is multiplied by 10,000 we obtain a figure which is called the *plate count* (the colony count times the dilution factor). The plate count indicates roughly the number of living bacteria per milliliter of the saliva that were capable of growth into visible colonies under these conditions. It is not as exact as the direct microscopic count, and it is always smaller for two reasons: first, many bacteria will fail to grow into countable colonies; second, a clump of bacteria, such as a packet of sarcinae, containing a number of organisms, will grow into just one colony.

When we investigate a material such as drinking water that contains at most only a few hundred bacteria per milliliter, we must rely entirely on cultural methods. We cannot find these few bacteria in a stained slide, for as we look at a single field under the oil immersion lens we see only about 1/500,000 of a milliliter of the material from which the slide was made. Other materials such as air and solid surfaces cannot be made into smears.

When our purpose is to discover morphologic types, we use direct microscopic examination wherever possible. When we want to determine the presence of physiologic types, cultures must be used. For example, in the study of a spoiled food, such problems as the presence of gram-negative rods, the relative number of free spores, and the total number of mold hyphae can be answered by direct microscopic examination. To determine the presence or numbers of acid formers or of anaerobic organisms, cultivation will be required.

From the previous discussions it is evident that colony formation on agar is helpful to the bacteriologist in three ways. First, he can often recognize and tentatively identify an organism from the appearance of its colony. Second, fishing a colony provides a simple method of procuring a pure culture. Third, the number of colonies gives evidence of the number of organisms in the original material.

Determination of Survival of Bacteria. When a plant or animal has been exposed to some unfavorable condition it is a simple matter to decide by direct observation whether it is alive or dead. It is much more difficult to decide whether a bacterium is still living or has been killed. In general, if an organism grows when transferred to a suitable medium, we consider that its survival has been proved; if it fails to grow, we assume that it was killed.

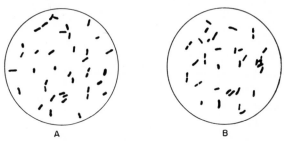

Fig. 6·5 Stained smears of *Escherichia coli* (*A*) and *Salmonella typhosa* (*B*). Note that it is impossible to distinguish these organisms by morphology alone.

This technique is the basis of many tests of methods of disinfection and sterilization.

Testing the Physiologic Reactions of Bacteria. In Chap. 4 many physiologic activities of bacteria were described. Knowledge of these processes has been gained by cultivation of pure cultures of organisms in special types of media. For example, on page 39 there is the statement, "the commonest bacillus of the intestine, *Escherichia coli,* has enzymes that can attack practically all sugars except sucrose (cane sugar)." This knowledge of the physiology of *E. coli* was obtained by inoculating a pure culture of the organism into a series of fermentation tubes each containing a different sugar broth. After incubation, acid and gas were found in the tubes of dextrose, lactose, xylose, and maltose broths; no acid or gas was found in the tube of sucrose broth (Fig. 6·2).

The Identification of Bacteria. Zoologists and botanists classify most types of organism by observing their structural characteristics. Bacteria cannot be completely classified by such means. Two kinds of bacteria indistinguishable under the microscope may belong to two entirely different species. The harmless *E. coli* cannot be told from the organism of typhoid fever, *Salmonella typhosa,* by any method of microscopic examination (Fig. 6·5). But

Agar stroke cultures

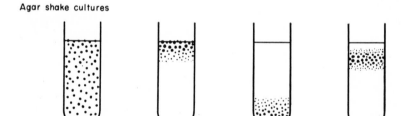

Beaded   Filiform   Echinulate   Spreading   Arborescent

Gelatin stab cultures

Stratiform   Crateriform   Infundibuliform   Saccate   Napiform

Agar shake cultures

Facultative   Aerobic   Anaerobic   Microaerophilic

FIG. 6·6 Growth characteristics in tube cultures.

physiologically they are very different. *E. coli* ferments many sugars with gas formation; *S. typhosa* forms acid from only a few and gas from none. Obviously they also differ in pathogenicity. Physiologic as well as morphologic characteristics will be needed to differentiate the two.

When the bacteriologist tries to classify an unknown organism he has to

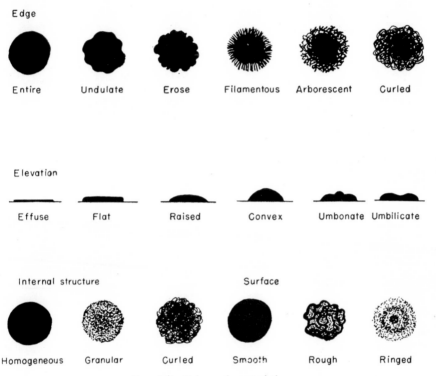

Fig. 6·7   Colony characteristics.

study both its morphology and its physiology. He must make a hanging drop to determine its motility, a simple stain so that he can describe its cell shape and groupings, a Gram's stain to determine its gram reaction. He studies its growth characteristics in tube media (Fig. 6·6) and its colony characteristics (Fig. 6·7). He must also inoculate the pure culture into fermentation tubes of sugar media to see which it ferments, make a gelatin stab to see if it liquefies gelatin, a milk culture to test its power to digest casein, etc. This long series of tests is usually referred to as the *systematic study of a pure culture*. It may also include animal inoculations to test pathogenicity and *serologic tests* to discover the reaction of the bacterium to immune substances in animal serums. The nature, methods, and practical

Name of organism *Escherichia coli* .... Studied by *Anne Smith* .... Culture No. *3*

Source *River Water* .... Habitat *Intestine of animals* .... Date *11/15/1950*

Descriptions (Underscore required terms.)	Sketches

CELL MORPHOLOGY Medium: *nutrient broth* Temp. *37* °C.

Vegetative cells: Age: *24 hrs.*
  Form and arrangement: *streptococci, diplococci, micrococci, sarcinae, rods, commas, spirals, branched rods, filaments*
  Motility in broth: +   Flagella:
  Size: Irregular forms:
Sporangia: *none, rods, spindles, elliptical, clavate, drumstick*   Age:
Endospores:
  Shape: *spherical, ellipsoid, cylindrical.*
  Position: *central to excentric, terminal, subterminal.*

X 2000

STAINING CHARACTERISTICS

Gram: *Neg.* Age: *24 hr.* Method: *see lab. manual*
Special stains:

AGAR STROKE Age: *24 hrs.* Temp. *37* °C.

Amount of growth: *scanty, moderate, abundant.*
Form: *filiform, echinulate, beaded, spreading, rhizoid*
Consistency: *butyrous, viscid, membranous, brittle.*
Chromogenesis: *none* ; *fluorescent, iridescent, photogenic.*

X 1/2

AGAR COLONIES Age: *24 hrs.* Temp. *37* °C.

Form: *punctiform, circular, filamentous, rhizoid, irregular.*
Elevation: *effuse, flat, raised, convex.*
Surface: *smooth, contoured, radiate, concentric, rugose.*
Margin: *entire, undulate, erose, filamentous, curled.*
Density: *opaque, translucent.*

X 3

NUTRIENT BROTH Age: *24 hrs.* Temp. *30* °C.

Surface growth: *none, ring, pellicle, flocculent, membranous.*
Subsurface growth: *none, turbid, granular.*
Amount of growth: *scanty, moderate, abundant.*
Sediment: *none, granular, flocculent, viscid, flaky.*

X 1/2

GELATIN STAB Age: *5 d.* Temp. *20* °C.

Liquefaction: *none, crateriform, infundibuliform, napiform, saccate, stratiform.*
Rate: *slow, moderate, rapid.*

OTHER MEDIA *agar shake* Age: *2 d.* Temp. *37* °C.

Growth throughout tube with gas formation

gas

X 1/2

FERMENTATION				Temp. *37* °C.	
Medium: *nutrient broth* Carbohydrate: *1* % Indicator:	Glucose	Lactose	Sucrose		
Acid in *2* days	+	+	−		
Acid in *5* days	+	+	−		
Gas in *2* days	+	+	−		
Gas in *5* days	+	+	−		

ACTION ON MILK		Temp. *37* °C.			
Indicator: *Brom cresol purple*		Days			
	1	*5*			
Reaction	*slA*	*A*			
Acid curd	−	+			
Rennet curd	−	−			
Peptonization	−	−			
Reduction (before coagulation)	−	−			

[*Fig. 6·8 continued on next page.*

ACTION ON NITRATES
Medium: *Nutrient nitrate* Temp. °C.
Nitrite: ...../....d. + ; ....d. ; ....d.
Gas (N): ...../.. d. — ; ....d. ; ....d.

INDOLE PRODUCTION
Medium: *Tryptone solution* Age: *24 hrs.*
Method: *Kovac* Temp. *37°C.*
Indole: *present, absent.*

HYDROGEN SULFIDE PRODUCTION
Medium: *Kligler's iron agar* Age: *24 hrs.*
H₂S: *present, absent.* Temp. *37°C.*

RELATION TO FREE OXYGEN
Medium: *Dextrose agar* Age: *2 d.*
Method: *Buchner tube* Temp. *37°C.*

Aerobic growth: absent, present, better than anaerobic growth, poorer than anaerobic growth.

Anaerobic growth: *present,* absent. *(gas formed)*

TEMPERATURE RELATIONS
Growth in refrigerator (*8* °C.): *present, absent.*
Growth at room temperature (*20* °C.): *present,* absent.
Growth at 37° C.: *present,* absent.
Growth at 50° C.: present, *absent.*

ADDITIONAL TESTS

Fat agar — *2 d. at 37°C. —no hydrolysis*
Starch agar — *2 d. at 37°C. —no hydrolysis*
Endo's agar — *1 d. at 37°C. —red colonies with metallic luster*

Fig. 6·8 Descriptive chart (student form) for recording characteristics of a pure culture. (*Society of American Bacteriologists, Biotech Publications, Geneva, N.Y.*)

importance of these serologic tests will be clear to students after they have studied the subject of immunity (Chaps. 18 and 19). The extent of systematic study is indicated by the chart prepared by the Society of American Bacteriologists on which the results of such study are recorded (Fig. 6·8).

Of course, a complete systematic study is not needed every time an organism is to be identified. Bacteria that are frequently encountered are recognized by a combination of a few specific unusual characteristics. If feces from a case of typhoid is streaked on Endo's medium, small white colonies are found that are readily distinguishable from the bright red colonies of *E. coli*. A pure culture can then be made from one of these colonies. If this culture can be shown to be a nonsporing, gram-negative, motile rod, which forms acid but no gas from dextrose and neither acid nor gas from lactose or sucrose, does not liquefy gelatin, and reacts in definite fashion with high dilutions of serum from an animal immunized against typhoid, the bacteriologist knows that he has isolated *S. typhosa*. Many illustrations of the methods of identifying the important pathogenic organisms will be discussed in later sections of this text.

METHODS USED IN THE STUDY OF SPECIAL TYPES OF MICROORGANISMS

The Cultivation of Autotrophic Bacteria. Autotrophic bacteria cannot be distinguished by their morphology. Since the obligate autotrophs build their own foods from inorganic compounds, they are grown in synthetic media free from organic chemicals. The composition of the synthetic medium depends on the requirements of the particular type of autotroph that is to be cultivated. Suppose we wish to grow a member of the genus *Nitrobacter,* which obtains energy by the oxidation of nitrites and builds protoplasm from nitrites, water, and carbonates. We will inoculate a bit of soil into a liquid medium composed of potassium nitrite, calcium carbonate, and other minerals in minute amounts. The culture will be practically a pure culture of *Nitrobacter,* since the medium will not support the growth of other genera.

Use of Animals as Culture Media. Artificial cultivation of organisms in the laboratory is referred to as cultivation *in vitro* (in glass), while cultivation in living animals is known as *in vivo* (in the living). Some supersentimental persons believe that scientists like to use animals for cultivation of microorganisms and for other experimental purposes. That is not true. Aside from any considerations of morality, which influence scientists fully as much as any other people, the expense involved, the time needed to care for animals, and the relative unreliability of results lead scientists to avoid the use of animals whenever they can. Animals are used only when in vitro experiments are impossible or inconclusive. (Human experimentation is used only when both in vitro and animal methods are impossible or inconclusive.) Animals are inoculated with microbes when the organisms cannot be grown successfully in nonliving media, when it is necessary to study the effects of infection on living tissue, or for the purpose of preparing immune sera. The organisms may be introduced in a great variety of ways. The method used in any particular case is described in anatomic terms such as *intradermal* (into the skin), *intranasal* (into the nose), *intraperitoneal* (into the peritoneal cavity), and *subcutaneous* (under the skin).

Anaerobic Cultivation. Many different methods have been devised by which oxygen may be excluded or eliminated from a culture so that anaerobic bacteria can be grown. Some methods involve the use of relatively expensive apparatus but allow the incubation of large numbers of cultures at one time. An example of such apparatus is the Brewer anaerobic jar in which a heated mass of platinized asbestos catalyzes the combination of the oxygen in the jar with hydrogen to form water. When such apparatus is lacking there are many simpler methods available. A few of these that are generally useful are listed below.

1. Buchner tube and Spray plate. Figure 6·9*a* and *b* shows these anaerobic systems. In the tube or in the special Spray culture dish two chemicals, pyrogallic acid and sodium hydroxide, are mixed to form a strong reducing compound which absorbs the oxygen from within the culture.

2. Thioglycolate and other special anaerobic media. Certain chemicals such as sodium thioglycolate and cysteine hydrochloride can be incorporated in agars or broths, where they act as constant reducing agents, combining with any oxygen present. Thioglycolate agar is often used in the Bray plate pictured in Fig. 6·9*c*.

3. Candle jar. If cultures are placed in a jar with a lighted candle and the jar is tightly sealed, the oxygen in the jar will be changed to carbon dioxide as the candle burns. The oxygen is not completely used up, but the reduced oxygen and the increased carbon dioxide are very favorable to the growth of some microaerophilic bacteria (Fig. 6·9*d*).

Fig. 6·9 Apparatus for cultivation with altered oxygen tension. (*a*) Buchner tube culture; (*b*) Spray plate; (*c*) Bray plate; (*d*) candle jar.

4. Agar shake culture. A tube of agar is thoroughly heated to drive off the dissolved oxygen. It is then cooled and inoculated. The organisms are mixed with the medium by rapid rotation of the tube rather than by shaking, which might introduce undesired air. If the organism is aerobic it will grow only at the top of the tube; if it is anaerobic its growth will be restricted to the bottom; and if it is facultative it will grow at all depths (Fig. 6·6).

Laboratory Study of Yeasts and Molds. Strictly speaking, these organisms can be identified by morphologic characteristics. Cultural characteristics are often helpful, however, since texture and pigment production of colonies provide simple means of recognizing common types. The useful microscopic preparations were indicated in the last chapter. Media with a pH decidedly on the acid side are often used, since they discourage bacterial growth without affecting the growth of yeasts and molds. Carbohydrates in comparatively large amounts (up to 5 per cent) are used in these media. For identification of saprophytic molds, a synthetic medium known as *Czapek's agar*

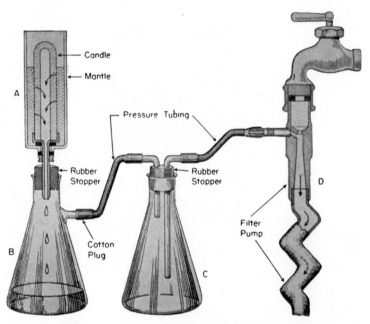

FIG. 6·10   Typical filtration apparatus. (*A*) Berkfeld filter; (*B*) filter flask; (*C*) safety flask (to prevent backflow of water from tap); (*D*) filter pump. (*From Belding and Marston, "A Textbook of Medical Bacteriology," Appleton-Century-Crofts.*)

with nitrogen salts instead of peptones is preferred. *Sabouraud's agar,* a sugar and peptone medium, and cornmeal agar are most frequently used for the cultivation of pathogenic fungi. Since colonies of these organisms grow to large size, it is customary to inoculate plates in only one to three spots and observe the development of *giant colonies* (Fig. 1·4).

Laboratory Study of Animal Forms. Protozoa, worms, and the ova and larvae of the worms are identified by their morphology alone. Cultivation is done in a very few instances.

Laboratory Study of Rickettsiae and Viruses. Microscopic study of these organisms requires the use of the electron microscope. They cannot be cultivated on artificial culture media, for they will grow only within living cells. The techniques of their cultivation in tissue cultures and in the developing chick embryo within the fertile egg and other special methods of laboratory virology will be considered in Chap. 33.

Filters and Filtration. Filtration is used in microbiology for the sterilization of liquids that might be injured by heat (page 116), for the separation of exotoxins and other products of microbial growth from cultures (page 232), and for the preparation of virus material and its study (page 457).

The types of filters most commonly used are

1. *Berkefeld filter*—made of plaster, asbestos, and diatomaceous earth in the form of a hollow candle. There are three grades: V, coarse; N, intermediate; and W, fine. Mandler filters are similar.

2. *Seitz filter*—a disk of compressed asbestos fitted into a metal holder.

3. *Sintered glass filter*—a disk of compressed ground glass fused into a glass holder.

4. Collodion membranes.

5. MF filters (see page 174).

Filters and filter flasks are sterilized by autoclaving. Suction is needed to draw the liquid through the very fine pores of these filters. It is provided by attaching the side tube of the filter flask to a vacuum pump or water faucet attachment. The usual arrangement of the apparatus is shown in Fig. 6·10. A mercury manometer is frequently connected between the filter flask and the trap flask in order to measure and regulate the negative pressure. This pressure should not be more than 45 cm. of mercury.

STUDY SUGGESTIONS

What information about the bacteriology of a material can be obtained from direct microscopic study? What information depends on cultural methods? Illustrate from your own laboratory experience.

Why and when is aseptic technique practiced in the hospital? Is it used for the same reasons in the laboratory? Is the technique essentially the same?

Study the illustrations that show cultures and stained microscopic preparations. Did you use these techniques? Were your results comparable? What advantages has an agar plate culture over a broth culture? Give examples from the text or your experience illustrating the use of a selective medium in obtaining a pure culture.

The genus *Serratia* consists of motile, nonsporing, gram-negative rods that inhabit natural waters and produce bright pink pigment when they are grown aerobically at temperatures from 20 to 30°C. How would a bacteriologist proceed to obtain a pure culture of *Serratia*? State the actual steps in detail. What tests could he use to check the purity of the culture that he had obtained?

The most commonly found species is *Serratia marcescens*. In addition to the generic characteristics listed above, it has the following physiologic characteristics:

it liquefies gelatin; it does not ferment lactose but may ferment dextrose very slightly; it digests milk and serum proteins but does not digest starch. How would the bacteriologist check these morphologic and physiologic characteristics?

SUGGESTED READING

Cultivation of Bacteria

FROBISHER, M., JR.: "Fundamentals of Microbiology." 5th ed., Saunders, Philadelphia, 1953. Chap. 16.

SOCIETY OF AMERICAN BACTERIOLOGISTS: "Manual of Methods for the Pure Culture Study of Bacteria." Biotech, Geneva, N.Y.

Leaflet III. The Study of Obligately Anaerobic Bacteria. 1945.

Leaflet V. Routine Tests for the Descriptive Chart. 1954.

Leaflet VI. Advanced Methods of Microbiological Chemistry. 1952.

Leaflet VII. Determination of Pathogenicity. 1948.

Necessity of Animal Experimentation

MOON, V. H., and D. G. WITTELS: They're trifling with your life. *Sat. Eve. Post* **221:**116 (July 2, 1948).

Stains and Staining Methods

BARTHOLOMEW, J. W., and T. MITTWAR: The Gram stain. *Bact. Rev.* **16:**1 (1952).

CONN, H. J.: "Biological Stains." 5th ed., Biotech, Geneva, N.Y., 1946.

SOCIETY OF AMERICAN BACTERIOLOGISTS: Staining Methods, Leaflet IV, in "Manual of Methods for the Pure Culture Study of Bacteria." Biotech, Geneva, N.Y., 1954.

Laboratory Study of Microorganisms Other than Bacteria

Fungi

SKINNER, C. E., C. W. EMMONS, and H. M. TSUCHIYA: "Henrici's Molds, Yeasts, and Actinomycetes." Wiley, New York, 1947. Chap. 2.

Rickettsiae and Viruses

BUDDINGH, G. J.: Chick-embryo Techniques, in T. M. Rivers's "Viral and Rickettsial Infections of Man." 2d ed., Lippincott, Philadelphia, 1952.

ENDERS, J. F.: Propagation of Viruses and Rickettsiae in Tissue Cultures, in T. M. Rivers's "Viral and Rickettsial Infections of Man." 2d ed., Lippincott, Philadelphia, 1952.

Nonmedical Microbiology

Although microbiology for nurses must stress the organisms pathogenic for man, these constitute only a small part of all microorganisms. It can truthfully be said that every kind of microorganism is important in one way or another. Many nonpathogens carry on activities important to the nursing profession, for, as was indicated in Chap. 1, they affect food, clothing, and many other materials on which nursing care depends.

MICROORGANISMS OF SOIL AND WATER; SOIL FERTILITY

Green plants continually use soil compounds for their growth, and yet under natural conditions where climate is favorable, the soil continues to supply material for new growth in each succeeding season. Obviously plant growth materials must be constantly renewed in the soil. This unfailing fertility of natural soils is principally due to the activities of three groups of fungi.

The Saprophytic Fungi. A *saprophyte* is literally a "rot plant." It is an organism that lives on nonliving matter and decomposes it. By their lipolytic, proteolytic, and carbohydrate-decomposing enzymes, the saprophytic molds, yeasts, and bacteria change the complex organic compounds in the dead bodies and wastes of plants and animals to simpler substances. Their true home is in the upper layers of the soil and in natural waters. Most of the end products which they produce are used directly by green plants. Some must undergo further changes by the action of certain highly specialized bacteria such as the nitrifying bacteria.

The Nitrifying Bacteria. Animals and saprophytic fungi excrete considerable amounts of nitrogen in the form of ammonia and ammonia compounds. These substances are seldom useful to animals and green plants. But in the soil there are two special groups of *nitrifying bacteria* that change ammonia to the nitrate compounds preferred by green plants for their protein synthesis. One group, including the genera *Nitrosomonas* and *Nitrosococcus,* oxidizes ammonia to nitrites; the other, the genus *Nitrobacter,* further oxidizes the nitrites to nitrates. These peculiar bacteria do not like organic food. Since they obtain their energy from the oxidations described above and build their protoplasm only from inorganic substances, they are obligate autotrophs.

The Nitrogen-fixing Bacteria. The atmosphere contains large amounts of nitrogen in the form of gas. Most organisms cannot use this at all. Plants use nitrogen in the form of nitrates, and animals require it in the form of amino acids or proteins. There are *denitrifying* bacteria that liberate free, gaseous nitrogen when they decompose nitrogenous material. This, of course, depletes the supply of nitrogen in forms usable by higher organisms. But fortunately there are other bacteria that can use this free nitrogen. They combine it into organic compounds and so balance the nitrogen loss. These bacteria are called *nitrogen-fixing.* The term *fixing* is used in its correct sense of fastening. Nitrogen fixation is carried on principally by two genera of simple bacteria. The members of the genus *Rhizobium* live in nodules on the roots of the legume plants such as beans, clover, and alfalfa. The members of the genus *Azotobacter* live free in the soil.

Organisms known as *sulfur bacteria* oxidize sulfur compounds such as hydrogen sulfide in the soil to sulfates that plants can use. Iron and other minerals of the soil are changed by bacterial action into forms usable by plants.

Where crops other than legumes are continuously harvested, the soil becomes poorer unless the farmer or gardener takes proper care of it. The scientific farmer has learned to provide organic material for his soil by adding to it animal wastes such as manure, plant material from ploughed-under crops, and commercial fertilizers. He encourages the growth of the bacteria which decompose these materials by his methods of cultivation and irrigation. At intervals in his rotation of crops, he plants legumes to increase the nitrogenous materials in the soil.

FOOD MICROBIOLOGY

Microorganisms spoil food, but they also help to keep it and to prepare it in palatable ways.

Food Spoilage. The same sorts of saprophytic fungi that decay the organic material in the soil spoil the foods in our kitchens, shops, and storage places. All foods spoil readily in their natural state and so do many prepared foods such as cooked meats, vegetables, and fruits. Some prepared foods and refined foods resist decomposition in varying degrees principally because of their low water content. Sugar and patented vegetable shortenings are examples. Flour, grain, and similar dry cereal products also keep well, though they may be attacked by insect larvae.

Food Preservation. Some methods of food preservation have been practiced for centuries, while others are relatively modern. Some are used to keep foods for short periods, while others preserve them for months and years. In daily practice in home and hospital we must be constantly alert to prevent waste by spoilage. Food must be obtained which is fresh and which has been properly handled and packaged so that its original microbial content is low. It must be kept in clean containers properly covered to prevent contamination from the air or by insects. Prompt and continuous refrigeration in a modern refrigerator at a temperature of 8°C. or less is the most valuable of all methods of combating food spoilage.

The methods used to keep foods for long periods include drying or dehydration; cold storage; freezing storage; preservation by the use of so-called "natural" preservatives such as salt, sugar, and vinegar; preservation by the addition of chemicals; smoking; and canning. In the past these methods were used mainly in the home. Now some are the basis of huge food industries. All except canning are obvious applications of methods that inhibit microbial growth. The canning process is a little more complicated.

When food is canned it is placed in an impervious container. The container and the food inside are processed by heat to kill the microorganisms present. The container is completely sealed while hot so that a partial vacuum develops in the can as it cools. Most nonacid foods have to be processed for a sufficient time to kill all organisms present, including mature spores. In other words, they have to be sterilized. Commercially they are always processed in a steam pressure apparatus, and in the home a pressure cooker should be used (Fig. 7·1). If the food to be canned is acid or has a high sugar content, the processing may be short and carried out in an open water bath at boiling temperature (100°C.). Then the canned product may not be sterile but will keep because the surviving organisms will be completely inhibited by the vacuum and the growth-inhibiting chemicals. Some foods are preserved by methods that really make use of a combination of two antimicrobial agents. For example, fish may be preserved by a combination of salting and drying, or by smoking and canning. When good food is preserved by proper methods it is healthful and economical. Proper food preservation enables us to enjoy a varied diet at all seasons and in all places without

FIG. 7·1   Commercial canning. Large stacks of cans are being lowered into pressure cooker. (*American Can Company.*)

excessive cost. Botulism, the only microbial disease spread by canned foods, will be discussed in Chap. 29.

Foods Prepared with the Aid of Microorganisms. Centuries ago people found that foods kept in certain ways changed into products that were agreeable to eat and that did not undergo further alterations that would be undesirable. For instance, if the juice of grapes was kept in a warm place in deep containers, exposed to very little air, it would ferment to form wine. If cabbage was shredded and packed in layers of salt, it would become the slightly softened product with a pleasantly acid taste that we know as sauerkraut. In the past these food products were produced at home and in small local industries, and the makers did not really know what was going on in the changing foods. Now these foods are often produced in large commercial establishments under constant laboratory control. Roquefort cheese, for example, has been made for centuries in a very limited area of southern France. The inhabitants make the curd from ewe's (sheep's) milk and transport it to cool, moist, limestone caves. There moldy bread is mixed with the curd and left to ripen. Now in the United States large cheese companies make American versions of Roquefort cheese. They use cow's milk and add laboratory-grown cultures of the mold *Penicillium roqueforti.* Then they ripen the cheese in curing rooms, where they carefully reproduce the conditions of temperature and humidity of the French caves.

It is impossible to discuss all the types of foods prepared with the aid of microorganisms, but the most important ones are noted briefly below.

1. Wines and other alcoholic beverages are prepared by allowing certain yeasts to grow in carbohydrate-containing solutions such as fruit juices and watery mixtures of malted grains. These materials are kept in deep, closed containers so that the conditions are anaerobic. Wine, beer, and other beverages of low alcoholic content are the fluids drawn from these containers. Whisky, gin, rum, and other beverages with high alcoholic content are distilled liquors. To produce them, the fermented material is heated until the volatile alcohol and part of the water vaporize. When this vapor condenses and is collected, it has a much higher alcoholic content than the original liquid.

2. Vinegar is made from the less expensive fermented fruit juices such as apple cider. The acetic acid bacteria belonging to the genus *Acetobacter* are encouraged by aerobic conditions to change the alcohol to acetic acid.

3. Fermented milks may be made in a variety of ways. In this country housewives often allow raw milk to sour by the growth of lactobacilli and use it in home cooking. Many nationalities have special forms of soured milk or cream, such as yoghurt, kumis, and Devonshire clotted cream, which they use instead of the raw liquids. The high acid content is unfavorable to the survival of disease bacteria, and so these fermented products are safer to drink than the unsanitary raw milk available in many countries. In this country yoghurt and cultured cream and buttermilk are now produced by many large dairy companies by the use of selected cultures of *Lactobacillus acidophilus.*

4. Cheese is made from casein, the chief protein of milk. Casein is curdled by the action of the lactic acid when milk sours. The liquid part called the *whey* is squeezed out. The curd also may be obtained by using *rennet,* the casein-coagulating enzyme extracted from the lining of the cow's stomach. Cottage cheese is fresh curd. Cream cheese is fresh curd with added cream.

Most other familiar cheeses undergo a ripening process which allows microorganisms of definite types to grow in them under controlled conditions. These microorganisms produce the characteristic changes in color, consistency, and flavor. Among them are members of the gas-producing genus *Propionibacterium,* which make the gas that forms the holes in Swiss cheese, and the blue-green penicillium molds of Camembert and Stilton cheeses.

5. Butter used to be made at home by churning sour cream until the fat lost its emulsified state and gathered into large lumps. Now most butter is made commercially from pasteurized cream, soured under controlled conditions by the actions of selected cultures of lactic acid bacteria and then churned. Butter so prepared has a constant flavor and consistency because of the controlled bacterial activity.

6. Fermented vegetable materials include sauerkraut, some types of pickles, and ensilage. Sauerkraut is prepared by allowing shredded cabbage mixed with salt to ferment in barrels or crocks. The salt draws water from the vegetable and inhibits the growth of many undesirable spoilage organisms. But the lactobacilli and false yeasts grow well. They form lactic acid from the dextrose in the vegetable. The best pickles are made by allowing cucumbers to undergo fermentation in salt brine, then washing and mixing with vinegar and spices.

Ensilage is similarly fermented vegetable material that is used for cattle feed. It is usually prepared from chopped corn, including stem and leaves. This is packed into a cylindrical building or lined pit called a *silo.* When winter comes, the material has been changed into a moist, moderately acid fodder which is excellent for dairy cattle. Ensilage contains large amounts of vitamin C made by the microorganisms as they grow. This is true of all foods fermented by lactic acid bacteria.

7. Leavened breads and other bakery products are among the most important and cheapest foods. From the beginning of history man has mixed grains with liquids and baked the mixtures into innumerable kinds of breads. Many of these have been of the sort called *unleavened* because no gaseous fermentation had taken place in the dough. But primitive cooks discovered that if the dough was left in a warm place it "rose," and that the raised, or leavened, bread was more palatable. They also discovered that a small amount of dough from one batch, added to the next lot of dough, would hasten its leavening in the desired manner. This is the way our great-grandmothers raised their breads and the Alaska "sourdoughs" made their raised biscuits. Louis Pasteur and other scientists learned that the yeast *Saccharomyces cerevisiae* is responsible for the rising of bread dough. Now cultures of that yeast are grown commercially and sold to housewives and bakers in the form of yeast cakes or dried yeast. Yeast works most rapidly in the dough when the temperature is around 30°C. and some sugar is

present from which it can form carbon dioxide gas. The coagulation of the grain proteins by the heat of baking traps the gas bubbles and so makes the bread light. The small amount of alcohol present is driven off by the heat of baking. Some bacteria also grow in the rising dough and help develop good flavor. They may make too much acid if the dough is kept in a place that is too cool for rapid yeast growth. Then the bread tastes sour. In some dark breads, such as those made from rye, this sourness is considered desirable.

Microorganisms as Foods. The rapidly increasing population of the world has created great interest in the possibility of using the microorganisms themselves as foods. Large quantities of false yeasts are being grown commercially in this country and added to animal feeds to provide increased vitamin and protein content. In several other parts of the world they are being grown for human food. Research indicates that single-celled green algae might well be cultivated on a large scale to provide abundant cheap food. The *plankton* (minute animal forms) of the ocean can be concentrated by sweeping the sea with nets and is another potential source of large quantities of food.

TEXTILE MICROBIOLOGY

Textile Spoilage. Textiles do not spoil as rapidly as foods because they are made from resistant animal and vegetable fibers and because the water content is usually very low. But if textiles are exposed to continued moisture and warmth, they do spoil. Then they are said to rot, or mildew. The term *mildew* is used when disintegration is accompanied by visible staining due to the growth of molds. Rotting of fabrics without noticeable staining may be due to bacteria or molds. Dirty spots on fabrics often rot and mildew more readily than other parts, because the dirt provides substances needed by the microorganisms for growth. It follows that keeping fabrics dry and clean is the best defense against spoilage.

When fabrics are used in damp, humid climates such as the tropics or when they are continually exposed to moisture as are tents, sails, and fish nets, it is desirable that they be treated with some antimildew chemical. Much equipment used in the tropics is mildew-proofed by treatment with special chemicals. Even the insulation on radio wires is treated.

Leathers, rubber, paper, paints, plastics, and even glass are subject to microbial deterioration. The newer synthetic textiles such as nylon and rayon are relatively resistant to microbial attack.

Microorganisms in the Preparation of Textile Fibers. Two important textile materials, linen and hemp, are made from the tough bast fibers in the stems of the flax and hemp plants, respectively. These fibers are freed from the other plant materials by a microbial process called *retting*. The harvested plants are tied in bundles and placed in a slow-running stream or in a vat of water. Here various aerobic and anaerobic bacteria attack the softer plant tissues. As these tissues are digested and become soluble, they are washed away, leaving the tough bast fibers from which linen cloth and hemp fabric are woven.

INDUSTRIAL MICROBIOLOGY

In so far as many of the processes already discussed are carried on commercially on a large scale, they are examples of industrial microbiology. In addition, there are certain others which are never carried on as domestic processes. They involve the production by microbial processes of specific chemicals needed in modern industry. Ethyl alcohol (grain alcohol) is the most important of these chemicals. Other chemicals produced commercially by microorganisms include higher alcohols, glycerin, acetone, and acids such as lactic acid and butyric acid. These are needed in laboratory procedures and in the preparation of drugs, cosmetics, foods, paints, adhesives, explosives, synthetic rubber, and plastics. Earlier processes of manufacture started with relatively costly ingredients such as sugar and grain. The tendency now is to develop methods which utilize cheap materials such as sawmill wastes, cornstalks, and low-grade potatoes. In order to obtain the highest possible yields, selected pure cultures of microorganisms are used and all conditions carefully controlled. The commercial production of alcohol will serve as an example.

Commercial alcohol was produced in the past by yeast fermentation of malted grains under very crude conditions. Most of the alcohol was used in beverages and a little for laboratory purposes. Now alcohol is made in huge industrial plants from a variety of organic materials, including sawdust. Carefully selected pure cultures of specific yeasts are used, and every step is checked by laboratory tests. The alcohol produced is so essential to industry and science that during the war the government drastically reduced the use of alcohol in beverages. It is likely that commercial production of alcohol will continue on a very large scale, since low-cost alcohol gives promise of being one of the important fuels of the future.

The commercial production of penicillin, streptomycin, and other antibiotics is the largest drug industry in the world. These antibiotics are all the products of bacteria, streptomycetes, or molds, grown under controlled conditions (see Chap. 11). Microorganisms are also grown commercially to produce large quantities of other products such as vitamins and specific enzymes. *Hyaluronidase*, used in many surgical and medical procedures to increase the permeability of tissues, is obtained from cultures of various bacteria. Cultures of the coccus *Leuconostoc mesenteroides* produce *dextrans*, the large-molecule sugar derivatives that are now widely used for intravenous injections to combat blood loss and shock. (See Fig. 7·2.)

FIG. 7·2 Commercial production of dextran. In the tank on the balcony *Leuconostoc mesenteroides* has been grown to produce large amounts of polymerizing enzyme. The enzyme mixture is now being added to the lower tank. Here cane sugar will be polymerized to form dextran, a substitute for blood plasma, used in the treatment of shock. (*Courtesy of "Pulse of Pharmacy," Wyeth Laboratories.*)

ANIMAL PATHOLOGY

All forms of animal and plant life are attacked by microorganisms. The diseases of lower animals that are of the greatest importance to us are those which can be spread from them to man. They will be discussed in later chapters. Almost as important are many diseases of the animals that serve man. Cattle, hogs, sheep, and poultry, as well as dogs, cats, and pet canaries, all suffer from microbial diseases. So do wild animals in their natural state. These infections are caused by all type of microorganisms. Hens are infected by coccidia, a type of protozoa; and hogs develop hog cholera, a virus disease. Various fungous infections such as ringworm attack the skin of dogs and cats; these animals may be thin and sickly because they have intestinal roundworms. Animal diseases are spread and controlled in the same ways as human diseases. The veterinary expert tells the poultryman how to disinfect his hen houses to control coccidiosis. He vaccinates hogs against hog cholera. He uses penicillin to control streptococcal infections in the udders of milk cows.

Lower forms of animal life also suffer from infectious disease. Tropical fish in aquariums develop mold infections of the skin where they have been injured in handling. Honeybee larvae die of virus infection in the beehives. Houseflies fall victims to a fatal mold infection. Other insect pests such as the gypsy moth succumb to virus disease.

PLANT PATHOLOGY

A limited number of plant diseases, such as cucumber wilt and potato scab, are caused by bacteria. Most plant infections are caused by fungi or viruses. Plant diseases are not transmissible to humans. (There is, however, one fungus which affects us indirectly. It grows in grain, causing the formation of a substance known as *ergot*. A serious poisoning called *ergotism* develops in any person or animal eating the infected grain.) The diseases of plants are important to us because of the extensive crop losses that result.

Plant diseases are spread by insects, by the spattering of raindrops, and by animals (including man) which carry the organisms from one plant to another. Destruction of infected plants and careful handling of plants help control these diseases. Sprays and dusts may kill or repel the insects or inhibit the growth of the pathogenic microorganism. They are more effective against the fungous diseases of plants than against those caused by viruses. Strong, healthy plants seem to resist many of the parasites. As far as can be determined, no immunity develops in infected plants and they cannot be immunized artificially. However, plant breeders work continually and successfully to develop disease-resistant varieties of our important plants.

STUDY SUGGESTIONS

Because this chapter deals with familiar material and because it contains few new scientific terms, it will seem easier to you than the preceding ones. It should, however, be carefully studied from two points of view.

First, can you relate the processes described here to what you have already learned about microbiology and chemistry? Have you a clear mental picture, which you can express in scientific language, of the microbial processes that go on when a dish of beef stew spoils? when the housewife cans string beans? when flax is retted? Check over the genera of microorganisms mentioned in the chapter. Look them up in Appendix B.

Secondly, can you relate this material to your own practical experience at home and in the hospital? If you have had farm or garden experience, what examples can you give of the relation of good agriculture to microorganisms and soil fertility? Note at least three examples of food or textile spoilage which you might have prevented, and tell what you should have done. What experience have you had in food preservation such as canning and quick-freezing? Have you helped to prepare any fermented beverages such as root beer or fermented milks? Have you made yeast-raised bread, cheese, or sauerkraut? What were the methods you used? Were they based on sound principles of microbiology? What examples of diseases of plants and animals have you encountered? What was done about them?

Many of the processes described in this chapter are of great economic importance. How has the scientific knowledge and control of these processes resulted in better living? What are some of the developments that we may expect in the future?

SUGGESTED READING

(The extension service of your state university can supply excellent material on many of these subjects.)

General References

GRANT, M. P.: "Microbiology and Human Progress." Rinehart, New York, 1953. Chaps. 16 and 17.

RAHN, O.: "Microbes of Merit." Ronald, New York, 1945.

Soil Microbiology

CONN, H. J.: The most abundant groups of bacteria in the soil. *Bact. Rev.* **12**:257 (1948).

WAKSMAN, S. A.: "Soil Microbiology." Wiley, New York, 1952.

WILSON, P. M., and R. H. BURRIS: Biological Nitrogen Fixation—a Reappraisal, in "Annual Review of Microbiology." Vol. 7, Annual Reviews, Inc., Stanford, 1953.

Food Spoilage, Preservation, and Processing

AMERICAN CAN COMPANY: "The Canned Food Manual." New York, 1947.

PRESCOTT, S. C., and B. E. PROCTOR: "Food Technology." McGraw-Hill, New York, 1937.

TANNER, F. W.: "The Microbiology of Foods." Garrard Press, Champaign, Ill., 1944.

Microbial Deterioration

GREATHOUSE, G. A., C. J. WESSEL, and H. G. SHIRK: Microbial Deterioration of Manufactured Materials, in "Annual Review of Microbiology." Vol. 5, Annual Reviews, Inc., Stanford, 1951.

Microbial Diseases of Plants and Animals

U.S. PRINTING OFFICE: "Yearbook of Agriculture. Keeping Livestock Healthy." Washington, D.C., 1942.
————: "Yearbook of Agriculture. Plant Diseases." Washington, D.C., 1953.

Industrial Microbiology

PRESCOTT, S. C., and C. G. DUNN: "Industrial Microbiology." 2d ed., McGraw-Hill, New York, 1949.

Foods from Microorganisms

THATCHER, F. S.: Foods and Feeds from Fungi, in "Annual Review of Microbiology." Vol. 8, Annual Reviews, Inc., Stanford, 1954.

PART TWO

The Control of Microorganisms

General Principles of Microbial Control

Man has advanced in civilization as he has learned to control his environment. He began very early in history to control the larger plants and animals. Not until much more recently has he learned something about the control of microscopic forms of life. When the scientists of the last century had discovered the basic facts of microbial morphology and physiology, man could begin to act intelligently to control communicable disease, surgical and other infections, and spoilage of food and other material. Now such knowledge is well advanced, but its effective application is still very incomplete. Not until the general public understands the necessity and methods of microbial control can its full benefits be realized.

The nurse cannot be one of the producers of this knowledge, but she is extremely important as one who applies it and passes it on to others. The well-educated nurse is constantly "bacteria-conscious" and knows that one of her chief functions is to control microorganisms. To do this intelligently, she must understand where bacteria are, how their growth can be controlled, and how they can be destroyed. This subject is often called *disinfection,* and that term might be used as the heading of this chapter, in which the factors that control microbial growth and life will be considered.

CONDITIONS THAT FAVOR MICROBIAL GROWTH

If we summarize the conditions under which bacteria will grow well, we will be able to see how their growth may be hindered or suppressed. Of course it is also true that under many conditions the growth of microorganisms is to be encouraged. Laboratory workers want their cultures to grow; housewives want their bread to rise. The conditions encouraging good growth of microorganisms are described below.

Suitable Temperature. The temperature at which an organism grows best is called its *optimum temperature.* Most nonparasitic microorganisms are able to grow over a rather wide range of temperatures, but strict parasites have a narrower temperature range close to that of their hosts' bodies. Most of the organisms that are important to us grow at temperatures ranging from 20 to 40°C., i.e., at temperatures ranging from cool room temperature to a little above human body temperature. Such organisms are called *mesophilic.* *Thermophilic* and *psychrophilic* bacteria are those that prefer high temperatures and very low temperatures. Thermophilic and psychrophilic bacteria are not pathogenic but may be troublesome in other ways. For example, thermophils may grow in milk while it is in the pasteurizing apparatus, and psychrophils may spoil food stored in refrigerators.

Moisture. All microorganisms need moisture for growth. They may grow in liquids or in materials that contain considerable available water.

Nourishment. The heterotrophic organisms, in which we are primarily interested, must have organic food. They demand the types of food which were enumerated in the discussion of the requirements of a good culture medium: nitrogenous food such as peptone, energy food such as sugars or peptone, minerals, and accessory growth substances. Many of the free-living saprophytic organisms utilize a great variety of foods. The parasitic kinds often require materials similar to the substances found in their hosts, such as whole blood or serum.

Neutral Reaction. The need for a neutral medium for most bacteria and the presence of buffer substances to prevent the rapid accumulation of excessive amounts of acid or alkali has already been discussed. Many molds and yeasts tolerate acid media.

Absence of Injurious Forms of Light. Green plants need light. The organisms we study in medical microbiology do not. They grow well in complete darkness. Moderately intense diffused light does not, however, interfere with their growth, though certain other types of light rays do.

Absence of Harmful Chemicals. No matter how good conditions are for microbial life and growth, if a chemical substance injurious to the organisms is present, growth will be inhibited or the organisms killed.

Suitable Oxygen Tension. While the facultative organisms will grow in a wide range of oxygen tensions, the strict aerobes and anaerobes must be provided with the conditions they demand.

If good microbial growth is desired, obviously the conditions outlined above must be provided. In the main, however, the problem of the nurse is not how to encourage the growth of microorganisms, but how to stop their growth or kill them. If the organisms are deprived of suitable temperature, food, etc., their growth will be stopped. If they are exposed to extremes of temperature, acid, drying, or harmful chemicals, they will be killed. The measures that can be taken against microorganisms are conveniently divided into physical and chemical agents. The specific methods of controlling microorganisms will be discussed in the next three chapters.

DEFINITIONS OF TERMS

Before specific antimicrobial methods are studied, the student must understand clearly the meaning of certain terms. Many of the terms signifying microbial control are carelessly used not only by nonprofessional people, but by some doctors and nurses, and even by teachers and writers who should know better. While the misuse of these terms may be unimportant under some conditions, it is very dangerous in hospital and public health practice. The division of these terms into three groups is helpful.

1. Terms that refer to complete destruction of all microorganisms present.

2. Terms that refer to the destruction of some particular group or species of undesirable organism.

3. Terms that indicate suppression of growth of microorganisms but not necessarily their death.

It should be noted that some of the terms are used in connection with medical science and the control of disease-producing organisms, while others are more general and may be used when any type of microorganism is discussed.

Terms Indicating Complete Microbial Destruction

Sterile—completely free from any living microorganisms. Such words as *sterilize, sterilization, sterility, sterilizer* should be clear. (Note that the term *sterile* is also used biologically to refer to something that is unfertilized, as a sterile egg.)

Aseptic—without infection. The noun *asepsis* is also used. These terms are used only when referring to the absence of pathogenic organisms. The term *sterile* may be used to indicate the absence of all types of microorganisms in food, soil, etc.

Surgical asepsis—the use of sterile materials and of techniques which exclude any contaminating microorganisms, as practiced in surgical procedures.

Surgically clean—used to refer to sterility in all surgical materials and techniques. This term was formerly more widely used in nursing than it is at present. It has no advantage over the term *sterile,* whose meaning is much clearer. Under no conditions should the word *clean* be used as a synonym for *sterile.* Anything that is clean is free from obvious extraneous matter, but it may be far from sterile.

Terms Referring to Destruction of Specific Undesirable Organisms

Disinfection—the destruction of pathogenic organisms. From the same root are derived the terms *disinfect* and *disinfectant.*

Medical asepsis—the techniques of handling and disinfecting all discharges and materials coming from patients with communicable disease, with the object of preventing the survival of the causative organisms.

Bactericide—an agent that kills bacteria. The adjective is *bactericidal. Germicidal* is also used but is *not* correct, since the true biologic meaning of *germ* is reproductive cell, not microorganism.

Terms Indicating Control of Growth of Microorganisms

Antiseptic—literally "against infection"—referring to anything that prevents growth and spread of harmful organisms. The word can be used as an adjective or as a noun denoting a substance with these properties. The noun *antisepsis* refers to any process or condition by which such control is exercised.

Bacteriostasis—condition in which any bacteria are prevented from growing and spreading. The adjective is *bacteriostatic.* These terms are more general than *antiseptic,* which is a medical term.

Antibacterial, antimicrobial—against bacteria, against microbes. These terms are coming into more common use. They are generally used with reference to inhibition of growth.

Similar terms are used in describing control of microorganisms other than bacteria. Note that the prefix *anti-* always means against; the prefix *a-* always means without; the suffix *-cide* means killing; and the suffix *-static* means stopping. The meanings of such terms as *fungistatic, viricidal,* and *antimycotic* should be clear.

PRACTICAL USES OF STERILIZATION, DISINFECTION, AND BACTERIOSTASIS

On some occasions it is necessary to kill all microorganisms; on others, to kill only certain types; on still others, to arrest the growth of certain types. A brief preliminary discussion of these occasions will aid in understanding the terms that have just been defined. The means commonly used to accomplish each purpose will be summarized here, but details of methods will be discussed in later chapters.

Sterilization. The complete destruction of all microorganisms present in or on any material is limited to three general situations.

In Surgical Procedures. For any surgical procedure, everything that will come in contact with the sterile tissues of the body must be made sterile. It must also be *kept* sterile by the extremely careful methods of handling which are called *aseptic technique.* Materials for use in surgical procedures are usually sterilized by steam under pressure in the autoclave.

In the Microbiology Laboratory. All media, glassware, and other materials used in experiments in microbiology must be initially sterile. Here also the methods of handling which keep the materials sterile are of great importance. Thus *bacteriologic technique* which must be practiced by all laboratory workers is essentially the same in purpose and method as aseptic surgical technique. Materials for bacteriologic laboratory work are sterilized in the autoclave and in the hot air oven.

In Canning of Nonacid, High-protein Foods. Neutral foods such as meats, fish, and peas must be canned by methods that accomplish sterilization. Here again, steam pressure sterilization is the method used, both commercially and in the home.

Methods of Sterilization. It would be no exaggeration to say that 95 per cent of all sterilization is done by steam under pressure in the autoclave. Dry heat in ovens is used for some glass and metal objects. Certain types of objects of glass, metal, or other impermeable material may be sterilized by prolonged boiling provided they are thoroughly clean. Sterilization by chemicals is always a questionable procedure. Wherever it is used as a routine method it should be replaced by steam pressure sterilization or baking.

Disinfection. The destruction of undesirable organisms is necessary in at least three situations.

In the Care of Cases of Communicable Disease. This is the most important practice of disinfection and the most rigorously carried out. Here disinfection is aimed in each instance at the destruction of the particular pathogen causing the disease. It must be carried out so thoroughly that not a single organism will survive to carry the disease to any other susceptible person. This process of disinfection is one of the chief responsibilities of the nurse.

In Personal and Public Sanitation. A less specifically directed type of disinfection is carried out continually in public and personal sanitation. It is not aimed at any one harmful organism known to be present, but at all pathogens likely to be present. Examples of bactericidal methods used in home and hospital include such desirable everyday procedures as thorough washing of the hands before eating and the use of hot water in dishwashing. Public health measures such as the pasteurization of milk and the chlorination of questionable water supplies are not expected to sterilize the milk or water, but rather to ensure the death of all pathogens which might be present.

In Agriculture and Industry. Outside the fields of medical microbiology there are many instances of the practice of disinfection. The boiling water bath is used in canning fruits and acid vegetables. Although the product is not always sterilized, the spoilage organisms are killed. The vineyard owner sprays his vines with copper sulfate solution to kill the spores of fungous disease. Some bakeries expose wrapped loaves of bread to ultraviolet radiation to kill mold spores.

Methods of Disinfection. Heat is very frequently used to accomplish disinfection. Boiling is the commonest of all methods, but lower temperatures may be used provided they are lethal for the particular pathogens to be killed. The other common method of disinfection is by the use of chemicals.

Bacteriostasis. Students often ask why inhibition of bacterial growth is ever a practical or useful procedure. Why should materials be treated so as to prevent the growth of microorganisms rather than disinfected or sterilized? Actually there are very good reasons why it is often preferable to control microorganisms by stopping their growth rather than to attempt to kill them. These reasons will become clear as the situations where bacteriostasis is practiced are discussed.

In Control of Microorganisms in or on the Body. If dangerous organisms are on or in a living body, any method by which they may be killed is likely to injure the living tissues of the host and delay their healing. If, however, a suitable antiseptic agent is utilized so that the multiplication of the pathogen is arrested, the body cells are uninjured. They are then capable of destroying the remaining organisms and rebuilding any destroyed tissues. This use of chemicals as internal bacteriostatic agents is called *chemotherapy.*

It is such an important aspect of microbial control that the whole of Chap. 11 will be devoted to it.

In Preservation of Foods and Textiles. Most methods of food preservation utilize bacteriostatic methods. So do methods of safeguarding textiles, leather, and woods from decay. There are two reasons why control of microbial growth is better than any attempt to kill the undesirable organisms that are present in the material. First, methods of disinfection or sterilization often change the materials in undesirable ways. For example, it is possible to sterilize fruits by processing them for long periods in cans, but the resulting product is soft and unattractive. Adding sugar to the fruits gives products that are much more palatable. Better still, the fruit may be frozen rapidly and kept at below-freezing temperature until it is to be used. Chemicals which would sterilize or disinfect canvas would injure the fibers, but anti-mycotic chemicals which prevent the growth of mildew mold spores can be used without injury. Secondly, methods of preservation must be continuous so that the material cannot be attacked at any time by spoilage organisms. It would be useless to sterilize canvas by steam before sending it to tropical areas. It would still be completely susceptible to mildew. But if it has been treated with antimildew chemicals before shipment, it will be continuously protected.

Bacteriostasis is, then, more desirable than disinfection or sterilization in chemotherapy and in preservation of various materials because it employs methods which do not injure tissues or materials and which are continuous in their action.

Methods of Bacteriostasis. Cold, drying, and selected chemicals are the most commonly used agents of microbial inhibition. They must be continuously present if they are to be effective, i.e., the material must remain dry, or in a very cold or frozen state, or the antimicrobial chemical must be constantly present in effective inhibitory concentration.

FACTORS IMPORTANT IN THE CONTROL OF MICROORGANISMS

In Bactericidal Techniques. Three important factors are discussed here which must always be taken into consideration when any attempt is made to kill microorganisms.

Concentration of the Chemical or Intensity of the Physical Agent Used. Directions for methods of sterilization and disinfection must always include the concentration of the chemical to be used or the degree of heat to be maintained. In a properly written nursing procedure book, the student nurse will never find such instructions as "Place this instrument in formalin" or "Place in hot water." The directions will state, "Place this instrument in a 1:100

solution of formalin" or "Place in actively boiling water." The nurse must always follow such directions exactly. If a weaker concentration of the chemical is used, or a lower temperature, some of the organisms that should be killed may survive.

A chemical disinfectant may be diluted by the material to which it is added. When 100 ml. of a 1:50 dilution of a disinfectant are added to 100 ml. of urine in a urinal, the actual concentration will be only 1:100. When boiling in water is used as a method of disinfection, the bubbling of the water is evidence that the proper temperature has been obtained. Nothing less than active bubbling should be considered as boiling. When baking, autoclaving, pasteurizing, and other forms of heat are used, the temperature must be constantly checked on a properly located thermometer.

Time Allowed. No chemical or physical agent of disinfection acts instantaneously. It always takes time to kill microorganisms. The student nurse will note that all satisfactory directions for sterilization and disinfection state the exact time needed. The nurse's watch is to be used not only to observe pulse and respiraton, but also to check exact times of disinfecting and sterilizing procedures. The time for chemical disinfection begins when the material is completely immersed in the chemical and completely saturated with it. The time for any method using heat begins when the temperature has reached the desired level.

Nature of the Material To Be Treated. If the material is of solid or semisolid consistency and microorganisms are not limited to the surface, a chemical disinfectant that has penetrating power must be employed. Unless the material to be disinfected is of negligible value, a method is chosen which injures it as little as possible. No chemical that combines with and coagulates albumin should be used when the material to be treated contains albuminous matter.

Type of Organism To Be Destroyed. Most nonsporing bacteria may be killed in 10 minutes at 70°C., but spore formers will require at least 15 minutes at 15 pounds pressure (121.5°C.) in the autoclave. Chemical disinfectants vary in their ability to kill different types of microorganisms. For example, carbolic acid kills vegetative bacteria readily but is much less effective against viruses.

In Bacteriostatic Techniques. Since methods of bacteriostasis must be continuous, the time element is not a factor. A food is not preserved by drying for 10 minutes or 1 hour. It is dried and kept dry until it is used. On the other hand, the concentration of a chemical bacteriostatic agent is important and so is the intensity of a physical agent. The housewife's jam will spoil if the sugar content is much less than 50 per cent. Foods in the refrigerator keep poorly unless the temperature maintained is below 45°F. As has been already noted, any satisfactory agent for control of microbial growth must not be injurious in the situation where it is used.

STUDY SUGGESTIONS

Why is the control of microorganisms important? Can you give one or more examples from your own personal experience to illustrate the serious consequences of failure to control undesirable organisms?

List the conditions encouraging bacterial growth. How are these fulfilled when bread dough is raised by yeast? How were they fulfilled in one culture that has been grown in your laboratory work?

Can you define and use the terms *sterile, aseptic, disinfect, bactericidal, antiseptic, bacteriostatic?*

Under what circumstances is it necessary to sterilize materials? List four things that you have used that had been sterilized. Why was each sterilized? What method was used?

Under what conditions is disinfection practiced? Have you or some other member of your family had a case of communicable disease recently? What procedures of disinfection were carried out? What was the reason for each? Describe some household and ward procedures that are essentially bactericidal or fungicidal although not directed at a specific pathogen.

Under what conditions is it desirable to inhibit microbial growth rather than try to kill the organisms? Give some examples from housekeeping experience, from agriculture, from medicine.

What is chemotherapy? Can you give an example?

What factors must be considered when disinfection is carried on? Give examples from your own hospital procedures that show consideration of these factors.

What factors must be considered in choosing a method of bacteriostasis or a chemotherapeutic agent?

SUGGESTED READING

General References

Burrows, W.: "Textbook of Microbiology." 16th ed., Saunders, Philadelphia, 1954. Chap. 5.

Davis, B. D.: Principles of Sterilization, in R. J. Dubos's "Bacterial and Mycotic Infections of Man." 2d ed., Lippincott, Philadelphia, 1952.

Frobisher, M., Jr.: "Fundamentals of Microbiology." 5th ed., Saunders, 1953. Chaps. 12, 17, 18, 19.

McCulloch, E. C.: "Disinfection and Sterilization." 2d ed., Lea & Febiger, Philadelphia, 1945.

RAHN, O.: "Physiology of Bacteria." Blakiston, Philadelphia, 1935.

REDDISH, G. F.: "Antiseptics, Disinfectants, Fungicides, and Chemical and Physical Sterilization." Lea & Febiger, Philadelphia, 1954.

WALTER, C. W.: "The Aseptic Treatment of Wounds." Macmillan, New York, 1948.

CHAPTER 9

Control of Undesirable Micro-organisms by Physical Means

HEAT

Heat is the most often used of all bactericidal agents, because it is the cheapest and the most readily controlled. The lowest temperature that kills, on 10 minutes' exposure, all the organisms of a 24-hour broth culture of a specific bacterium is its *thermal death point*. This term is sometimes abbreviated to *TDP*. The TDP of most nonsporing bacteria is between 55 and 65°C., but mature spores may survive 10 minutes to several hours of boiling temperature (100°C.).

Heat may be used in many ways. The actual methods will be discussed under four headings.

Incineration. Burning contaminated objects is an easy and effective way of destroying unwanted microorganisms, but it will obviously be usable only if the object to be disinfected is either worthless or completely resistant to fire. Paper handkerchiefs, soiled sputum cups, and similar objects should be burned. In the laboratory, the inoculating needle is sterilized by flaming. All the material on the needle is destroyed, but the needle, which is not permanently affected by heat, becomes sterile.

It is sometimes a temptation to attempt to sterilize other objects by passing them through the flame. Aside from the fact that it is unsafe to rely on this method to kill bacteria, flame destroys the cutting edge of instruments and weakens glass. The practice of dipping objects in alcohol and then flaming is to be condemned. Although the process looks dramatically effective, the surface of the object is never well heated, since it is covered with a layer of vaporized alcohol.

Baking in Hot Air (Dry Heat). Dry heat does not penetrate as readily as moist heat. The temperature needed to kill an organism by baking will be considerably higher than that needed to kill it with moist heat. High temperatures are easily obtained with insulated ovens, but many materials are injured by these high temperatures. Baking is, however, the method of choice for some supplies.

In the laboratory, glassware such as petri dishes and pipets in metal containers are sterilized in the oven for 1 to 2 hours at a temperature of 170°C. or over. In the hospital such materials as bulk talcum powder, petroleum jelly, glycerin, coated gauze, oils, and bone wax should be sterilized in the oven because steam cannot penetrate such materials. They should be packaged in small quantities and baked at 160°C. for 1 to 2 hours. Hypodermic needles and syringes are often sterilized in the oven, since the heat will enter the small bore of the needle and they will be absolutely dry after baking. They are placed in tubes or petri dishes and heated at 160°C. for 1 hour. Rusting of suture needles is avoided by sterilizing them in the same way. Surgical instruments may be sterilized by baking in specially designed electric ovens.

Moist Heat at Boiling Temperature or Below. When water is heated in any container that is not completely sealed, the maximum temperature that can be reached is 100°C. (at sea level, less at higher levels). When the water reaches that temperature it becomes steam. The transformation of the water to steam is shown by the active bubbling of the water. So *boiling temperature* (100°C., 212°F.) can be detected without the aid of a thermometer. The steam that is evolved from the boiling water also has the temperature of 100°C. and rapidly heats objects with which it comes in contact. The Arnold steam sterilizer in which articles are exposed to streaming steam was commonly used in hospitals and laboratories before the days of good autoclaves. Jets of steam may be used in some modern hospital apparatus such as the bedpan sterilizer pictured in Fig. 9·1.

Disinfection and Sterilization by Boiling. Disinfection by boiling is a safe method. Since the great majority of the organisms of communicable disease are not spore formers, short periods of exposure to boiling temperature are effective in destroying most pathogens. Materials designed for nonsurgical uses that must be free from possible infection and materials that have received possible infection as they were used are frequently disinfected by boiling for 10 to 30 minutes. Among such materials are patients' dishes, urinals and bedpans, clothing and bedding.

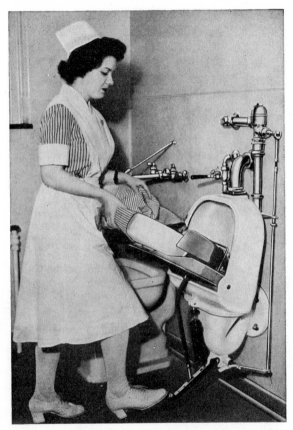

FIG. 9·1 Bedpan sterilizer. The nurse has opened the hopper with the foot pedal. After placing the bedpan inside, she will transfer her foot to the small pedal at the right to flush with cold water. With her elbow she will then turn on the small lever above to flood the chamber with live steam for 1 minute. (*American Sterilizer Company.*)

Instrument sterilizers of the type pictured in Fig. 9·2 are often employed for the sterilization of instruments and certain other equipment. The water is brought to the boiling point, the instruments are completely submerged, and active boiling is continued for at least 20 minutes. The instruments are removed as soon as the heat is turned off, and care must be taken to avoid contamination from the air. Baking and steam pressure sterilization of in-

FIG. 9·2 Instrument boiler-sterilizer. (*American Sterilizer Company.*)

struments (described below) have several advantages over the boiling method: less discoloration of metal, less likelihood of contamination after processing, and greater certainty of complete sterilization. The attempted sterilization of surgical basins and hypodermic needles by boiling should be replaced wherever possible by other, safer methods.

Pasteurization. Temperatures considerably below the boiling point may also be used to kill nonsporing bacteria. Louis Pasteur found that heating wine to 60°C. for a suitable time would kill spoilage organisms and allow the wine to be shipped long distances. The same type of process, which we call *pasteurization,* is used to kill dangerous organisms in milk. In the home the use of hot dishwater and rinsing water acts to disinfect our eating utensils. In home and commercial laundering, hot rinse water destroys microorganisms in clothing and bedding.

Steam under Pressure. The steam pressure sterilizer (also called *autoclave*) is used for the sterilization of most materials in both the hospital and the laboratory. The home pressure cooker and the processors used in canning and some other industries operate on the same basic principle as the autoclave and are essentially similar in construction. The apparatus always consists of a chamber that fills with steam. The steam displaces the air in the

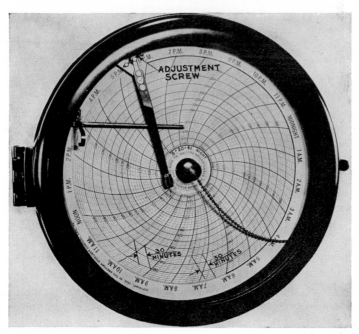

FIG. 9·3 Recording thermometer for steam pressure sterilizer. (*American Sterilizer Company.*)

chamber, forcing it out through a single outlet. When all air has been evacuated, this outlet is shut by hand or by an automatic, thermostatically controlled valve. As more steam continues to enter the chamber the pressure rises and with it the temperature. Pressure cookers and older models of sterilizers are often equipped with only a pressure gauge, which is the sole

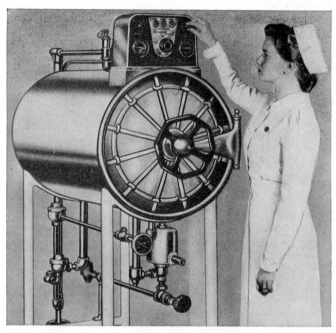

FIG. 9·4 Modern steam pressure sterilizer with automatic controls. The nurse is setting the timer at the exposure period needed for effective sterilization of this particular load. (*American Sterilizer Company.*)

guide to the operation of the sterilizer. If, and only if, all air has been evacuated and the chamber is completely filled with steam, the pressure and the temperature will rise together. A temperature of 251°F. (121.5°C.) is then indicated by a pressure reading of 15 lb. (to the square inch); a temperature of 260°F. (126.5°C.) by a pressure of 20 lb.

All modern hospital and laboratory sterilizers are equipped with thermometers. The thermometer is placed in the chamber outlet. The operation of the sterilizer is guided by this thermometer, and the outlet pipe is closed by a thermostatically controlled valve which expands with heat to close the opening. In addition, many are equipped with a recording thermometer (Fig. 9·3), which makes a permanent record of the temperature for each day on a paper chart. This is invaluable as a check of times and temperatures for all sterilizer runs.

A small type of hospital sterilizer is shown in Fig. 9·4. Figure 9·5 indicates diagrammatically the structure of the same unit. For sterilization of

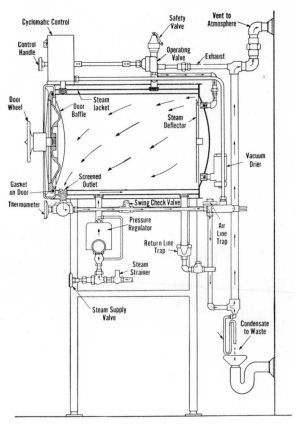

FIG. 9·5 Diagrammatic section through steam pressure sterilizer. (*American Sterilizer Company.*)

larger objects such as bedding or large amounts of surgical supplies, many hospitals have bulk sterilizers such as the one shown in Fig. 9·8. These types are built with double-walled chambers that aid in the drying out of materials after the exposure to steam. The sterilizer used in the laboratory is usually single-walled, since drying out is not required.

Two recently developed forms of steam pressure apparatus are the specially designed emergency sterilizer (Fig. 9·6), which sterilizes instruments at a temperature of 132°C. within a period of 5 minutes, and the instrument washer-sterilizer (Fig. 9·7), which washes and then sterilizes the instruments.

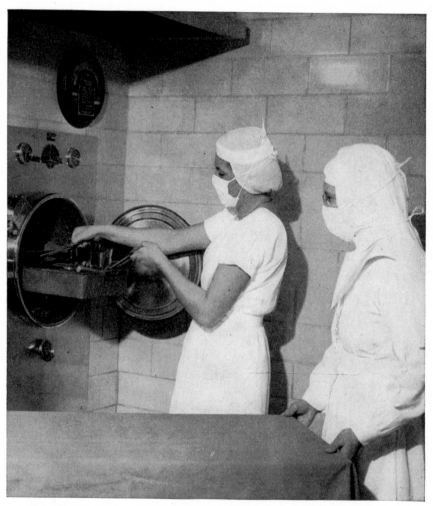

Fig. 9·6　Emergency instrument sterilizer. (*Wilmot Castle Company and Resurrection Hospital, Chicago.*)

Operation of the Steam Pressure Sterilizer. Although our modern hospital sterilizers are constructed to work correctly with a minimum of attention, they are not foolproof, and many hospitals have older installations that must be operated with great care and attention. The consequences of incomplete

sterilization of surgical supplies may be very serious. Incomplete sterilization of canned foods or laboratory supplies may be troublesome but is soon
detected. The incorrect operation of the operating-room sterilizer may be

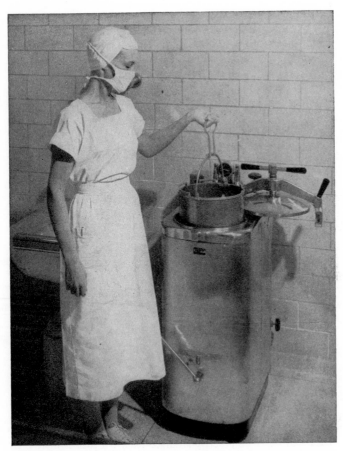

FIG. 9·7   Instrument washer and sterilizer. (*Wilmot Castle Company and Sherman
Hospital, Chicago.*)

undetected until a fatal case of bacterial infection has occurred. Every nurse
and technician must become thoroughly familiar with the operation of any
machine for which she is responsible. The manufacturers provide explicit
and clear directions for operation. If they are not available, one or more of
the books referred to at the end of this chapter should be consulted. When
a new operator takes over, she should first observe the operation of the
sterilizer as carried out by an experienced person and then operate it at least

once under supervision. Regardless of the type or make of the apparatus, there are certain basic requirements which must always be followed. They may be summarized as follows:

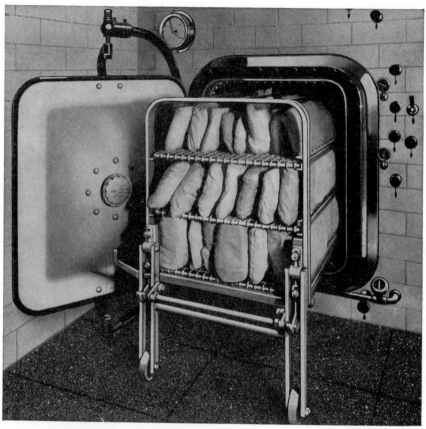

FIG. 9·8 Bulk sterilizer with properly arranged load. No pack is more than 12 by 12 by 20 inches. All packs placed on end with spaces between to allow circulation of steam. (*American Sterilizer Company.*)

1. Temperature. Since it is the temperature rather than the pressure that accomplishes sterilization, we should always define conditions in terms of temperature. The operator must watch the *thermometer* rather than the pressure gauge. The supervisor must check the temperature records conscientiously. The development of sufficiently high temperatures within the autoclave depends mainly on the proper evacuation of air. To ensure this in the older types of apparatus, the operator must be certain that the chamber

is completely filled with steam before she closes the outlet. The plug screen (strainer) in the chamber outlet must be cleaned daily. If it is clogged, air will be trapped in the chamber and the temperature will not rise to the effective sterilization level. Any increase in the time needed for the temperature to reach the prescribed range indicates defects in the outlet and should be promptly attended to. Improper packing of the chamber so that air pockets are formed or free drainage of air to the outlet is stopped will also prevent the development of sterilizing temperature in parts of the chamber.

2. Full exposure of all articles to steam. The proper packaging of materials for sterilization and the proper packing of the steam pressure sterilizer have

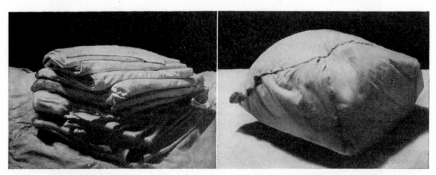

Fig. 9·9 Large pack with contents properly arranged. A total of 46 items are arranged in this pack so as to give space for steam circulation. (*American Sterilizer Company.*)

been the objects of cooperative study by doctors, nurses, and engineers of the sterilizer industry. Their recommendations should be followed, though they may be contrary to long-established hospital traditions. Three essentials must never be neglected.

a. Packing the chamber loosely so that steam can circulate freely and air drain readily (Fig. 9·8).

b. Making packages of suitable limited size with contents so arranged that the steam can pass freely through them (Fig. 9·9).

c. Using coverings or containers through which steam penetrates easily. Cloth and many types of paper are suitable coverings, since steam passes through them readily. Rubber, cellophane, and some of the newer plastics should never be used, for they are steamproof. Steam has no opportunity to reach objects placed in closed glass, tin, or enamelware containers. They should be perforated or their covers should be completely or partially removed during processing. Nonperforated containers and basins and trays must be placed on their sides in the sterilizer chamber so that all air can drain out and be replaced by steam. Layers of rubber in rubber gloves or other rubber articles must be separated by gauze or paper stuffing to allow steam to reach all surfaces. Rubber tubing should be open throughout its length, loosely spiraled around towels, and so placed in the sterilizer that air can drain freely from the lower end as steam enters from above (Fig. 9·10).

3. Correct timing of sterilization process. In operating the steam pressure sterilizer, the time rather than the temperature is varied, depending on the

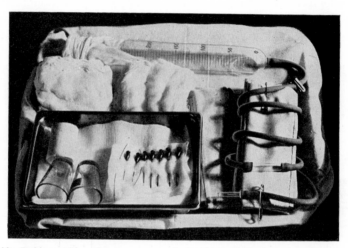

FIG. 9·10   Rubber tubing, instruments, and dressings properly arranged in a tray for sterilization. The tray is wrapped and placed on its side in sterilizer so that air will drain from glasses and tubing and be replaced by steam. (*American Sterilizer Company.*)

nature and packaging of the materials. Periods that are too short are obviously dangerous. Prolonging the time of sterilization not only takes up valuable time but is injurious to many substances. The time is reckoned from the moment when the thermometer indicates the temperature of 240°F. (115.5°C.) as it climbs to its maximum range of 250 to 254°F. This maximum temperature is regulated by automatic control in most sterilizers. The time ends when the inflow of steam is stopped by the operator. Unless the apparatus is fitted with an automatic temperature recorder, the operator must keep a concurrent written record of times and temperatures. In order to operate the sterilizer most effectively, the load for any one run should consist of similar materials requiring the same length of exposure. It is obviously bad practice to sterilize mattresses and packs of cotton pledgets at the same time. Five minutes is adequate for the sterilization of clean instruments in an emergency, though 10 minutes should be routine. When instruments are packaged in double muslin covers, or scalpel blades in cotton-stoppered glass vials, 15 minutes' exposure is required. Fluids in test tubes are readily sterilized in 15 minutes, but fluids in heavy-walled gallon jugs need 40 minutes. Single basins in double musin covers are processed for 10 minutes, while mattresses (placed on edge, not rolled) need 30 minutes. These figures are given here as examples, not as specific instructions. The operator of a steam pressure sterilizer must follow exactly the directions prepared by the hospital authorities or the manufacturers' instructions approved by her hospital. (See references at end of this chapter.)

COLD AND FREEZING

Microorganisms are not readily killed by low temperatures. In fact, cold is used to preserve organisms. Agar slant cultures of bacteria are kept for months in refrigerators. Pure cultures are frozen in a vacuum to preserve them for years. However, when materials are frozen under ordinary conditions, some of the bacteria may be crushed mechanically between expanding ice crystals. Repeated freezings and thawings tend to decrease the microbial content of natural waters and soils. Some parasites that flourish in semitropical climates, such as the hookworm, are unable to survive in the cold soil of more northern regions. Cold and freezing may decrease the numbers of microorganisms but cannot be relied on to disinfect or sterilize.

On the other hand, cold is one of the best methods of bacteriostasis. Materials kept in cold environments or carefully frozen undergo a minimum of chemical and physical change. Temperatures of 8°C. or below in good refrigerators and cold storage plants are effective in keeping most foods for comparatively long periods, since spoilage organisms will grow very slowly if at all. If materials are rapidly frozen to a solid state, the growth of all microorganisms is stopped. Such frozen materials must then be kept at below-freezing temperature (below 0°C.). For centuries freezing has been the method of food preservation in arctic regions. Now with the development of home and commercial freezing units, it promises to become our most important method of food preservation.

DRYING

Like cold, drying is an effective method of inhibiting growth but a very unreliable way of killing microorganisms. All spores are resistant to drying. Anthrax spores have been found alive in bandages after 40 years. Under some conditions vegetative cells are killed by drying, but under other conditions, which are not completely understood, they survive for surprisingly long periods in the dry state. Sputum, feces, and pus, even when apparently dry and actually pulverized into dustlike material, may still contain sufficient moisture to allow the survival of streptococci and other dangerous bacteria. The cysts of protozoa and the ova of some parasitic worms can withstand drying. Filtrable viruses are very resistant to drying. Obviously, then, drying is not to be used practically as a disinfecting or sterilizing agent.

But microorganisms of all kinds fail to grow in dried material. This is because of the lack of water for physiologic processes and the increased concentrations of inhibitory chemicals in the dried substances. For example, dried fruits such as raisins and prunes keep well though they are still quite moist, because the partial desiccation has increased the sugar concentration. Preservation of food is the chief practical use of drying.

RADIATION

Daylight and sunlight undoubtedly play an important part in the destruction of pathogenic organisms in nature. The sun and certain sources of artificial light give off rays invisible to us, called *ultraviolet* rays because they are beyond the violet end of the visible light spectrum. Certain wavelengths of this ultraviolet light are strongly bactericidal—those between 2,540 and 2,800 Å. (Ångström units) in length. Viruses seem to be more resistant than the other microorganisms to lethal types of light.

Ultraviolet light from the sun cannot pass through ordinary glass. It does not penetrate opaque materials or even dusty atmosphere. Sunlight is not reliably or rapidly bactericidal except outdoors on bright, clear days, and then only the organisms on directly exposed surfaces will be killed. Sunning and airing of bedding, clothing, and other supplies are desirable for many reasons but cannot be expected to accomplish sterilization or disinfection.

Within the last few years, special lighting tubes that emit a reliable and effective amount of bactericidal light have been developed. These "sterilizing" lamps are now relatively low in cost, require little attention except occasional cleaning, and have a life of several thousand hours. They are used in operating rooms, infants' wards, respiratory disease wards, schoolrooms, and barracks. (See Fig. 16·6.) They are also used to kill bacteria in the preparation of vaccines, to control food spoilage, to ensure the sanitary cleanliness of bottles in bottling plants, and to keep down contamination of cultures and working surfaces. (See Fig. 11·6.)

FILTRATION

When gases or liquids containing microorganisms pass through material with very fine pores, the microorganisms may be strained out. Cotton plugs in culture tubes, paper covers on flasks of fluids for parenteral use, and gauze face masks are all examples of filters. They do not destroy microorganisms, but they keep them out of places where they are not wanted. Modern ventilation systems have air filters built in the intake pipes to remove both bacteria and dusts. Liquids that might be injured by heat may be sterilized by filtration through sterile filters of earthenware, asbestos, or glass fiber into sterile flasks (Fig. 6·10). Obviously filtrable viruses cannot be removed by filtration.

STUDY SUGGESTIONS

Which physical agents are used primarily for killing organisms? Which are used primarily for suppressing microbial growth?

What are the ways in which heat is used to kill microorganisms? Make a list of the pieces of apparatus in your hospital that are used to accomplish complete sterilization of materials. What others are there that may accomplish sterilization but whose primary function is to ensure disinfection? Give examples of the practical use of these installations. Study the diagram of the steam pressure sterilizer. When the steam pressure sterilizer is demonstrated to you, be sure you understand its parts and their functions.

Do the methods of sterilization given in your hospital procedure book, discussed in your nursing classes, and practiced where you have been on duty or observation follow the principles discussed in this chapter? If you have noted any apparent discrepancies, ask the instructor to discuss them in class. Give examples of the application of methods of sterilization and disinfection by heat which you have noted in the laboratory or used at home.

Be prepared to describe practical uses of cold, freezing, filtration, and drying. Where have you seen installations of sterilizing lamps? What was the purpose of these lamps?

SUGGESTED READING

General References (See also page 101.)

Perkins, J. J.: Principles and methods of sterilization. *The Manual* (American Sterilizer Company) **12**:1 (1953).

Rahn, O.: Physical methods of sterilization of microorganisms. *Bact. Rev.* **9**:1 (1945).

Underwood, W. B., and J. J. Perkins: "Textbook of Sterilization." 3d ed., Charles C Thomas, Springfield, Ill., 1955.

Sterility Testing

Vera, H. D.: Sterility testing: the control of efficiency of sterilizing techniques. *Appl. Microbiol.* **1**:117 (1953).

Cold

HUTTON, R. S., R. J. HILMOE, and J. L. ROBERTS: Some physical factors that influence the survival of *Brucella abortus* during freeze-drying. *J. Bact.* **61**:309 (1951).

Radiation

NICKERSON, J. T. R., B. E. PROCTOR, and S. A. GOLDBLITH: Public health aspects of electronic food sterilization. *Am. J. Pub. Health* **43**:554 (1953).

CHAPTER 10

Chemical Disinfectants
and Their Use

Antimicrobial chemicals have two important uses in medicine. The first is the destruction of organisms of disease outside the human body. It may be called *environmental disinfection*. The second is the inhibition and destruction of pathogens in and on the body. This chapter is concerned with the first of these uses. The succeeding chapter on *chemotherapy* will consider the second. In Chaps. 7 and 8, we have discussed other uses of antimicrobial chemicals outside the medical field.

THE IDEAL DISINFECTANT

It would be very convenient if there were one chemical that could be used for all purposes of disinfection. Unfortunately no such ideal chemical disinfectant has been discovered. Every known disinfectant has some qualities that make it undesirable for universal use. To meet each situation involving disinfection we must select the one that will be most effective. Before the specific chemicals commonly used in disinfection are discussed, it will be helpful to list the qualities that are desirable in a disinfectant.

1. The ideal disinfectant should kill all types of microorganisms within a short period of time.

2. It should not be inhibited by the presence of protein, nor should its action be unfavorably altered by changes in pH or temperature.

3. It should be cheap and plentiful, and should keep well even if exposed to the air.

4. It should not be toxic to tissues, poisonous if ingested or inhaled, or injurious to fabrics or metals.

5. It should mix easily with water in any desired concentration to make a permanent solution or emulsion.

EVALUATION OF CHEMICAL DISINFECTANTS

The effectiveness of a disinfectant must be tested by many laboratory experiments before it is used in actual nursing practice. The nurse does not carry out these experiments, but she should understand the procedure and significance of the standard method of testing. This is the Food and Drug Administration (*F.D.A.*) method of determining the *phenol coefficient.* The term is frequently abbreviated to *PC.* The PC is an arithmetic expression of the ability of a chemical to kill cultures of a test organism, *Salmonella typhosa* or *Staphylococcus aureus,* as compared with that of pure phenol (carbolic acid) when tested under the same standard conditions. The method of determining the phenol coefficient of a chemical can be illustrated by the following examples. A 1:90 dilution of phenol will kill *S. typhosa* in 10 minutes but not in 5 minutes. If the same result is obtained with a 1:900 dilution of substance X, it is obvious that X is ten times as strong a disinfectant as phenol. So its PC is 10. If the substance Y has to be used in a 1:45 dilution to kill the test organism in the same time interval, it is only half as effective as phenol in this test, so its PC will be 0.5.

The PC of a commercial disinfectant is often stated on its container, but it should be noted that the PC tells us only a very small part of what must be known about a chemical disinfectant and represents only a small part of its complete laboratory study. Adequate testing must also include experiments that reproduce practical conditions as faithfully as possible. Excellent examples of such experimentation are the two papers of Sommermeyer and Frobisher cited in the bibliography of Chap. 13.

COMMONLY USED CHEMICAL DISINFECTANTS

In the following pages the chemicals most commonly employed in nursing techniques and in environmental sanitation will be considered briefly. The chemicals used in and on the human body will be described in the next chapter. Substances used in controlling insects and rodents will be discussed in Chap. 16. As a help in checking the disinfectants, their names are italicized in the following paragraphs. Many commonly used disinfectants are special solutions of these chemicals. Unfortunately they are often called by names which are not specifically descriptive, e.g., Bard-Parker Germicide (a formaldehyde solution) and Lysol (a cresol, phenol, and soap solution).

Halogens and Their Derivatives. Two of the halogens, iodine and chlorine, have marked disinfectant action. Iodine is most frequently used in the form of an alcoholic solution, *tincture of iodine,* though an aqueous solution is better. Its use as a skin disinfectant will be discussed in Chap. 11. Because of its expense and staining properties, it is not used for environmental disinfection.

Chlorine gas is purchased as a compressed liquid in special metal cylinders. It is poisonous if inhaled. Its use is limited to disinfection of water, sewage, and some foods. The compounds of chlorine are effective only as they give off free chlorine. The amount of chlorine that may be given off is called the *available chlorine.* The more unstable a chlorine compound is, the more rapidly effective it will be and the faster it will deteriorate if it is kept for any length of time. The inorganic chlorine compound most commonly used is *chlorinated lime.* This is known as *bleaching powder* and owes its action to the liberation of chlorine. It is a very inexpensive compound used widely for disinfection of carcasses before burial, privies, barns, and freight cars. A chlorinated lime paste may be used for disinfection of skin and for decontamination of infected areas on floors and solid objects. The cans of powder must be kept tightly sealed and solutions made up fresh for each use. All chlorine compounds have bleaching and corrosive effects. They impart unpleasant tastes and odors. *Dakin's solution* and *Zonite* are forms of sodium hypochlorite. Other useful chlorine compounds are the *chloramines,* substances in which the chlorine is combined with a nitrogen atom. They are relatively more expensive.

Heavy Metals. Compounds of mercury, silver, copper, arsenic, and zinc are used as disinfectants. The ions of the metals have great antibacterial power. Their lethal effect is due to their ability to coagulate bacterial protein. Unfortunately, they are also injurious to tissue protein.

Mercuric chloride (bichloride of mercury) has been used for many years. Despite its past popularity it has so many disadvantages that it is now replaced by other materials. It is a violent poison, is inhibited by the presence of albumin, and corrodes metals. It is bacteriostatic in high dilutions. Although early bacteriologists believed that it would kill all bacteria, including spores, later experiments disproved this contention. It is not capable of sterilizing catgut or instruments as some have claimed. An organic mercury compound called *merthiolate* is commonly used as a preservative for vaccines and sera. It and other organic mercury compounds used on skin and mucous membranes will be discussed in Chap. 11.

Copper sulfate in very high dilutions inhibits the growth of algae (green scum plants) in water reservoirs. It is an important ingredient of agricultural sprays used to control fungous diseases of plants.

Alcohol. Seventy per cent ethyl alcohol (grain alcohol) is more often used than 95 per cent alcohol or absolute alcohol. All three are now known to be equally useful. Dilutions below 50 per cent are ineffective. The value of alcohol as a disinfectant has been much overrated in the past. It will not kill spores and takes up to 1 hour to kill vegetative bacteria. It is expensive and evaporates on standing. It is a tissue poison. It might well be replaced by other substances in many disinfection techniques where it is still used.

Alcohol has valuable bacteriostatic action. It is a useful but expensive preservative for biologic specimens. Since it is a fat solvent as well as a disinfectant, it is used in some cleaning procedures such as the preparation of the skin for hypodermic injection.

Formalin. Formalin is a 40 per cent solution of formaldehyde gas in water. It is effective in relatively high dilutions as a bacteriostatic agent and in lower dilutions as a bactericidal agent. It is not affected by the presence of proteins. It is a true *deodorant* (odor destroyer). It is somewhat irritating to the nose and throat and loses strength if exposed to the air. Its disinfecting power is greatly increased if it is used hot. It is inexpensive and is one of the best chemical disinfectants for hospital use. Special solutions containing a small amount of alkali and proprietary forms such as Bard-Parker Germicide are often used for disinfecting transfer forceps and rubber sheets.

Coal Tar Derivatives. *Phenols* and *cresols* in crude mixtures are obtained by the destructive distillation of coal. They are very inexpensive and are generally effective against bacteria and fungi but not against viruses. Purified phenol (carbolic acid) is more expensive and less effective than the crude products. Solutions of the cheaper compounds are often mixed with soap to form a permanent emulsion, since these compounds are not readily water-soluble. These emulsions are sold under trade names such as *Lysol*. The chief use of cresol and phenol compounds is in the disinfection of utensils and other objects in homes, hospitals, farms, and commercial establishments.

Soaps. Soap is primarily a cleansing agent. It loosens dirt and embedded microorganisms and aids in their removal. Strong soap solutions acting over long periods have definite disinfecting action. But the concentrations and short periods of exposure ordinarily used in washing do not accomplish disinfection. It is inadvisable to combine soap with chemical disinfectants, for some are actually inhibited by soap. Research indicates that the diphtheria organisms, the streptococci, and the pneumococci are more readily killed by soap than are most other forms. Many so-called germicidal soaps fail to show any advantage over ordinary toilet soaps in laboratory tests. Laboratory experiments support the use of green soap and other soft soaps containing certain unsaturated fatty acids in preference to the commoner hard soaps. Soaps containing compound G-11 (a dihydroxyhexachlorodiphenylmethane) and related compounds have been shown to reduce the bacteria of the skin.

Detergents; the Quaternary Ammonium Compounds. Within the past decade, dozens of cleansing agents other than soaps have been developed. The actions and chemical nature of these substances, which are called *surface-active compounds,* or *detergents,* vary widely. They all act primarily by their ability to depress the surface tension of water. Those that are acid in nature, the *anionic* detergents, are very effective in cleaning but less effective against microorganisms. The bactericidal effectiveness of many of those used for cleaning purposes has not been adequately investigated. The most widely used cleaning detergent, trisodium phosphate, is practically useless as a bactericide.

On the other hand, certain *cationic* detergents, the *quaternary ammonium compounds,* are very effective bacteriostatic and bactericidal agents. These quaternary ammonium compounds are complicated organic substances, each having at least one long carbon chain radical combined with the basic $\equiv$ N—OH group. Because of their very long and awkward chemical names, these compounds are almost invariably called by their trade names. Those in most common use include *Zephiran* (also sold as *Roccal* and *BTC*), *Phemerol* (*Hyamine 1622,* or *Polymine D*), *CTAB* (*Cetavon*), and *Ceepryn.* They may all be referred to as *quats.* These substances have been proved effective against both gram-positive and gram-negative bacteria. They are less effective against acid-fast bacteria and should not be used against bacterial spores and viruses. Quats are inactivated by the presence of soap or anionic detergents and by the presence of protein-containing materials such as milk, serum, or pus.

New Disinfectants. For many years only the chemicals that were commonly available were used as disinfectants. Within the last 20 years, chemists have collaborated with microbiologists to produce new chemicals that would be specifically useful and powerful against microorganisms. Many of these newer substances have marked advantages over the traditional disinfectants. Among the earliest to be developed was *hexylresorcinol.* This compound is sold as a glycerin and water solution under the name of *S.T. 37. Amphyl,* a mixture of alkyl and halogenated phenol compounds, kills certain patho-genic fungi as well as bacteria. Tile and other impermeable surfaces treated with amphyl retain bactericidal properties for as long as 1 week. The quaternary ammonium compounds and many special preparations of chlora-mine and buffered hypochlorite compounds are additional examples of sub-stances developed primarily for their disinfecting action.

Gases and Vapors: Fumigation. Fumigation is the use of a gas or a vapor to combat harmful organisms. Fumigation is used to destroy both organisms of disease and insects and other pests that spread disease.

Formaldehyde gas was commonly used in the past in an attempt to disinfect rooms and their contents after cases of communicable disease. This procedure has been abandoned as ineffective and impractical, but formaldehyde gas is still used for the disinfection of objects in small enclosed spaces such as closets. Aerosols, chemical mists made by vaporizing bac-tericidal chemicals of very low surface tension, are the most effective chemical means of disinfection of the atmosphere. The two most commonly employed for destruction of pathogenic bacteria in air are *propylene glycol* and *tri-ethylene glycol.* They are sprayed into the air of hospital wards, dormitories, and auditoriums. Tests show that they are capable of destroying a large proportion of dangerous streptococci in the air.

PRACTICAL DISINFECTION BY CHEMICALS

In Chap. 8 it was noted that sterilization is seldom accomplished by chemical means. The term *chemical sterilization* still appears in textbooks, but hospitals now limit the employment of chemicals for sterilization to a few procedures where more reliable methods are injurious or inexpedient. Many techniques used by dentists and doctors in private practice should be termed *disinfection* rather than *sterilization.* Experimentation and practical experience lead all authorities to discourage the general use of attempted sterilization by chemical solutions and to recommend the substitution of methods employing heat wherever feasible. On the other hand, there is no question of the efficacy of chemical methods of disinfection if the chemical is intelligently selected and properly used.

The Selection of a Method of Disinfection. Disinfection may be accom-plished by either physical or chemical means. In actual practice the choice is usually between heat and a chemical. Many uses of heat in disinfection were discussed in Chap. 9. It should also be noted that since chemical destruction of spores is so uncertain, heat is used for disinfection in the care of cases of anthrax, gas gangrene, and tetanus.

When a chemical is to be used, its choice will depend largely on the type of organism to be killed and the nature of the material to be disinfected.

Chemicals vary in their effects on different species of microorganisms. For example, soaps are effective against diplococci but ineffective against staphylococci; viruses are susceptible to the action of alkalies but are not destroyed by dilutions of phenol compounds that kill bacteria. The chemical chosen must be one that does not injure the material to be treated. Obviously the same disinfectant cannot be used on sheets, sputum cup holders, clinical thermometers, and bedside tables. Sometimes it will be advantageous to use a disinfectant that is also a deodorant. If the pathogens are in pus, sputum, or feces, a disinfectant is chosen which is not affected by the presence of protein and which has penetrating power. When large amounts of disinfectant are needed the cost must be considered.

Ordinarily the nurse is guided by past experience and experimentation as reflected in standardized nursing procedures. She does not have to take the responsibility of choosing a method every time she has something to disinfect. Acceptable methods are specified in procedure manuals and other hospital handbooks. However, the nursing profession must be continually critical of traditional methods and willing to adopt improved methods backed by scientific evidence. Too often questionable traditional methods persist long after better and safer methods have been discovered.

Disinfection in the Care of Cases of Communicable Disease. In the past, great emphasis was placed on disinfection of room, bed and bedding, and personal belongings when a patient had recovered from a communicable disease and was removed from isolation. This was *terminal disinfection* and generally included fumigation of the room with formaldehyde gas. Since pathogenic organisms leave the patient not just at the time of recovery but throughout the course of a case of communicable disease, disinfection should be practiced continuously. This constant destruction of all dangerous organisms leaving the patient is known as *concurrent disinfection,* or *bedside disinfection.*

The conditions of isolation and the routine of concurrent disinfection in a specific communicable disease will depend primarily on the nature of the causative organism and the way it leaves the patient's body. Therefore there is no single set of rules for the care of all diseases. There is one set of procedures for cases of known or suspected intestinal infections (*enteric precautions*), another for respiratory infections, etc. Sometimes these "precautions" seem needlessly detailed and burdensome to the nurse. But they must be carried out with intelligent attention, for only then will the nurse accomplish her purpose of preventing the escape of even a single pathogen. Details of isolation and disinfection vary in different hospitals, but they are all formulated to accomplish this one end.

Sanitization in the Care of All Patients. Not all dangerous organisms come from patients ill with communicable disease. They are also spread from patients ill with other types of disease and from hospital personnel, including the nurse herself. Cleanliness is the basic means of preventing spread of organisms from person to person in the hospital or any other environment. No good nurse tolerates uncleanliness in any situation. An important result of the training of the nurse is an appreciation of true cleanliness and a knowledge of efficient, time-saving methods of maintaining it. Because the term *clean* is usually taken to mean freedom from grossly visible dirt, the adjective *sanitized*, the verb to *sanitize,* and the noun *sanitization,* all implying freedom from undesirable contamination, have been quite generally adopted by the foods industries and are useful additions to the nursing vocabulary. Sanitization implies disinfection as well as apparent cleanliness. The housewife or restaurant employee who wipes up a table with any handy wet rag will say that she is cleaning the table. When the nurse on the ward cares for the patient's bedside table, she must have a much more exacting purpose and must do the job with a technique that has been proved to sanitize that surface. It is, of course, this conception of purpose and this application of definite scientific method that contribute professional status to many nursing tasks that thoughtless people consider menial. They also color these tasks with professional interest for the nurse who carries them out thoughtfully.

STUDY SUGGESTIONS

Recheck your comprehension of the terms and principles of disinfection (Chap. 8). Your chemistry and materia medica texts will give you additional information about the chemicals listed in this chapter.

Make a table for your notebook with the following headings: *Disinfectant; Chemical nature; Principal uses; Defects.* Fill in this table for the important disinfectants.

Should the home medicine closet and kitchen have a varied supply of disinfectants for frequent use, or should the home supply be limited to those specifically prescribed by the physician? On what methods of disinfection and sanitization should we rely in ordinary housekeeping procedures?

If the label on a bottle of disinfectant states that its phenol coefficient is 3, is this disinfectant stronger or weaker than phenol? What else will you need to know about this disinfectant in order to use it intelligently?

Name some chemicals that are being used less frequently than formerly. What types of disinfectants are being developed at the present time? What chemical disinfectants are used in your hospital? What chemical methods of disinfection are prescribed in your procedure book or practical nursing text for use in cases of enteric disease? In each case why was that particular chemical chosen? If any chemical disinfectant not mentioned in this chapter is used in your hospital, look it up in one of the books listed at the end of this chapter.

Have you ever observed any example of chemical sterilization? What method of heat sterilization might be substituted? What methods of disinfection by heat have you noted in the hospital? Why was heat used in these cases rather than a chemical?

Describe at least three examples of sanitization in the routine care of the patient. Cite some possible examples of carelessness by yourself or others in carrying out these duties. In each case evaluate the dangers of such carelessness.

SUGGESTED READING

General References (See also page 101.)

BUCHBINDER, L., and P. ZARETSKY: Cessation of bacterial motility as a rapid test for germicidal action. *Am. J. Pub. Health* **41**:537 (1951).

"Conference on the Mechanisms and Evaluation of Antiseptics." *Ann. New York Acad. Sc.* **53**:1 (1950).

REUHLE, G. L. A., and C. M. BREWER: "Methods of Testing Antiseptics and Disinfectants." Circular 198, U.S. Department of Agriculture, Washington, D.C., 1931.

WYSS, O.: Chemical Disinfectants, in "Annual Review of Microbiology." Vol. 2, Annual Reviews, Inc., Stanford, 1948.

Sterilization by Ethylene Oxide

PHILLIPS, C. R., *et al.:* Symposium on gaseous ethylene oxide. *Am. J. Hyg.* **50**:270 (1949).

Specific Disinfectant Chemicals

GLASSMAN, H. N.: Surface active agents and their application in bacteriology. *Bact. Rev.* **12**:105 (1948).

KLARMANN, E. G., E. S. WRIGHT, and V. A. SHTERNOV: Prolongation of the antibacterial potential of disinfected surfaces. *Appl. Microbiol.* **1**:19 (1953).

ROBERTSON, O. H.: Disinfection of the air by germicidal vapors and mists. *Am. J. Pub. Health* **36**:390 (1946).

SMITH, C. R., *et al.:* The bactericidal effect of surface-active agents on the tubercle bacillus. *Pub. Health Rep.* **65**:1588 (1950).

CHAPTER 11

Control of Organisms on and in
the Human Body: Chemotherapy

It is much more difficult to destroy pathogenic microorganisms on and in the animal body than it is to destroy them in the external environment. Most physical and chemical agents that injure microbial protoplasm are definitely toxic to human cells. Obviously the commonly employed physical and chemical methods of disinfection cannot be applied to human tissue.

The term *chemotherapy* is susceptible of several different interpretations but may be most usefully defined as the prevention and treatment of infections by the use of chemical agents that are capable of destroying or inhibiting the pathogen without serious injury to the animal host. Drugs that are used in chemotherapy are called *chemotherapeutic agents*. Atabrine used in the control of malaria and penicillin used to prevent the development of streptococcal infection are chemotherapeutic agents; salts given as cathartics and digitalis prescribed for a heart condition are not.

Some of the most useful chemotherapeutic agents are obtained from microorganisms. These drugs are called *antibiotics*. The most important antibiotic is penicillin, which is obtained by culturing the mold *Penicillium notatum*.

The term *antimicrobial agent* is now frequently used for both antibiotic and nonantibiotic substances used for internal therapy directed against the causative agents of disease.

DEVELOPMENT OF CHEMOTHERAPY

Chemotherapeutic agents such as quinine for malaria and pomegranate bark and pumpkin seeds for intestinal worms have been used for centuries. The early use of such drugs was based entirely on practical experience: it was *empirical*. Empiricism is still the basis of the use of many old and many new drugs. However in recent years available drugs have been systematically and scientifically studied. In many cases we have in vitro and in vivo laboratory evidence of the effectiveness of a drug. In a smaller number we have gained some knowledge of the mechanisms by which the drugs act on the microorganisms. With the advances of modern organic chemistry it has been possible to synthesize new types of compounds and test their actions in the laboratory before trying them on man.

The pioneer in the modern development of scientific chemotherapy was Paul Ehrlich, the German biochemist. Fifty years ago he defined the characteristics that are required for a satisfactory chemotherapeutic agent and synthesized the drug *salvarsan* (*arsphenamine*), the first successful drug for the treatment of syphilis.

In 1934 Domagk in Germany reported the ability of a red dye, *Prontosil*, to cure streptococcal infections. Shortly after it was found that the active part of the dye was a *sulfonamide* compound, *sulfanilamide*. Since then several thousand other sulfonamide derivatives (*sulfa drugs*) have been synthesized and a considerable number used clinically.

In England in 1929 Fleming noted and studied the action of a mold, *Penicillium notatum* (*P. chrysogenum*) that interfered with the growth of staphylococci on a culture plate. But it was not until nearly 10 years later that two other English workers, Florey and Chain, prepared a concentrated, clinically usable form of the drug, *penicillin*. In the early 1940s the American government laboratories developed methods of practical large-scale production of this first successful antibiotic. The laboratory techniques used now by microbiologists in their search for new antibiotics were developed about this time by the two American bacteriologists Waksman and Dubos.

In the last 15 years many thousands of cultures have been tested for their antibiotic ability. More than a dozen antibiotics are now in commercial production. The prevention and the treatment of infection have been revolutionized by their use. There is also at the present time increased interest in the development of new chemotherapeutic compounds that are synthetic chemicals rather than antibiotics. New knowledge of the essential processes of cells has given scientists important new clues as to the types of chemical compounds that might prove to be effective antimicrobial agents. The antituberculosis effect of the compound *isoniazide* (*isonicotinic acid hydrazide,* or *INH*) was discovered in this fashion.

NATURE AND ACTION OF CHEMOTHERAPEUTIC AGENTS

Most chemotherapeutic agents are bacteriostatic in their action. Some are bactericidal in high concentrations. Effective bacteriostasis is usually sufficient for the control of infection. The majority of microorganisms in the body that cannot reproduce will die within a short period. Nonmultiplying cells will be incapable of further invasion of tissues and will be destroyed by the defensive mechanisms of the body.

Specificity of Chemotherapeutic Agents. The chemicals used for the destruction of microorganisms within the body are much more selective than those used in environmental disinfection. Each antibiotic has what is called its *spectrum.* Broad-spectrum antibiotics such as chloramphenicol are active against nearly all types of bacteria and against rickettsiae as well. The spectra of others are more limited. Penicillin is most active against the gram-positive bacteria, while streptomycin is most active against the gram-negative bacteria and the mycobacteria. One simple method of demonstrating the spectrum is illustrated in Fig. 11·1.

Action on Microorganisms. To be effective an agent must interfere with some essential life process of the microorganism. To do this it must be able to penetrate within the organism and unite with its cell substance. At the same time it must not seriously injure the tissues of the host.

There is no reason to believe that all antibiotics act in the same way on susceptible cells. Determining the exact way in which each antibiotic acts has proved a very difficult problem. It is known that sulfonamides prevent bacteria from utilizing *para-aminobenzoic acid* (*PABA*), a substance which susceptible cells need in order to form an enzyme essential for their own growth. The chemical structure of the sulfa drug is the same as that of PABA except for one radical. The drug therefore competes with PABA for combination with cell substance. If the cell substance does combine with the drug, the bacterium cannot take up enough PABA to continue its normal growth. Since the drug inhibits a process of normal metabolism it is an *antimetabolite*. The concept of antimetabolites and their action, gained largely from the study of chemotherapeutic agents, is now being applied to the study of many other problems of cell physiology, including cancer.

Penicillin interferes with the cell's use of essential amino acids in its synthesis of nucleic acids. Streptomycin is believed to inhibit the action of certain respiratory enzymes.

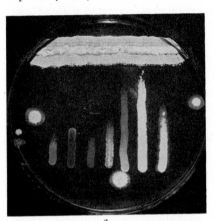 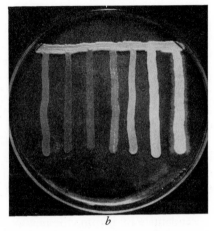

FIG. 11·1   The effect of two selected cultures on the growth of seven representative microorganisms. (*a*) The effect of *Penicillium* is definitely antibiotic. (*b*) The unidentified bacterium lacks antibiotic properties. The seven microorganisms streaked at right angles to the organism being tested are (reading from left to right) *Micrococcus pyogenes* (gram-positive coccus), *Escherichia coli* (gram-negative intestinal bacterium), *Brucella bronchiseptica* (gram-negative respiratory bacillus), *Mycobacterium tuberculosis* (acid-fast bacillus), *Saccharomyces pastorianus* (yeast), *Candida albicans* (parasitic yeast), and *Trichophyton rubrum* (parasitic mold). (*Eli Lilly and Company.*)

PROBLEMS OF CHEMOTHERAPY

The drug introduced into the infected body affects the host tissues, the invading microorganisms, and frequently also other microorganisms that are normally present in the host. Because both the host and the microorganisms are living things, their reactions may be multiple and varied. These biologic reactions are the bases of many of the difficult problems of chemotherapy.

Toxicity for Host Tissues. It is unlikely that any chemotherapeutic agent is entirely lacking in toxicity if it is given in sufficiently high concentrations. However some drugs including penicillin are so relatively nontoxic that they can be safely given in quantities much greater than the minimum needed for effective treatment. Unfortunately, certain other useful drugs are toxic in concentration only very slightly higher than the effective dosage. Sulfa drugs injure the kidneys, antimalarial drugs cause jaundice, and streptomycin therapy often results in vertigo and deafness because of nerve injury. Frequently compounds used on lesions in skin or mucous membranes prevent the growth of bacteria, but at the same time they prevent the growth of tissues needed for healing.

Hypersensitivity. Persons who have been previously treated with an antibiotic may show signs of hypersensitivity if they are given the drug again. They are then said to be *allergic* to the drug. This allergy differs from toxicity. The severity of the reaction is not related to the size of the dose; it does not occur the first time the drug is given; it develops only in certain people who are constitutionally predisposed to allergies. Moreover, the symptoms are varied and appear in a variety of tissues, while the effects of the toxicity of a drug are similar in all persons.

Development of Resistant Strains of Microorganisms. Mutant microorganisms tolerant of a specific antibiotic appear spontaneously in very small numbers in any population of drug-susceptible cells, whether the drug is present or not. If the drug is present, it prevents the majority of the cells from multiplying, but the drug-tolerant mutants can still grow, and their descendants soon become the new population. In this way a microorganism "becomes resistant" in a culture containing the antibiotic or in a person treated with the antibiotic. In most cases the increase in resistance resulting from each mutation is small. The new population will be suppressed by a concentration of the drug only two to five times that needed for the original cells. High degree of resistance develops only after serial exposure to increasing concentrations. On the other hand, tubercle bacilli may develop mutants that are resistant to a thousand times the originally effective concentration. This sort of mutation is much more likely to cause failure of the antibiotic therapy. There is also danger that these highly resistant forms may spread to other persons, causing infections refractory to treatment.

Alteration of the Body's Normal Flora. It will be remembered that in many parts of the body there are mixed populations of bacteria, fungi, and protozoa, all harmless under normal conditions. (See page 147.) When a person is treated with an antibiotic, some of these normally present forms may be inhibited. Others, normally present in very small numbers but naturally tolerant of the drug, may grow with unusual rapidity. Although these organisms are of kinds that are usually considered avirulent, their abnormal numbers may lead to diarrhea, membranous colitis, pharyngitis, pyelitis or cystitis, and even to septicemia. The microorganisms most often identified in these cases are pyogenic staphylococci, the yeast *Candida albicans* (causing the condition usually known as *moniliasis*), and certain antibiotic-tolerant gram-negative rods, species of *Proteus* and *Pseudomonas*.

IMPORTANT CHEMOTHERAPEUTIC AGENTS

Chemotherapeutic Agents Used in Superficial Infections. Many dyes have strongly selective antimicrobial action. Their use in selective culture media has already been noted. *Gentian violet, acriflavine,* and *proflavine* are the ones most used in medicine. Gentian violet is particularly effective against the gram-positive cocci and the flavines against the gram-negative neisseriae.

Because mercury and its inorganic compounds are so toxic, a number of organic mercury compounds less injurious to tissues have been synthesized. Among them are *mercurochrome, merthiolate, metaphen,* and *mercurophen.* Mercurochrome is the weakest of them. The 1 or 2 per cent aqueous solutions usually sold are unreliable. A 5 per cent solution in acetone and alcohol is more effective. *Silver nitrate* and the organic silver compounds *argyrol* and *protargol* are used on infected membranes. Special preparations of zinc peroxide have a very favorable effect in wounds invaded by anaerobic bacteria.

Quaternary ammonium compounds have been suggested as wound disinfectants. Weak freshly made solutions of hypochlorites such as *Dakin's solution* and the organic chlorine compounds known as *chloramines* are used as antiseptic irrigants for wounds and infected cavities. It should be noted that a number of chemicals including 1 per cent aqueous iodine, picric acid, Zephiran, and lime paste are used to disinfect the intact skin but are too toxic to be used in or on wounds.

The Sulfa Drugs. There are two important groups of sulfa drugs, the sulfonamides and the sulfones. Most compounds belonging to the first group have a low solubility and are injurious to kidney tissue. The form in most common use is *sulfadiazine.* This drug and certain other sulfonamides are most often used to treat bacterial dysenteries and some forms of meningitis. A newer and more soluble sulfonamide, *Gantrisin,* is useful for some infections of the urinary tract. Sulfones are used principally in the treatment of leprosy.

Drugs Used for the Treatment of Tuberculosis. In the last 10 years several groups of chemical compounds have been found useful in treating various forms of tuberculosis. *Para-aminosalicylic acid* (*PASA*) is only mildly tuberculostatic but is used very effectively in combination with streptomycin and other drugs. German doctors employ a group of compounds known as *thiosemicarbazones. Tibione* and *Conteben* are two forms of such compounds. *Isonicotinic acid hydrazide* (also known as *isoniazide* and *INH*) has recently received much publicity in this country. The chemotherapy of leprosy and of tuberculosis is covered more fully in Chap. 30.

Penicillin. Penicillin was the first, and is still the most important, of the antibiotics. It is the most powerful and the least toxic of them all. It is effective against all except a few strains of streptococci and micrococci, and against the neisseriae and the spirochetes. (See Fig. 11·2.)

Streptomycin. The name of this antibiotic indicates its origin from a species of the genus *Streptomyces*. It has very marked antibacterial action, notably against gram-negative bacteria and *Mycobacterium tuberculosis*. However its usefulness in most bacterial infections is limited by its toxicity, its allergenicity, and its tendency to allow the growth of resistant mutants. It is, however, our chief reliance in the therapy of tuberculosis. By using it in combination with PASA, some of its bad effects are avoided. Streptomycin is often referred to as SM, and its closely related derivative, *dihydrostreptomycin,* as DSM.

The Tetracyclines. Two other antibiotics obtained from streptomycete cultures have been used since 1950. (See Fig. 11·3.) They were originally named *Aureomycin* and *terramycin*. More recently it has been shown that they are both forms of a complex organic substance named tetracycline (TC). This compound has also been found to possess marked antibiotic properties. Aureomycin is now more properly called *chlortetracycline* (abbreviated to CTC), and terramycin is *oxytetracycline* (OTC). The three tetracyclines are "broad-spectrum" antibiotics, for they act against rickettsiae and certain large viruses (page 449) as well as against the gram-negative bacteria. They can be given by mouth and are absorbed from the alimentary canal. They are relatively nontoxic, though they do cause some digestive disturbances.

Chloramphenicol. Another broad-spectrum antibiotic, *Chloromycetin,* was originally obtained from still another streptomycete. It is now produced by chemical synthesis rather than from microbial culture, and the pure, synthesized form is properly called *chloramphenicol*. Its rapid absorption from the alimentary canal makes it especially effective against the bacteria of typhoid fever. Under some conditions it injures the red blood cells and causes a serious form of anemia.

Other Antibiotics. Although thousands of other antibiotics have been tested in the laboratories, only a relatively small number are produced commercially and licensed by the Food and Drug Administration for general use. *Neomycin* is most effective for the preoperative disinfection of the alimentary canal. *Viomycin* is possibly useful in the treatment of tuberculosis. *Erythromycin* is effective against penicillin-resistant strains of micrococci. All these drugs are obtained from cultures of specific streptomycetes.

Tyrothricin, first of the antibiotics developed in America, cannot be used internally because it destroys both red and white blood cells. Its main use is in salves and ointments for the treatment of chronic skin ulcers. It is obtained from cultures of a sporing bacillus. *Bacitracin* and *polymyxin* also come from cultures of bacilli. They are also toxic but are sometimes used to treat infections due to penicillin-resistant cocci or gram-negative rods such

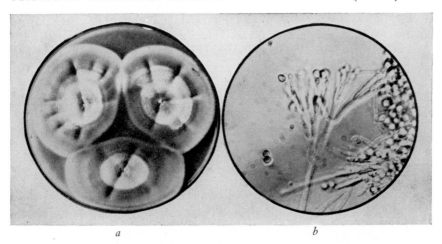

a   *b*

FIG. 11·2   *Penicillium crysogenes.* (*a*) Three giant colonies on modified Czapek's agar; (*b*) fruiting bodies. ×2,000. (*Courtesy of Dr. Kenneth B. Raper, from J. Bact. 48:643.*)

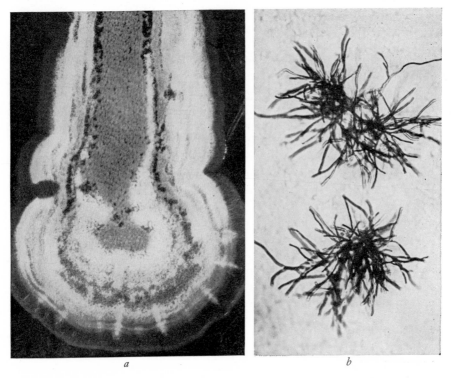

a   *b*

FIG. 11·3   *Streptomyces aureofaciens,* the producer of chlortetracycline. (*a*) Growth on agar. ×20. (*b*) Characteristic morphology. ×1,500. (*Lederle Laboratories Division, American Cyanamid Company.*)

as *Pseudomonas* that are not affected by other antibiotics. The chemotherapy of the parasitic, mycotic, and viral infections is discussed in the chapters on these organisms. We should note, however, that while many effective drugs are used against animal parasites, there are relatively few that are useful in the diseases due to fungi. And up to the present time no antibiotic has been discovered that has any effect on the infections due to the small viruses, although several antibiotics act against rickettsiae and the larger viruses.

MICROBIOLOGIC TECHNIQUES IN THE STUDY OF ANTIMICROBIAL AGENTS

Laboratories in the universities, in government agencies such as the Food and Drug Division, and in the drug companies carry on continuous research designed to discover new antibiotics and improve those already in use. Hospital and other clinical laboratories perform routine tests that help to ensure effective chemotherapy for the patients.

Discovery of a New Antibiotic. Bacteria of soil samples collected from many different environments are isolated. Each culture is tested for its possible antimicrobial effect on a number of representative species. Figures 11·4 and 11·1 illustrate these steps. The cultures that show promise are then grown in larger amounts and filtrates of these cultures tested. The biochemists concentrate and purify the active fractions of the filtrates.

New nonantibiotic chemicals are usually prepared by slight modification of the molecular structure of some compound known to have antimicrobial properties. The action of each new compound is tested for its effect on the growth of specific microorganisms.

Basic Study of a New Antimicrobial Agent. Several groups of scientists must cooperate in the development of any new agent. Pharmacologists determine the toxicity of the drug by tests on animals. They determine safe concentrations and safe methods of administration. They study the rate of absorption from the alimentary canal and from intramuscular injections, and the rate of excretion by the kidneys. Chemists determine the stability and solubility of the drug. They determine its exact chemical composition and find ways of preparing it in pure form. Bacteriologists experiment with cultures to discover the conditions that will provide optimum conditions for growth and the maximum production of the antibiotic substance. Engineers develop methods of large-scale production and design huge commercial plants (Figs. 11·5 and 11·6). Teams of physicians in large hospitals carefully test the new drug on selected patients under controlled conditions. Finally the Food and Drug Commissioner, after study of all reports, may certify the drug and allow its general sale. Thereafter each batch of the drug is tested for purity, strength, and other characteristics by the government laboratories before it is allowed on the market.

Further Study. New dosage forms are developed mainly by the drug companies. For example, an antibiotic may be sold as a sterile soluble salt for intramuscular injection, as a dusting powder for wounds, as tablets for oral use, as troches to be sucked, etc.

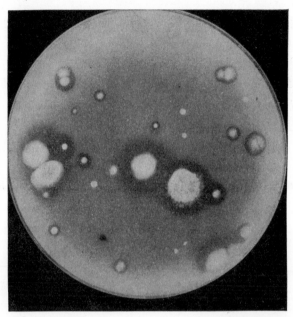

FIG. 11·4   Detection of antibiotic-producing bacteria. The plate has been heavily seeded with a pure culture of a bacterium. Its surface has been inoculated with soil. The clear zones around some of the colonies of soil bacteria show that they produce substances antagonistic to the growth of the pure culture. (*Courtesy of Dr. Selman A. Waksman.*)

Repository Compounds. A very important advance in chemotherapy is the use of long-acting compounds (*repository compounds*) that make frequent injections unnecessary. The soluble forms of penicillin, for example, are excreted so rapidly that parenteral injections used to be given every few hours. Fortunately it has been found that combining the antibiotic with any one of several substances will result in a slower but steady release of the drug into the general circulation. Peanut oil, beeswax, procaine, and aluminum stearate have all been used for this purpose. Procaine penicillin in oil with aluminum monostearate is an effective repository form. One large dose gives effective blood levels for as long as 2 days. The action of penicillin

FIG. 11·5 Streptomycin production in 15,000-gal. tanks (only the tops of the tanks can be seen). (*Merck and Co., Inc.*)

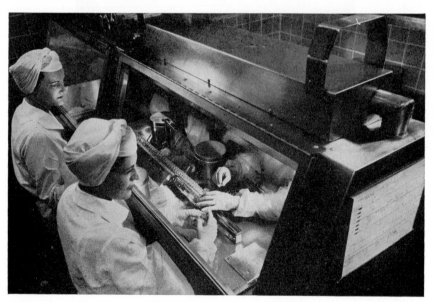

FIG. 11·6 Filling and stoppering vials of dihydrostreptomycin. The operators work through built-in rubber gloves in a sealed cubicle irradiated by ultraviolet light in order to ensure sterility of the final product. (*Merck and Co., Inc.*)

can also be prolonged by the addition of chemicals that slow down penicillin excretion in the kidneys. A single massive dose of bicillin (benzethacil penicillin) gives adequate blood levels for more than a week.

Increased Drug Production. The price of the important antibiotics is being brought down as more economical methods of production are found. Slow-growing types of *Penicillium* have been replaced by strains that grow rapidly in submerged cultures and produce much greater amounts of the active chemicals. A cheap nutrient, the previously wasted liquid from factories making cornstarch and corn oil, is the basis of the thousands of gallons of culture medium used in the large penicillin tanks. It is fortified with carbohydrates, minerals, and phenylacetic acid. With the improved strains and improved media over 100 times as much penicillin can be obtained in a given culture as could be produced in 1940.

Combined Therapy. When two antimicrobial agents are administered together, they may interfere with each other, the effect may be the sum of the action of the two drugs, or an extraordinary increase in effectiveness may be noted (synergistic effect). In the treatment of an infection in which the causative bacterium tends to develop drug resistance, the emergence of resistant strains is suppressed or delayed by the use of two carefully selected synergistic drugs. So, for example, at the present time tuberculosis is usually treated by *combined therapy,* employing both streptomycin and para-aminosalicylic acid. The clinical use of combined therapy should always be based on careful in vitro and in vivo laboratory research.

Measuring the Strength of Antibiotics. The strength of most antibiotics is now expressed in micrograms (μg) of the pure chemical per milliliter of the dosage form. Chemical tests are therefore used for the exact measurement of the strength of preparations of these substances. However the strength of penicillin, bacitracin, and some of the newest antibiotics is measured in biologic units. The unit of penicillin is the amount that will have a bacteriostatic effect equal to that of a standard unit provided by the Food and Drug Administration. (See Fig. 11·7.) The strength of commercial preparations is checked in this way by the government laboratories. The concentration of an antibiotic in blood, spinal fluid, urine, or other body substances may be assayed by similar appropriate chemical or biologic methods.

Sensitivity Determinations. The bacteriologist often assists the physician in choosing the agent to be used in the chemotherapy of an infection. He tests the bacteria from the patient to determine which antibiotics will suppress their growth. Such tests may be done before treatment is begun, or when an antibiotic has been used but has failed to bring about improvement in the patient's condition, or when a relapse suggests that a drug-resistant strain of the microorganism may have developed.

The disk method is most commonly used. Bacteria isolated from the patient or the pathologic specimens such as blood or pus are used. The inoculum may be mixed with the agar to make a *seeded plate,* or it may be heavily streaked over the surface of the hardened medium. Five or six disks are then placed at even intervals on the surface of the plate. Each disk is a small circle of filter paper that has been saturated with a chosen concentration

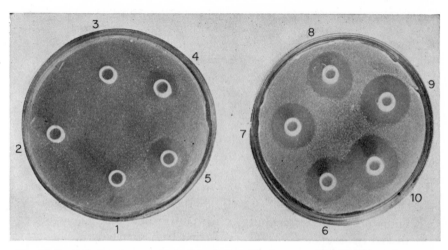

FIG. 11·7 Cylinder-plate method of testing antibiotic concentration. These plates are seeded with *Micrococcus pyogenes.* Penicillin solutions of increasing strength were placed in cylinders numbered 1 to 10. The size of the zone around number 7 indicates that the concentration of penicillin used in that cylinder equals 1 unit of penicillin per milliliter.

of an antibiotic and then dried. Disks may be purchased from drug supply houses. They are colored, each color indicating a different antibiotic. (As is appropriate, penicillin disks are green, and Aureomycin disks are yellow.) Each disk is also marked in some way to designate the concentration of the drug. Usually three concentrations are available—low, medium, and high. The plates are examined after suitable incubation. The degree of bacteriostatic action is judged by the area around each disk in which the organisms have failed to grow. If an organism is sensitive to a given antibiotic, definite halos will be found around the disks of medium and low concentrations. If an organism is resistant, even the high-concentration disk will lack a halo. A typical test is shown in Fig. 11·8.

Tube dilution tests are done when more exact information is needed. They are too time-consuming for routine use. Serial concentrations of the antibiotic are made in tubes of suitable broth medium. The bacterium is inoculated

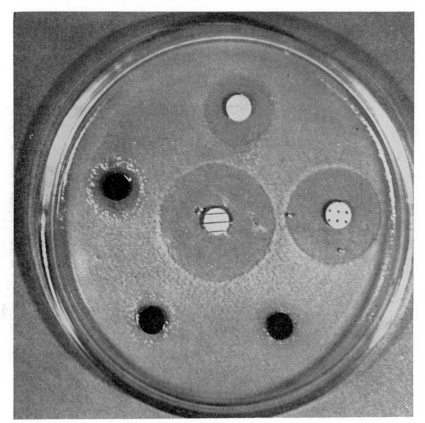

FIG. 11·8 Disk method of testing sensitivity to antibiotics. The bacterium seeded in the agar, a nonsporing rod, is clearly inhibited by the disks of chlortetracycline (light colored) but not by the disks of bacitracin (dark). (The striped disk contains a high concentration of the antibiotic; the dotted disk, a medium concentration; and the unmarked disk, a low concentration.)

into each tube. After incubation the tubes are examined for cloudiness or other evidence of growth. The negative tube with the least amount of antibiotic indicates the minimum inhibitory concentration for that bacterium. A tube dilution test is shown in Fig. 11·9.

STUDY SUGGESTIONS

Define *chemotherapy*. Define *antibiotic*. Are all chemotherapeutic agents antibiotics? Name important ones that are not.

Describe the discovery and development of penicillin. Name three diseases for which penicillin is the chief treatment. What other antibiotics are in common use? Compare them with penicillin.

What is your concept of the action of a chemotherapeutic agent? Can a person become resistant to an antibiotic? Can a bacterium become resistant to an anti-

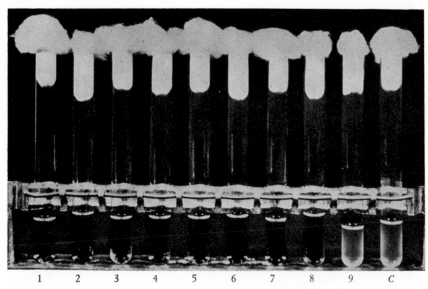

FIG. 11·9 Tube dilution method of determining sensitivity to an antibiotic. Tubes 1 through 9 contain decreasing concentrations of oxytetracycline in broth. Each tube has been inoculated with *Streptococcus pyogenes*. Tube *C* is a control containing no antibiotic. The minimum concentration that will inhibit growth is that of tube 8 (0.39 μg per milliliter). (*Chas. Pfizer & Co., Inc.*)

biotic? What is the true explanation of this business of resistance? What measures help to prevent the development of resistance?

Streptomycin is not an ideal antibiotic for the treatment of tuberculosis. Why? Many laboratories are now trying to find a better tuberculostatic drug. Just how will they proceed in trying to solve this problem?

What are the advantages of combined therapy? of repository compounds? How can research laboratory workers study the effects of combined therapy in cultures and in animals? How can they measure the effectiveness of a repository compound?

Sometimes patients receive antibiotic therapy which effectively combats their original disease. Yet they may be made more ill than they were before. Give three possible explanations for this.

SUGGESTED READING

General References

Burrows, W.: "Textbook of Microbiology." 16th ed., Saunders, Philadelphia, 1954. Pages 133–148.

Davis, B. D., and W. McDermott: Principles of Chemotherapy, in R. J. Dubos's "Bacterial and Mycotic Infections of Man." 2d ed., Lippincott, Philadelphia, 1952.

Eagle, H., and A. K. Saz: Antibiotics, in "Annual Review of Microbiology." Vol. 9, Annual Reviews, Inc., Stanford, 1955.

Fleming, A.: Twentieth-century changes in the treatment of septic infections. *New England J. Med.* **248:**1037 (1953).

Goldstein, A.: Medical progress. Antibacterial chemotherapy. *New England J. Med.* **240:**98; **240:**137; and **240:**180 (1949).

Karelitz, S.: Choice of an antibiotic; an interpretive review. *J. Pediat.* **42:**478 (1953).

Waksman, S. A.: "Microbial Antagonisms and Antibiotic Substances." 2d ed., Commonwealth Fund, New York, 1947.

Welch, H.: "The Manual of Antibiotics. 1954–1955." Medical Encyclopedia, Inc., New York, 1954.

Mode of Action of Antibiotics

Brownlee, G.: Antibiotics (with special reference to mode of action), in "Annual Review of Microbiology." Vol. 5, Annual Reviews, Inc., Stanford, 1951.

Umbreit, W. W.: Mechanisms of Antibacterial Action, in "Annual Review of Microbiology." Vol. 8, Annual Reviews, Inc., Stanford, 1954.

Wyss, O., et al.: Symposium on the mode of action of antibiotics. *Bact. Rev.* **17:**17 (1953).

Problems of Antimicrobial Therapy

Garrod, L. P.: Acquired bacterial resistance to chemotherapeutic agents. *Bull. Hyg.* **25:**539 (1950).

Jawetz, E., and J. B. Gunnison: An experimental basis of combined antibiotic therapy. *J.A.M.A.* **150:**693 (1952).

Woods, J. W., I. H. Manning, and C. W. Patterson: Monilial infections complicating the therapeutic use of antibiotics. *J.A.M.A.* **145:**207 (1951).

Special Reports on Specific Antibiotics

Finland, M., et al.: Clinical and laboratory observations of a new antibiotic, tetracycline. *J.A.M.A.* **154:**561 (1954).

HAIGHT, T. H., and M. FINLAND: Laboratory and clinical studies on erythromycin. *New England J. Med.* **247**:227 (1952).

WAKSMAN, S. A.: Streptomycin: background, isolation, properties, and utilization. *Science* **118**:259 (1953).

Laboratory Methods

HUMPHREY, J. H., H. M. MUSSETT, and W. L. M. PERRY: The 2nd international standard of penicillin. *Bull. WHO* **9**:15 (1952).

ROUTIEN, J. B., and A. C. FINLAY: Problems in the search for microorganisms producing antibiotics. *Bact. Rev.* **16**:51 (1952).

SPAULDING, E. H., and T. G. ANDERSON: Selection of antimicrobial agents by laboratory means. *J.A.M.A.* **147**:1336 (1951).

PART THREE

Sources and Modes of Infection

CHAPTER 12

Sources of Pathogenic Organisms

This chapter and the three following discuss the sources from which pathogenic organisms come and the ways in which they are spread. In every case
of communicable disease, a cause, a source of infection, and a mode of infection are involved. The *source of infection* is always some person or animal
who is discharging living pathogenic organisms. The *mode of infection* is
the way or means by which the living pathogen, the cause of the disease,
travels from the source of infection to the next victim. Effective control of
any infectious disease depends on knowledge of the cause of the infection,
its exact sources, and its modes of transfer. A fourth factor, the immunity
or susceptibility of the possible victim, will be the subject of the next part
of this book (Chaps. 17, 18, and 19).

MICROBIOLOGY OF THE NORMAL HUMAN BODY

Microorganisms of the Body Surface and Mucous Passageways. Microorganisms are always present on the outer surfaces of the body and in the

cavities and tubes that have direct connections with the outside of the body. Some of these organisms are chance invaders that do not persist in these places, but many of them are parasitic organisms that grow there continually. The parasites of each place in the body are usually limited to a few definite types which are said to constitute the *normal flora* of that part. There is considerable variation from person to person, but in general the types enumerated in the following paragraphs are considered the normal flora of that part. Certain types, normally present in small numbers, may increase rapidly when antibiotic therapy diminishes the number of the predominant microorganisms. The yeast *Candida albicans,* the green pus bacterium *Pseudomonas aeruginosa,* and others may cause troublesome local irritation under these conditions.

The skin acquires chance contaminants constantly, but the organisms that are persistently present are staphylococci, streptococci, and diphtheroids. They grow in the openings of the skin glands and in the hair follicles.

The mouth also receives all sorts of organisms, but the saliva destroys many types quite rapidly. Gram-positive sporing bacilli must get into the mouth frequently, but they are almost never found in cultures made from the mouth. The most typical and universally present bacterium is the green-producing streptococcus named *Streptococcus salivarius.* Neisseriae, staphylococci, and certain vibrios are also common. Some degree of dental decay is so often present, even in healthy people, that several types of decay organisms are very common. They include the *Endamoeba gingivalis,* lactobacilli, spirochetes, and other higher bacteria.

The nasal passages, if healthy, do not favor the growth of bacteria, although they are constantly contaminated by the organisms breathed in with the air. The nasal sinuses are normally sterile because of the antibacterial effect of the mucous secretions and the mechanical cleaning action of their ciliated linings.

The throat flora resembles that of the mouth. The lymphoid tissue of normal tonsils guards against infection in the throat. But if the tonsils are diseased, their crypts may harbor unusual numbers of streptococci.

The stomach receives all the bacteria in the food. The highly acidic and proteolytic gastric secretions destroy many of them promptly. Others survive and pass on into the intestines. Only when gastric secretions are abnormal do bacteria grow in the stomach.

In *the duodenum* the duodenal and pancreatic secretions destroy many more bacteria, and the bile actually is able to dissolve many types, including the gram-positive diplococci. As the food material passes on through the jejunum and ilium, several surviving types of bacteria begin to grow.

The lower small intestine and the large intestine have, therefore, a luxuriant growth of a limited number of species. The one found in the largest numbers in cultures made from the feces is the sugar-fermenting, nonsporing rod named *Escherichia coli* (the colon bacillus). Others are *Streptococcus faecalis,* certain species of clostridia, and many anaerobic non-spore-forming rods. The characteristic odor and consistency of feces are largely due to these organisms. The gases that are formed in the lower bowel when certain types of food are ingested are due to the action of these organisms on carbohydrates. There are literally millions of these organisms in each gram of feces. A harmless ameba, *Endamoeba coli,* is found in the feces of 50 per cent of normal people. Molds and yeasts in small numbers are often present.

The infant's intestine is sterile at birth but very soon acquires a typical flora consisting mainly of lactobacilli, with *Lactobacillus bifidus* predominating. The acid reaction and the odor of the feces of healthy, milk-fed infants are due to these organisms. As the child's diet becomes more varied, these bacteria are replaced by the adult intestinal flora.

The external genitals, particularly the folds of the prepuce and the clitoris, harbor an acid-fast organism known as the smegma bacillus. The normal skin bacteria are also present, and the region is constantly contaminated with fecal organisms.

The vagina normally harbors a growth of *Lactobacillus acidophilus,* sometimes called *Doederlein's bacillus.* It increases the acidity of the vaginal secretions and helps to keep down the growth of undesirable organisms. The sphincter muscles of the uterine cervix prevent bacteria from entering the uterus, and that organ is normally sterile.

The trachea and lungs are protected by the ciliated epithelium and the cough reflex. The few bacteria that reach the alveoli are engulfed by leukocytes and by the cells of the alveolar lining. Inspired air contains many organisms, but expired air is normally practically sterile.

The Sterile Parts of the Body. There is evidence that small numbers of organisms constantly make their way into the body tissues and fluids and that some of them may remain there in a latent (nonactive) state for some time. In normal persons their numbers are very small—so small as to be negligible for practical purposes. The internal parts of the body are therefore regarded as sterile. These parts include the blood and lymph, the body cavities, and all the organs except those with direct outside connections as discussed above.

Factors That Prevent Microbial Invasion. Many of the factors already noted decrease the bacteria on and in the body. Other factors act to prevent their penetration into tissues, and still others to destroy the majority of those that succeed in gaining entrance. Some of these are described briefly below. They are referred to as the *natural defenses* of the body.

1. The intact skin with its covering of stratified epithelium presents an almost impenetrable barrier to the entrance of microorganisms. It is com-

mon experience that skin infections start either with some mechanical injury to the skin or with the blocking of glands or hair follicles.

2. The intact mucous membranes do not provide as effective a mechanical barrier as the skin, but their mucous secretions trap microorganisms and their cilia carry them outward. In addition, antibacterial and antiviral substances are present in the mucous secretions. One such substance, called *lysozyme,* is present in lacrimal, nasal, and salivary secretions.

3. Body excretions such as tears, urine, menstrual flow, and even fecal discharge have a mechanical cleansing action. Although many bacteria are

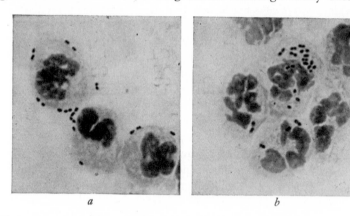

a   *b*

FIG. 12·1   Phagocytosis of pneumococci by leukocytes. (*a*) Leukocytes have been unable to engulf the cocci. (*b*) Cocci engulfed by leukocytes. The fibrin in the coagulated plasma has provided a solid material against which the blood cells have been able to "pin" the bacteria. (*Courtesy of Dr. Mary Ruth Smith, Science 110:187.*)

always present around the urethral meatus, the urethra and bladder are sterile.

4. Phagocytic cells are present not only in blood and lymph, but in all loose connective tissue and in many organs, notably in the liver, spleen, and lungs. The prefix *phag-* means "to engulf." *Phagocytes* are cells that engulf foreign materials. The process is called *phagocytosis.* The chemical attraction which serves to bring phagocytes in contact with the foreign particles is called *chemotaxis.* After the protective cell has engulfed the microorganism it usually digests it, although some pathogenic types taken in by phagocytes are able to remain alive within these cells. (See Fig. 12·1.)

5. Antimicrobial chemical substances in blood and tissues, the exact nature of which is not understood, are important in the destruction of organisms that have succeeded in getting past the outer defenses of the body. They are sometimes called *natural antibodies.* These defense substances and the other defenses discussed above are comparatively nonspecific in their

actions—i.e., they act against many types of organism. These natural defenses are an important part of the general resistance to infection that is known as *natural immunity.* The specific immunity to individual infections that results after invasion of the body by a specific pathogen will be discussed in the chapters on immunity.

Practical Applications. The laboratory technician examines specimens of sputum, feces, and other body materials from cases of disease. If she finds an organism that is not normally found in the material, she reports its presence to the physician as an aid in diagnosis. If the material examined is one that is normally sterile—e.g., blood—the detection of any organism is significant.

When examining milk, water, and certain foods, the sanitary bacteriologist looks for *E. coli.* Since this is the typical organism of feces and does not grow anywhere else in nature, its presence in milk, water, or food indicates recent pollution and unsanitary conditions. In the same fashion, the presence of large numbers of *S. salivarius* or certain lactobacilli in the atmosphere indicates that it is contaminated with mouth bacteria, an indication of a dangerous condition resulting from overcrowding and improper ventilation.

Doctors and nurses carry out all procedures involving the sterile parts of the body with aseptic (surgical) technique. Procedures involving nonsterile parts of the body do not require sterile materials and aseptic technique, e.g., giving an enema is not an aseptic procedure. The enema can and tube, the water, and the nurse's hands must be clean and free from pathogenic bacteria, but they need not be sterile, for the colon is known to contain large numbers of organisms. On the other hand, catheterization of the urinary bladder is a surgical procedure. It must be carried out with a sterilized catheter handled by an exacting technique which guarantees that it will be uncontaminated when it passes up the urethra and enters the bladder, since these parts are normally sterile.

SOURCES OF INFECTION

Most pathogenic organisms grow in nature only in the bodies of their hosts. They can be termed strict or *obligate* parasites. (Some biologists prefer to reserve this term for organisms that have never been grown in culture media, but it is only a matter of time until scientists will have found the growth requirements of the most fastidious organisms.) The source of any infection is, therefore, the person or animal who is discharging the specific pathogen.

The organisms may leave the person or animal in the ordinary body excretions such as the feces, urine, or saliva. They may also be discharged in abnormal excretions such as sputum expectorated from the lungs or pus discharged from suppurating lesions. Some leave the body only when blood is withdrawn by biting or sucking insects or for transfusion. Sometimes these body materials are spoken of as the sources of infection, but it is better to regard the infected individual from which they come as the source. Each species of pathogen has its characteristic means of leaving the body. Intestinal pathogens leave in the feces and occasionally in the vomitus; the organisms of most pulmonary diseases leave in the sputum; the parasites of malaria and certain other diseases are removed from the body only by specific insects.

The human or animal source of the infection in any particular disease may belong to any one of the categories described below.

Cases of Disease. *Recognized cases of disease* are the most important sources of infection in primitive communities and under war conditions where isolation and concurrent disinfection are inadequate. In well-organized civilized communities, recognized cases of the more dangerous communicable diseases are promptly reported. The infected persons are isolated in home or hospital, so that their dangerous excretions are prevented from reaching susceptible persons.

Even in the most progressive places, many cases of disease are not correctly diagnosed. Many cases may be so mild that no doctor is consulted. Such *missed cases,* which are sometimes called *atypical cases* or *walking cases,* move about freely and scatter pathogens as they go.

In some diseases cases may fail to develop what are considered the typical clinical symptoms. In poliomyelitis and in epidemic meningitis, for example, many cases do not show any involvement of the central nervous system. Such cases, called *abortive cases,* are often undiagnosed and therefore not properly isolated.

In many diseases early symptoms are not distinctive, and diagnosis and isolation may be delayed although the person is already spreading infection. This period, called the *prodromal stage,* often comes before the eruption of a distinctive rash. In a typical case of measles, for example, the rash does not appear until the third day of the disease. During the prodromal stage, the child's respiratory secretions are loaded with the virus, but he is often allowed to go to school, play with his friends, and thus spread the disease freely.

Carriers. A carrier is a person or animal who harbors and discharges living pathogenic organisms although he is free from any effects of the infection. He seems to be at least partially immune to the organism, although it continues to grow in some part of his body. Carriers are frequently not detected until they have passed the disease on to others. The term *carrier* may be modified in various ways.

Chronic carriers are those in whom the carrier state persists for long periods. Persons recovering from typhoid fever have been known to discharge *Salmonella typhosa* for as long as 30 years.

Temporary carriers discharge the organism for short periods only.

Convalescent carriers are temporary carriers who discharge organisms after their apparent recovery from an attack of disease. Convalescent carriers are common in diphtheria and in scarlet fever.

Contact carriers are individuals who acquire and harbor some pathogen for a while as the result of close contact with a case of communicable disease. The contact carrier state is not uncommon among persons who have been caring for cases of diphtheria or streptococcal infections.

Casual carriers are contact carriers in the general population whose contact with clinical cases cannot be traced.

Animals as Sources of Infection. A considerable number of the infectious diseases of lower animals also attack man, and so infected animals may be sources of infection for human cases. These diseases are seldom communicable from man to man. The animals that are hosts to these infections are usually *mammals*—the warm-blooded, hairy animals that suckle their young. Cattle pass on tuberculosis to human beings; dogs give us rabies; and rodents are sources of at least half a dozen important human diseases. Diseases that may be acquired from animals other than mammals include two respiratory infections from birds—psittacosis and ornithosis—and broad tapeworm infestation from fresh-water fish. As research in sources of infection progresses, scientists are finding more and more animal sources of infectious disease. The population of infected animals from which man may acquire infection is called the animal "reservoir" of the disease.

It should be noted that insects are not considered sources of infection. Since their role is to carry infection from one animal or person to another, they are considered modes of infection. As such they will be discussed in Chap. 16.

Control of the Sources of Infection. Persons with cases of the serious communicable diseases are isolated in order to prevent the further spread of infection. *Isolation* is the separation of the patient for the period of communicability of the disease from other persons who might acquire the infection. The techniques used in the isolation of any specific disease depend on the ways in which the disease is spread. The person with smallpox is rigidly isolated, since his disease can spread by material from the skin lesions as well as by respiratory discharges. All the isolation needed in malaria is screening to keep away the mosquitoes that are the sole means by which the disease can reach another person. Animals as well as persons may be isolated because of infection.

Persons who have been exposed to infection may be quarantined. *Quarantine* restricts the freedom of contacts for a period equal to the longest usual incubation period of that disease. Quarantine may be complete or modified.

Persons entering this country from areas where plague or cholera is epidemic are rigidly quarantined. Modified quarantine is more common. The person who has been exposed to scarlet fever may not be allowed to handle food; children exposed to measles are excluded from school. Frequently contacts are kept under *surveillance*. They are examined at intervals to detect the earliest possible signs of infection.

Unfortunately there is no really effective way of detecting carriers. Once a carrier has been identified, the public health authorities have the power to restrict his activities so that he does not infect others.

Diseases in domestic animals may be controlled by the same general methods as are used in human disease. In addition, animals with infections serious to man may be killed in order to protect both man and their own species. Control of infection in a wild animal population is much more difficult. Rats and related rodents are the most important animal reservoirs of human disease. The only truly effective campaigns against rodents are those that deprive them permanently of their food supply and their nesting places. This requires the proper disposal of all trash and garbage and the ratproofing of all places where food is stored. Rat poisons such as *Warfarin* (a Dicumarol derivative) are best used over a wide area as a community project under the direction of a trained exterminator. Rats in grain elevators, warehouses, ships, and freight cars are killed by fumigation with hydrocyanic acid gas.

THE NURSE'S ROLE IN THE CONTROL OF SOURCES OF INFECTION

The Nurse as a Source of Infection. The student nurse and her family often fear that she may catch some infection from her patients. Of course that is possible, but such danger is effectively avoided by careful nursing technique. Much less attention is usually given to the ever-present possibility that the nurse may be a source of infection for her patients. The conscientious nurse must keep the following possibilities in mind:

1. She may be suffering from an actual case of dangerous infection. Prompt reporting of all illness to the proper authorities safeguards not only her own health but that of her patients. A mistaken sense of duty should never prompt her to hide illness. Mild respiratory infections, diarrhea, unusual vaginal discharge, or sores on the face, mouth, or hands may not seem serious or disabling to the nurse but may spread organisms of infection to her patients.

2. She may be a carrier of specific disease. Women who have had typhoid fever should not work as bedside nurses because of the distinct possibility that they may be chronic carriers of that disease. Contact outside the hospital with any case of communicable disease should be reported. If this precaution is neglected, a nurse who is a contact carrier of diphtheria or who has a case of measles in the prodromal stage may infect her patients.

3. She may have very dangerous types of organisms in her mouth and throat. In crowded communities, particularly during the colder months, many persons become casual carriers of dangerous types of streptococci and pneumococci. They may be relatively immune to these organisms themselves but can spread them to others who are not immune. Infants and persons who are already ill are particularly likely to succumb to such infections. Respiratory streptococci are so dangerous in obstetric nursing that some hospitals culture all nurses' throats and bar from obstetric work all those who are found to be carrying dangerous types. It is impossible to extend this practice to all services, but each nurse must regard her saliva and her nose and throat secretions as dangerous and never allow them to reach her patients.

4. She has dangerous organisms on her skin. The skin staphylococci and streptococci are not dangerous in nonsurgical procedures. But if they contaminate sterile surfaces and tissues in surgical procedures they can cause local and generalized infections. These organisms persist on the hands even after vigorous washing and disinfection. Therefore the nurse wears sterile rubber gloves in many procedures. In others, she employs sterile forceps to handle sterile materials.

The Patient as a Source of Infection. The nurse is responsible for preventing the spread of infection from the patient to other persons, including herself. The diligence with which she must carry on bedside disinfection was discussed in Chap. 10.

The Nurse as a Tracer of Sources of Infection. Under some circumstances the nurse becomes a detective, endeavoring to find sources of infection. When employed in public health services dealing with cases of tuberculosis, syphilis, and gonorrhea, one of her chief functions is to discover from whom the patients have acquired their infections. Then these dangerous individuals can be properly treated and prevented from continuing their spread of infections.

STUDY SUGGESTIONS

Can you define *cause of infection, source of infection,* and *mode of infection?* Make a list of the parts of the body that have a normal flora. Opposite each part list the organisms usually found there. Can you give the morphologic and physiologic characteristics of each of the groups of organisms listed? If not, take this occasion to review.

What parts of the body are sterile? What natural defenses of the body keep them so? Have you observed any nursing techniques designed to keep these parts sterile? Describe them.

How do pathogens leave the body? List the types of cases and carriers that may be sources of infection. From your present knowledge can you indicate what persons or animals in your community would be the most likely sources of cases of measles? common colds? malaria? infantile paralysis? typhoid fever? rabies? In what ways are you a possible source of infection? You should deliberately practice thinking of yourself as a possibly dangerous spreader of respiratory, fecal, and skin bacteria. Why are the skin bacteria particularly dangerous in surgical procedures? Suppose saliva were colored bright blue and feces bright orange, what objects in the environment of a careless nurse (you?) would be stained? Review your day's activities. In what ways must you change your everyday habits to avoid spreading these dangerous microorganisms?

SUGGESTED READING

General References on Sources and Modes of Infection

Anderson, G. K., and M. G. Arnstein: "Communicable Disease Control." 3d ed., Macmillan, New York, 1953.

Burnett, F. M.: "Natural History of Infectious Disease." Cambridge, New York, 1953.

Burrows, W.: "Textbook of Microbiology." 16th ed., Saunders, Philadelphia, 1954.

Maxcy, K. F.: Principles of Epidemiology, in R. J. Dubos's "Bacterial and Mycotic Infections of Man." 2d ed., Lippincott, Philadelphia, 1952.

Tracing Sources and Modes of Infection

Prescott, S. C., and M. F. Horwood: "Sedgwick's Principles of Sanitary Science and Public Health." Macmillan, New York, 1936.

Rouiché, R.: "Eleven Blue Men." Little, Brown, Boston, 1954.

Smith, G.: "Plague on Us." Commonwealth Fund, New York, 1941.

Winslow, C.-E. A.: "The Conquest of Epidemic Disease." Princeton University Press, Princeton, N.J., 1943. Chaps. 13, 16, and 28.

Normal Flora of the Human Body

Rosebury, T.: Bacteria Indigenous to Man, in R. J. Dubos's "Bacterial and Mycotic Infections of Man," 2d ed., Lippincott, Philadelphia, 1952.

Natural Body Defenses

Nungester, W. J.: Nonspecific Factors in Immunity, in "Annual Review of Microbiology." Vol. 8, Annual Reviews, Inc., Stanford, 1954.

Raffel, S.: "Immunity." Appleton-Century-Crofts, New York, 1953. Chap. 2.

CHAPTER 13

Spread of Infection from Person to Person

DIRECT AND INDIRECT MODES OF INFECTION

The modes of infection are the means by which pathogenic organisms pass from the source of infection to the victim of infection. It is customary and convenient to divide these modes of infection into direct and indirect. The *direct modes* of infection are also called *person-to-person* and include all those methods by which the organisms pass directly from one individual to another. The time of transfer is very short—generally only a few minutes—and the material is fresh and unaffected by external conditions. Direct modes of transfer include actual bodily contact; transfer by infected hands, by saliva, and other body discharges; and transfer by freshly contaminated objects (sometimes referred to as *fomites*). Congenital transfer of infection from the mother to the unborn child and transfer by transfusion are also included.

Indirect modes of infection include spread by the vehicles of infection, air,

157

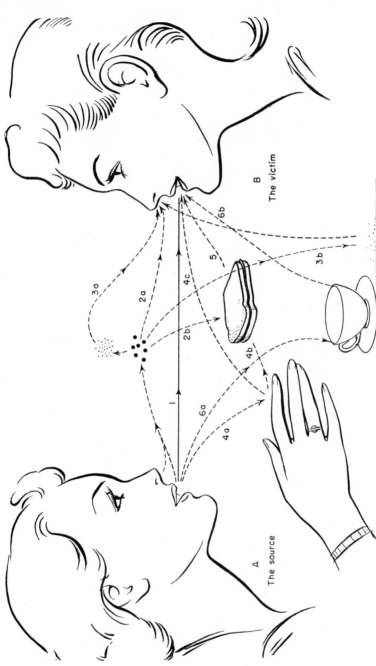

FIG. 13·1 Spread of respiratory infection. (1) Direct contact—*A* kisses *B*; (2*a*) droplets from *A* inhaled by *B*; (2*b*) droplets from *A* contaminate food; (3*a*) droplet nuclei suspended in air, later inhaled by *B*; (3*b*) droplet nuclei fall and mix with dust, later inhaled by *B*; (4*a*) *A* contaminates hand from mouth or nose; (4*b*) *A* contaminates food by handling; (4*c*) *A* uses contaminated hand in *B*'s mouth; (5) contaminated food eaten by *B*; (6*a*) *A* contaminates object (cup) in mouth; (6*b*) *B* places object in own mouth.

sewage, water, milk, and foods; and by *vectors* (insects). The time interval is usually long. Two weeks may elapse between the time typhoid organisms are discharged in the feces of a person suffering from the disease and the time they are swallowed in infected water by a possible victim. The organisms are exposed to external conditions and must be capable of surviving in numbers that will cause infection. The path traveled by a pathogenic organism from one host to another is often quite involved. For example, feces from a typhoid carrier may be washed into soil and eventually into a river. Oysters taken from oyster beds at the mouth of the river may contain the bacteria and infect the person who eats them. Here the spread of infection is by feces, sewage, soil, water, and oysters. In describing this infection the public health authorities would say simply that it was acquired from infected oysters, and the intelligent reader would supply the other steps in his own mind.

Knowledge of modes of infection is essential to both personal and public hygiene. In general, the individual is responsible for the control of infections that are spread directly from person to person, while control of water, milk, and food is largely a government function. Some of the principal pathways of direct transmission are illustrated in Fig. 13·1.

In discussing the modes of spread of any particular disease, it is not sufficient to state that they are direct or indirect; specific ways must be listed. Moreover, it must be remembered that the prevailing modes of infection in any disease will vary with the conditions in the community. In most urban American communities the few typhoid cases that now occur are food-borne; in poorly sanitated parts of the world, fly-borne, milk-borne, and water-borne typhoid are common. Milk-borne tuberculosis is uncommon in this country because our milk comes from tuberculosis-free cattle and most of it is pasteurized. In Europe, where herds are heavily infected with tuberculosis and pasteurization is uncommon, childhood tuberculosis acquired from infected milk is distressingly prevalent.

FACTORS DETERMINING THE MODES OF INFECTION

Each communicable disease is spread in one or more rather definite ways. Malaria, for example, is normally spread in only one way—by the bite of the infected female anopheles mosquito. Typhoid can be spread in many ways—by articles freshly contaminated with feces; by flies; by water; by milk; and by salad vegetables, oysters, and other foods. The modes of infection in any particular disease are determined by three factors.

The Way in Which the Pathogen Leaves the Source of Infection. Obviously organisms excreted in the feces are started out on a different path from those discharged in the sputum.

The Portal of Entry. If a specific pathogen is to cause disease, it has to enter through some channel favorable to its development. Certain dangerous bacteria, such as many of the staphylococci, can be swallowed with impunity but will cause infection if they penetrate the skin. Others, such as the dysentery bacilli, are harmless if rubbed on the skin but cause disease when ingested. So each pathogen is said to have its favored *portal of entry*. It is clear that organisms whose favored portal of entry is the alimentary canal will be likely to be spread by water, milk, and food. Organisms that have to be inoculated directly into the blood, such as the malaria protozoan, cannot be transferred under natural conditions except by an insect that bites more than one person in succession.

Ability of the Pathogen To Survive Outside Its Hosts. Organisms that are quickly killed by exposure to air, light, etc., can be spread only by direct contact or by insects. The spirochete of syphilis is a very fragile organism of this type, and as a result, syphilis is spread by direct bodily contact in 99 per cent of all cases. The rickettsiae of typhus are strict parasites that live only in the human and rodent hosts and in certain insects. They are spread by the insects.

Many pathogens can survive for varying periods in excretions such as feces and sputum. Most common pathogenic bacteria belong to this group. Therefore such diseases as diphtheria, tuberculosis, and whooping cough are spread by articles contaminated by body discharges or by respiratory discharges suspended in the atmosphere. The intestinal bacteria and the cyst stages of protozoan parasites survive for still longer periods in water, milk, and foods if they are protected from drying and sunlight. Streptococci and many viruses survive in dust.

A few pathogenic bacteria are spore-forming, and so are some of the pathogenic fungi. They can survive on dry surfaces and in the soil for indefinite periods. So anthrax, caused by *Bacillus anthracis,* may be spread by dust from infected sheep's wool, by dry animal hides, by bristles of infected shaving brushes, and by fodder containing spores from infected farm soil. Some pathogenic worms have ova that resist prolonged drying.

PERSON-TO-PERSON MODES OF INFECTION AND THEIR CONTROL

Direct Bodily Contact. Actual contact between the skin of one person and the skin of another is not dangerous under most conditions. When the skin is healthy and unbroken it forms an effective barrier against the penetration of most microorganisms. But such contact is dangerous if one person is suffering from a disease in which the organisms are discharged through the skin and if the other person has a cut or abrasion through which the organisms may enter.

Contact between moist mucous membranes is fraught with much greater danger. Kissing, where the lips of two individuals are in contact, allows the transfer of the potentially dangerous upper respiratory tract organisms. It provides a frequent mode of transfer of *herpes simplex* (cold sore) and many respiratory diseases and may be the mode of spread in syphilis. Cheek-to-cheek kissing and kissing the baby on the back of the neck are more sanitary techniques. The custom of the gentleman kissing the lady's hand used to imply respect; it might well be adopted today as a health measure. In sexual intercourse, microorganisms of the genitals of one person can be transferred directly to the genital organs of the other. The diseases that are so transferred are called *venereal diseases*. Syphilis and gonorrhea are the most important of these infections.

Hands. The hands of human beings are the parts of their bodies by which they are constantly in contact with others and with their environment. The staphylococci and streptococci of the skin are always present on the hands. To them are constantly added organisms from the environment. Many of these are harmless saprophytes of soil origin whose presence is not significant. Some may be pathogens acquired by caring for sick people or carriers or by handling excretions from such persons. At intervals the hands are contaminated by the person's own fecal bacteria. At much more frequent intervals the person's fingers go into his nose or mouth and are covered by potentially dangerous respiratory organisms. With his hands, man transfers microorganisms from person to person, from objects to people, and from people to objects in his environment. With his hands he introduces pathogenic organisms into his own body and distributes his own bacteria to others.

Everyday Hand Hygiene. When this consists of washing only whenever the hands appear grossly dirty, it is not sufficient. The hands should be washed after each use of the toilet, before each meal, and whenever they have been contaminated by handling any questionable material. The washing should include thorough soaping with a mild soap and thorough rinsing, preferably under running water. Complete drying after washing and the use of a mild skin cream will help to keep the hands smooth when washing has to be frequently repeated. All homes and working places should provide proper hand-washing facilities. Modern industries do well in this respect, but some hospitals still fail to provide adequately for the hand hygiene of their ward and kitchen employees.

Contaminated objects should not be handled directly if this can be avoided. If they are small, they should be picked up with forceps or some other instrument. If large, they may be handled by holding onto some uncontaminated part or by using a disposable piece of paper to protect the hands. Everyone should practice a safe technique in the use of toilet paper, so as to protect the hand from pollution while satisfactorily cleaning the anal region, and such a technique should be taught to children. In addition, everyone should avoid careless hand habits such as finger sucking, nail biting, fingering the lips and mouth, running the fingers through the hair, and cleaning the nose with the fingers. Any nurse who has such a habit should make a conscientious effort to get rid of it.

In Care of Communicable Disease and Handling of Food and Milk. Special attention must be given to hand disinfection in these procedures. When doctors first attempted to destroy harmful organisms on the hands they used strong chemicals. Hands were soaked in solutions of phenol and chlorine compounds. Sometimes chlorinated lime and sodium carbonate were made into a paste and rubbed into the skin. There is no doubt that such methods were effective in disinfecting the skin, but when frequently repeated, they proved so injurious to the skin that they had to be abandoned and milder methods substituted. Thorough washing with disinfectant soap or green soap under running water, using a hand brush, is the basis of all hand disinfection. This may be followed by a bactericidal soak or rub using a mild chlorine solution, alcohol, or one of the newer disinfectants such as Zephiran. The student nurse should make it a point to find out exactly what hand hygiene techniques she is to use for medical asepsis and to follow those techniques faithfully.

In Surgical Procedures. Sterile hands are essential in surgical asepsis. Although the methods outlined above are successful in removing or destroying all contaminating microorganisms on the hands, they do not sterilize the hands. The typical skin streptococci and staphylococci persist in the skin openings and irregularities. The only solution to the problem appears to be the wearing of sterile rubber gloves. The hands are scrubbed for at least 5 minutes or by a prescribed technique that cleans all surfaces. After rinsing in sterile water, an alcohol spray or soak is used both as a bactericide and as a means of drying the skin. Zephiran or other chemicals which leave an actively bactericidal film on the skin may be used. Sterile towels or air blowers are used to dry the hands. They are then dusted with sterile powder and sterile gloves are drawn on in such a way as to avoid any possible contamination of the outer surface of the gloves. The wet glove technique in which the wet scrubbed hands are inserted into sterile gloves in a Zephiran bath is also used.

In certain minor procedures, such as perineal care of the obstetric patient and urethral catheterization, the nurse does not always wear gloves. She cleanses her hands carefully and then handles the implements, towels, etc., in such a fashion that her hands do not touch any surface that must be kept sterile.

Articles Contaminated with Infected Discharges. All body discharges are possible spreaders of infection. All must be handled with care and disposed of in sanitary fashion. In civilized communities, feces, urine, menstrual discharge, and pus are generally regarded as unclean material, and there is usually provision for their disposal. Children are taught habits that prevent the spread of these materials in the environment, and people have developed an attitude of mind toward them which has satisfactory sanitary results. It is very difficult for persons brought up in most American homes and communities to comprehend conditions that exist where such sanitary habits are not practiced. But it is unfortunately true that in most of the world, and even in many parts of the United States, people literally live in filth. Here is a description of home conditions in one part of the Philippines, as observed by medical officers of the U.S. Navy.*

Most natives pass their stools on the ground in the yards and but a little way from the immediate region of the house. Not a few pass their stools through a hole in the floor to the ground below or into a coconut shell or on a piece of paper which is then tossed out of the window to fall where it may.

Disposal of excretions from the respiratory tract is still very unsatisfactory even in the most civilized communities. These discharges are generally not regarded as being so objectionable because they do not smell or look bad. They are less noticed because they leave the body in small amounts at frequent intervals in a variety of ways. For the same reason they are much more difficult to deal with. It would be impossible to list all the various articles that are commonly contaminated by discharges of the mouth and nose. Only a few examples can be discussed here.

Eating and Drinking Utensils. The microorganisms of the mouth contaminate all eating utensils directly or indirectly. Dishwashing should be a method of disinfecting dishes as well as making them clean. Whether it is done by hand or by machine, the dishes must be exposed to sufficiently hot water for a long enough time to kill pathogens that may be present. Excessively hot water used for washing may interfere with cleaning because it coagulates the protein of food particles. Therefore a period of exposure to very hot rinse water is an essential part of the process. Soaps and anionic detergents are helpful because they dissolve fat and so aid in mechanical removal of embedded organisms, but they cannot be depended on for disinfecting action. Where hot water is not available, or where its use is objectionable because it leaves drinking utensils too warm for immediate use, dishes can be soaked in chlorine-containing solutions. The chlorine content of such rinses must be kept at an effective level and the dishes must be completely immersed.

Handkerchiefs and Sputum Cups. These articles are grossly contaminated with respiratory discharges. Handkerchiefs should be collected in special

* MAGATH, T. B., and D. R. MATHIESON, *Am. J. Hyg.* **43**:152 (1946).

containers. When a person has a cold or other respiratory infection, he should use handkerchiefs of waste cloth or paper, place them in paper bags himself, and see that they are burned. Even when there is no sign of respiratory infection, handkerchiefs should be regarded as dangerous. The common habits of constantly fingering used handkerchiefs and of leaving them "any old place" are sanitary misdemeanors. Whenever material from the lungs is expectorated disease is present, since sputum cannot be raised by a healthy person. Disposable paper cups must be used to receive the sputum. Expectorating into washbowls, sinks, or anywhere else is dangerous.

Clothing and Bedding. These may carry the organisms of digestive, respiratory, and skin infections. Laundering must disinfect as well as clean. Modern commercial laundering with the newest types of equipment and methods is much more effective in this respect than old-fashioned washing by hand. Bedding and clothing from patients with infectious diseases must be handled with care to prevent contamination of the nurse's hands and of the patient's environment. The nurse may be responsible for the preliminary disinfection of such articles before they go to the laundry, or they may be sent to well-equipped laundries in special containers marked for special treatment. Special treatment for blankets will be described in the section on airborne infection in Chap. 16.

Congenital Transfer of Infection. *Congenital infection* is the transfer of disease from mother to child before birth. Such prenatal infection is not inherited disease. Communicable diseases cannot be inherited. They are all caused by living pathogenic organisms. Such organisms cannot become part of the ovum or sperm.

Although there is normally no exchange of blood between the maternal and fetal circulations, the tissue between them is very thin. Some pathogenic organisms are able to penetrate it and reach the fetal tissues. Such *intrauterine infection* is tragically common in syphilis and occasionally occurs in tuberculosis, smallpox, and some other diseases.

During childbirth, organisms in the vagina may infect the baby. The severest form is conjunctivitis of the newborn caused by the *Neisseria gonorrhoeae.*

Transfer of Infection by Transfusion. The modern medical technique of transferring blood or blood derivatives from one individual to another has introduced another possible mode of infection. It is obvious that only healthy persons should be used as donors of fresh whole blood. Diseases that have been unsuspected in donors and sometimes acquired by transfusion include syphilis, quartan malaria, and one type of viral jaundice. Infection may also be transferred by sera of human or animal origin used in the prevention or treatment of disease, by human plasma, albumin, and other blood derivatives prepared by blood banks. Extreme care must be exercised in the collection and preparation of these materials.

Sterility of transfusion apparatus and aseptic technique are essential. It is not true, as is sometimes claimed, that "a few bacteria do no harm." One authority, Kolmer, states, "It cannot be too often said that intravenous therapy requires absolute sterility and that any method which does not guarantee it is working on the brink of disastrous negligence."

STUDY SUGGESTIONS

Define *mode of infection*. What does *direct mode of infection* imply? What are the principal direct modes of infection? What is meant by *indirect mode of infection?*

What are the factors that determine the modes of infection in any specific disease? *Diplococcus pneumoniae* is the cause of lobar pneumonia. It is capable of surviving for a short time in body discharges. By what modes of infection will it probably be spread? Give reasons for your answers.

Hemophilus ducreyi causes a genitourinary infection called chancroid. It is a very delicate parasite, unable to survive outside the body. How will it be spread?

Clostridium perfringens is a spore-forming anaerobe. It is the organism chiefly responsible for the epidemics of gas gangrene infection of wounds that spread in the past through surgical wards. How do you suppose it was spread in those days? Why would such an epidemic be considered a disgrace in any modern hospital?

Review your actions since you got out of bed this morning. What have you done that might spread your respiratory organisms to your classmates?

What techniques of housekeeping and home habits need revision in the typical American home? (Is there a common drinking glass in your home bathroom or over your kitchen sink?)

List the articles used in routine care of bed patients that are or may be contaminated with their discharges. What have you learned about their sanitization?

SUGGESTED READING

(See also page 156.)

Nurse's Role in Control of Person-to-person Spread of Infection

BOWERS, A. G., and E. B. PILANT: "Communicable Diseases." 7th ed., Saunders, Philadelphia, 1953. Chaps. 2 and 3.

BRADLEY, F. R.: A 6-year report on the care of communicable disease. *Hospitals* 24:62 (1950).

FROBISHER, M., JR.: Practical disinfection in hospitals. *Am. J. Nursing* 38:226 (1946).

NEW YORK STATE DEPARTMENT OF HEALTH: "Guide for the Handling of Communicable Disease in the General Hospital." Albany, 1950.

SHETLAND, M.: Communicable disease nursing. *Pub. Health Nursing* **40**:543 (1948).

VETERANS ADMINISTRATION: "Basic Principles of Aseptic Technique." Veterans Administration Manual M10–2, Washington, D.C., 1946.

WALTER, C. W.: "The Aseptic Treatment of Wounds." Macmillan, New York, 1948. Chap. 20.

Person-to-person Modes of Infection

Hands

SEASTONE, C. V.: Observations on the use of G-11 (Hexachlorophene) in the surgical wash. *Surgery* **2**:290 (1949).

WALTER, C. W.: "The Aseptic Treatment of Wounds." Macmillan, New York, 1948. Chap. 12.

Eating and Drinking Utensils

GOVERNMENT PRINTING OFFICE: "Instructor's Guide—Sanitary Food Service." Washington, D.C., 1952.

————: "Ordinance and Code Regulating Eating and Drinking Establishments." Pub. Health Bull. 280, Washington, D.C., 1943.

Proposed method for control of food utensil sanitation. *Am. J. Pub. Health* **39**:255 (1944).

SHIFFMAN, M. A.: Field studies on two- and three-compartment sink manual dishwashing. *Am. J. Pub. Health* **43**:1563 (1953).

SPANGLER, C. D., R. F. CLAPP, and G. J. CLARK: A field test for efficiency of detergents. *Am. J. Pub. Health* **40**:1402 (1950).

Clothing and Bedding

CHURCH, B. D., and C. G. LOOSLI: The role of the laundry in the recontamination of washed bedding. *J. Infect. Dis.* **93**:65 (1953).

Clinical Thermometers

SOMMERMEYER, L., and M. FROBISHER, JR.: Laboratory studies on the disinfection of oral thermometers. *Nursing Research* **1**:32 (1952).

————: Laboratory studies on the disinfection of rectal thermometers. *Nursing Research* **2**:85 (1953).

Blood Transfusion

PITTMAN, M.: A Study of bacteria implicated in transfusion reactions. *J. Lab. & Clin. Med.* **42**:273 (1953).

Spread of Infection by Sewage and Water

This chapter will deal with the wastes of homes, institutions, and industries and with water. The other indirect modes of infection—milk, food, insects, and air—will be dealt with in the following chapters.

SEWAGE

Sewage is the waste water supply of a community. It is a slightly turbid liquid which contains about one teaspoonful of organic matter and one teaspoonful of sand and other inorganic matter in each 50 gal. Besides many varieties of saprophytic organisms, it always contains harmless and pathogenic bacteria from the skin, respiratory tract, and intestinal tract. The fecal bacteria are of the greatest importance, since they are capable of survival in the sewage, while most other parasitic organisms die rapidly. It must not be assumed that the intestinal bacteria grow in this environment; the majority die as a result of unfavorable conditions and the action of sewage bacteriophage (see page 473). Out of the enormous numbers originally present, a few will survive for periods as long as several weeks. So organisms of intestinal diseases, such as typhoid and amebic dysentery, may infect water and food that come in contact with the sewage.

The amount of sewage coming from a modern community is appalling— about one hundred gallons per person per day—and its safe disposal is one of the principal problems of sanitary engineering. There are only two possible methods of disposing of sewage. It can be allowed to flow into some body of water or it can be allowed to flow into the soil. Any satisfactory method of disposal must protect the inhabitants of the region from the dangerous organisms that may be present. It must also result in destruction of the organic material in the sewage without the development of *sanitary nuisances,* such as unsightly places and bad odors. As the population of an area increases, it becomes more and more difficult to dispose of sewage without some type of treatment. The methods of treatment include (1) removal of large objects and mineral matter by screening and flow through settling tanks; (2) holding in tanks under either aerobic or anaerobic conditions to allow microbial decomposition, stabilization of organic matter, and destruction of most parasitic microorganisms; (3) filtering under aerobic conditions through coarse filters which accomplish the same results; and (4) chlorination or other methods of chemical disinfection, usually of liquids after tank or filter treatment.

Disposal of Sewage from Homes and Institutions. When homes and institutions are located in areas not served by municipal systems, they must provide for disposal of their own wastes. Two methods are considered acceptable by public health authorities. The simplest is the *sanitary pit privy.* It is the recommended installation for camps, farms, and rural homes that lack plumbing. The second is the *septic tank.* This is more expensive and will be used in homes and institutions provided with flush toilets. The septic tank is a closed underground chamber in which the sewage undergoes anaerobic decomposition.

GARBAGE AND OTHER WASTES

Garbage is the waste portion of the food supply. Because it undergoes rapid decomposition with the development of unsightly appearance and smells, people have often believed it to be a "breeding place of disease." Of course that is not true. Organisms of disease cannot grow in garbage, or in waste paper, ashes, or tin cans. There are, however, two points of sanitation that must be kept in mind in the disposal of such material. First, raw garbage should not be fed to pigs. The roundworm that causes trichinosis may be present in garbage containing raw pork and will infect the hogs that eat the garbage. They in turn may give the disease to humans when they are eaten. Secondly, the disposal of household wastes should not provide food or breeding places for rats or insects.

WATER

The atmosphere is the source of all water supplies. The rainfall of any region remains in part on the surface of the earth; the rest sinks into the soil. Brooks, rivers, ponds, and lakes are *surface waters. Reservoirs* are storage places for surface waters. *Ground water* forms a layer or layers at varying depths from the surface of the soil in all except areas of solid rock. Ground water is obtained from springs, shallow or deep wells, or drilled artesian wells which tap water that lies between layers of impervious rock.

The Microbiology of Natural Waters. Natural waters contain many types of saprophytic organisms. When the organic content of these waters is high— e.g., in swamps—many saprophytic protozoa, bacteria, and algae (scum plants) grow, and there may be thousands of microorganisms in every milliliter. When water is polluted with human wastes the typical intestinal bacteria, notably *Escherichia coli,* will always be present. If the human pollution includes excreta from persons with intestinal disease, the intestinal pathogens, such as *Salmonella typhosa* and *Endamoeba histolytica,* will also be present. These parasitic types never grow in the water. The longer the interval—in *time,* not in *space*—since the pollution occurred, the fewer they will be, but some may survive for days. Ground waters are freed from much of their microbial flora by filtration through the soil and ordinarily have a lower bacterial content. But since ground waters can be polluted either from the surface or through fissures in the soil, a water supply must not be considered safe just because it is a ground water.

The diseases most often spread by water are the intestinal infections typhoid fever, paratyphoid fever, bacillary dysentery, amebic dysentery, and Asiatic cholera. Other diseases including leptospirosis (page 429) and brucellosis (page 317) may also be sometimes spread by water. All these diseases are said to be *water-borne.*

Sanitary Examination of the Water Supply. The safety of a water supply is determined by field surveys to detect possible sources of pollution and by various examinations in public health laboratories. The laboratory examinations include (1) physical and chemical study, (2) microscopic examination, and (3) bacteriologic examination by means of cultures. The American Public Health Association and the American Water Works Association publish a volume entitled *Standard Methods for the Examination of Water and Sewage,* 10th edition, 1955.

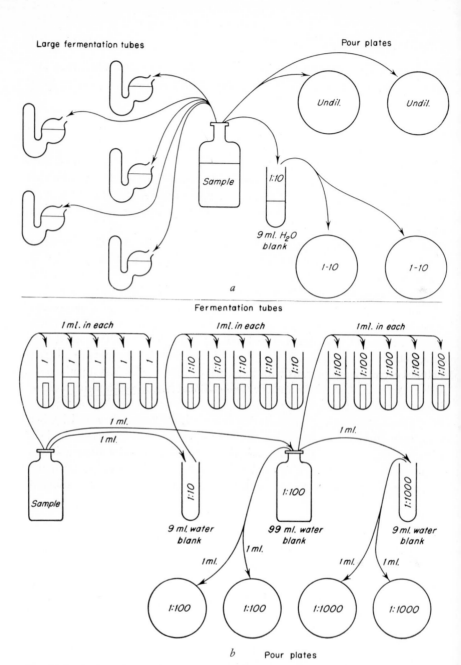

Large fermentation tubes

Pour plates

Undil.

Undil.

Sample

1:10

9 ml. H₂O
blank

1-10

1-10

a

Fermentation tubes

1 ml. in each

1 ml. in each

1 ml. in each

1

1:10

1:100

1 ml.

1 ml.

1 ml.

Sample

1:10

9 ml. water
blank

1:100

99 ml. water
blank

1:1000

9 ml. water
blank

1 ml.

1 ml.

1 ml.

1 ml.

1:100

1:100

1:1000

1:1000

b   Pour plates

Fig. 14·1 Sanitary bacteriology of water. (*a*) Examination of water of good quality. Arrows at left indicate transfers of 10-ml. amounts of the water to large tubes of lactose broth. Arrows at right indicate transfers of 1-ml. amounts of the water and dilutions to agar pour plates. (*b*) Examination of water of poor quality. Preparation of dilutions and inoculations of small tubes of lactose broth and agar plates.

Physical and Chemical Study. The color, odor, and turbidity (degree of cloudiness) are studied in the physical tests. The amounts of such substances as lead, iron, and copper are determined by chemical analysis. If excessive amounts of chlorine, sulfur, and nitrogenous compounds are found, pollution is suspected, since these substances are products of organic decomposition.

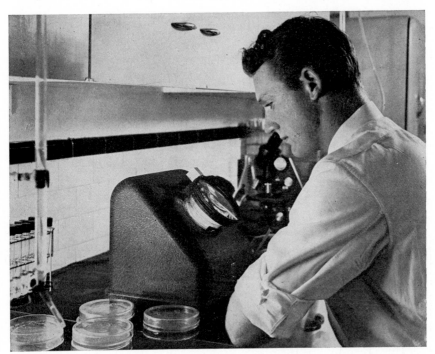

F<small>IG.</small> 14·2   Quebec colony counter being used to determine the number of colonies on an agar plate. (*American Optical Company, Instrument Division.*)

Microscopic Examination. Samples of water concentrated by filtration are examined with lower powers of the microscope and the numbers and types of algae, protozoa, and other water forms determined. Excessive numbers of these organisms are associated with objectionable color, turbidity, odors, and tastes in drinking water.

Bacteriologic Examinations. The bacteriologic examination consists of two tests: (1) determination of numbers of bacteria by a plate count and (2) determination of presence and numbers of coliform bacteria.

1. Plate count. Undiluted or suitably diluted samples of water are plated, using nutrient extract agar and incubating at 37°C. for 24 hours. (See Fig. 14·1.) From the number of colonies developing on these plates the number of bacteria per milliliter of the water can be determined, since each colony

represents a bacterium in the original inoculum. The numbers will vary from less than one per milliliter in artesian well waters to thousands in water from stagnant pools or polluted streams.

2. Tests for coliform bacteria. The term *coliform bacteria* is used to indicate *Escherichia coli* and certain other closely related nonpathogenic

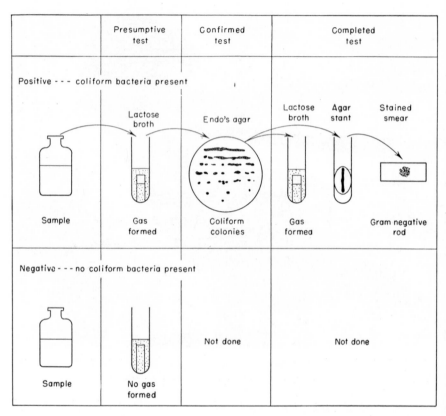

FIG. 14·3   Technique of testing water for coliform bacteria.

types of intestinal origin, principally *Aerobacter aerogenes* and *Escherichia freundii*. These organisms are all gram-negative, nonsporing rods which ferment lactose with gas formation and grow aerobically on standard solid media. Their presence indicates probable recent fecal pollution of the water, and their absence indicates that pollution has not occurred.

The actual test is performed in three steps, as shown in Fig. 14·3.

a. The *presumptive test* consists of inoculating measured amounts of water into tubes of lactose broth. If gas is formed, the test is positive; if it is not formed, the test is negative. If all tests are negative, the conclusion is that coliform bacteria are not present in that sample of water. Positive results require further testing.

b. The *confirmed test* is done by streaking plates of Endo's agar or eosin methylene blue agar with single loopfuls from the lactose broth tubes that

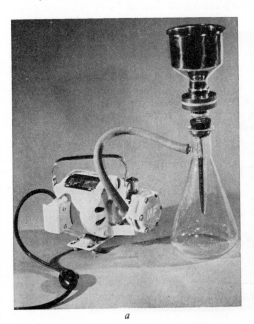
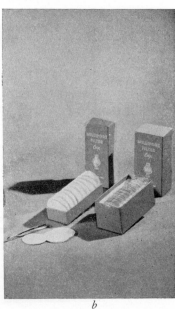

a   *b*

FIG. 14·4 Molecular filter used in sanitary bacteriologic examination of water. (*a*) Assembled filter with collection flask and pump. (*b*) At left—package of paper-thin molecular filter disks and absorbent pads to be saturated with culture medium, on which the filter disks are placed for incubation; at right—package of small, disposable, plastic petri dishes. (*Millipore Filter Corporation.*)

show gas formation. On these plates, coliform bacteria form deeply colored colonies with metallic surface luster. Several isolated colonies of this sort are used in the third test.

c. The *completed test.* In this step, each selected colony is inoculated into lactose broth and also streaked on an agar slant. If gas develops in the lactose broth and the organism grows on the agar slant, and if a stained slide shows that it is a pure culture of a non-spore-forming, gram-negative rod, the presence of coliform bacteria in the original sample has been proved. The numbers of coliform bacteria in the water can be approximately estimated from the amounts of water giving positive tests, provided that a sufficient number of presumptive tests (usually five for each sample amount used) are done and confirmed. The *most probable number* (*MPN*) of coliform bacteria per 10 ml. of the water is then determined by consulting a table provided in the standard methods manual.

3. Examination for coliform bacteria with the aid of membrane filters. *Membrane* (molecular) *filters* (*MF*) are small thin disks of cellulose esters

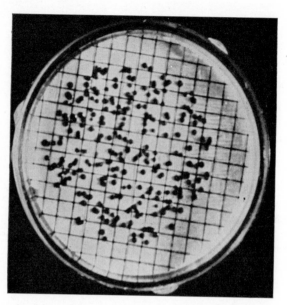

FIG. 14·5 Growth of bacterial colonies on molecular filter disk in small plastic petri dish. The disk has been incubated on an absorbent pad saturated with a fluid culture medium. (*Millipore Filter Corporation.*)

having many pores of uniform size. A sterile MF is placed in a steel funnel and an amount of water expected to produce 50 to 300 bacterial colonies is filtered through (Fig. 14·4). The membrane is then removed with sterile forceps and placed on a sterile pad saturated with a nutrient culture medium. Small metal "pill boxes" are used instead of petri dishes. For the discovery and enumeration of coliform bacteria, the pad is saturated with an enriched broth. After 2 hours' incubation the MF is transferred to another pad saturated with a liquid Endo medium. After a total of 15 hours' incubation the colonies are counted. The coliform bacteria form lustrous red colonies; the colonies of other bacteria are pale pink. (See Fig. 14·5.) The MF method allows the rapid and convenient determination of the safety of large quantities of water.

Students often wonder why laboratories do not examine the water for *Salmonella typhosa* and the other organisms of enteric disease. The reason is that the presence of any specific pathogen even in highly polluted water would be intermittent and its absence would not mean that the water was safe. The coliform organisms provide a much safer index of actual and potential danger, since they will always be present if the water is polluted. Even when pathogens are present, their numbers are often so few and their identification is so difficult that laboratory tests are unsatisfactory.

The Good Water Supply. A good water supply will possess the following qualities:

1. It will be adequate in amount at all times and seasons. At least 100 gal. per person per day will be needed for a public supply.

2. It will be clear, odorless, tasteless, and colorless. It should be cold.

3. It will be free from harmful chemicals such as lead.

4. It will be free from pollution. The area around a source of water supply must be kept free from animal wastes. Chemical tests must show a low content of nitrates and other products of organic decomposition. Bacteriologic tests must show a low total number of organisms and practical freedom from coliform bacteria.

The Public Health Service has formulated a rather complicated set of standards for the bacteriology of drinking water. In general not more than 10 per cent of all 10-ml. samples examined should show coliform bacteria. The details of these standards can be found in the *Public Health Report* article listed in this chapter's bibliography.

For housework and many industrial processes a soft water is preferable, but a very soft water, free from dissolved minerals, is probably bad for the teeth of those who drink it. Dental and public health authorities are agreed that fluorine should be added to most American water supplies to improve the quality of our teeth. Some iodine should also be present, since the body needs it to form normal thyroid secretion.

Water Treatment and Purification. In uncongested regions, where rainfall is plentiful, the waters may not need treatment. Otherwise most public water supplies need treatment in one or more ways to correct their defects. The method or methods chosen will depend on what needs to be done to the water. The following are the methods most commonly used in the treatment of public supplies:

1. Storage in reservoirs for sufficient time to allow parasitic types to die out.

2. Slow filtration through beds of fine sand. These beds are called *slow sand filters.*

3. Coagulation of suspended matter by means of a chemical coagulant (usually sulfate of aluminum), followed by rapid filtration through sand.

These two filtration methods remove 90 to 99 per cent of the bacteria present, but this action is nonselective and cannot be depended on to disinfect the water if the original pollution is great. Rapid sand filtration is very useful in removing suspended silt from turbid waters.

4. Chlorination by the addition of chlorine gas is the accepted method of disinfection of water. It is most effective when used to treat water after storage or filtration.

Two other methods used to treat public supplies should be noted. One is aeration, which restores dissolved oxygen to stored waters. The other is the treatment of reservoirs with copper sulfate to prevent the growth of algae.

Home and emergency treatment of water is best done by heat. Bringing water to a boil is sufficient. After cooling, it should be shaken or poured from one utensil to another to restore the oxygen content. Emergency chlorination can be accomplished in a number of ways when disinfection by heat is impractical. Home filter installations, particularly the type supposed to be attached to the water faucet, are completely unreliable.

Water for Other Uses. *Ice.* Freezing of water does not destroy its microbial content. Infected ice has been shown to be responsible for outbreaks of intestinal disease. Natural ice should be harvested from unpolluted waters, and artificial ice should be manufactured from water of proved purity.

Ice should be handled in a sanitary fashion. Unless the ice supply is known to be ideal it should never be allowed to come in contact with food or drink. Do not add ice to the drink; put the liquid in a container on the ice! Ice cubes made from an accepted water supply in the electric refrigerator may be added to drinks and food if care is taken to avoid contamination when they are removed from the tray.

Swimming Places. Bathing in polluted water is dangerous. Typhoid bacilli and other organisms of intestinal disease may be swallowed. Respiratory and skin organisms may be spread from person to person, causing otitis media, sinusitis, and impetigo. Fungous infections of the skin and virus infections of the eyes have been traced to swimming pools, and skin irritations due to animal parasites to outdoor bathing places. Outdoor bathing places must be protected from untreated sewage. Swimming pools must be supplied with pure water and continuously chlorinated. Only clean persons free from infections should be allowed to use public bathing places.

Water for Special Medical Uses. Water suitable for ordinary purposes is not considered pure enough for infant feeding. It may contain bacteria, particularly the *Clostridium perfringens,* that are responsible for digestive disturbances in babies. These organisms and others that are present in acceptable water supplies make them unsuitable for surgical use. Therefore in modern medical practice, water for these two uses is sterilized either in special tanks (Fig. 14·6) or in flasks in the steam pressure sterilizer. Water for use in

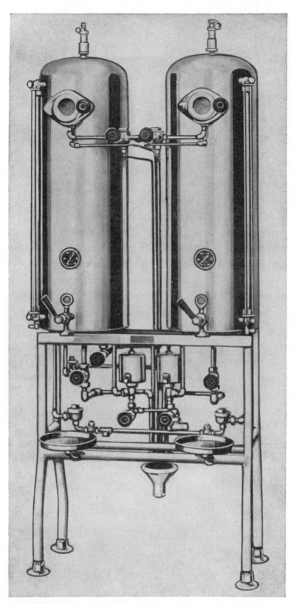

FIG. 14·6 Hospital water sterilizer. (*American Sterilizer Company.*)

preparation of parenteral fluids is sterilized and purified from all irritating or pyrogenic (fever-producing) chemicals by distillation in special apparatus.

STUDY SUGGESTIONS

Is your home connected with a sewage disposal system or do you have a domestic system? Describe your home or community system and tell why it is good or how it might be improved. What happens to the sewage of your hospital? What is done with the garbage from your hospital?

What are the sources of the water supply of your home? of your hospital? Are these water supplies treated? If so, how and for what purposes?

How do dangerous bacteria reach water supplies? How is their probable presence detected? Can you define *coliform bacteria?* Why is this group an "index of pollution"?

What are the steps in the bacteriologic examination of water? What results would you expect in each test if the water came from a sewage-polluted river? from a swamp in practically uninhabited country? from a good well? from a water treatment plant after filtration and chlorination? How do the sanitary bacteriologic tests on water utilize the technique of isolation by use of selective media? the identification of bacteria by means of specific physiologic reactions?

Suppose the water supply of the hospital is found to be unsafe; what rules and regulations would need to be issued to the hospital staff? (Would directions to boil all water used for drinking be all that would be necessary?)

What regulations should an institution have concerning the source of its ice supply and its use? Can you cite some examples from your own experience of probably unsafe ice or improper use of ice?

Where do you swim? Is it a safe place from the sanitary point of view, or do you suspect that it is potentially dangerous? Why?

If you have had the opportunity to observe the sterilization of water for any hospital use, describe the method and apparatus used. Why is a good community water supply unsafe for certain hospital purposes?

SUGGESTED READING

General References—Environmental Sanitation

Drinking water standards. *Pub. Health Rep.* **61**:371 (1946).

GOVERNMENT PRINTING OFFICE: "Environment and Health." Public Health Service Publication 84, Washington, D.C., 1951.

HOPKINS, E. S., and F. B. ELDER: "The Practice of Sanitation." Williams & Wilkins, Baltimore, 1951.

MAXCY, K. F.: "Rosenau's Preventive Medicine and Hygiene." 7th ed., Appleton-Century-Crofts, New York, 1951.

Water

American Public Health Association: "Standard Methods for the Examination of Water and Sewage." 10th ed., New York, 1955.

Moore, E. W., E. W. Brown, and E. M. Hill: Sanitation of crushed ice for iced drinks. *Am. J. Pub. Health* **43**:1265 (1953).

Prescott, S. C., C.-E. A. Winslow, and M. H. McCrady: "Water Bacteriology." Wiley, New York, 1946.

Walter, C. W.: "The Aseptic Treatment of Wounds." Macmillan, New York, 1948. Chap. 16.

CHAPTER 15

Spread of Infection by Milk and Other Foods

MILK

Milk is the lacteal secretion of the mammary glands of mammals. It is the most important of all foods from a bacteriologic point of view because it is obtained from animals that suffer from infections that also attack man; because it is a medium for the growth of some pathogens; because it is one of the few animal foods that is eaten without previous cooking; and because it is such an important food for infants and sick people.

The Bacteriology of Milk. Like all secretions, milk is sterile when it is formed in the mammary glands. But during the processes of production and distribution it acquires many organisms from the cow's udder, from human handlers, from utensils and containers, and from the atmosphere. For most of these organisms milk is a good culture medium, but one type, the *Streptococcus lactis,* outgrows all the others. This bacterium forms lactic acid from the lactose sugar of the milk, making the milk sour and eventually causing it to curdle with a soft acid-type curd. If the milk is kept at refrigerator temperatures, 8°C. or below, the growth of microorganisms will be slow. At 20°C. or above it will be very rapid. By the time the milk reaches the consumer it may contain millions of organisms per milliliter if it was produced from dirty, unhealthy cows on unsanitary farms, processed and distributed by unclean dairies, handled by dirty, careless people, or kept at warm temperatures. On the other hand, a milk ideally produced and handled will have a bacterial count of less than 1,000 per milliliter.

Milk-borne Diseases. Pathogenic organisms in milk may come from human beings or from the milk-producing animal.

Diseases of Human Origin. Both respiratory and intestinal pathogens may be spread by milk. They may get into the milk directly from the polluted hands of a milker or indirectly when milk is placed in contaminated receptacles or infected by flies. The human diseases most frequently spread by milk are dysentery (particularly bacillary dysentery of infants), typhoid fever, paratyphoid fever, and scarlet fever. Epidemics of poliomyelitis and diphtheria have also been traced to milk.

Diseases of Animal Origin. Two diseases, tuberculosis and brucellosis (undulant fever), are commonly spread from infected cows to human beings by milk. Bovine tuberculosis, caused by the bovine variety of *Mycobacterium tuberculosis,* is a very important disease of dairy cattle. The cow swallows sputum containing the bacteria and they get into the milk when it is contaminated by her fecal material.

Brucellosis of cattle is called *contagious abortion* because the infection results in the premature birth of calves. In goats the infection is called *Malta fever.* Both infections are spread to man in raw milk. The causative organisms are *Brucella abortus* and *B. suis* in cattle and *B. melitensis* in goats. Though the rickettsiae of Q fever may be present in milk, the disease is believed to be spread mainly by dust containing dried manure. In countries where foot and mouth disease of cattle is common, milk from infected cows may spread the disease to man.

Septic Sore Throat. Mastitis (mammary gland infection) is very common and troublesome in dairy cows. These infections are usually due to *Streptococcus agalactiae,* a species seldom pathogenic to man. Occasional cases of mastitis are due to types of streptococci that are virulent for man. These organisms are members of the *S. pyogenes* group. They infect the cow's udder from the hands of a milker who harbors the organism in his throat. Milk from a cow with an acute case of this type contains millions of dangerous streptococci. If the milk is used raw, it gives rise to an explosive epidemic of septic sore throat and other streptococcal infections. Although the cow is truly the source of the infection, in dealing with such an epidemic the public health authorities try to trace the course of infection back to the infected human.

The Production of Satisfactory Milk. The health and cleanliness of the cows and the milk handlers, correct equipment and techniques in barns and dairies, and effective pasteurization all play important parts in the preparation of good milk.

Cows. American dairy herds are kept free from tuberculosis by repeated tuberculin testing of all cattle and the elimination of all those that show positive reactions. Brucellosis is still present in a considerable portion of our herds. Progressive farmers have their cattle tested for the disease and prevent its development in young animals by vaccination. Dairy sanitation and competent veterinary supervision reduce the incidence of all types of mastitis.

Milk Handlers. Persons who have had typhoid should not be employed as milk handlers because of the likelihood that they may be carriers. No one who is suffering from any infection should be allowed to work in contact with milk. The most modern dairies and milk plants provide medical examination and supervision for their employees. The need for cleanliness must be thoroughly taught to all employees, and they should be instructed in the techniques for maintaining it.

Equipment and Techniques. Modern dairy equipment—milking machines, steam sterilizers for utensils, refrigerating apparatus, and bottling machines—helps the farmer and milk processor to give the public clean milk at reasonable cost, but it does not by itself ensure good milk. Complicated equipment needs careful supervision, and special methods of cleaning must be carried out day after day. The equipment and techniques used in a well-run modern dairy represent the most thorough practical application of sanitization. On farms and in dairies where equipment is not ideal, there is still greater need for scrupulous cleanliness. In many it is achieved, but in others it is imperfect or entirely lacking. Prompt delivery to the ultimate consumer is also important.

Pasteurization. Pasteurization is disinfection of milk by heating at temperatures below the boiling point. Two methods of pasteurization are generally approved by authorities.

1. The *holding method,* in which the milk is held at a temperature of 142 to 145°F. for 30 minutes, followed by rapid cooling to 50°F.

2. The *high-temperature, short-time method,* in which the milk is heated to 160°F. for 15 seconds, followed by cooling to 50°F.

These times and temperatures are sufficient to ensure the killing of all species of pathogenic organisms that may be in milk. Pasteurization is the final safeguard against milk-borne infection. All milk should be pasteurized before distribution. At present, most milk sold in urban areas in America is pasteurized. In our rural areas and in other countries the proportion of pasteurized milk is increasing rapidly.

Sanitary Control of the Milk Supply. The sanitary quality of the milk supply is safeguarded by the cooperative activities of government agencies, private organizations such as the Association of American Medical Milk Commissions (see page 186), the milk dealers, and associations of dairymen. Inspections of farms and milk processing plants, chemical and biologic tests of the milk, and bacteriologic studies are carried out at frequent intervals. The tests described here are those that are directly concerned with the sanitary quality of the milk supply. The methods described below are those approved by the American Public Health Association and published in *Standard Methods for the Examination of Dairy Products,* 10th edition, 1953.

Tests of Total Bacterial Content. The sanitary quality of a milk is inversely proportionate to the numbers of bacteria found in it. A low-count milk is one that has been carefully produced and marketed; a high-count milk is one that has been carelessly handled and that may be dangerous. Methods of detecting specific pathogens in milk are difficult and are not used routinely. The three methods described below are quantitative methods used to determine the total numbers of bacteria in milk.

1. The plate count method. Milk plate counts are made with an enriched culture medium, tryptone glucose yeast agar. Since milk seldom has less than 1,000 bacteria per milliliter and often has many times that number, the agar plates are always made with dilutions of milk ranging from 1:10 to 1:1,000 or even higher. The plates are incubated at 32°C. for 48 hours. Colony counts are made and averaged and multiplied by the dilution factors. The resulting figure is reported in round numbers as the *standard plate count* per milliliter.

2. Direct microscopic examination. A smear of 0.01 ml. of milk is spread over an area of 1 sq. cm. on a clean glass slide. The smear is dried quickly and the fat removed by immersion in xylene. It is then stained with a special solution of methylene blue and examined with the oil immersion objective. Three types of observations may be made on such smears.

a. Bacterial clump counts. The number of clumps of bacteria plus the number of separate single bacteria are counted in from 10 to 100 representative fields. The average count per field is multiplied by a known *microscopic factor.* With a standard compound microscope using the 10× ocular and the oil immersion lens, the microscopic factor is 500,000 (because each field seen under the microscope contains one five hundred thousandth of a milliliter of the milk).

b. Rapid grading by microscopic examination. Experienced workers can determine the general quality of a milk and assign it to a grade by a rapid survey of the stained smear. A simple suggested grading is as follows:

Grade 1. Less than 0.1 bacterium per field—good milk
Grade 2. Between 0.1 and 1 bacterium per field—fair milk
Grade 3. Between 1 and 10 bacteria per field—poor milk
Grade 4. More than 10 bacteria per field—milk nearly or actually sour

c. Recognition of causes of high counts. Three reasons for high bacterial counts in milk—udder infection, dirty utensils, and insufficient cooling—can be recognized with considerable accuracy by the appearance of the stained milk smear. The appearance of a good raw milk and of typical high-count milks is shown in Fig. 15·1.

3. Reduction of dyes (*reductase tests*). A milliliter of a standard solution of methylene blue thiocyanate is added to 10 ml. of milk. The mixture is incubated at 35.5°C. The bacteria present in the milk produce reductase enzymes which fade the blue color to white. The greater the number of bacteria, the quicker the color will be lost. Good milks retain the color for at least 6 hours. A similar test uses another dye, *resazurin*. The original blue color changes to purple, mauve, and pink, and then to white. These changes are more rapid than the fading of the methylene blue, and the result can be determined in from 1 to 3 hours.

Other Laboratory Tests. In addition to the tests already described, certain others are often done to detect special defects and dangers.

1. Tests for coliform bacteria. Since pasteurization kills the bacteria of the coliform group, their presence in milk after pasteurization indicates contamination after processing. Organisms of this group are detected by gas formation in highly selective liquid media such as brilliant green lactose bile broth, or by finding typical dark red colonies on special plating media such as violet red bile salt agar. Very high counts of coliforms in raw milk indicate contamination of milk with manure, incomplete cooling, or udder infection with these bacteria.

2. Laboratory pasteurization tests. Samples of milk from individual farms or of pooled raw milk are often pasteurized in tubes in the laboratory. Plate counts are made of the samples after heating. These counts indicate the milks that contain excessive numbers of thermoduric bacteria that will not be killed by pasteurization. These heat-resistant bacteria get into the milk from unclean utensils. If a farmer's milk has a high count after laboratory pasteurization, he must improve his dairy sanitation.

3. Sediment test for presence of visible dirt. A pint of milk is forced through a cotton disk by air pressure. A sediment score is given the milk on the basis of comparison with a set of standard disks on which definite

amounts of dirt have been deposited. Poor scores are caused by dirty methods on the farm and failure to use efficient milk strainers.

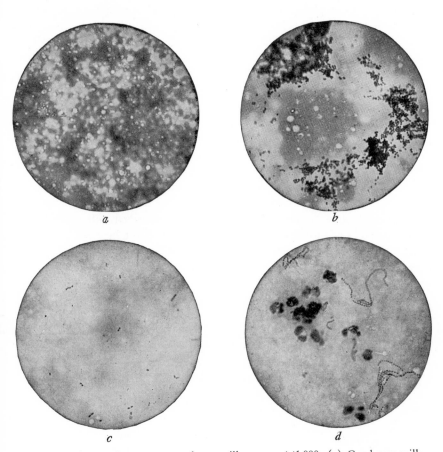

FIG. 15·1 Microscopic appearance of raw milk smears. ×1,000. (*a*) Good raw milk— few if any bacteria per field; fat vacuoles clearly seen against background of precipitated protein. (*b*) Milk from dirty utensils—many bacteria in clumps. (*c*) Milk not promptly cooled—frequent short-chain streptococci. (Good milk after several days' storage may also look like this.) (*d*) Milk from cow with udder infection—long chains of streptococci (or sometimes groups of micrococci) and many pus cells. (*From "Standard Methods for the Examination of Dairy Products," American Public Health Association.*)

4. Phosphatase test. *Phosphatase* is an enzyme present in raw milk. It is destroyed by pasteurization. The chemical test for the enzyme is, therefore, positive in raw milk, in milk insufficiently heated, and in milk that has been

diluted with as little as one part in 100 of raw milk. A simplified form of the test is described here, the modified Sharer test.

One milliliter of milk is added to 10 ml. of a disodium phenyl phosphate solution. If phosphatase is present in the milk, it will split off the phosphate radical, liberating phenol. The solution is then tested for free phenol by adding a solution of *BQC* (2,6-dibromoquinonechloramide) and a little copper sulfate as a catalyst. With these reagents the free phenol forms a blue-colored compound. If the milk has been well pasteurized, the color will remain white, for pasteurized milk will be free from phosphatase and no color will have been freed to form the blue compound.

Milk Grades and Standards. Legal standards and grades of milk differ from one community to the next. The Public Health Service "Milk Ordinance and Code" allows 50,000 bacterial plate count for raw Grade A milk and 30,000 for pasteurized Grade A milk. Grade B milk if raw may not have a plate count of over 200,000; if pasteurized the count cannot be over 50,000. Most large cities allow only the sale of pasteurized milk which must be "approved" or "satisfactory." The standards in effect in New York City are summarized in Table 15·1.

Table 15·1

Summary of Milk Standards of New York City *

Types	Number of bacteria per milliliter		
	Before pasteurization after shipment from country plant	Before pasteurization at place of production	After pasteurization and when delivered to consumer
Approved milk.........	400,000	150,000	30,000
Approved cream.......	500,000	250,000	100,000
Certified milk.........	†	10,000	500

* Data from New York City Milk Regulations amended to June, 1953.
† All certified milk has to be pasteurized at place of production.

Certified Milk. This is milk very carefully produced and tested under the direction of a local unit of the American Medical Milk Commissions. The first of these organizations was formed in 1893, when good, safe milk was extremely rare. Its purpose was to "certify" the quality of milk produced on contracting farms so that physicians could safely recommend it to their patients for infant feeding. For many years a large part of the certified milk was sold raw, but at the present time most of it is pasteurized. It may not contain more than 10,000 bacteria per milliliter when raw or more than 500 after pasteurization. Its high cost limits its use to cases of infant malnutrition and to the very prosperous.

Homogenized Milk. This is milk that has been forced through very small apertures under high pressure to break up the fat globules and prevent them from rising to form a cream layer. The process is not bactericidal.

Some Special Considerations. The provision of a safe milk supply is a function of government in our modern civilization. But after milk reaches the home or institution the health authorities are no longer in control and the proper care of milk becomes an individual responsibility. Emergency treatment of milk and care of special types of milk are also responsibilities of the individual.

Care of Milk after Delivery. Three rules for the care of milk should always be observed.

1. It should be immediately and continuously refrigerated in the coldest nonfreezing part of the refrigerator.

2. It should never be placed in any but clean, preferably sterilized, containers. This is particularly important in institutions when the milk is purchased in large containers and transferred to smaller ones after delivery.

3. It should be handled only by clean, healthy people.

Milk Formulas for Infant Feeding. In all modern hospitals a special room is set aside for the preparation of milk formulas for infants. It is equipped with apparatus for sterilizing milk bottles and nipples and for pasteurizing or sterilizing the formulas. Air contamination is avoided by cleanliness, special ventilation, and the use of ultraviolet lamps. Nurses and attendants working in the milk room wear special gowns and masks, keep the hair covered, and follow careful techniques of hand hygiene. Figure 24·6 shows a modern formula room.

Breast Milk. When an infant is breast-fed by its own healthy mother, it receives practically sterile milk with a composition exactly fitted to its needs. Sometimes infants are breast-fed by other lactating women. These *wet nurses* must be clean and healthy or the infant may acquire dangerous organisms through the milk or from contact with the woman. Some hospitals now maintain breast-milk stations. The milk is obtained from healthy women by means of the breast pump, rapidly cooled, transported immediately to the hospital, tested frequently by the hospital laboratory, pasteurized, and bottled for feeding special infant cases.

Emergency Treatment of Milk. Heat is the only method recommended for purifying milk in an emergency. Where no satisfactory milk can be purchased for homes or institutions the emergency may be said to be continuous. Some form of pasteurization must then be practiced as routine treatment of milk. Bringing milk to a boil is effective in disinfecting it, but the flavor is undesirably altered. Pasteurization is therefore preferable. Many types of apparatus for home and institutional pasteurization are on the market. Their efficiency will depend on the care and intelligence with which they are used. The milk may be placed in the top of a double boiler the bottom of which is filled with very hot water. It is stirred until it reaches a temperature of 160°F. This should, of course, be checked with a thermometer. The hot water should then be replaced with very cold water so that the temperature falls to below 50°F. This method is said to eliminate all possible pathogens without altering the milk flavor.

The Microbiology of Milk Products. Milk products include milk preserved in various ways, cream, butter, cheeses, and frozen desserts. All are potential vehicles of the organisms present in the milk from which they are prepared.

Canned Milks. Milk is usually canned after the removal of part of the water content. If canned with added sugar it is called *condensed milk;* if without sugar, *evaporated milk.* The quality of canned milks has greatly improved in recent years. When clean milk is properly canned, the product is sterile. Canned milk for infant feeding should be carefully selected on the basis of laboratory tests, and the formulas made with it should be handled and processed with the same care as those made with fresh milk.

Dried Milk (Dehydrated Milk). Dried milk always contains some bacteria. Processes of drying differ greatly in their bactericidal efficiency. When dehydrated milk is made from clean milk by drying on rollers, it is usually free from intestinal and respiratory bacteria, but spore formers survive and the fate of *Mycobacterium tuberculosis* is doubtful. *Reconstituted milk* is made from dried milk, butter, and water by an apparatus called the "mechanical cow." Reconstituted milk should be pasteurized.

Frozen Milk. Frozen milk and cream are recent developments. The milk and cream must be of high quality and must be pasteurized before freezing, since freezing does not destroy pathogens that may be present.

Fermented Milks. These were discussed in Chap. 7. The acid resulting from the rapid growth of lactobacilli suppresses the growth of other organisms, and pathogenic bacteria are destroyed. Fermented milks produced commercially should always be prepared from clean pasteurized milk.

Butter and Cheese. These should be made from pasteurized cream and milk. Because typhoid fever has several times been traced to cheese, laws in some places require the storage of unpasteurized cheese for at least 60 days. Laboratory tests have shown that coliform types die out completely during that period.

Frozen Desserts. Frozen desserts may be very dangerous if made from raw milk and cream and eaten immediately, since the freezing process will have relatively little effect on the bacteria. Commercial ice creams are usually safeguarded by pasteurization of the "mix" before freezing and by the practice of storing the ice cream at low temperatures for several weeks before its sale.

FOODS

Certain aspects of food microbiology dealing with food spoilage, preservation, and fermentation have been considered in Chap. 7. In this chapter we are concerned with food as a mode of infection.

How Foods Become Infected. The food may be derived from an organism that is itself a host of disease. Pork from infected hogs may contain the larval form of *Trichinella spiralis,* the organism of trichinosis. Rabbit meat may contain *Pasteurella tularensis,* the organism of tularemia (rabbit fever). More frequently the food may be infected during its production, distribution, processing, or use. This infection may come in many ways. Some of the important ones are discussed here.

Soil. In many parts of the world farm lands are routinely fertilized with human excreta. In this country there have been numerous instances of the use of polluted water for irrigation. Oysters are harvested from areas along the coast where sewage-laden rivers empty into the ocean. So it is not surprising to find that typhoid and other intestinal infections may be spread by salad vegetables and shellfish.

Utensils. Dirty processing machinery, containers, and cooking utensils add many organisms to food. The greater such contamination, the greater the chance that some of them may be pathogens. While modern sanitization in food industries and careful food packaging are designed primarily to guard food quality, they are also important in preventing infections. Contamination of food receptacles by the feces of rats and mice may introduce organisms of the *Salmonella* food-poisoning group or ova of the dwarf tapeworms.

Milk and Water. Milk is used as an ingredient of many prepared foods. If it is not pure its dangerous organisms will be incorporated in the food and may even grow there. Only approved pasteurized milk should be used for any food purpose. Pathogenic organisms in impure water may be introduced into food when the food is washed, when the water is used in recipes, or by the use of improperly washed utensils. When the water supply is of dubious quality it should be boiled before it is used in food preparation. Foods may also be infected by contact with infected ice.

Air. Good ventilating systems and air disinfection are desirable in kitchens and food-processing plants. They help to prevent contamination with organisms of spoilage and reduce the likelihood that respiratory organisms will infect exposed foods. All foods not already suitably packaged should be placed in covered containers to avoid such air-borne contamination.

Insects. See next chapter.

Handlers. Sick persons and carriers of disease who work as food handlers are probably the most important means of infecting food. The most dramatic food-borne epidemics are those initiated by undetected typhoid carriers working as cooks. Less spectacular, but much more common, are epidemics of gastroenteritis and respiratory diseases started by food handlers.

Spread of Disease by Specific Foods. Processed foods such as fats and oils, flour and other dry cereal products, sugars and sirups, salt, spices, and many types of preserved food are seldom if ever spreaders of disease.

Vegetables and Fruits. Asiatic cholera, dysentery, typhoid, and other intestinal infections are often spread by fruits and vegetables in countries where human excreta is used as fertilizer. In most parts of this country vegetables are not grossly polluted, but they should be thoroughly washed before serving.

Fish and Shellfish. In a few instances, these lower forms of animal life transmit worm infestations to human beings. Most of these diseases are not found in North America. However, in certain regions of the Middle West some species of fresh-water pike are infected with the broad tapeworm. If these fish are imperfectly cooked, persons eating them may acquire the disease. (See Chap. 38 for further discussion of these diseases.)

Oysters and clams raised in polluted coastal waters may contain large numbers of intestinal bacteria. Since oysters are so often eaten raw, oyster-borne epidemics of typhoid fever have been quite common in this country. Shellfish should not be taken from polluted areas. In some places they are chlorinated before they are sold.

Meat. In addition to trichinosis, two tapeworm infestations may be spread from pigs and cattle to man in meat. Bacterial diseases that may be spread from diseased animals to man in meat include bovine tuberculosis, all forms of brucellosis, salmonella infections, and tularemia. Hunters, employees in slaughter houses and meat markets, and cooks may be infected with these bacterial diseases when they handle the raw meat. Government meat inspection, prolonged storage, and thorough cooking are the best safeguards against meat-borne disease.

Canned Foods. The usual food-borne diseases are not spread by canned foods. The heat of the canning process kills all common saprophytic and pathogenic bacteria. The canned food is protected from further contamination by the sealed container. There is, however, one species of anaerobic bacterium, *Clostridium botulinum,* whose spores sometimes survive if the processing has been done at too low a temperature or for too short a time. The spores germinate in the stored canned food, and the resulting vegetative cells produce a very powerful exotoxin. Persons eating the food develop *botulinus poisoning,* a severe and often fatal toxemia. This can be avoided by 10-minutes' boiling of the food before it is served, for the toxin is easily destroyed by heat. The bacteriology of botulism is discussed in Chap. 29.

Eggs. Many species of the *Salmonella* bacteria have been found on the shells and in the contents of eggs. These bacteria can survive the process of drying and have been common in commercial egg powder presumably made from improperly cleaned eggs.

Prepared Foods. Foods which require handling and which are then served without further cooking are the most dangerous. Such foods include nonacid types of salads, sandwich fillings, and custard fillings for various bakery products. Hashes, meat pies, casserole dishes, croquettes, and even stews and creamed dishes are often imperfectly heated before serving. When such materials are baked or cooked in the double boiler the food in the center often fails to reach bactericidal temperature. These foods support the growth of food-poisoning bacteria if they are kept at warm temperatures. All such foods should be prepared from clean, fresh ingredients in clean utensils by clean, healthy persons. The time and temperature used in cooking and in reheating such foods should be sufficient to kill nonsporing bacteria. These foods should always be stored in the refrigerator.

Food Poisoning. In addition to typhoid, cholera, botulism, and other specific diseases that are food-borne, there are thousands of cases each year of milder, transitory gastrointestinal illnesses that follow within a few hours the ingestion of food containing various bacteria. The term "ptomaine poisoning" for these outbreaks has survived from the time when they were thought to be due to specific chemical poisons ("ptomaines") produced from proteins during bacterial spoilage of the food. We are now certain that specific bacteria not related to spoilage are responsible. At least one of these illnesses is caused by a bacterial exotoxin and can be called a food poisoning, but the others are infections of the alimentary canal and should be called *gastroenteritis* (plural *gastroenteritides*). These bacteria grow well in suitable foods kept at higher-than-refrigerator temperatures. The foods usually do not show signs of spoilage, but persons eating them receive large doses of infective bacteria.

Many types of bacteria have been implicated in outbreaks of gastroenteritis. In this country staphylococcal food poisoning due to strains of micrococci that produce *enterotoxin* (enteric poison) are most common. Three kinds of bacteria that produce little or no toxin but do cause infections when ingested in large numbers are (1) certain species of *Salmonella,* (2) some types of hemolytic streptococci, and (3) certain heat-resistant strains of *Clostridium perfringens.* Other organisms that may cause gastroenteritis under some conditions include strains of *Escherichia coli* (see page 312), *Pseudomonas* species, and possibly *Bacillus cereus.* Botulinus poisoning, already described in this chapter, is sometimes included in lists of food poisonings. The chief characteristics of the important forms of these illnesses are summarized in Table 15·2. The causative bacteria will be described in greater detail in the chapters on specific pathogens.

Table 15·2

Common Forms of Gastroenteritis (Food Poisoning) *

	Staphylococcal food poisoning	Salmonella gastroenteritis	Clostridium perfringens gastroenteritis	Streptococcus gastroenteritis
Causative organism	Enterotoxin-producing micrococci	S. typhimurium, S. choleraesuis, etc.	C. perfringens heat-resistant strains	Strains of S. faecalis, etc.
Nature of illness..	Injury to digestive system by pre-formed enterotoxin	Infection of alimentary canal	Infection of alimentary canal	Infection of alimentary canal (?)
Chief symptoms..	Diarrhea, vomiting, nausea, cramps	Cramps, chills and fever, prostration	Cramps, diarrhea	Mild nausea, cramps
Occurrence.......	Very common	Common	?	Rare
No. of hours between eating and onset of symptoms......	1–5	12–24	8–22	6–18
Foods most commonly involved	Cream-filled bakery goods, ham and tongue products	Stews, meat pies	Steamed or boiled meats	Sausage, meat stuffings

* Data from Dack, Hobbs, *et al.*, and Meyer.

Bacteriologic Examination of Foods. The techniques used in the sanitary examination of foods are the same basically as those used for the examination of water and milk. The methods include (1) direct microscopic examination of liquid mounts or stained smears of the food; (2) plate counts to determine total numbers of viable bacteria; (3) selective cultivation to determine the presence of types indicating undesirable conditions of production or handling; and (4) tests for the presence of specific pathogens. An example of the first is the microscopic study of preparations of canned tomato products to hunt for filaments of molds. Legal standards for ice creams are based on plate counts. Examination of oysters for coliform bacteria safeguards the public from shellfish taken from polluted waters. The presence of staphylococci, streptococci, and salmonella is investigated in foods suspected of responsibility for outbreaks of food poisoning.

STUDY SUGGESTIONS

What are the milk-borne diseases? How do the organisms of each disease get into milk? Define *pasteurization*. What does it accomplish? How do the authorities determine that a milk has been pasteurized?

What is your milk supply at home? in the hospital? Are these supplies satisfactory? In what ways should they be improved?

What milk standards are enforced in your community? How does a modern community check on the safety of its milk? How does an up-to-date milk-company laboratory protect milk purchasers?

Why is the number of bacteria in milk generally accepted as the most satisfactory index of its quality? What methods are used to discover the numbers of organisms in milk? Describe other laboratory tests that safeguard the milk supply.

Have you ever visited a dairy farm or a milk plant? Describe the equipment and methods critically.

How should milk be handled in home and hospital? Give examples of improper handling. If you have had any experience in emergency home pasteurization or in the preparation of infant formulas, describe the apparatus and techniques that you used.

The last few chapters have had diagrams illustrating various modes of infection. Design diagrams to show how oysters spread typhoid; how lettuce might spread typhoid; how rat-contaminated foods might spread salmonella food poisoning; how a cook with a salmonella infection might spread it.

Suppose a family ate a meal consisting of home-canned string beans, chicken croquettes, bread and butter, cream puffs from a small commercial bakery, and tea. The next day all members become severely ill. Four out of five die within a few days. What type of food poisoning did they have? What food was responsible? How could this have been prevented?

After eating a similar meal, another family develops symptoms within 3 hours. They are all nauseated and have cramps. Some of them vomit. The next day all are well again. What type of food poisoning was it? What food was probably responsible? How could this have been prevented?

Answer the same questions, supposing the symptoms had developed about twelve hours after the meal with similar symptoms accompanied by prostration.

List the measures that should be practiced in all eating places to prevent all types of food-borne infections and poisonings. Make your rules specific. Have you ever been a victim of food poisoning? Describe the circumstances.

SUGGESTED READING

General References—Milk and Food

Adams, H. S.: "Milk and Food Sanitation Practices." Commonwealth Fund, New York, 1947.

Hopkins, E. S., and E. B. Elder: "Practice of Sanitation." Williams & Wilkins, Baltimore, 1951. Chaps. V and VI.

Maxcy, K. F.: "Rosenau's Preventive Medicine and Hygiene." 7th ed., Appleton-Century-Crofts, New York, 1951.

Milk

American Public Health Association: "Standard Methods for the Examination of Dairy Products." 10th ed., New York, 1953.

Andrews, J. A., and A. W. Fuchs: Pasteurization and its relation to health. *J.A.M.A.* **138**:128 (1948).

Elliker, P. R.: "Practical Dairy Bacteriology." McGraw-Hill, New York, 1949.

Feemster, R. F.: Milk-borne disease in Massachusetts, 1946–1950. *Am. J. Pub. Health* **41**:1275 (1952).

Government Printing Office, "Milk Ordinance and Code." Pub. Health Bull. 220, Washington, D.C., 1949.

Foods (See also pages 89 and 314.)

Dack, G. M.: "Food Poisoning." Rev. ed., University of Chicago Press, Chicago, 1949.

Feig, M.: Diarrhea, dysentery, food poisoning, and gastroenteritis. *Am. J. Pub. Health* **40**:1372 (1950).

———: The investigation of food-borne outbreaks of acute gastroenteritis. *Am. J. Pub. Health* (1952).

Griswold, D. M.: Food poisoning. *Am. J. Pub. Health* **40**:1398 (1950).

Meyer, K.: Food poisoning. *New England J. Med.* **249**:765 (1953).

CHAPTER 16

Spread of Infection by Insects and by the Atmosphere

True insects belong to the *hexapods* because they have six legs. Flies, mosquitoes, lice, fleas, and bugs are all true insects. A few orders of insects, including the cockroaches and the true bugs, have immature forms (*larvae,* sing. *larva*) that are similar to the adult forms. Most other insects go through four stages of development: the egg (*ovum*) stage; the wormlike, actively feeding, larval stage; the nonfeeding, resting stage (*pupa,* pl. *pupae*); and the sexually mature, usually winged, adult stage (Fig. 16·1). The related octopods, which have eight legs, include the ticks and mites. All these organisms belong to the phylum *Arthropoda* ("having jointed legs"). In this chapter the term *insect* will be used in the popular sense to include the ticks and mites as well as the six-legged forms. Insects injure and annoy people by their bites. They are also of great importance as the means by which many diseases are spread from one human to another or from animals to humans. Table 16·1 lists the important insect-borne diseases. Insects that

195

spread disease are called *vectors*. Arthropods that parasitize man and cause specific pathologic conditions such as scabies are discussed in Chap. 38.

HOW INSECTS SPREAD DISEASE

Certain insects, such as flies, pick up bacteria on their bodies or swallow them and discharge them in feces and vomitus. Since they breed in human

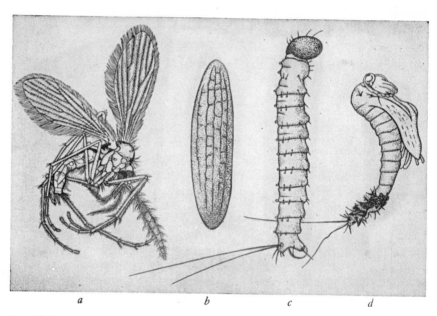

FIG. 16·1 Stages in the development of an insect (sand fly). (*a*) Adult, ×10; (*b*) ovum, ×100; (*c*) larva, ×10; (*d*) pupa, ×10. (*From Belding, "Textbook of Clinical Parasitology," Appleton-Century-Crofts.*)

fecal waste or animal manure and then may feed on exposed human foods, it is easy to see how they transfer pathogenic intestinal bacteria. Such transfer is known as *mechanical* transfer.

Other insects transfer dangerous microorganisms by *biologic* transfer. In them, the pathogenic organisms pass definite stages of their life cycles. The best-known example is the transfer of malaria by anopheline mosquitoes. The protozoan parasites conjugate in the mosquito's stomach. The zygote migrates through the stomach wall and forms a cyst in which thousands of new parasites grow. Some of these spread to the insect's salivary glands and are injected into the next person bitten. (See Fig. 37·3.)

The diseases transferred mechanically are bacterial diseases. The diseases transferred biologically are caused by viruses, rickettsiae, and higher animal forms—organisms that often have more complicated life cycles than the bacteria. If an insect is a biologic vector, it is usually the only natural mode of transfer of the disease. Diseases spread by mechanical vectors can be spread in other ways. Malaria is ordinarily spread only by the anopheline mosquitoes and can be eradicated if all mosquitoes are destroyed or prevented from biting humans. Water-borne, milk-borne, and food-borne typhoid may still occur where there are no flies.

The bacteria of bubonic plague are ingested by rat fleas when they feed on infected animals. The bacteria of tularemia are ingested in the same way by deer flies. The bacteria multiply in the intestines of these insects but do not pass through any life cycle there. This, therefore, may be considered as a special form of biologic transfer, though some bacteriologists consider it mechanical transfer.

In a few cases—notably the ticks that spread spotted fever, the mites that spread scrub typhus, and the deer flies that spread tularemia—the infected female insect may produce infected offspring. These offspring may transmit the diseases, although they have never fed on an infected animal.

THE IMPORTANT VECTORS

Ticks. Ticks are eight-legged forms of arthropods. The tick does not live on its animal victims continuously but attaches itself to an animal or human host at three different stages of its development, each time engorging itself with a huge meal of its host's blood. For example, the tick found in the Rocky Mountains feeds during its larval and nymph stages on rabbits and other small animals. In the adult stage it feeds on larger animals, such as dogs and man. If the tick's first meal was on an infected animal, the organisms of disease may be spread to its later host. (See Fig. 16·2.)

Mites. Mites are closely related to ticks. They feed on animals only during their larval stage, when they are known as *chiggers,* or *red bugs.* The adults pass on the infection to the next generation of larvae. All chiggers produce intense irritation. The members of a few species spread the mite-borne rickettsial infections. (See Fig. 16·2.)

Lice. The sucking lice that live on man are small, flattened, wingless insects (Fig. 16·2). There are three common types of louse, the head louse, the pubic louse (popularly called crab louse), and the body louse. When a person is infested with any type he is said to have *pediculosis.* The first two types are bothersome but are not involved in the spread of specific diseases. The louse-borne diseases are spread only by the body louse. It lives mainly in the clothing of its host, occasionally biting the host's skin and securing a meal of blood. Close contact between human beings or exchange of clothing

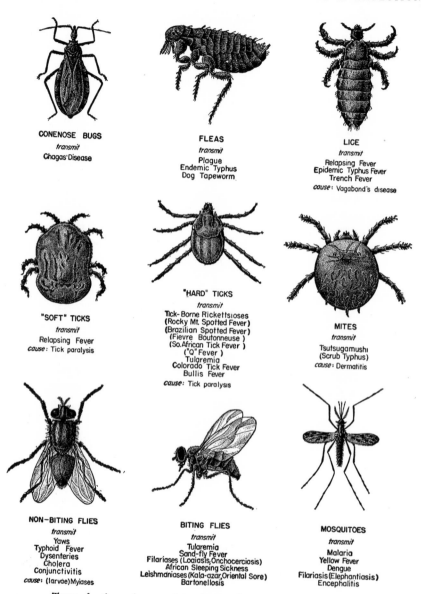

CONENOSE BUGS
transmit
Chagas'Disease

FLEAS
transmit
Plague
Endemic Typhus
Dog Tapeworm

LICE
transmit
Relapsing Fever
Epidemic Typhus Fever
Trench Fever
cause: Vagabond's disease

"SOFT" TICKS
transmit
Relapsing Fever
cause: Tick paralysis

"HARD" TICKS
transmit
Tick-Borne Rickettsioses
(Rocky Mt. Spotted Fever)
(Brazilian Spotted Fever)
(Fievre Boutonneuse)
(So.African Tick Fever)
("Q" Fever)
Tularemia
Colorado Tick Fever
Bullis Fever
cause: Tick paralysis

MITES
transmit
Tsutsugamushi
(Scrub Typhus)
cause: Dermatitis

NON–BITING FLIES
transmit
Yaws
Typhoid Fever
Dysenteries
Cholera
Conjunctivitis
cause: (larvae)Myiases

BITING FLIES
transmit
Tularemia
Sand-fly Fever
Filariases (Loaiasis,Onchocerciasis)
African Sleeping Sickness
Leishmaniases (Kala-azar,Oriental Sore)
Bartonellosis

MOSQUITOES
transmit
Malaria
Yellow Fever
Dengue
Filariasis (Elephantiasis)
Encephalitis

Types of arthropods transmitting human diseases (selected examples).

FIG. 16·2   Types of insects that transmit disease. (*From Stitt, Clough, and Branham, "Practical Bacteriology, Hematology, and Parasitology," McGraw-Hill, Blakiston Division.*)

may result in transfer of lice from one person to another. The louse does not inject the pathogenic organisms when it bites. But its bite is so irritating that the victim sooner or later scratches himself and the bacteria or rickettsiae from the louse's feces or vomitus or from the crushed body of the louse itself enter the resulting abrasions.

Bugs. Bedbugs are very objectionable insects, but there is no conclusive evidence that they transmit disease. The only bugs that are proved disease vectors are the large, spotted reduviid bugs of South and Central America. (See Fig. 16·2.) They are popularly called by many names, such as "assassin bugs" and "kissing bugs." They feed on many animals as well as on man, usually biting around the face during sleep. They spread the flagellates of Chagas' disease.

Fleas. Fleas are hard-shelled, wingless insects. They are laterally flattened and have powerful legs with which they jump long distances (Fig. 16·2). Rat fleas spread several infections from rats to man. The microorganisms enter the human in the same general fashion as in louse-borne diseases.

Table 16·1

Important Diseases Spread by Insects

Disease	Cause	Vector	Source of infection
Typhoid and other intestinal infections..........	Bacteria	Houseflies	Man
Tularemia...............	Bacterium	Deer flies, hard ticks	Rabbits, other game animals
Bubonic plague..........	Bacterium	Rat fleas	Rats, wild rodents
Relapsing fevers..........	Spirochetes	Ticks (in America), ticks and lice (in Europe, Asia, Africa)	Rodents, man
Yellow fever.............	Virus	Aëdes, other mosquitoes	Man and monkeys
Various types of encephalitis..................	Viruses	Mosquitoes, other insects	Birds and animals
Epidemic typhus..........	Rickettsia	Body louse	Man
Murine typhus............	Rickettsia	Rat fleas	Rats
Spotted fevers............	Rickettsiae	Ticks	Rodents
Tsutsugamushi fever.......	Rickettsia	Mites	Rodents
Malaria.................	Sporozoa	Anopheles mosquitoes	Man
African sleeping sickness...	Flagellates	Tsetse flies	Man
South American leishmaniasis..................	Flagellate	Sand flies	Man
Chagas' disease..........	Flagellate	Reduviid bugs	Armadillos, dogs, cats, etc.
Filariasis................	Roundworms	Mosquitoes	Man

Mosquitoes. Adult mosquitoes are two-winged insects. The three principal types are shown in Fig. 37·2. Mosquitoes lay their eggs in water. The eggs develop into aquatic larvae and pupae. Some species breed in swamps, others in streams, and still others in small amounts of water such as collect in empty tin cans. The female mosquito bites because she requires animal blood for the development of the ova; the male does not bite. The adult female may live for months and bite many different persons and animals during that time. If she bites a person infected with malaria and later an uninfected person, she may transfer the disease. The pathogenic organisms that are mosquito-borne all pass through stages of their life cycles in the insect host and are usually injected with the saliva when the insect bites.

Flies. Flies belong to the same group as mosquitoes. Some of them are bloodsucking. These include the deer flies that transmit tularemia, the sand flies that spread various flagellate infections, and the tsetse flies that are vectors of African sleeping sickness. (See Fig. 16·2.)

The common housefly, on the other hand, does not bite. It transfers disease by mechanical pollution of human food and drink. Flies lay their eggs in manure, garbage, animal litter, and human excreta. The larval and pupal stages are passed in the same environment. They are dangerous when unsanitary disposal of animal excrement provides them with breeding or visiting places where they may acquire organisms of human disease. Flies are scarce when such breeding places are eliminated. The winged adult flies leave their breeding places and fly to places where foods are exposed. There they can pollute the food in several ways: (1) by bacteria adhering to the sticky hairs of their feet and legs; (2) by bacteria in their feces; (3) by bacteria in their vomitus, since they soften foods before eating by regurgitating liquid from the upper alimentary canal; and (4) by organisms within their bodies, which may be released in food if the fly is crushed or drowned in the food.

In addition to pollution of food, flies have been suspected of carrying bacteria such as anthrax spores to wounds and dressings. Ova of worm parasites and cysts of the ameba of dysentery are also spread by flies. Other flies and cockroaches are believed to spread intestinal diseases in the same general way.

CONTROL OF INSECT-BORNE INFECTION

Successful control of the insect vector results in the elimination of the disease in those instances where the insect is the only means of spread. If the insect is a mechanical vector its control will definitely lower the incidence of infection but will not affect the spread of the disease by other means.

Elimination of Sources from Which Insects Acquire the Organisms. If the source of the disease is man, cases of the disease must be promptly diagnosed.

All insects on the patient or in his environment must be promptly killed
and he must be protected from the insects as long as he carries the infection.
Therefore typhus patients must be deloused, malaria patients must be kept
in screened wards, and the excreta of typhoid patients must be protected
from flies.

Protection of Possible Victims. The chief methods of protecting people
against dangerous insects are the use of screens and the use of repellents.
Dimethyl phthalate and other repellents developed during the Second World
War are much more effective than those formerly used. A few drops on
the skin repel all types of insects for several hours. Clothing and bedding
treated with a 5 per cent solution remain repellent for several weeks.

Chemical Control of Insects. "Swat the Fly" has been a popular slogan but
represents a very ineffectual method of dealing with dangerous insects. That
and other older methods have been superseded by the use of chemicals in
killing adult insects. Some of the chemicals kill the insects on contact. These
are the "knockdown" compounds that are sprayed or dusted directly at the

FIG. 16·3 Typhus control by dusting Russian prisoners of war in Germany with DDT
to rid them of body lice. (*Armed Forces Institute of Pathology, No. B814.*)

insects. The "residual" sprays or dusts are dispersed on surfaces, where they remain actively insecticidal for months, killing any insect that lands there. *DDT* (dichloro-diphenyl-trichloroethane) is the best known of these residual insecticides. (See Fig. 16·3.) Others commonly used are *chlordane, dieldrin,* and *BHC* (benzene hexachloride). Certain dialkyl phosphates such as *malathione* are mixed with sugar or sirup to attract and kill flies in dairy barns and other places with high fly populations. Lice and other ectoparasites in clothing are killed by placing the clothing in chambers that are filled with steam or methyl bromide gas.

Some insects, notably houseflies and mites, readily produce mutants resistant to the insecticide that is being used against them. It is then necessary to use another chemical to control the newly developed population of resistant insects.

Prevention of Insect Breeding. Killing larvae or adult insects is never as satisfactory as preventing the breeding of the species. In the long run the cost is not greater and the problem of insecticide resistance is avoided. Yellow fever in cities and towns was completely eradicated by the vigilance of special sanitary squads which inspected every part of the community, emptying, destroying, or treating with insecticide every small water container in which the yellow fever mosquito could breed. Drainage of swampy areas is the most effective measure against malaria, for its mosquito vectors breed in these bodies of stagnant water. The fly-free community is the one where flies can find no exposed manure, garbage, or animal litter in which to lay their eggs.

SPREAD OF MICROORGANISMS THROUGH THE AIR

The atmosphere is never a source of infection. All microorganisms in the air have come from soil, water, human excretions, or other sources. None grow in the air. Organisms of human disease are present in air in three forms: (1) in particles of dust from solid materials, (2) in droplets of moisture, and (3) in droplet nuclei. *Droplet nuclei* are the minute solid residues of small droplets.

Infected air spreads organisms of respiratory disease. Large droplets and particles in inhaled air are filtered out of inspired air before it reaches the lungs, but the majority of particles of 1 to 10μ in size reach the lung tissue. Infected inhaled material is also found in the alimentary canal, since most mucous secretions of the respiratory tract are swallowed. Sterile supplies exposed to air for any length of time are contaminated by organisms from dust. The air-borne contamination of open wounds and of burns and other extensive skin lesions has been shown to be an important cause of infection.

Dangerous Dusts. Dust in barracks, dormitories, and hospital wards has been shown to contain dangerous organisms of respiratory origin, particularly streptococci. The number is highest in the air of the room after sweeping or bedmaking. Most of the bacteria come from the bedding, which is grossly contaminated by coughing and sneezing and by the infected hands of the inmates. The most effective measures against the dust-borne organisms are oiling of the floors and treatment of the bedding. Blankets and sheets are treated with a mineral oil emulsion added to the last rinse water when

FIG. 16·4 A violent unstifled sneeze. Photograph taken with special lighting and a high-speed camera. (*Courtesy of Dr. M. W. Jennison.*)

the bedding is laundered. Oiled bedding does not shed bacteria-laden lint. The treatment of bedding with certain bactericidal detergents has been suggested as a means of making its surfaces lastingly antimicrobial. It is also important that no cleaning, bedmaking, or other process that might distribute microorganisms be carried out in any operating room or ward for some time before any surgical procedure.

The intakes of modern ventilating systems are provided with dust filters to remove outside dust. Very effective filtration is needed to provide dust-free air for operating rooms.

Droplets. Sneezing, coughing, hawking, and violent talking expel large numbers of droplets of respiratory secretion into the air. They are clearly shown in pictures taken with the aid of special lighting and high-speed cameras (Fig. 16·4). These droplets are laden with bacteria and viruses. The larger droplets are spread only a few feet and tend to settle out rapidly, infecting nearby surfaces as they fall. The spread of these large droplets is avoided by the proper use of handkerchiefs and face masks; by the isolation of persons who sneeze and cough; and by *spacing out* (the provision of

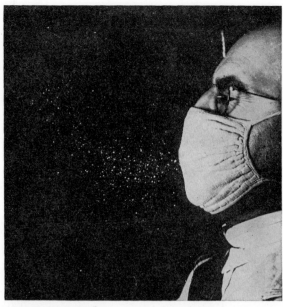

FIG. 16·5   The effect of a surgical mask on the spread of droplets from a sneeze. (*Courtesy of Dr. M. W. Jennison.*)

sufficient space between units occupied by people, such as beds in wards and desks in schools). Normal, quiet breathing through the nose or mouth and normal talking do not spread respiratory secretions.

Face Masks. Face masks are worn in the operating room and in the infants' wards as a routine procedure to prevent the spread of respiratory organisms. They are also worn by workers in drug plants who are engaged in the preparation of vaccines, etc. Some authorities have advocated their general use in influenza epidemics. Masks are useless unless they are properly constructed and properly worn. They are made of several layers of gauze, special paper or plastic, or cotton flannel combined with gauze. Cloth masks should be laundered before use. The mask should be tied so that is covers both mouth and nose and fits tightly around all edges (Fig. 16·5). A flexible wire may be built into the mask so that it will fit snugly over the bridge of

the nose. If the mask becomes damp it should be promptly replaced, since
only a dry mask is an effective filter.

Droplet Nuclei. The large droplets from the respiratory tract settle out
rapidly. The much more abundant small droplets remain suspended in the

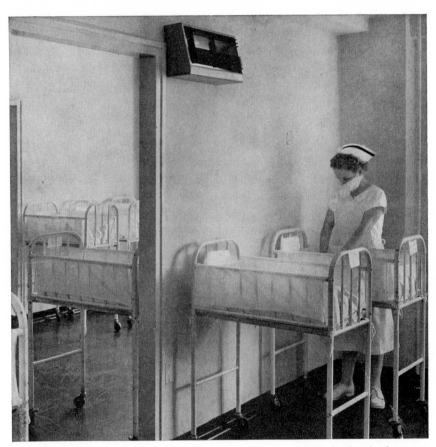

FIG. 16·6 Ultraviolet lamp in use in an infant ward. (*General Electric Company,
Lamp Division.*)

air for hours or even for days. The moisture in these small droplets evaporates, leaving minute bits of matter that often contain one or more microorganisms. The dried residues are called *droplet nuclei*. Dust-control measures
do not affect the droplet nuclei. Continuous effective air change by good
ventilation reduces their number. Ultraviolet light is effective in killing these
air-borne microorganisms. A modern ultraviolet light installation for this
purpose is shown in Fig. 16·6. Aerosol vapor, particularly propylene glycol,

is also effective, but its use is limited by the technical difficulty of obtaining an even dispersion of the vapor.

TESTING AIR FOR THE PRESENCE OF MICROORGANISMS

The simplest method of testing the atmosphere for the presence of microorganisms is the exposure of a sterile agar plate for 15 minutes. The number of colonies developing on the plate is a rough approximation of the number of fungus-carrying and bacteria-carrying dust particles per cubic foot of the air in the place where the plate was exposed. To detect streptococci, blood agar plates are used. Plates held in front of the face while sneezing or coughing will indicate the numbers of expelled droplets bearing bacteria. More accurate methods utilize air-sampling apparatus that collects a definite quantity of air and directs its flow against the surface of an agar plate. Each droplet or particle containing one or more growable bacteria or fungi will develop into a colony. The numbers of infected particles per cubic foot can then be calculated.

STUDY SUGGESTIONS

Do not try to memorize the material in Table 16·1, but use it as a frequent reference.

Define *octopod, hexapod, mechanical vector, biologic vector*. Give one or more examples of each.

Make and study a table with the following headings: *Insect type; Description; Examples; Diseases transferred; Methods of control*. It will be best to list houseflies as a separate type from the biting flies.

What effective measures of insect control have you observed or used at home? in your community? in your hospital?

Is the air a source or a mode of infection?

What techniques have you been taught in practical nursing or seen used in the hospital that work against insect-borne and air-borne disease?

The use of Steril lamps and glycol vaporizers is quite new. Have you seen any such installations? Describe them. Where in your hospital or community might it be desirable to install such apparatus?

SUGGESTED READING

Control of Air-borne Infection

Buttolph, L. J., and H. Haynes: "Ultraviolet Air Sanitation." General Electric (Lamp Division), Cleveland, 1953.

Hopkins, E. S., and F. B. Elder: "Practice of Sanitation." Williams & Wilkins, Baltimore, 1951. Chap. X.

Loosli, C. G.: Dust and its control as a means of disinfection of air. *Am. J. Pub. Health* **37**:353 (1947).

Maxcy, K. F.: "Rosenau's Preventive Medicine and Hygiene." 7th ed., Appleton-Century-Crofts, New York, 1951.

"Progress in the Control of Airborne Infections." American Journal of Public Health Yearbook, 1949–1950. Page 82.

Puck, T. T. L.: The mechanism of aerial disinfection by glycols and other chemical agents. *J. Exper. Med.* **85**:729 (1947).

Rooks, R. L., J. Craley, and M. E. Burman: Hospital masks: their bacterial filtering efficiency and resistance to air flow. *Pub. Health Rep.* **56**:1111 (1941).

Walter, C. W.: "The Aseptic Treatment of Wounds." Macmillan, New York, 1948. Chap. XIII.

Insects

General References

Belding, D. T.: "Textbook of Clinical Parasitology." 2d ed., Appleton-Century-Crofts, New York, 1952. Sec. VI.

Government Printing Office: "Insects." Yearbook of Agriculture, 1952, Washington, D.C., 1952.

Herms, W. B.: "Medical Entomology." 4th ed., Macmillan, New York, 1950.

Mackie, T. T., G. W. Hunter, and C. B. Worth: "A Manual of Tropical Medicine." 2d ed., Saunders, Philadelphia, 1954. Sec. XI.

Winslow, C.-E. A.: "The Conquest of Epidemic Disease." Princeton University Press, Princeton, 1943. Chap. 17.

Control

Andrews, J. M.: Advancing frontiers of insect vector control. *Am. J. Pub. Health* **40**:409 (1950).

Hopkins, E. S., and F. B. Elder: "Practice of Sanitation." Williams & Wilkins, Baltimore, 1951. Chap. XIII.

Insecticides and Rodenticides, 1952. *Pub. Health Rep.* **67**:455 (1952).

Maxcy, K. F.: "Rosenau's Preventive Medicine and Hygiene." 7th ed., Appleton-Century-Crofts, New York, 1951.

PART FOUR

Infection and Immunity

CHAPTER 17

Microorganisms and Disease

Not all diseases are caused by microorganisms, but it is conservatively estimated that they are responsible for over 50 per cent of all illnesses. In uncivilized countries the proportion is certainly much greater. All communicable diseases, all diseases that are thought of as infections, and some others are caused by living organisms. Some illnesses are the results of past infections. Nonmicrobial diseases include those resulting from mechanical and chemical injuries, those resulting from malnutrition including vitamin deficiencies, those resulting from congenital malformations, and tumors and cancers.

A microbial disease is a complicated interreaction of the cells of two living organisms, the invading pathogen and the host. The ways in which microorganisms injure the body, the ways in which the body reacts to the microorganisms, and the practical applications of our knowledge of these reactions constitute the subject matter of this part of the text.

211

INFECTION AND VIRULENCE

Infection. The invasion of the body of a host by a microorganism constitutes *infection*. Infectious microorganisms are capable of invading living organisms and establishing themselves within the hosts' tissues at least temporarily. However infection does not always result in disease. Potentially dangerous microorganisms may infect the body but be quickly overcome by its defense mechanisms without causing clinically detectable symptoms. In some diseases, notably tuberculosis, the microorganisms may continue to exist within certain tissues for long periods of time. At a later date in a relatively small number of these infected persons overt disease may develop. Infections frequently persist after clinical recovery. This is the essence of the carrier state.

Infection is such a common occurrence in the lives of all living things, and disease is so relatively uncommon, that we may well agree with Dubos that "infection is in many cases the normal state; it is only disease that is abnormal."

Virulence. Fundamentally the term *virulence* means pathogenicity—the ability to cause disease and death. The term is most frequently used when alteration in ability to cause disease or measurement of disease-producing ability is being described. A mutant of a pathogenic microorganism that has lost its ability to cause disease is said to be *avirulent*. Virulence of pathogenic organisms is often diminished by cultivating them in artificial media or in unusual animal hosts. The resulting strains are said to be of *attenuated virulence*.

Virulence is best measured by tests that lead to the computation of the size of the inoculum that will cause the death or recognizable characteristic injury in 50 per cent of tests animals. (Fertile eggs or tissue cultures are often used in testing viruses.) The figure obtained is the LD_{50} (median lethal dose) or the ID_{50} (median infective dose). The median infective dose of some bacteria is very small. A single treponeme of syphilis is believed to cause clinical disease.

PROOF THAT A MICROORGANISM CAUSES A SPECIFIC DISEASE

The usual steps in the proof that a specific microorganism is the causative agent of a particular disease are summarized in what are known as *Koch's postulates*.

1. The organism must be found in every case of the disease.
2. It must be isolated and grown in pure culture.

3. The organism from the pure culture must cause the typical disease when it is inoculated into a susceptible animal.

4. The same organism must be recovered from the inoculated animal.

It is not always possible to follow these steps. Some organisms observed in human disease cannot be grown in culture media, others cannot be grown in animals or, if they are grown, do not produce the typical disease. A few including the leprosy bacillus and the virus of infectious jaundice have never been grown in media or animals. Even when all the postulates cannot be fulfilled we are often justified in accepting an organism as the cause of the disease on the basis of other lines of evidence. Such evidence will be better understood after your study of this section of the text. For example, a preparation of the organism (vaccine) may protect susceptible people against the disease; the blood serum of a diseased or recovered person may react specifically with the suspected microorganism (serologic reaction); or persons infected or recovered may show specific skin reactions to preparations containing the organism or its products (allergic skin reaction).

HOW MICROORGANISMS INJURE THE BODY

There is no single simple way in which microorganisms injure the body. Even the smallest microorganism is a complex living thing, and its host's body is made up of millions of individual cells, each capable of many varied reactions. No two species of pathogenic microorganisms injure their hosts in exactly the same fashion, and no two hosts react in exactly the same way. But related organisms do cause similar reactions in their hosts, e.g., all rickettsial diseases have generally similar courses and symptoms. All human hosts tend to show somewhat similar responses to infection with a specific pathogen. All persons with measles develop a set of symptoms that can be recognized as the typical *syndrome* (complex of symptoms) of that disease. In the later chapters of this text many of the effects of specific pathogens will be described.

Toxins. The word *toxin* is a general term for poison. The poisons that are formed by microorganisms, particularly the bacteria, may be exotoxins or endotoxins.

Exotoxins are poisonous substances formed by the organisms and secreted into the surrounding tissue or medium. Only a limited number of pathogens form exotoxins. The pathogenicity of the organisms of diphtheria, tetanus, and botulinus poisoning is due almost entirely to their exotoxins. The organisms of gas gangrene, the streptococci of scarlet fever, certain strains of micrococci, and some other bacteria owe at least part of their injurious effects to their exotoxins.

Exotoxins are nitrogenous substances. They can be separated from the bacteria that form them by filtration of broth cultures through fine filters. Highly purified crystalline toxins have been prepared from the filtrates by chemical methods. Exotoxins are readily destroyed by heat and are altered when treated with formaldehyde or certain other chemicals. Some of the exotoxins are the most powerful poisons known to man. For example, the lethal dose of tetanus (lockjaw) toxin is one two-hundredth of the lethal dose of strychnine. A guinea pig can be killed by 1/1,000,000 ml. of a filtrate of a *Clostridium botulinum* culture. There is evidence that the toxins act by blocking some essential step in the metabolism of the host cells.

The exotoxin-forming organisms grow in some one place in the body and have little tendency to spread from these chosen localities. But their poisons are absorbed and carried to distant organs. Exotoxins have affinities for special tissues with which they unite firmly and rapidly. When present in sublethal amounts, exotoxins stimulate the body cells to form definite protective substances called *antitoxins*. Each antitoxin is specific for the toxin that causes its formation. Exotoxin is one form of antigen, and antitoxin is a form of antibody. Antigens and antibodies will be discussed in detail later in this section. When the word *toxin* is used in connection with microorganisms it ordinarily means exotoxin.

Endotoxins are poisonous substances that stay within the microorganism until it disintegrates. They cannot be separated from cultures by filtration and are not readily destroyed by heat. Their actions are much weaker and less specific than those of exotoxins. They do not cause the formation of antitoxins. The substances that older texts refer to as endotoxins are now considered to be somatic antigens (see page 217).

Mechanical Injury. Mechanical injury to tissues may be caused directly or indirectly by the presence of microorganisms. Hookworms attach themselves to the lining of the small intestine by their sharply toothed mouths and so cause hundreds of small hemorrhages, resulting in anemia in the host. Adult filaria worms plug large lymphatics, and tangled chains of anthrax bacilli clog capillaries in internal organs. In malaria the erythrocytes are ruptured by the rapid intracellular growth of the protozoa. The injury to cells invaded by viruses and rickettsiae may be due in part to mechanical factors.

Chemical Injury. In studying the effects of various bacteria, scientists have found many substances that injure tissues in specific ways.

Cell-destroying Substances. Certain microorganisms secrete substances resembling proteolytic enzymes. *Hemolysins,* which destroy red blood cells, are formed by many streptococci. *Leukocidins,* which act against white blood cells, are commonly formed by pathogenic micrococci. Some micrococci also form *necrotoxins,* which cause necrosis of skin tissues. One species of wound-invading clostridia has such marked ability to digest tissues that it is named *Clostridium histolyticum* (tissue-dissolving).

Tissue-altering Enzymes. Some bacteria possess the power to cause the coagulation of blood by means of *coagulases.* This ability may protect the bacteria against the action of the white cells. Other bacteria form substances that enable them to spread rapidly through tissues. Many streptococci secrete *streptokinase,* one of several kinases that dissolve coagulated fibrin in blood vessels and in intracellular spaces. Another enzyme of some streptococci is *dornase* (desoxyribonuclease), which splits nucleoproteins. Carbohydrate-splitting enzymes of the gas gangrene organism form gas bubbles in muscle and other tissues, forcing the cells apart. Streptococci, micrococci, and other bacteria form an enzyme, *hyaluronidase,* which decomposes hyaluronic acid, an intracellular substance that holds cells together in tissues. (This enzyme is also known as the *spreading factor* and the *Duran-Reynals factor.*)

Substances That Affect Body Temperature. Pyrogens (fever-producing substances) are formed by many bacteria. On the other hand the bacillus of the Shiga type of dysentery forms a *hypothermic* (temperature-lowering) factor.

Substances That Stimulate or Attract Cells. Various substances from invading microorganisms stimulate unusual forms of cell growth. The leprosy mycobacteria cause proliferation of fibrous tissue to form subcutaneous nodules. The mycobacterium of tuberculosis stimulates the formation of multinucleated giant cells. The pathogenic intestinal worms cause the appearance of abnormally high numbers of eosinophilic granulocytes in the blood.

Leukocytes are attracted to the site of invasion of many bacteria. This is a chemical attraction and is called *chemotaxis.* Dilatation of small blood vessels is common, bringing increased numbers of blood cells and increased amounts of tissue fluid to the area of infection.

Nutritional Injury. The rapid growth of pathogens within the body—often actually within the cells—must rob the tissues of needed nutrients. Some bacteria definitely lower the blood-sugar level. In vitro, many pathogenic bacteria will not grow without supplies of accessory growth substances identical with animal vitamins. When these same organisms grow in the body they must take needed vitamins from the tissues. The amino acids of the cells and body fluids must be used by invading organisms for their growth. Viruses growing intracellularly use substances that are needed for the synthesis of the nucleoproteins of their host cells. More obvious activities of this sort are the use of digested food in the intestine by tapeworms and the ingestion of erythrocytes by intestinal amebas.

ANTIGENS

An *antigen* is defined as any substance which, when introduced into the body, stimulates the formation of a specific antibody.

Characteristics of Antigens. Substances that act as antigens are very varied as to nature and origin, but all have certain properties in common.

1. Antigens are substances foreign to the circulation of the body. Substances normally present in the circulating fluids of the body do not act as antigens. A few normal body proteins that do not ordinarily reach the general circulation may act antigenically in the same species of animal from which they are taken. The protein of the lens of the eye is an example. Such an antigen is called an *isoantigen*.

2. Antigens are organic substances of high molecular weight. Proteins and protein-containing substances act as antigens. It is considered likely that some very complex carbohydrates such as glucosides may act as antigens. Other simpler carbohydrates are not antigenic but form antigenic compounds by uniting with protein molecules. Such carbohydrates and other organic radicals that act in combination with proteins are called *haptens,* or *partial antigens.* Enzymes are antigenic. Fats do not act as antigens. While it is frequently stated that antigens are soluble in body fluids, this is not the true solubility of crystalline substances. Antigens are colloids.

3. Antigens cause the tissues to form antibodies. The animal body is well equipped to rid itself of diffusible substances. They can be excreted by the kidneys, lungs, and skin. Foreign solids in tissues may cause trouble but can generally be walled off from functioning cells. But foreign colloidal substances are not localized, cannot be excreted, and tend to spread through the body, uniting with fluid and cellular substances. A special and complicated method for dealing with such material, the development of specific antibodies, has developed in the animal body. The formation of a specific antibody is evidence of the presence of an antigen. Our modern conception of these antibodies is discussed in the next chapter.

4. Antigens are specific. Each substance of definite chemical structure acts as an independent antigen, causing the formation of a specific antibody. This specificity is dependent on the exact chemical nature of a small part of the huge protein molecule. This portion of the antigen molecule is known as the *determinant group.* Two otherwise unlike protein molecules both possessing the same determinant group may act as identical antigens.

Microorganisms as Sources of Antigens. Nonmicrobial antigens will be discussed in Chap. 20.

Microorganisms are made up of many organic compounds. Therefore it is not surprising to find that each pathogenic microorganism is the source of a number of antigenic substances. To use an expression suggested by the bacteriologist Nicolle, each bacterium is a *mosaic of antigens.* This is also true of pathogenic worms, protozoa, fungi, rickettsiae, and the animal viruses. It is possible that some of the smaller plant viruses are composed of only one antigenic substance. The antigenic structure of the bacteria has been most extensively studied. Among the classes of antigenic compounds found in various bacterial species are the following:

1. Cell products. The true exotoxins act as effective antigens. Certain other materials secreted by bacterial cells or easily separated from them also have antigenic properties, e.g., hyaluronidase and some hemolysins.

2. Surface substances. The flagella of motile pathogens contain substances that are important antigens. They are called *flagella antigens,* or sometimes *H antigens.* The *H* is derived from the German word *hauch,* meaning "film," and refers to the spreading type of colony formed by certain flagellated bacteria. These H antigens are very easily destroyed by heat. The capsular polysaccharides of bacteria are partial antigens. Each type of pneumococcus, hemolytic streptococcus, and salmonella has its specific capsular substance. The capsular and flagella antigens are very important because of this type specificity and because, being on the surface of the organisms, they are the antigens most commonly involved in reactions between antigens and antibodies.

3. Somatic substances. The materials of the internal protoplasm of the bacteria also act as antigens. They are called the *somatic antigens.* The term *O antigen* is also used. The letter *O* stands for the German phrase *ohne hauch,* meaning "without film," because somatic antigen is most readily identified in nonflagellated bacteria which do not form filmlike colonies. The O antigens are heat-resistant. Most bacteria that have been thoroughly studied have been found to have somatic antigens in common, e.g., the same somatic antigens are present in all pneumococci.

Antigenic Formulas. The salmonellas and some other bacteria have now been so thoroughly studied that bacteriologists are able to use a system of letters and numbers to indicate the antigens to be found in each type. In the salmonellas, the identified somatic antigens are designed by Roman numerals; the flagella antigens common to several species, by small letters; and the specific flagella antigens by Arabic numerals. The salmonella of paratyphoid A fever has the formula I,II,XII; a. The salmonella of paratyphoid B fever has the formula I,IV,V,XII; b; 1,2. The salmonella of mouse typhoid, an organism that causes food poisoning in human beings, is very closely related to the paratyphoid B organism. Its formula is I,IV,V,XII; i; 1,2.

TYPES OF INFECTION AND INFECTIOUS DISEASE

Although, as was stated earlier in this chapter, infection does not necessarily imply active disease, the word infection is very loosely used. It is frequently used when the better term would be *infectious disease,* designating a disease resulting from an infection.

Acute and Chronic Infectious Disease. An infectious disease is said to be acute when it has a definite duration. A chronic disease is of indefinite duration. For example, a case of measles always terminates within 2 weeks, while the termination of a case of tuberculosis is unpredictable.

In an acute infectious disease certain events or stages are clearly indicated. They develop in the following order:

1. Exposure. The living pathogenic organisms enter the body of the prospective victim.

2. Incubation period. After exposure there is a definite period before the symptoms of disease appear. This is the *incubation period.* In each acute communicable disease the incubation period is of characteristic length. The incubation period of measles is 10 to 12 days; that of scarlet fever, 2 to 3 days. During the incubation period three things are taking place: the organisms are spreading to the parts of the body where they do the damage; they are growing to sufficient numbers to cause trouble; and some tissues in the body may be developing hypersensitiveness to the invading organisms.

3. Prodromal stage. In some diseases there may be several days when the person is not well but fails to show recognizable symptoms of the specific infection. This is the *prodromal stage.*

4. Period of actual disease. Sickness in an acute infectious disease may have a sudden onset or it may develop gradually. If the onset is so slow as to be scarcely noticeable it is said to be *insidious* (treacherous). The course of an acute disease is marked by a combination of characteristic symptoms, the *syndrome* of the disease. The illness may terminate suddenly by *crisis,* or recovery may be slow. In the latter case it is said to end by *lysis.*

5. Death. Death will result when essential cells are destroyed or disabled so that they can no longer carry out their functions.

6. Convalescence. If death does not supervene, there is a shorter or longer period of convalescence as the patient returns to normal health. During this period injured cells are repaired and resume their normal activities. The individual who has recovered from an infection is not quite the same person he was before the infection. He has developed specific defensive antibodies so that he has at least a temporary immunity to reinfection with the same organism. He may have permanent sequelae resulting from incomplete repair of tissue injuries. He may have become a carrier of the organism.

General and Local Infections. In a *general infection* the organisms spread throughout the body. Frequently they can be found at least temporarily in the blood stream, a condition called *bacteremia*. In some infections there is a persistence of blood stream infection and an actual growth of organisms in the blood. Such a condition is called *septicemia*. The terms bacteremia and septicemia are often used interchangeably. When organisms in the blood localize in various tissues, giving rise to local inflammations, the condition is known as *pyemia*.

In a *local infection* the organisms remain in one limited area. The term *focal infection* implies a center (*focus*) of infection from which organisms spread to other parts of the body. A boil on the arm is an example of a local infection. Infected tonsils from which streptococci or their products spread, giving rise to repeated attacks of rheumatic fever, is an example of focal infection.

Communicable, Infectious, and Contagious Disease. A disease is considered *communicable* if it can be transmitted directly or indirectly from man to man or from animals to man. *Communicable disease* is the term most commonly used in public health. Some communicable diseases are contagious—transmitted by actual contact. All communicable diseases and many others are *infectious diseases*—diseases that result from the invasion of the tissues by pathogenic microorganisms.

When a disease is constantly present in an area it is said to be *endemic*. If cases occur in unusual numbers in a community, the disease is *epidemic*. When an epidemic is present over a large part of the world at one time, the disease is *pandemic*. These words can be used as adjectives or as nouns.

Primary and Secondary Infections. A *primary infection* is the original infection causing an illness. A *secondary* infection is an infection developing in a person already suffering from disease. Most acute communicable diseases are primary infections, e.g., measles, typhoid, amebic dysentery. Bronchopneumonia developing in a child with measles, septicemia following a compound fracture of the leg, and gingivitis (inflammation of the gums) in an infant suffering from scurvy are examples of secondary infections.

Primary infections are due to truly virulent organisms possessing marked invasive ability. Secondary infections are usually caused by organisms of low virulence which take the opportunity to invade weakened tissues. Such organisms may be called *opportunists*, a name suggested by the great American bacteriologist Theobald Smith. Primary infections are usually caused by organisms that come from outside the victim's body. Their origin is said to be *exogenous*. Organisms of secondary infections may be exogenous or they may be opportunists already present in the person's respiratory tract or other organs. Then the infection is said to be *endogenous*.

Most infections are due to the growth of a single species of microorganism in or on the body. In some infections, however, disease seems to develop only when two organisms are present. The classic example of this is *Vincent's angina* (popularly called trench mouth), which is supposedly caused by the combined attack of a fusiform bacillus and a spirochete. The association of an opportunist bacterium with a virus is very common. Green-producing streptococci are present in cases of measles.

Specific and Nonspecific Infections. A *specific infection* is an infection caused by a virulent microorganism and showing a typical clinical picture. Typhoid fever is an example of a specific infection. It is caused by a definite species of bacterium, *Salmonella typhosa*. It has a definite course characterized by an incubation period of about two weeks, an initial bacteremia, followed by ulceration of lymphatic areas in the intestinal lining, a typical fever curve, etc.

A *nonspecific infection* is caused by relatively avirulent opportunist microorganisms invading abnormally susceptible tissues. The symptoms are poorly defined and variable. Most nonspecific infections are given names combining the name of the part involved with the suffix -*itis,* which means "inflammation of." Examples are sinusitis, tonsillitis, gastritis, otitis media, appendicitis, cystitis. Many nonspecific infections are chronic or recurrent. Effective immunity is seldom developed.

Specific infections are generally communicable and tend to become epidemic, but nonspecific infections are frequently not communicable. If they do spread it is among groups of persons already ill, e.g., thrush, a fungous disease of the mouth, spreads in wards of poorly nourished infants. The opportunist organism causing a nonspecific infection may not cause the same set of symptoms in all its victims. Streptococci from the mouth of a healthy nurse may, if she is careless, cause puerperal sepsis in a postpartum patient or bronchopneumonia in a baby suffering from measles.

Hard and fast division into specific and nonspecific infections is impossible. Many infections, including such important ones as tuberculosis and some streptococcal infections, have an intermediate position.

NONINFECTIOUS DISEASES DUE TO MICROORGANISMS

There are some microorganisms that can cause disease without invading the body. The clostridium of botulism forms a strong poison while growing in canned foods, and the ergot fungus forms a poison when it grows as a parasite on grains. Persons eating the food or grain suffer from poisoning, not from infection. Some authorities consider the organisms of tetanus and gas gangrene as noninfectious. These clostridia grow in the fluids and dead tissue of deep wounds. They do not invade living tissue. Their pathogenicity is due mainly to the exotoxins they secrete. Some illnesses are sequelae to previous infections. Persons with deformities due to previous infection with infantile paralysis or those with heart-valve abnormalities due to previous attacks of rheumatic fever may need treatment, but they are no longer harboring the causative organisms.

STUDY SUGGESTIONS

Make a list of new terms used in this chapter. Can you define them all?

The chapter is divided into three distinct sections. If you find it difficult it may help to study each one separately and master it before you go on to the next.

Can you summarize the ways in which microorganisms injure the body?

Explain the nature of an antigen. What is an antigenic formula? The organism of typhoid fever has the antigenic formula IX,XII; d. What antigen does it have in common with the salmonellas of paratyphoid and mouse typhoid? Is this a somatic or flagella antigen? (Students should not attempt to learn antigenic formulas, but they should understand their significance.)

As far as your knowledge will permit, classify the following diseases as specific or nonspecific, exogenous or endogenous, acute or chronic, primary or secondary, local or general:

Common cold	Mumps	Bronchopneumonia
Tonsillitis	Syphilis	Ringworm of the feet
Bronchitis	Infected tooth	Malaria
Carbuncle	Undulant fever	Streptococcal septicemia

SUGGESTED READING

General References on Immunity

BOYD, W. C.: "Fundamentals of Immunology." 2d ed., Interscience, New York, 1947.

RAFFEL, S.: "Immunity." Appleton-Century-Crofts, New York, 1953.

ZINSSER, H., J. F. ENDERS, and L. D. FOTHERGILL: "Immunity: Its Principles and Applications in Medicine and Public Health." 5th ed., Macmillan, New York, 1939.

Parasitism, Infection, and Virulence

BURNET, F. M.: "Natural History of Infectious Disease." Cambridge, New York, 1953.

BURROWS, W.: "Textbook of Microbiology." 16th ed., Saunders, Philadelphia, 1954. Chap. 8.

DUBOS, R. J.: "Biochemical Determinants of Microbial Diseases." Harvard University Press, Cambridge, 1954.

MACLEOD, C. M., and A. M. PAPPENHEIMER, JR.: Properties of the Bacteria Which Enable Them To Cause Disease, in R. J. Dubos's "Bacterial and Mycotic Infections of Man." 2d ed., Lippincott, Philadelphia, 1954. Chap. 8.

SMITH, T.: "Parasitism and Disease." Princeton University Press, Princeton, 1934.

The Theory of Immunity; Antibodies

Immunity means resistance to infection. The general defenses of the body have already been discussed. Immunity to each specific disease of microbial origin is due to the presence of specific antibodies. The interaction of antibody with antigen usually has the result of protecting against disease and hastening recovery. Sometimes, however, the body develops a state of *hypersensitivity* as a result of antigen-antibody reaction. The hypersensitive individual reacts in undesirable ways when antigen-antibody reactions take place in his tissues. Hypersensitivity is discussed more fully in Chap. 20.

TYPES OF IMMUNITY

Immunity may be natural or acquired. Acquired immunity may be either active or passive.

Natural immunity is immunity that is part of an animal's biologic heritage. When an animal is naturally immune to an infection that attacks other species of animals, it is said to have *species immunity*. Man has species immunity against the distemper of dogs. *Racial immunity* refers to natural immunity of a race or variety of animal to organisms pathogenic for other races or varieties of the same species. Scientists have bred strains of laboratory animals that show greatly increased or decreased susceptibility to specific infections. The existence of racial immunity in man is rather difficult to prove. It is true that in the United States the death rate for tuberculosis is much higher among Negroes than among whites, but this may be due to generally better nutrition and living conditions among white people. In countries where malaria is endemic, the Negro population seems to be more resistant than the white population. However, this relative racial resistance is attributable to immunity acquired from childhood infection rather than to any inborn racial resistance.

Acquired immunity results from an attack of communicable disease or from specific artificial immunization. Generally speaking, natural immunity seems to be due to the general defense mechanisms of the body, while acquired immunity depends upon the development of specific antibodies.

Active immunity is immunity resulting from the formation of antibodies within the person's or animal's own body. Since antibodies are formed only when the tissues are invaded by antigens, it follows that active immunity to microbial disease develops only after the introduction of microorganisms or their products into the body. Active immunity may be acquired in four ways:

1. By an actual attack of the disease.

2. By deliberate introduction of dead microorganisms into the body. Vaccination against typhoid is an example.

3. By deliberate introduction into the body of living organisms of disease. Organisms of attenuated virulence are used. Vaccination against smallpox is an example.

4. By deliberate introduction of materials prepared from cultures of the organisms. Active immunization against diphtheria by the use of diphtheria toxoid is an example.

Passive immunity is immunity that results from the introduction into the body of antibody-containing blood serum from another animal or person who is already immune. The recipient of the serum is immune because he now has antibodies made by the tissues of the other organism.

Newborn infants are passively immune to many diseases because of antibodies that they have received from the maternal circulation. This immunity lasts for several months. It is sometimes called *congenital immunity* or *natural passive immunity*.

ANTIBODIES

An *antibody* is a specific substance produced by a living organism in response to the introduction of a specific antigen and capable of uniting with that specific antigen. The following discussion deals primarily with antibodies that act against bacterial antigens. It is believed that the antibodies acting against other types of microorganisms are essentially similar.

Nature. In the presence of a specific antigen a portion of the gamma (γ) globulin, one of the proteins of the body, is modified to form specific antibody. Antibody is made only within the living body and only when specific antigen is present as a stimulus. Antibody is formed in the cells of the spleen, liver, lymph nodes, bone marrow, and possibly other tissues. The most extraordinary aspect of antibody formation is that it continues for years. We do not yet know just how the antigen molecule causes the alteration of the globulin, nor by what means this process continues after antigen is presumably no longer present.

Location. Some antibodies remain in the tissues. These are called *sessile antibodies.* They are of great importance in local infections. For example, the effective immunity to erysipelas appears to be due to sessile antibodies in skin areas that have been attacked by this streptococcal infection. In most infections antibody is found in the blood. This is *circulating antibody.* Here it is ready to react with the antigen should it again enter the body.

If blood is allowed to clot, the antibody remains in the liquid portion, the *serum.* Serum containing antibody is called *immune serum* (or *antiserum*). Proteins other than globulin can be removed from the serum by selective precipitation with salts. The antibody globulin can be further purified by digesting the unmodified globulin with pepsin (proteolytic enzyme). "Serum" used to immunize and to treat infection is really purified and concentrated antibody prepared from immune serum.

Antibodies against Microbial Disease. It has already been noted that bacteria are not single antigens but antigenic mosaics. As a result a number of different antibodies will develop in the body of an infected animal—one specific kind of antibody for each antigenic component of the invading organism. These antibodies are designated as antitoxins if they act against exotoxins, as somatic antibodies, H antibodies, etc. It has also been previously noted that certain bacterial antibodies are not species-specific—e.g., many salmonellas share the same somatic antigens. It follows that all persons with these salmonella infections develop some of the same somatic antibodies. However, since other antigens of the salmonellas are species-specific, definitely species-specific antibodies will also develop in the body of each infected individual.

ANTIGEN-ANTIBODY REACTIONS

As was indicated in the last chapter, antigen-antibody reactions enable the body to deal with colloidal foreign materials of microscopic and sub-microscopic size. The methods by which this is accomplished have been partially but not wholly explained by the extensive studies of immunologists.

Nature of the Antigen-Antibody Reaction. Our present-day explanations of antigen-antibody reactions are based on modern chemical and physical concepts. The specific determinant group of the antigen molecule combines with the specific group of the antibody molecule (altered globulin). The union is by adsorption rather than by chemical means. The combination of the antibody with the antigen alters the surface characteristics of the antigen. There is more than one determinant group in some antibodies and in some antigens. In that case each antigen unit can combine with several antibody units and each of these antibody units with several more antigen units. The result will be a large group of joined molecules.

When whole bacterial cells with their complex structure of many antigens take part in an antigen-antibody reaction, the action will be principally between the surface antigens (flagella antigens, etc.) and their homologous antibodies. Changes in surface tension and cell permeability result. Reactions between somatic antigens and antibodies become important and demonstrable only when surface antigens have been destroyed by heat or chemicals or when the microorganisms have disintegrated, freeing the internal antigenic substances.

Laboratory Demonstration. When an antigen and its specific antibody are mixed in a test tube, on a test plate, or on a microscope slide, certain reactions may take place that can be seen with the unaided eye or with the microscope. (See Figs. 22·3, 22·6.) Sometimes, however, a living animal has to be used to test the result of the reaction. These tests are *serologic tests*.

Test Materials. Two basic materials are always used in these tests. The first, the antigen, is always a culture of the microorganism or a preparation made from such a culture. The second, the antibody, is always material from the body of an animal or person, usually blood serum since that is easiest to obtain and use. If this serum contains antibodies specific for the antigen it is called a *homologous serum*. When a test is done with an antigen and its homologous serum there will be an observable result. If the antigen and antibody do not "match," the expected reaction does not take place.

Commonly Observed Antigen-Antibody Reactions. The practical uses of these reactions are discussed in Chap. 22.

1. Agglutination. A suspension of a specific organism is clumped by its homologous serum. The name *agglutinin* is given to antibody in the serum which causes this reaction.

2. Precipitation. A filtrate of a broth culture of a bacterium, or other material containing antigens from the organisms, is precipitated by antibodies in homologous serum. The name *precipitin* is used to designate the antibody involved.

3. Capsular swelling. The capsules of encapsulated bacteria become denser and more granular when the organism is mixed with homologous serum. This reaction is also known as the *quellung reaction* and the *Neufeld reaction*.

4. Increased phagocytosis. In the presence of homologous serum, white blood cells show increased phagocytic activity. The antibody involved is called *opsonin*.

5. Bacteriolysis. Suspensions of organisms are *lysed* (dissolved) by homologous serum. The antibody taking part in the process is called *lysin* (or *bacteriolysin*). In this reaction a third substance, *complement* (*alexin*), also takes part. Complement is present in all normal blood. It is nonspecific and can combine with any lysin and antigen. Unlike the antibodies it is readily destroyed by heat. In any lytic reaction the antigen and antibody combine first. Then the alexin joins the combination and causes the lysis of the antigen.

6. Neutralization tests. The ability of antibody in serum to combine with and neutralize antigen is tested on animals, since the results of in vitro tests listed above do not always give a satisfactory estimate of the protective power of a serum. Protective power may be determined by testing the ability of a serum to protect a susceptible animal against usually infective or lethal doses of an organism. The chick embryo or tissue culture is used in this way in the study of viruses.

REACTIONS OF ANTIGEN AND ANTIBODY WITHIN THE BODY

The function of antibody is to protect the body cells from the harmful antigen. Although it is certain that the in vitro reactions just listed are not the whole story of protective action, they do indicate some ways in which the antibodies carry out their task. Agglutination and precipitation form antigenic substances into aggregates that can be engulfed by phagocytic cells. Capsular swelling may indicate the breakdown of the protective action of the capsules. Lysed antigenic substance will be more easily excreted than the colloidal material from which it is made. Investigators have noted other ways in which the antibodies may act. They have found, for example, that antiserum inhibits the reproduction and physiologic activities and stimulates mutation of some bacteria. Reproduction of protozoa is also inhibited by the presence of antibodies, and antibodies stunt the growth of the larval forms of worm parasites.

THE UNITARIAN HYPOTHESIS

We have already noted that when antigen-antibody reactions take place in the laboratory, various things seem to happen. Sometimes the bacteria are clumped, sometimes they are dissolved, sometimes their capsules are altered. Various names—agglutinin, lysin, etc.—have been assigned to what would seem to be different antibodies. But we have also noted that all antigen-antibody reactions have the same physical and chemical basis. It is the present belief of immunologists that all antibodies are alike in their nature and basic reactions. Under certain conditions the antibody may cause agglutination, under other circumstances lysis or capsular swelling. This concept is called the *unitarian hypothesis*. It does not, of course, invalidate our knowledge that an antibody is specific for the antigen that caused its formation.

Two types of experimental evidence confirm this theory and also help to explain it. In the first, a serum is shown to be capable of more than one type of in vitro reaction—e.g., when diphtheria exotoxin (the antigen) is mixed with serum from an immunized horse, the exotoxin is no longer capable of killing a guinea pig. This indicates that the serum contains antibody that neutralizes the toxin. If the same antigen and antibody are mixed in a test tube with a suitable amount of an electrolyte, a flocculent precipitate will be formed. Here the same antibody is acting as a precipitin. In the same type of experiment it may readily be shown that antipneumococcic serum will agglutinate pneumococci, cause their capsules to swell, or form a precipitate with a filtrate of a pneumococcus culture.

In the second type of test the serologist uses an antibody-containing serum that has been shown capable of several types of reaction with a specific antigen—e.g., a serum from an animal immunized to a certain bacterium may be shown to agglutinate a culture of the bacterium. An aliquot portion of the same serum may be shown to precipitate a filtrate of a broth culture of the same bacterium. If, however, the agglutinated bacteria from the first test are filtered out, thus removing the adsorbed agglutinating antibody, the remaining serum is incapable of further agglutination and is also incapable of precipitation.

STUDY SUGGESTIONS

How do immunity and hypersusceptibility differ? Are they alike in any way? How do natural and acquired immunity differ? active and passive immunity? List two diseases to which you have a species immunity. List three diseases to which you have an acquired immunity. How did you acquire the immunity to each of these? Is the immunity active or passive? Do the materials (vaccines) given to confer active immunity contain antigen or antibody? Do the materials (antisera) given to confer passive immunity contain antigen or antibody?

Can you define *antibody?* State briefly but clearly the nature of antibody. Where and when are antibodies formed?

Describe five reactions that may be observed when an antigen is combined with its specific antibody in the laboratory. What is the nature of the material used as antigen in such tests? What is the nature of the material used as antibody? How would a laboratory prepare a serum that would cause agglutination of typhoid bacilli (typhoid-agglutinating serum)? Would your blood serum agglutinate typhoid bacilli? Give reasons for your answer.

What are some of the ways in which antibodies actually work to help the body resist infection or fight already existing disease?

At one point in this chapter the statement is made that "all antibodies are specific"; at another, various names are given to antibodies according to the observable reactions that they cause. Later in the chapter it is stated that "all antibodies are alike in their nature and basic reactions" (the unitarian hypothesis). Explain fully why these views are not contradictory.

SUGGESTED READING

(See also page 221.)

Antibody Nature and Formation

Coons, A. H.: Labelled Antigens and Antibodies, in "Annual Review of Microbiology." Vol. 8, Annual Reviews, Inc., Stanford, 1954.

Francis, T., Jr.: Response of the Host to the Parasite, in R. J. Dubos's "Viral and Rickettsial Infections of Man." 2d ed., Lippincott, Philadelphia, 1952.

Nungester, W. J.: Mechanisms of man's resistance to infectious diseases. *Bact. Rev.* 15:105 (1951).

Raffel, S.: "Immunity." Appleton-Century-Crofts, New York, 1953. Chaps. 4, 5, and 6.

Nature of Antigen-Antibody Reaction

Pardee, A. B., and L. Pauling: The reaction of simple antigens with purified antibody. *J. Am. Chem. Soc.* 71:143 (1949).

Raffel, S.: "Immunity." Appleton-Century-Crofts, New York, 1953. Chaps. 7 and 9.

Treffers, H. P.: Serology and Immunochemistry, in R. J. Dubos's "Bacterial and Mycotic Infections of Man." 2d ed., Lippincott, Philadelphia, 1952.

Basic Serologic Reactions

Society of American Bacteriologists: Serological Methods, Leaflet VIII, in "Manual of Methods for the Pure Culture Study of Bacteria." Biotech, Geneva, N.Y., 1947.

CHAPTER 19

Practical Applications of Immunology

Although our knowledge of the principles of immunology is very incomplete, great progress has been made in practical immunology. The first part of this chapter deals with the substances used in practical immunology, the *biologicals*. The second part considers how these materials are used for protection against infection, for treatment of infection, and for testing immunity.

TYPES OF BIOLOGICALS

All biologicals are either antigenic or antibody in nature. The antigenic ones are living or killed microorganisms or materials derived from such organisms. The antibody-containing materials are always sera from immune persons or animals, derivatives of such sera, or other antibody-containing

230

materials from the immune body. (The plural of the word serum is *sera*. Some bacteriologists prefer to use the anglicized plural, *serums*.)

The antigenic biologicals may be roughly divided into (1) living cultures, (2) killed cultures, and (3) derivatives of cultures. This third group may be divided into exotoxin preparations, crude extracts of cultures, and purified derivatives of microorganisms. The antibody-containing biologicals may be divided into (1) sera from immune animals and relatively crude preparations of such sera, (2) highly purified derivatives of sera, and (3) other antibody materials.

Living Cultures. There is no term that refers specifically to this class of biologicals. They belong to the general group of substances called *vaccines* (see below), but this term in its broadest sense includes all antigenic biologicals. In speaking and thinking about vaccines the student must be careful to differentiate those which are used in the living state from those which consist of killed organisms.

Preparation of Living-culture Biologicals. These biologicals are made by growing the chosen organism under carefully controlled conditions and then preparing a suspension of the living cells. Viruses and rickettsiae are grown in animal tissues, in tissue cultures, or in the developing chick embryo. Freedom from bacterial and other contamination is tested by cultivation. The efficiency of the preparation and the amounts to be used are ordinarily determined by tests on animals.

Uses. Living-culture vaccines are used when killed cultures are not effective and the organism does not make toxin. The dangers of inoculation with living cultures are minimized in one or more of the following ways:

1. Most commonly the culture is one of attenuated virulence. This alteration to a mutant culture of diminished virulence has been accomplished by growth in an unusual animal host or in the laboratory under unusual conditions. However the culture must have retained its *antigenicity*, i.e., its ability to cause the production of antibody.

2. The culture may be introduced into a resistant tissue rather than through the usual portal of entry.

3. A dose of specific antiserum may be given at the same time as the living organisms so that the injurious effects of the organism are limited.

Killed Cultures. Killed cultures of microorganisms are called *vaccines*. The terms *vaccine* and *vaccination* are commonly used to refer to all antigenic biologicals, though some authorities would prefer to have them used only in reference to killed cultures.

Preparation of a Vaccine. The preparation of a bacterial vaccine involves the following steps:

1. A fully virulent pure culture of the organism is obtained. It must have all the essential antigenic components.

2. The organism is grown in large cultures on a solid synthetic medium.

3. The surface growth of the organism is removed and suspended in normal salt solution.

4. The organisms are killed by heat at a temperature just above the thermal death point or by the addition of a chemical. Two newer methods are also used: exposure to ultraviolet radiation and treatment with supersonic vibration (vibration more rapid than that of audible sound waves).

5. The number of dead organisms present per unit of the preparation is estimated by comparing the turbidity (cloudiness) of the material with known turbidity standards. The material is diluted with normal saline to a concentration that is standard for that particular vaccine.

6. The sterility of the vaccine is tested by plating on suitable media.

7. A bacteriostatic concentration of a chemical such as merthiolate is added to prevent growth of any contaminating organisms.

Usually a vaccine contains only one species of microorganism. Occasionally *mixed vaccines* are used. For example, a vaccine containing paratyphoid A and paratyphoid B organisms as well as *Salmonella typhosa* may be used to confer immunity against all three intestinal infections.

The efficiency of a vaccine may be enhanced by the addition of a non-antigenic substance which concentrates or delays the absorption of the antigenic material from the site of injection. Such substances are called *adjuvants*. The two kinds of adjuvants most commonly used are salts such as aluminum phosphate that precipitate the vaccine and fatty substances such as lanolin.

Uses of Vaccines. Since killed cultures are obviously safer to use for immunization than are living cultures, the tendency is to use them wherever possible. Active immunization with killed cultures is successfully employed in many bacterial diseases and in some diseases due to viruses and rickettsiae. Vaccines are also used in the treatment of infections (see below).

Exotoxins. The term *toxin* (or more exactly *exotoxin*) is used for the biologicals that are filtrates of broth cultures of exotoxin-producing organisms. These preparations are never pure exotoxin. They contain large amounts of soluble substances from the culture medium and impurities from the bacteria.

Preparation. The following steps are taken in the preparation of a toxin:

1. A pure culture of a strain known to be a good toxin producer is grown in a suitable container of liquid medium.

2. The culture is filtered through a bacteria-proof filter to remove all microorganisms.

3. The sterility of the preparation is tested by attempted cultivation in suitable media.

4. The strength of the toxin is measured by the effect of graded amounts on susceptible animals. In this way a unit of toxin, the amount that has a definite biologic effect on a selected animal, is determined.

5. The preparation is diluted so that a standard number of units is present in a given dose.

6. A chemical preservative may be added.

Modification. Four forms of toxin are used.

1. Unmodified toxin. This is given in small repeated doses to avoid severe reactions at the site of injection.

2. Toxoid. *Toxoid* is toxin altered by the addition of a chemical, usually formalin, which lessens the local reaction of the toxin without destroying its ability to cause antitoxin formation. The term *FT* is also used, indicating fluid toxoid.

3. *Alum-precipitated toxoid.* Fluid toxoid can be precipitated by the addition of small amounts of potassium-alum or aluminum phosphate as adjuvants. Since the precipitate dissolves slowly in the tissues, it acts over a long period of time and fewer injections need be given. Alum-precipitated toxoid is also referred to as *APT*. (In the past toxin mixed with antitoxic serum to form a mixture called *toxin-antitoxin* (*TAT*) was used for active immunization against diphtheria.)

Uses. These toxins are used to actively immunize persons and animals against the diseases caused by toxin-forming bacteria. They are also used to test immunity to these disease.

Crude Extracts of Cultures. Filtrates of bacterial cultures contain antigenic substances other than exotoxin that come from intact bacteria and from disintegrated cells. Extracts of larger microorganisms including the fungi and pathogenic worms are also of antigenic nature. These preparations are used principally in skin tests for hypersensitivity.

Purified Derivatives of Organisms. The use of highly purified derivatives of microorganisms is a recent development in immunology. The potency of these preparations is so great that very small amounts are needed, reactions are clear-cut, and undesirable reactions due to impurities are minimized. These materials are used for active immunization and for testing hypersensitivity. Two outstanding examples are the *purified protein derivative* of *Mycobacterium tuberculosis* (also designated as *PPD*) and the polysaccharide preparations from pneumococci which have been used as a means of active immunization against pneumococcal pneumonia.

Antisera. The biologicals discussed up to this point are all antigenic substances prepared from microorganisms. The next three are all antibody-containing substances obtained from immune animals.

The fluid part of the blood of an immune person or animal is called *antiserum* (or *immune serum*). The person or animal from whom the serum is obtained may be immune because of a previous attack of an infection or because of artificial immunization. Immune sera are most often obtained from actively immunized horses. The horse is capable of developing antibodies against many infections and can be bled repeatedly for many months. Cows, rabbits, and other animals are also used as sources of immune sera. Sera from human beings are used for some diseases.

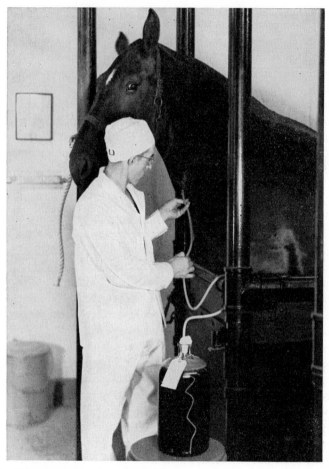

FIG. 19·1 Collection of antitoxin-containing serum from horse that has been repeatedly immunized against diphtheria. (*Division of Laboratories and Research, New York State Department of Health.*)

Preparation of a Typical Antiserum. The steps in the preparation of an antiserum from a horse are as follows:

1. A healthy horse is given repeated injections of exotoxin or killed or living cultures. At intervals small samples of serum are obtained and tested for antibody content.

2. When antibody content is found to be sufficiently high, the horse is bled from the jugular vein. (See Fig. 19·1.) As much as 4½ liters of blood can be taken at one time.

3. The blood cells and fibrin are allowed to clot, and the clear serum is removed.

4. The antibody material in the serum is concentrated and purified by precipitation and dialysis.

5. The sterility of the preparation is tested by cultivation and animal inoculation. The potency is tested by animal-protection (neutralization) tests. A small amount of antimicrobial chemical is added as a preservative.

Varieties of Antisera. A serum containing antibodies induced by killed or living cultures is called an *antibacterial serum.* It may be more specifically designated by the name of the pathogenic organism. We speak of an *antimeningococcic serum* and an *antipneumococcic serum.* When the animal has been immunized by the introduction of exotoxin, the serum is an *antitoxic serum,* or, less accurately, an *antitoxin.* Examples are diphtheria antitoxin and tetanus antitoxin. Serum from a human being recently recovered from an infection is called *convalescent serum.* A *polyvalent serum* is one that contains antibodies against more than one type or species of organism. Polyvalent antimeningococcic serum is obtained from a horse immunized against several strains of *Neisseria meningitidis.* An antiserum developed by repeated reimmunization of an animal or person and containing unusually high amounts of antibody is called *hyperimmune serum.*

Human Gamma Globulin. Concentrated antibodies of human origin are obtained from blood donated to the Red Cross and other agencies. The gamma globulin fraction is separated from the pooled bloods by precipitation with alcohol at low temperature. Only 7 ml. of a 16 per cent solution can be extracted from the usual blood donation of 500 ml. This *gamma globulin (GG)* contains antibodies against childhood diseases that the adult donors have experienced in the past. It is now recommended for the complete or partial passive immunization of young children against measles (page 487). Its use for protection of persons exposed to viral jaundice is generally accepted (page 491). It contains antibodies against poliomyelitis, but we are not yet certain of its usefulness in preventing that disease (page 509).

Other Antibody Materials. Whole blood from persons who have recovered from a specific infection is sometimes given intramuscularly for passive immunization. Fluid extracts from human placentas contain the antibodies present in the blood of the mothers. This *placental extract* or *placental globulin* has been used to prevent measles and other childhood diseases.

THE MANUFACTURE AND DISTRIBUTION OF BIOLOGICALS

Biologicals for general use are produced in two types of laboratories, state and Federal laboratories and the laboratories of certain drug companies. The government laboratories make only a limited number of biologicals of proved value in the control of communicable diseases. The commercial laboratories prepare a wider range of biologicals. (See Fig. 19·2.)

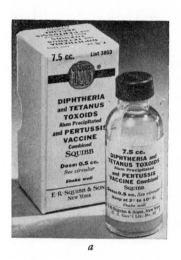 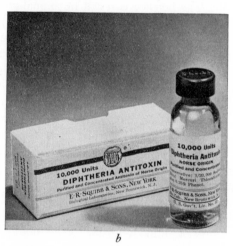

a   *b*

FIG. 19·2 Typical biologicals: (*a*) A combined vaccine preparation used to immunize small children against diphtheria, tetanus, and whooping cough. (*b*) Antitoxin from immunized horse, used to treat cases of diphtheria. (*E. R. Squibb and Sons.*)

Most biologicals essential in the control of communicable disease are distributed free by government health agencies. Licensed physicians obtain them from their state health departments. Local boards of health may act as distributing agencies. During the Second World War and since, the armed services purchased large amounts of biologicals such as yellow fever vaccine from drug houses. Doctors desiring biologicals not furnished by the state purchase them from drug houses.

Standardization of Biologicals. Manufacture of biologicals in this country is supervised by the National Institutes of Health. This agency sets very high standards for the methods of manufacture and the potency of biologicals and licenses only those laboratories that keep up to these standards. The World Health Organization (WHO) of the United Nations has set up international standards of preparation and potency for many biologicals.

Care of Biologicals. All biologicals are plainly marked with lot numbers, expiration dates, and directions for storage (Fig. 19·3). No biological should be used after the stated expiration date, as it may have lost its potency. Each biological should be stored as directed. It is particularly essential that small-pox vaccine be kept at freezing temperature. Directions for use are given on enclosed sheets. If there is anything abnormal about the appearance of a

---

SMALLPOX VACCINE

10 Capillary Tubes for Vaccinating   Lot No.
Persons against Smallpox   Exp. Date
                              If kept below 5°c (41°F)

Keep preferably below 0°C. (32°F)

Massachusetts Public Health Biologic Laboratories

Boston 30, Mass.   U. S. License No. **64**

Preservative: Glycerine 40%, Phenol 0.5%

Caution: Federal Law Prohibits Dispensing

Without Prescription

IMPORTANT
Read Enclosed Directions. Keep record of Lot Number.
Do not use this product after Expiration Date.
Return expired or unused packages

Fig. 19·3   The labels on a package of a biological. Note lot number, date, conditions of storage, and U.S. license number. (*Institute of Laboratories, Massachusetts State Department of Health.*)

biological or if the clinical results are not as expected, a report should be sent immediately to the state department of health or to the drug house. The lot number should always be noted in this report.

IMMUNIZATION AGAINST INFECTION

Scientific immunization against infection began with Pasteur's work with rabies and anthrax in the 1880s. It has progressed so that at the present time susceptible people can be immunized against many of the important communicable diseases. As has already been noted, acquired immunity may be of two kinds, active or passive.

Methods of Active Immunization. There are three characteristics of active immunity that must be kept in mind: (1) it is always accomplished by the introduction of antigenic material, (2) it develops slowly, (3) it is ordinarily quite lasting, though it is doubtful if it is ever permanent. Active immunization is accomplished by the introduction of a vaccine. The nature of the vaccine varies. Immunization against smallpox is accomplished by the use of a living culture, immunization against typhoid by a killed culture, and immunization against diphtheria by the use of toxoid.

Most vaccines are given by hypodermic injection into subcutaneous tissue. The directions as to the filling of the syringe should be carefully followed so that exactly the right amount will be given. Tincture of iodine is used to paint the skin area before injection, and rigid asepsis is carried out in the procedure. A few antigenic biologicals are given by other methods. Smallpox vaccine and BCG for protection against tuberculosis are scratched or pricked into the superficial layer of the skin.

Whenever possible a single dose of vaccine is given, but it has been found that an effective immunity against many diseases requires two or more injections, given at intervals of one to several weeks. The development of effective immunity requires from a week to several months. Then it does not remain constant but tends to diminish. If, however, another dose of antigen is given after 6 months or a year, the concentration of antibody again rises rapidly and reaches a greater concentration than after the original immunization. Such single doses given at intervals to keep immunity high are called *booster doses* or *recall doses.*

Because active immunity takes so long to develop but is so generally durable, it is the method used to protect persons against infections to which they may be exposed in the future. Babies are immunized against diphtheria, smallpox, and whooping cough, diseases to which all school children are exposed. Nurses are immunized to typhoid fever. Soldiers are immunized to tetanus (lockjaw), since they are liable to infection in battle wounds.

Vaccination against some infections may be useful after exposure. Typhoid and smallpox vaccination during the incubation periods may modify these diseases even if they do not prevent them. Effective active immunization against rabies is accomplished by the Pasteur treatment after the person has been bitten by a rabid animal. This is possible because of the very long incubation period of this viral infection.

Methods of Passive Immunization. In contrast to the materials of active immunization, those of passive immunization are all antibody-containing substances. The biologicals used will be antisera from animals, convalescent sera from humans, gamma globulin, pooled adult blood, or placental extract. The immunity will be effective just as soon as the antibodies are circulating in the body fluids. But this immunity is of very short duration, since these foreign antibodies are rapidly excreted.

Passive immunization is given as an emergency protection against a disease to which a susceptible person has been exposed. In actual practice this prophylactic treatment is now employed to a very limited extent, principally against measles, tetanus, and diphtheria. Since this type of immunity disappears within 2 weeks, immunization has to be repeated if there has been continued or renewed exposure to the disease. If diminished amounts of the antiserum are used or if the immunization is delayed until near the end of the incubation period, the resulting immunity may not be complete and a mild attack of the infection may result. This is done deliberately in measles so that the child will acquire a lasting active immunity.

The amount of serum used is considerably greater than the amount of vaccine used in active immunization. The sera are given by intramuscular injection so that absorption will be rapid. The site of injection is previously painted with iodine, and sterile precautions are observed throughout the procedure.

TESTING IMMUNITY

When minute amounts of antigenic material are introduced into the skin or the conjunctival membrane of the eye, reactions occur that indicate immunity or susceptibility or indicate allergy. The reactions indicative of allergy are discussed in the next chapter. Only those that indicate the presence or absence of immunity to exotoxins are discussed here.

Two important skin tests, the Schick test and the Dick test, disclose the presence or absence of immunity to diphtheria and scarlet fever toxins, respectively. Since the Dick test is simpler in interpretation, it is used as the example here. The toxin is injected just under the skin on the forearm. The amount used is a *minimum skin test dose,* the least amount that will cause a definite reaction in the skin of a susceptible human being. If the person has sufficient specific antitoxin, the toxin will be neutralized and no reddened area will develop on the skin. If the person has never developed streptococcus antitoxin, the toxin will injure the skin tissue and cause an area of reddening. This reaction can be observed in from 20 to 24 hours (Fig. 19·4). (The Schick test will be discussed in the chapter on the diphtheria bacilli.)

TREATMENT WITH BIOLOGICALS

Antisera have been of great value in the treatment of certain communicable diseases. In a few instances vaccines have also been used for therapy. The antibiotics and other chemotherapeutic agents have now largely replaced both in the treatment of infections.

Serum Therapy. The therapeutic administration of specific antitoxic serum is still the most important means of treating diphtheria. In the past antipneumococcic serum, antimeningococcic serum, scarlet fever antitoxic serum, and a number of others were commonly used. All these were prepared by immunizing horses to the specific organisms. Hyperimmune human serum is sometimes used to treat cases of mumps and whooping cough. It is prepared from the blood of persons who have had the disease and then been given repeated doses of the antigen to increase the antibody content of their blood. Hyperimmune gamma globulin is a concentration of the antibody from such serum.

Serum therapy to be effective must be administered as soon as the infection is diagnosed. Usually a single large dose is given intramuscularly. In

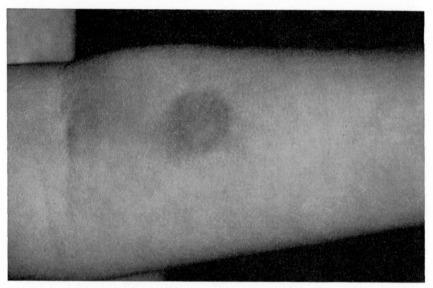

FIG. 19·4 Positive Dick test. (*"Medichrome," Clay-Adams Co., Inc., Dr. Gregory Shwartzman, Mt. Sinai Hospital.*

very severe cases part of the serum may be given intravenously. Aseptic techniques must be carried out in all steps of serum administration. Serum recipients may develop hypersensitivity reactions. These reactions and their prevention will be discussed in the next chapter.

Vaccine Therapy. Certain chronic infections such as furunculosis (boils), colitis, and pyelitis may occasionally be treated by the use of vaccines. A commercial mixed vaccine may be used containing dead organisms of the species most likely to be the cause of the patient's infection. Sometimes an *autogenous vaccine* is prepared. An autogenous vaccine is made from a pure culture of the bacterium isolated from the patient's own lesions. Vaccines for therapy are given in many small divided doses. The expectation is that the antigenic material in the vaccine will stimulate increased production of circulating antibody.

Sometimes vaccines, such as typhoid vaccine, or other protein substances are used in what is termed *nonspecific protein therapy*. The fever and other physiologic reactions that they cause may have a favorable effect on arthritis and some allergic conditions.

Study first the section on Types of Biologicals. Make a table with the following headings: *Type of biological, Antigen or antibody, Nature and preparation, Uses, Examples,* and fill out for the six types discussed.

Study the section on Manufacture. What are the sources of the biologicals used in your hospital? What responsibilities does the nurse have in the care and use of biologicals?

Study the section on Immunization against Infection. How do active and passive immunization differ in materials used and resulting protection? When is it desirable to actively immunize people? to passively immunize them? Give examples. Make a list of the diseases to which you have been immunized. Describe as far as your present knowledge will allow the materials used, the methods used, and the results. Have you had any booster doses? What is the purpose of the booster dose?

Study the rest of the chapter. Which seems more reasonable to you, treatment of disease by sera or treatment by vaccines? Explain. Describe any personal experiences with serum and vaccine therapy.

In your reading, thinking, and discussion try to avoid careless use of immunologic terms. When you use the word *toxin* be sure you know whether it refers to an exotoxin or an endotoxin, to a pure antigen or to a crude toxic filtrate. When you use the word *vaccine* be sure you know whether the material is a living or a killed culture or a culture derivative. Every time you refer to a biological, note mentally whether it is an antigen or an antibody preparation. Every time you refer to a state of immunity, note whether it is active or passive. Be careful not to fall into the common error of calling all biologicals "sera." What is the biologic meaning of the word *serum?*

Biologicals and Their Use

AMERICAN ACADEMY OF PEDIATRICS: "Report of the Committee on Immunization and Therapeutic Procedures for Acute Infectious Diseases." Evanston, 1955.

EDSALL, G.: Immunization, in "Annual Review of Microbiology." Vol. 9, Annual Reviews, Inc., Stanford, 1955.

McGUINESS, A. C.: Review of current trends in active and passive immunization. *J.A.M.A.* **148:**261 (1952).

NATIONAL RESEARCH COUNCIL: Distribution and use of gamma globulin. *Pub. Health Rep.* **68:**660 (1953).

SAUER, L. W., and W. H. TUCKER: Immune response to diphtheria, tetanus, and pertussis, aluminum phosphate adsorbed. *Am. J. Pub. Health* **44:**784 (1954).

SCOTT, T. F. M.: Trends in Immunization Concepts. Seminar (Sharp and Dohme), Summer, 1953.

WADSWORTH, A. B.: "Standard Methods." 3d ed., Williams & Wilkins, Baltimore, 1947. Pages 615–836.

CHAPTER 20

Nonmicrobial Antigens and Antibodies: Allergy

The theoretical and practical aspects of immunity in microbial diseases have been discussed in the last three chapters. This chapter deals with nonmicrobial antigen-antibody reactions, with hypersensitivity, and with allergy.

NONMICROBIAL ANTIGENS AND ANTIBODIES

Colloidal organic materials from microorganisms are not the only antigenic substances that may enter the body. Normal skin, digestive and respiratory tract epithelium, and placental tissue allow only the passage of soluble, diffusible substances, but under abnormal conditions foreign proteins of nonmicrobial origin may enter. Intravenous injection, blood transfusions, and similar procedures may introduce foreign materials into the tissues. Insect and snake bites also introduce antigenic substances.

243

The nonmicrobial antigenic substances introduced by these routes are similar to microbial antigens in structure, in specificity of action, and in ability to cause the formation of specific antibodies. They differ from microbial antigens in their origin and in their inability to increase by growth within the tissues. They also differ in that the observed reactions in the animal usually are those of hypersensitivity rather than protective immunity.

The antibodies produced are frequently of the sessile type, remaining attached to the cells and concentrated in certain tissues. However, circulating antibodies are also produced. Sera from individuals who have developed such antibodies will ordinarily precipitate suspensions of the specific antigens.

HYPERSENSITIVITY

Hypersensitivity (or *hypersensitiveness*) is the state that results when antigen-antibody reactions within the body produce undesirable results. The term *anaphylaxis* (literally, without protection) is used to indicate serious reaction in sensitized laboratory animals. It is also used to refer to serious reactions in man. The term *allergy* (literally, altered reaction) is generally applied to the hypersensitive state in man, particularly when the reactions are relatively mild.

Animal Experiments. Much of our knowledge of the nature of hypersensitivity has come from animal experimentation. Three basic types of these experiments are described here.

Anaphylactic Shock. If 0.1 ml. of horse serum is injected into a healthy guinea pig, nothing appears to happen. If 2 weeks later 1 ml. of the same serum is injected, the animal dies within a few minutes. Its death is due to asphyxia because of the contraction of smooth muscle in the walls of the bronchi. A rabbit similarly treated dies of heart failure due to contraction of the musculature of the pulmonary artery. In the sensitized dog, death is due to the contraction of the hepatic vein. These are all examples of *anaphylactic shock*. The essential conditions of the experiment are a small *sensitizing dose* of an antigenic substance followed at a suitable interval by a larger *shock dose* of the same material. The larger the shock dose and the more rapid its introduction, the more quickly fatal the result will be. Certain drugs, notably epinephrine, will prevent the development of anaphylactic shock if given at the same time as the shock dose.

Passive Sensitization. If a normal animal is given a dose of serum from a sensitized animal, the second animal will become hypersensitive and subject to anaphylactic shock if it is given a shock dose of the specific antigenic substance. This indicates that the sensitized animal developed transferable antibodies.

Desensitization. If an animal that has received a sensitizing dose of an antigen is given a single small dose of the same material after 10 days or so, he will not die though he may show signs of modified shock. This second dose will desensitize him so that thereafter he will not react to a full shock dose. Desensitization can be more effectively and safely carried out by a series of very small injections of the antigen. Such desensitization may not be permanent but may be renewed by the repetition of the desensitizing process.

Characteristics of the Allergic State. From such studies on animals and from observation of the allergic reactions in man, the characteristics of the allergic state become clear. They may be summarized as follows:

1. Hypersensitivity is induced by the introduction of specific antigenic substance into the tissues (the sensitizing dose).

2. Hypersensitivity is present in the individual after a short period and may be demonstrated by a sizable dose of the antigen (shock dose). The larger the dose and the more rapid its introduction, the more violent will be the reaction.

3. The reactions are generally due to smooth-muscle contraction. The reacting tissues vary in different animals and in different human beings. The reactions often occur at the site of introduction of the shock dose, but they may also appear in distant tissues.

4. Hypersensitivity may be passively transferred.

5. Desensitization may be accomplished by a single dose or repeated doses of the antigen. It is not always lasting.

6. Heredity seems to be a factor in the development of hypersensitivity. If parents show clinical manifestations of allergy, their children are likely to develop allergic conditions.

Theoretical Explanations. Students often assume that hypersensitivity is the opposite of immunity. That is not true. Hypersensitivity and immunity are considered to be different manifestations of the same basic reactions within the body. Both result from the combination of antibody with antigen. A prominent American bacteriologist, Bronfenbrenner, has suggested that we may think of the apparently contradictory results of such antigen-antibody combinations as comparable to the results of combustion. We are all glad of the warmth and light of a fire, yet we all dread its possible destructive effects. We recognize that both good and bad effects arise from the same process.

Immunologists cannot completely explain the mechanisms of these undesirable allergic reactions, but the histamine theory seems to provide the most satisfactory explanation at this time. *Histamine* is a chemical substance known to be formed in tissues during allergic reactions. When it is experimentally used on normal tissues it causes effects indistinguishable from those of allergy. Moreover, certain drugs known to destroy histamine have been found very effective in the treatment of both experimental and natural allergies.

PRACTICAL ASPECTS OF MICROBIAL ALLERGY IN MAN

Certain aspects of hypersensitivity, such as serum sickness and allergic reactions to vaccines, are obviously closely related to our subject of microbiology.

Allergic Reactions in Communicable Disease. Some of the clinical manifestations of communicable diseases are known to be allergic reactions. Only a few examples can be given here. In fungous infections of the skin, lesions called *ids* may develop in situations far distant from the site of actual infection. These ids do not yield the causative fungus. They are considered to be localized allergic reactions. The painful joints of rheumatic fever are allergic reactions to products of hemolytic streptococci. Many of the manifestations of the worm infection filariasis, including the hugely swollen limbs that are called elephantiasis, are due to tissue hypersensitivity to the antigens released from worms that have been destroyed in the patient's body.

Reactions to the Injection of Sera. It has already been noted that antisera are not pure antibody materials but contain other substances from the animal's blood. Persons receiving sera may be allergic to these substances and so may develop undesirable and sometimes dangerous reactions. Their sensitivity to serum proteins may be due to previous serum injection, including immunization with toxin-antitoxin mixtures. They may be persons who already show hypersensitivity to animal proteins by attacks of asthma or rhinitis when exposed to horses or other animals.

Four reactions that may occur in response to the injection of serum are (1) *acute anaphylactic shock*, a severe but rare reaction resembling anaphylaxis in animals; (2) chills and fever; (3) serum sickness, a delayed reaction characterized by urticaria and fever; (4) the *Arthus reaction*, a sterile ulceration at the site of injection.

Prevention. Serum is not given to persons who have a history of hypersensitivity to horses or to those who have had serum injections within a period of 1 week to 3 months. Two tests for sensitivity should be done before serum is administered to any patient. The *ophthalmic test* is performed by placing a drop of 10 per cent solution of normal horse serum in one eye, leaving the other eye as a control. Reddening, itching, and watering of the test eye will develop within 30 minutes in an allergic patient. The *skin test* is done by injecting 0.1 ml. of a 1 per cent dilution of the serum into the skin of the forearm. If the patient is allergic to horse serum, the area will become red and swollen within a few minutes. Patients who have positive reactions to the tests should not be treated with antiserum from horses.

When serum therapy seems imperative in a possibly sensitive person, the doctor will give it in multiple graduated doses at intervals of 30 minutes starting with a dose of only 0.005 ml. or less. It is also sometimes possible to obtain sheep or rabbit antiserum to use on a patient who is hypersensitive to horse serum.

An intravenous syringe containing fresh epinephrine is always kept at hand when serum is administered, for this drug counteracts most of the reactions of hypersensitivity. Careful nursing minimizes the less serious effects such as chills and the urticaria of serum sickness.

Reactions to Active Immunization. Many of the unpleasant effects of vaccination against such diseases as tetanus, typhoid, and rabies are allergic reactions. They include fever, headache, and local inflammation. The allergic substance may be some constituent of the medium in which the culture was grown. The increasing use of synthetic, protein-free media for the preparation of vaccines has resulted in a marked decrease in troublesome reactions. Purification of virus vaccines grown in embryonated eggs is an object of present research, since traces of egg proteins may cause bad reactions in persons allergic to such material.

Skin Reactions to Microbial Antigens. During the course of an infection the patient's tissues develop specific allergy against the cell substances of the causative organism. This sensitivity can be readily detected by the local skin reaction that appears when minute amounts of extracts of the organisms are placed in or on the skin. In general, such a positive reaction indicates that the person is harboring an infection with that type of organism. The infection may be active or latent. A negative test means that the person is free from the infection.

The most commonly used test of this sort is the tuberculin test. An extract of a tuberculosis culture is placed in or on the skin. If the person has an active or latent infection with tuberculosis, an area of edema will appear within 2 days. This test and others are more fully discussed in later chapters.

NONMICROBIAL ALLERGY

Nonmicrobial allergies such as asthma, urticaria due to foods, and blood incompatibilities are not actually part of microbiology but are considered briefly here because they are also examples of the basic pattern of hypersensitivity.

The long and varied life of human beings results in their having a much greater diversity of allergic reactions than is found in any animal. Although most people escape all serious forms of allergic reaction, mild types occur sooner or later in the majority of human beings. Most common of these are reactions to such substances as foods, pollens, dusts of animal origin, and drugs.

Types of Allergic Reaction. Allergic manifestations in man are so varied as to defy complete classification. Some of the commoner types are described here.

Respiratory Allergies. Asthma and hay fever are the commonest forms of respiratory allergy. Asthma is characterized by recurrent obstruction to breathing due to contraction of lung bronchioles, hay fever by abnormal nasal discharges and congestion of the nasal mucous membranes. Most respiratory allergies are due to the inhalation of dusts of animal origin or of wind-borne pollens. Some are due to foods or drugs.

Gastrointestinal Allergies. Disturbances of the alimentary canal, all the way from canker sores in the mouth to mucous colitis, may be due to hypersensitization. They are usually caused by the ingestion of foods to which the person is said to have an *idiosyncrasy.*

Migraine. The severe type of headache known as migraine is often related to the ingestion of foods to which a person is hypersensitive.

Cutaneous Allergies. Allergic reactions localized in the skin may be called *allergic dermatoses* (sing. *dermatosis*). Urticaria (popularly called *hives*) and eczema are usually due to food allergies but may also be caused by sera or inhaled antigens.

Diagnosis. The three methods of diagnosis of allergic conditions are essentially methods for the identification of the allergic substance. The first method is the examination of the person's history to determine when, where, and how his attacks occur. The second method consists of deliberate clinical trials in which the patient is exposed to or protected from the suspected substances under controlled conditions. The third method, skin testing, gives the most specific results. The method is essentially the same as for the skin testing of sera and microbial extracts. Extracts of the suspected materials are introduced by the *scratch test,* in which a bit of the extract is applied by a superficial scratch on the skin; by intradermal injection; or by the *patch test* (*contact test*), in which the material is applied to the skin on a small square of cloth or paper. (The method is similar to the tuberculin test shown in Figs. 30·7, 30·8.) Reactions can be read within 15 minutes.

Treatment. There are three possible methods of treating allergic states. The first is by the elimination of the irritating material from the patient's life. The second method, desensitization, consists in giving the patient a series of increasing doses of the material to which he is hypersensitive, beginning with a very small amount. The third method is treatment by drugs. Epinephrine, ephedrine, and ergotamine counteract the undesirable tissue reactions. Benedryl, Pyribenzamine, and several others destroy histamine.

Some Practical Aspects of Allergy in Relation to Nursing. Nurses are prone to develop contact dermatitis of the hands as the result of frequent exposure to such chemicals as formalin, phenol, and linseed oil. Skin hypersensitivity to antibiotics, particularly to streptomycin, has become a very common occupational dermatitis among nurses. Care should be taken to avoid spilling antibiotics. Containers should be carefully handled to avoid skin contamination.

The nurse should be constantly on the alert for signs of allergy in her patients. When such conditions as migraine, eczema, or urticaria develop, the nurse's careful observation of the patient's habits and environment may provide valuable clues to the cause of the condition.

Human Blood Groups. The antigens and antibodies related to human red blood cells, their interactions, and their clinical importance can only be touched on here. For further information the references listed at the end of this chapter should be consulted.

The red blood cells of each human being contain an assortment of complex nitrogenous substances that act as antigens when these cells are introduced into the body of another person who lacks them. When red cells of a blood donor contain an antigen for which the recipient's plasma has matching antibody the donor's cells are agglutinated and the recipient becomes ill and sometimes dies because of the blocking of small blood vessels.

The AB Blood Groups. Every human being has one, both, or neither of the red cell substances A and B. His blood can therefore be classed as A, B, AB, or O (lacking both antigens). His blood serum will contain isoagglutinins for the antigen(s) that he does not have. This is true even though he has never been injected with these antigens. His blood serum will be b (if his erythrocytes are A), a (if his erythrocytes are B), o (if his erythrocytes are AB), and ab (if his erythrocytes have neither antigen).

The Rh and Other Blood Factors. Many other antigenic substances may be present or absent in a person's erythrocytes. The most completely studied of these other factors is the Rh substance (now known to include three components, called D, C, and E). Others are designated by additional letters —M, N, S, etc. Antibodies against these factors do not appear in a person's blood until he has received some of the specific antigen. If, for example, Rh-positive blood is given to an Rh-negative recipient, the latter will develop specific antibody. If he should then receive a second transfusion of Rh-positive blood he may die from the resulting hemagglutination. An Rh-negative woman may develop Rh antibody if she is pregnant with an Rh-positive fetus.

These antibodies may cause the death of an Rh-positive fetus in a subsequent pregnancy (*erythroblastosis*). They may cause her death if she later receives a transfusion with Rh-positive blood.

Safety of Transfusions. The blood of the donor and the blood of the recipient must be *compatible;* they must not contain matching antigen and antibody. This is tested by mixing the red cells of each with the serum of the other. No agglutination of the red cells occurs in either test if the bloods are compatible.

STUDY SUGGESTIONS

What is meant by hypersensitivity? anaphylaxis? allergy?

How does a person or animal become hypersensitive? How can it be shown that an animal is hypersensitive? that a person is hypersensitive? What is meant by desensitization? How is it accomplished?

What are the four important allergic reactions to the administration of serum? What materials in serum cause these reactions? How can the doctor determine if serum treatment would be dangerous to the patient? What precautions must be used in the actual administration of serum and in the aftercare of persons receiving serum?

Skin tests for three different purposes are described in this chapter. Name them and describe the nature of the material used in each. What is the significance of a positive result in each? What three techniques may be used in skin tests? In the last chapter another sort of skin test was described. Describe such a test and its significance.

Describe any personally experienced allergic reactions to microbial or non-microbial materials or any such experience among your family and friends.

SUGGESTED READING

General References

CHASE, M. W.: The Allergic State, in R. J. Dubos's "Bacterial and Mycotic Infections of Man." 2d ed., Lippincott, Philadelphia, 1952.

COOKE, R. A., *et al.:* "Allergy in Theory and Practice." Saunders, Philadelphia, 1947.

CRIEP, L. H.: What is allergy? *Am. J. Nursing* **45**:721 (1945).

HAWN, C. V. Z., and C. A. JANEWAY: Histological and serological sequences in experimental hypersensitivity. *J. Exper. Med.* **85**:571 (1947).

Practical Aspects

FEINBERG, S. M.: Histamine and antihistaminic agents. *J.A.M.A.* **132**:702 (1946).

KOJIS, F. G.: Serum sickness and anaphylaxis. Analysis of 6,211 patients treated with horse serum for various infections. *Am. J. Dis. Child.* **64**:93, 313 (1942).

PENNINGTON, E. S.: Allergic conditions in infants and children. *Am. J. Nursing* **46**:85 (1946).

Special Problems

CARR, E. A.: Allergy to drugs. *New England J. Med.* **245**:892, 935 (1951).

LEVINE, P.: Human Blood Groups, in R. J. Dubos's "Bacterial and Mycotic Infections of Man." 2d ed., Lippincott, Philadelphia, 1952.

PART FIVE

Introduction to the Study of Pathogens

CHAPTER 21

The History of Microbiology

This chapter will summarize some of the facts of the history of microbial science. Because of the limitations of space, many related developments in communicable disease control, sanitation, aseptic surgery, modern nursing technique, and other similar subjects cannot be included. The student will learn about them in other courses and should correlate that information with the history in this chapter. Many of these related aspects of history are admirably treated in the references listed in the bibliography at the end of this chapter.

    The history of microbiology can be conveniently divided into three periods: the period of speculation preceding the development of the compound micro-scope (from prehistoric times to 1850), the "golden age" of microbiology when the microscopic organisms other than the rickettsiae and the viruses were discovered (1850 to 1910), and the modern period (1910 to the present).

THE PERIOD OF SPECULATION

All through the ages philosophers, medical men, and other scientists tried to answer certain questions: how do living things originate? (the problem of biogenesis); what happens when food and other materials undergo spoilage and other changes? (the problem of fermentation); how and why do certain illnesses spread? (the problem of contagion); and what happens in wounds that causes them to become inflamed and discharge pus? (the problem of suppuration). During these centuries many scientists postulated the existence of invisible living things, but they had no way of proving or disproving their conjectures. Many of their ideas seem ridiculous to us. Others are quoted reverently because they turned out to be correct.

The Law of Biogenesis and the Disproof of Spontaneous Generation. For centuries people believed that living things could arise from nonliving matter —flies were supposed to come from putrefying meat, mice from moldy hay, lice from dirty clothing. The Italian physician and scientist Francesco Redi (1626–1697) proved by carefully controlled experiments that fly larvae come from the ova deposited by previous generations of flies. He insisted that all animal forms have parents. His observations were confirmed by many others, and the belief in the spontaneous generation of visible organisms was discredited. But most scientists still believed that microscopic forms could be generated spontaneously, and some of their experiments seemed to support this belief. In the next century another Italian, Lazzaro Spallanzani (1729–1799), sealed infusions of organic matter in flasks, heated them thoroughly, and noted that they did not spoil or show the development of any microorganisms. Similar unheated and opened flasks developed microorganisms of specific forms. Spallanzani declared that it was absurd to suppose that these definite types developed from amorphous matter. Other workers who attempted similar experiments had varied results that were hard to explain, for at that time no one suspected the existence of spores that could survive boiling. The controversy was not fully settled until Cohn in 1877 showed the heat resistance of the spores of *Bacillus subtilis*.

Fermentation and Food Spoilage. For many centuries food spoilage and fermentations were believed to be the result of chemical changes. When yeasts and other microorganisms were seen in fermenting materials they were explained as the result rather than the cause of the fermentations. In the 1830s, with the aid of the newly perfected compound microscopes, three different biologists studied yeast cells in fermenting solutions and expressed their belief that the plant cells were responsible for the alcohol formation, but the stubbornness of Liebig and other chemists of the period kept their ideas from general acceptance. Not until 1860 was the question settled by Pasteur's work on fermentations.

Contagion and Infection. Many ancient peoples knew that diseases spread from person to person. Laws concerned with the proper disposal of excreta and with the segregation of lepers are found in the Old Testament. In the Middle Ages three terrible epidemic diseases overran Europe—leprosy, bubonic plague, and syphilis. Many doctors and philosophers tried to explain the nature of these diseases and their spread. Among the most famous of these was Fracastorius (1478–1553), who wrote a monumental work on syphilis and a book on contagion. He believed in the specificity of diseases and their causation by some sort of self-propagating entity. A century and a quarter later Athanasius Kircher (1602–1680) wrote on the methods of spread of infection and included most of those that we recognize today. He was familiar with the use of the microscope and had observed microorganisms in various organic materials. He combined his microscopic and epidemiologic observations and decided that contagious disease might be due to *effluvium animatum* (living vapor). Unfortunately his ideas were not accepted.

By the middle of the nineteenth century the medical men and government officials in England were thoroughly convinced that diseases originated from filth—excreta and other decaying organic material. They came to believe that sanitation was the function of government. Though they did not know that microorganisms were involved, their sanitary measures did help to control disease.

During this period some problems of contagion were clarified by the work of three pioneer epidemiologists. In 1847 the Danish physician Peter Panum (1820–1885) investigated an epidemic of measles in the isolated Faroe Islands and was able to trace the course of the epidemic through the population. The other two epidemiologists were Englishmen, John Snow (1813–1858) and William Budd (1811–1880). Dr. Snow solved the mystery of an explosive epidemic of Asiatic cholera that occurred in 1854. He showed that all those infected had used drinking water from a public well in London's Golden Square and that the well was heavily polluted from a nearby privy. Dr. Budd traced the spread of rural typhoid fever and showed that it, too, came from polluted water.

As with the two other problems that have been discussed, the final solution of the problem of contagion had to wait until the specific causes of disease were recognized and studied by Pasteur, Koch, and other early bacteriologists.

Suppuration. In the years before the practice of disinfection and sterilization, pus formation in wounds was so common that it came to be regarded as the normal exudate of disintegrating tissues. It was obvious that the absorption of this putrid matter into the blood stream resulted in septicemia and pyemia. In the early part of the nineteenth century many physicians carried out experiments in which they showed that such conditions might be transmitted from one animal to another by injection but not by ingestion.

The fact that minute amounts of putrid material, filtered and heated, still had the ability to cause infection led these scientists to the belief that the factor responsible was a protein acting as a ferment and that suppuration

a   *b*

FIG. 21·1   Reconstruction of a Leeuwenhoek microscope. Actual size. (*a*) Front view; (*b*) side view. The lens is in the round hole seen in the front view. The object to be examined is placed on the point shown in the side view and brought into focus by manipulating the two screws. (*Courtesy of Dr. A. C. Lonert, General Biological Supply House, Inc.*)

was a form of fermentation. Not until Pasteur showed that fermentation was caused by microorganisms did it occur to doctors that suppuration was due to the growth of living things. (See discussion on page 265.)

Three Scientific Investigators in the Period of Speculation. Experimental science as we know it today was not practiced in ancient times or in the Middle Ages. Nevertheless the scientific temperament of some men led them to carry out investigations that involved the scientific approach to their problems.

Antonj van Leeuwenhoek (1632–1723) was a prosperous Dutch business-man with a hobby of grinding lenses and constructing microscopes. A reconstruction of one of his many microscopes is shown in Fig. 21·1. It is believed that he used a dark-field method of illumination and that his greatest magnification was around 270. From 1674 until the year of his death van Leeuwenhoek corresponded with the Royal Society of London, describing the many things that he saw with the aid of microscopes. In one of his early letters he described protozoa seen in drops of lake water. Two years later he noted that "little animals—incredibly small" swam around in a pepper infusion. Among them were spiral as well as rodlike forms. In 1683 he examined tartar from his own and other peoples' teeth and drew pictures of cocci, bacilli, filamentous forms, and spirochetes that he saw. He also described at least one intestinal protozoan of man, *Giardia,* and several parasitic worms.

Fig. 21·2   Antonj van Leeuwenhoek (1632–1723).

Francesco Redi (1626–1697) was a highly educated and cultured Italian, a poet and court physician as well as an experimental scientist. He is best known for his experiments disproving spontaneous generation of visible organisms (see page 256). He has been called the "grandfather of parasitology," for he dissected hundreds of animals and discovered many of the parasitic worms. He was the first to show that ascaris worms come from ova and one of the first to describe the life cycles of insects. Two of his collaborators, Bonamo and Cestoni, inspired by his teaching, discovered the scabies mite (the cause of "the itch" of man and mange of animals). They also demonstrated that the disease is spread by transfer of these arthropods. This was in 1687 and is believed to be the first proof of the communicability of a specific cause of disease.

Agostino Bassi (1773–1856) was an Italian government employee who gave up his job to pursue his interest in science. He is best known for his discovery of the fungus that causes the muscadine disease of silkworms. In 1835 he demonstrated its presence in the sick larvae. He showed that it could be transferred by a pin (the first inoculating needle!) to healthy larvae and that it could also be spread by contact and by contaminated mulberry leaves (the staple food of the silkworm). He became convinced that human infections are similarly due to microorganisms and similarly spread. During the later years of his life he wrote treatises explaining his belief in the communicability of smallpox, cholera, typhus, and similar diseases. These writings included well-reasoned recommendations concerning isolation and disinfection.

THE GOLDEN AGE OF BACTERIOLOGY

Microbiologic science could develop only as the tools and techniques enabling scientists to work with normally invisible things became available. The development of the microscope, methods of staining, and other techniques, combined with use of the methods of scientific investigation and the scientific mental approach to all problems, set the stage for the extraordinary development of microbiology during the latter half of the nineteenth century.

Development of Tools and Techniques. Compound microscopes had been made by lens makers prior to 1800, but they were variable in quality and performance and unsuitable for work at high magnifications. In the first quarter of the nineteenth century many improvements were made, and by 1835 several commercial firms were manufacturing satisfactory instruments. Early bacteriologists cultivated microorganisms in animals, in infusions and broths, and sometimes on slices of potato or other vegetables. They were seldom able to obtain pure cultures. In 1881 Koch demonstrated cultures streaked on solidified gelatin poured on flat plates of glass. Two years later he described the poured plate method. The use of agar-agar as a substitute for gelatin was the result of the suggestion of Frau Hesse, the wife of one of Koch's assistants. She had received the agar-agar from friends living in the Dutch West Indies, where this seaweed product was used for thickening preserves. In 1887 the inconvenient and easily contaminated flat glass plates were replaced by the covered dishes designed by another assistant, Richard Petri. In 1877 Koch first used dried, fixed, and stained films of bacteria in his microscopic work. Previously almost all microscopic examination had been of liquid, living material. Koch used the new aniline dyes, and his methods were adaptations of those of the pathologist Carl Weigert and the biochemist

Paul Ehrlich. The Gram stain was developed by the Dane, Christian Gram, in 1884. The crude filters of the early microbiologists were replaced by the more accurate filters of unglazed porcelain first used by Chamberland in Pasteur's laboratory in 1887 and the Berkefeld filter of diatomaceous earth first used in Germany in 1891. Methods of anaerobic cultivation and of sterilization of media and glassware were also perfected during these years.

The Identification of Specific Pathogenic Microorganisms. It is often difficult to decide on the discoverer and date of discovery of any specific pathogen. For example, many parasitic worms were seen by early investigators, but their life cycles and their animal and insect hosts were not known until much later. In 1882 the American Sternberg and the Frenchman Pasteur both found pneumococci in rabbits inoculated with human saliva; but not until several years later was the organism definitely shown to cause pneumonia.

With his newly developed agar media and his meticulous methods of aseptic technique, Koch was the first bacteriologist who could rely on the purity of his cultures and prove without question that a specific bacterium was the cause of a specific disease. In the classic report on his discovery of the organism of tuberculosis he described the steps that must be followed in the identification of a pathogen. These rules, known as Koch's postulates, still hold good and are followed by all bacteriologists. (See page 212.)

In Table 21·1, the discoverers and the discovery dates of many important pathogens are listed. The student will note that many of the parasitic worms and the fungi of superficial infections were the first to be recognized; that the majority of bacteria and protozoa of human infections were first identified in the years from 1875 to 1900; but that the discovery of the rickettsiae and viruses belongs to a still later period.

Other Developments. Although the last half of the nineteenth century is thought of as the period in which bacteria were discovered, many other important theoretic and practical aspects of microbiology were investigated at this time. Some of them are discussed below.

Immunology. Immunization against smallpox by inoculation of healthy children with material from the lesions of mild cases and, after 1800, with the cowpox vaccine of Edward Jenner was a purely empirical procedure. Immunology as a science began with the work of Pasteur. In 1880 he found that the chicken cholera organism lost its ability to cause the disease in inoculated birds if it was allowed to grow for many months in broth. Furthermore, these inoculated birds were refractory to subsequent inoculations with fully virulent cultures. Employing the same general principle of attenuated virulence, he developed a vaccine against the cattle and sheep disease, anthrax, in 1881, and against rabies in man in 1885. The other important early develop-

Table 21·1. Chronological Table

Date	*Tools and techniques*	*Worms*	*Protozoa*
Before 1850		Pinworm (Lineus) Whipworm (Roederer) Trichina (Tiedemann)	
		Intestinal fluke (Busk)	Vaginal trichomonad (Donné)
		European hookworm (Dubini)	
1850	Perfected compound microscope	Blood fluke (Bilharz)	
1860 1870		Filaria (Demarquay) Liver fluke (McConnell)	Balantidium (Malmsten) Giardia (Lambl)
	Koch's culture techniques Improved bacterial stains		Endamoeba (Lösch)
1880		Lung fluke (Ringer)	Malarial plasmodium (Laveran)
1890			
1900		American hookworm (Stiles)	Leishmania (Leishman) Trypanosome (Forde)
1910			
1920 1930	Chick embryo culture technique		
1940	Perfected electron microscope		

of Discoveries in Microbiology

Fungi	Bacteria	Rickettsiae and viruses	Date
			Before 1850
Ringworm fungi (Langerbeck) (Schoënlein)			
(Grisby)			
			1850
			1860
	Borrelia recurrentis (Obermeier)		1870
	Bacillus anthracis (Koch) *Mycobacterium leprae* (Hansen) *Mycobacterium tuberculosis* (Koch)		1880
Coccidioides (Posadas)	*Corynebacterium diphtheriae* (Klebs) *Vibrio cholerae* (Koch) *Brucella melitensis* (Bruce) *Neisseria meningitidis* (Weichselbaum) *Actinomyces bovis* (Israel) *Neisseria gonorrhoeae* (Neisser)		1890
Blastomyces (Gilchrist)	*Hemophilus influenzae* (Pfeiffer) *Pasteurella pestis* (Yersin)		
	Clostridium perfringens (Welch) *Shigella dysenteriae* (Shiga) *Shigella paradysenteriae* (Flexner)		1900
Histoplasma (Darling)	*Treponema pallidum* (Schaudinn)		
	Hemophilus pertussis (Bordet) *Pasteurella tularensis* (McCoy)	*Rickettsia rickettsiae* (Ricketts) *Rickettsia prowazekii* (Ricketts)	1910
		Bacteriophage (Twort)	1920
		Rickettsia typhi (Wolbach) Virus of common cold (Dochez)	1930
		Virus of western equine encephalitis (Meyer) Virus of St. Louis encephalitis (Mackenfuss)	
		Virus of influenza A (Andrewes) Virus of influenza B (Francis) *Rickettsia akari* (Huebner)	1940

ments in immunology were the discovery of the filtrable exotoxins of the tetanus and diphtheria organisms by von Behring and Kitasato in Germany in 1890 and their resulting development of antitoxic sera for passive immunization. Paul Ehrlich (1854–1915), already mentioned for his development of staining methods, was the first to elucidate a clear theory of immunology, in 1897, based on biochemical concepts. Ehrlich was also the first to develop the chemotherapy of a specific infection on a scientific basis when he synthesized and used the compound arsphenamine for the treatment of syphilis.

FIG. 21·3 Paul Ehrlich (1854–1915).

Disease Transmission. Even before the discovery of the enteric organisms the epidemiologists had shown the probability of the spread of enteric disease by milk, water, and food. The isolation of the bacteria from these materials completed the proof of their part in the spread of such infection. The actuality of person-to-person spread and spread by fomites was readily proved experimentally. Because of the importance of these methods of transfer, the spread of pathogens by air was unfortunately minimized for many years.

In 1884 Loeffler noted the presence of diphtheria organisms in the throats of healthy persons, and 10 years later William H. Park in New York studied the carrier state in convalescents and its relation to the spread of the disease. The year before in Germany, Koch had published evidence that there were healthy carriers of typhoid fever.

The parasitologist Manson saw filaria worms in the mosquito in 1879, but the first proof of insect transmission of disease was the work of Theobald Smith of the U.S. Bureau of Animal Industry. In 1889 the investigation of Texas cattle fever under his direction proved that the cattle tick was responsible for the spread of that disease. During the next 10 years Bruce in Africa showed that African sleeping sickness is transferred by the tsetse fly, Ross in India and Grassi in Italy proved that the anopheline mosquitoes are the vectors of malaria, and Reed and his associates of the American Yellow Fever Commission implicated the aëdes mosquito in the transmission of yellow fever.

Control of Infection in Surgical and Other Wounds. Both French and German bacteriologists used their microscopes to study the infected wounds of soldiers in the Franco-Prussian War of 1870. In 1878 Robert Koch published his work on the etiology of wound infections and described the bacteria found in six forms of septicemic infections. In 1877 Pasteur and Joubert cultivated an anaerobic bacterium of wound infection which they called *Vibrion septique* (*Clostridium septicum*). These and other discoveries confirmed the necessity for antiseptic technique in surgery, which had been introduced in Scotland and England by Joseph Lister.

The Great Men of the Golden Age. Two men, Louis Pasteur of France and Robert Koch of Germany, were the undisputed leaders of bacteriology in the last half of the nineteenth century. Not only were they the leading experimental investigators of the newly developing science, but they were also the leaders of important research laboratories and teachers of the next generation of microbiologists.

Louis Pasteur (1822–1895) was educated as a chemist. In 1856 during investigations into the production of lactic acid and alcohol he utilized the compound

FIG. 21·4   Louis Pasteur (1822–1895).

microscope for the study of sediments and became convinced that the "globules" (yeast cells) present were responsible for the chemical changes. For the next 15 years he made a thorough study of fermentations, including the relation of bacteria to vinegar formation and of fungi to the spoilage of wines. This work was notable not only because it solved the age-old problem of fermentation but also because it was the first comprehensive scientific study covering a field of microbiology. As he studied fermentation he became convinced that there could be no spontaneous generation of microorganisms, and he performed crucial experiments showing that heated liquids would not undergo fermentation if all contamination, including that from the air, was kept out.

In 1865, at the request of the French Government, he undertook an investigation of the disease of silkworms that had devastated the silk production industry of the country. His experiments proved that the diseases—for there turned out to be two—were of microbial origin, and he found that by microscopic examination healthy silkworm moths could be selected that would give rise to larvae free from these infections.

FIG. 21·5   Robert Koch (1843–1910).

From 1875 until his death Pasteur worked on medical aspects of bacteriology. At first he was concerned with the identification of pathogens and studied the organisms of puerperal fever, staphylococcal infections, and anthrax. Then he turned his attention to the problems of immunity. In 1888 the Institut Pasteur in Paris was erected with funds contributed by his admirers. He was its first director, and under his leadership it became and has continued to be one of the most important centers of bacteriologic research in the world.

Robert Koch (1843–1910) began his career as a country doctor, and his first work on anthrax was done alone and with very little equipment. He was able to grow the organisms in minute cultures, utilizing the aqueous fluid of the ox eye as the culture medium. Studying these cultures under the microscope he was able to see the processes of spore formation and germination. His subcultures were capable of causing the disease in inoculated animals. In 1876 the famous German botanist Ferdinand Cohn invited Koch to demonstrate his results at his University of Breslau laboratory and generously published Koch's first paper.

From 1880 until the end of his life Koch worked and taught in Berlin. The technical developments that were worked out in his laboratory have already been noted. He and his pupils discovered the organisms of tuberculosis, typhoid, diphtheria, cholera, and gonorrhea. Pupils from all over the world came to learn his methods and returned to their own countries to pass them on to others.

Microbiology in America. Syphilis and bubonic plague did not occur in epidemic form in colonial America, but epidemics of cholera, smallpox, typhoid, and diphtheria raged among the Indians and the settlers. Malaria was endemic in most parts of both North and South America, and a new and mysterious disease, yellow fever, occurred in the tropical regions and spread to all except the most northern cities of the Atlantic Coast. Benjamin Rush (1745–1813), the Revolutionary patriot-physician of Philadelphia, and Noah Webster (1758–1843), the author of the dictionaries and spelling books, were among the investigators who tried to determine how the disease was spread. It was obvious to them that it did not spread directly from one person to another nor was it a filth disease, but the relationship of the mosquito to the disease did not occur to them.

The government's responsibility for health was accepted from the very beginning by the American colonies. In 1797 Massachusetts passed a law providing for the formation of local boards of health. A landmark in the development of public health is the *Report of the Sanitary Commission of Massachusetts,* more commonly called the *Shattuck Report* after its author, Lemuel Shattuck. The report was submitted in 1850. It contained a set of recommendations which can still serve as a plan for public health organization. The most extraordinary thing about the report is that Shattuck was convinced that disease is preventable and that the government must assume the task of prevention.

In 1851 in Buffalo, New York, a lens maker, Charles Spencer, started a microscope manufacturing business and made instruments that were the equal of any in Europe. But in all other respects America lagged behind Europe in the development of microbiology during the "golden age." The reasons for this delay were many. The great unexplored fields of the zoology and botany of the continent tended to make American biologists into naturalists. American doctors and other scientists preferred to spend their time on practical matters rather than on subjects the usefulness of which had not been proved. Most important of all was the lack of universities with well-equipped laboratories and trained staffs such as were common at that time in Europe and Great Britain.

In the 1880s Americans studying in Europe were impressed by the work of the microbiologists there. Some of them worked in the laboratories of Pasteur, Koch, and others. Americans who did not go to Europe began to read with interest the publications telling of the newly discovered pathogenic forms of life. American biologists and doctors began to look for microorganisms through their own microscopes and to show them to their students. In a few places botanists and pathologists began to give a few lectures on bacteriology as part of their regular courses. Dr. Harold Ernst, the professor of pathology at Harvard, gave six lectures on bacteriology in 1885. A general biologist, E. A. Birge, taught the first complete course in bacteriology at the University of Wisconsin in 1886.

Fig. 21·6 William H. Welch (1850–1934).

Fig. 21·7 Theobald Smith (1859–1934).

Fig. 21·8 William H. Park (1863–1939).

Fig. 21·9 Howard T. Ricketts (1871–1910).

Laboratories modeled after those in Europe were founded. In 1887 the state of Massachusetts established the Lawrence Experiment Station, where Professor William T. Sedgwick, of the Massachusetts Institute of Technology, and others carried out many important studies on the microbiology of water and sewage. In the same year the U.S. Public Health Service established a bacteriologic laboratory in its Staten Island hospital. The laboratory had only one room, but it was equipped with apparatus modeled after that in Koch's laboratory and its director was a young scientist, Dr. Joseph J. Kinyoun, who became the first head of the Hygienic Laboratory (now the National Institutes of Health). When cholera threatened New York City in 1892, the city's Health Commissioner, Dr. Hermann Biggs, persuaded Dr. William H. Park, a young physician who had recently returned from study in Europe, to take charge. This was the first municipal laboratory, but many others were started before 1900. In 1894 Massachusetts established a laboratory for the preparation of antitoxin and for bacteriologic diagnosis. Dr. Theobald Smith, whose proof of the tick transmission of Texas fever has been noted, was its first director.

Early American contributions to microbiology by William H. Park, Theobald Smith, and Walter Reed have already been mentioned. Others included the discovery of the principal clostridium of gas gangrene, *Clostridium perfringens,* by William H. Welch of Johns Hopkins in 1894; Simon Flexner's discovery of one of the organisms of dysentery, *Shigella paradysenteriae,* in 1900; and the cultivation of the bacterium of tularemia, *Pasteurella tularensis,* by George McCoy of the U.S. Public Health Service in 1910.

MODERN MICROBIOLOGY

The History of Virology. Just as the actual discovery of the bacteria had to wait until the development of a satisfactory light microscope, so the actual study of the viruses had to wait for the development of the electron microscope. The early bacteriologists suspected the existence of filtrable microorganisms, e.g., Pasteur in his work on rabies indicated that he believed the disease to be caused by a filtrable living substance. The credit for proof of the existence of viruses is generally given to Iwanowski, a Russian microbiologist. In 1892 he described the persistence of the infectious agent of tobacco mosaic disease (so called because of the mottling of the infected tobacco leaves) in bacteria-free filtrates of juice from infected plants. The nature of this filtrable substance was further studied by Beijerinck, a Dutchman, in 1898. In the same year Loeffler and Frosch in Germany showed that foot-and-mouth disease of cattle is caused by a filtrable substance. Three years later the members of the American Yellow Fever Commission showed that yellow fever is a virus disease, and in the next few years the virus nature

FIG. 21·10 1887: First U.S. Public Health Service laboratory—one room in the Stapleton Marine Hospital, Staten Island. (*Public Health Service, Department of Health, Education and Welfare.*)

FIG. 21·11 1954: The National Institute of Health at Bethesda, Maryland. This is only one of the present research centers of the Public Health Service. (*Public Health Service, Department of Health, Education and Welfare.*)

of a number of other infections was established. None of these workers actually saw or cultivated the viruses; their experiments consisted of the demonstration that bacteria-free filtrates of infected tissues would cause the typical infection in susceptible animals. The cell inclusions and elementary bodies of smallpox and cowpox were seen by Buist in 1887 and those of rabies by Negri in 1903, but their true nature was not determined until 20 years later. The American Howard Ricketts identified the rickettsia of spotted fever in 1906 and the rickettsia of typhus in 1910.

During the 1930s many important advances were made in the techniques of virology, most of them by American scientists. In 1930 Woodruff and Goodpasture showed that a single elementary body of fowl pox is infective. In 1931 Elford of England developed a more perfect type of filter of collodion, which could be prepared with pores of graded sizes. The chick embryo method of cultivation was first described by Goodpasture in 1931. In 1935 Wendell M. Stanley was able to adapt the methods of purification previously used in the preparation of enzymes to the purification of the tobacco mosaic virus. During these years physicists and engineers were perfecting the electron microscope and commercial models were developed. As a result of these and other technical advances, most of the important viruses have now been seen and their morphologic characteristics studied. Most of them have been grown in the chick embryo and tissue culture and purified. No longer do we think of viruses as "living fluids." We know that they are micro-organisms with definite sizes, shapes, and other characteristics. Some important dates in the history of virology are given in Table 21·1.

Other Important Modern Developments. Next to research in virology, the most important aspect of modern microbiology is the development of specific chemotherapy, with recent concentration on the discovery and development of antibiotics (Chap. 11).

During the earlier years of the modern period great advances were made in immunology and sanitary bacteriology. In the 1920s and 1930s the variation of bacteria and the life cycles of fungi and animal forms claimed the attention of many workers. A characteristic of the work of more recent years is the emphasis on the study of microorganisms with the tools and methods of chemical, physiologic, physical, genetic, and even mathematic research. The details of bacterial cytology have been clarified by study with the electron microscope and other techniques. The chemical nature of cell substances, including microbial enzymes, is now investigated qualitatively and quantitatively as part of the modern research on the nature of living matter. There is no longer a distinct cleavage between the medical research and other aspects of microbiology. Biologists, biochemists, biophysicists, and geneticists are finding that essential processes of living things can be studied more profitably in microorganisms than in larger organisms; and medical men

Fig. 21·12   Alice Evans.

Fig. 21·13   Wendell M. Stanley.

Fig. 21·14   Selman A. Waksman.

Fig. 21·15   René Dubos.

are realizing that the true nature of disease processes and their control cannot be understood until the biologic nature of microorganisms is made clear.

Microbiology Today and Tomorrow. Most modern research is carried on by teams of workers, and these teams include experts in related sciences as well as in microbiology. Almost all early microbiologists worked in laboratories of universities, and a great deal of work is still carried on in teaching institutions. In addition scientists now work in laboratories provided by the government (such as the National Institutes of Health, the regional laboratories of the U.S. Department of Agriculture, and the laboratories of many states); in laboratories of special research foundations (such as the Rockefeller Institute); and in the laboratories of industrial plants (such as those of the large drug houses).

We are in the middle of the history of microbiology. Since this book went to press important discoveries will have been made and some things in this book will be outdated. The intelligent student will make a definite and continuing effort to learn of the advances in medical microbiology as they occur. To keep up-to-date in any medical or other field of microbiology one must belong to professional associations, attend their meetings, and read their publications. Other literature that will be useful is described in Appendix A.

STUDY SUGGESTIONS

State four puzzling natural phenomena that had to wait until the development of microbiologic science for their solution. List some of the scientists and their discoveries that led to the solutions. In the light of their discoveries how would you now explain these phenomena?

Many scientifically disproved ideas still persist as popular superstitions. Has your scientific education led you to discard any such ideas? What were they and what scientific concepts have replaced them in your mind?

In the past, people have credited the occurrence of disease to evil spirits, to the positions of the heavenly bodies, to night air, and to filth. Was there any truth in these beliefs?

In what ways were van Leeuwenhoek and Redi different from most learned men of their times? Compare and contrast Louis Pasteur and Robert Koch and their discoveries.

What techniques were principally responsible for the rapid development of microbiology in the 1800s; of virology in the last 20 years?

Who were the following and what do we remember them for?

Bruce	Spallanzani	Budd
Ross	Fracastorius	Liebig
Bassi	Loeffler	Ehrlich
Petri	von Behring	Iwanowski

What part did the following play in microbiology and sanitation in America?

Shattuck	Park	Spencer
Noah Webster	Zinsser	Rush
Bergey	Theobald Smith	Ricketts

How many important present-day American microbiologists can you name? In what lines of research has each been active?

Consult one or more of the journals listed on page 574. Check through the numbers for the last 3 years. In what lines of study are microbiologists principally engaged at the present time?

SUGGESTED READING

General References

BULLOCH, W.: "The History of Bacteriology." Oxford, New York, 1938.

FORD, W. W.: "Clio Medica: Bacteriology." Hoeber, New York, 1939.

WINSLOW, C.-E. A.: "Man and Epidemics." Princeton University Press, Princeton, 1952.

Biographic

DOBELL, C.: "Antony van Leeuwenhoek and His Little Animals." Harcourt, Brace, New York, 1932.

DUBOS, R. J.: "Louis Pasteur—Free Lance of Science." Little, Brown, Boston, 1950.

FLEMING, D.: "William Welch and the Rise of Modern Medicine." Little, Brown, Boston, 1954.

GOODLEE, R. J.: "Lord Lister." Macmillan, New York, 1918.

SMILLIE, W. G., *et al.:* Lemuel Shattuck—still a prophet. *Am. J. Pub. Health* **39:**135 (1949).

VALLERY-RIDOT, R.: "The Life of Pasteur." Garden City, Garden City, N.Y., 1926.

Popular Presentations

DE KRUIF, P.: "Microbe Hunters." Harcourt, Brace, New York, 1926.

HAGGARD, H. W.: "Devils, Drugs, and Doctors." Garden City, Garden City, N.Y., 1929.

CHAPTER 22

The Study of Specific Pathogens;
Laboratory Diagnosis

*Essential Information Concerning Each
Pathogenic Microorganism*
The Diagnostic Laboratory
  The laboratory and its functions
  The collection of specimens for the laboratory
  Choice of techniques in laboratory diagnosis
  Interpretation of results
*The Methods of Microbial Laboratory
Diagnosis*

Detection and identification of pathogenic organisms—by direct microscopic examination; by cultivation in artificial media; by inoculation of laboratory animals, tissue cultures, or fertile eggs; by reaction with specific antibodies—agglutination test, precipitation test, capsular-swelling test
Detection and identification of specific antibodies—complement-fixation test

The first part of this text has been devoted to a discussion of the general characteristics of the medically important groups of microorganisms. Their structure and actions, their classification, their control, their methods of spread, and the reactions they cause in infected bodies have been described. The remaining chapters of the text will consist of detailed discussions of the specific microorganisms causing important diseases in man. This chapter is an introduction to the study of these specific pathogens.

ESSENTIAL INFORMATION CONCERNING EACH PATHOGENIC MICROORGANISM

The essential information needed by the nurse can be summarized under the following headings:

1. History—name of discoverer, approximate date of discovery of the specific organism, and other significant names and dates.

275

2. Name, nature, and importance of disease caused.

3. Morphology and staining—size, shape, groupings, flagellation, sporulation, Gram's stain, etc.

4. Physiology—characteristic enzyme activities (effects on proteins, carbohydrates, etc.); effects of physical and chemical agents (methods of killing, methods of inhibiting growth, thermal death point, etc.); cultivation (media and methods used).

5. Sources and modes of infection.

6. Treatment—limited to treatment by specific chemotherapy and by sera and vaccines.

7. Diagnostic methods—limited to those methods involving microbiology and serology.

8. Prevention and control—by sanitation; by specific immunization (including methods of active and passive immunization and methods of determining immunity).

9. Nursing considerations—protection of patients against the infection; prevention of spread of infection from the patient with the infection; protection of the nurse against the infection.

The outline given above will have to be modified to some extent when organisms other than bacteria are discussed. In general, the more important the organism is, the fuller will be the discussion of these points. It is suggested that the student should make out a card or sheet using the topics given above as headings. By making out such a sheet for each important pathogen, the student fixes the basic facts in her own mind and prepares useful reference material.

THE DIAGNOSTIC LABORATORY

By *diagnosis* is meant the determination of the exact nature of the disease from which the individual is suffering. The patient's history, the results of physical examination, the patient's symptoms as reported by the nurses' charts, and the results of various types of laboratory tests are all considered by the doctor in making the diagnosis. In this text we can consider only those aids to diagnosis that are based on the methods of microbiology and serology. Many laboratory methods such as blood counts and chemical analysis of blood and urine do not come within the scope of this book.

The Laboratory and Its Functions. Every well-equipped hospital has a bacteriologic laboratory whose chief function is the detection and identification of specific pathogens. Since each communicable disease is caused by a specific pathogen, this identification is of primary importance in its diagnosis. The bacteriologic laboratory may also carry out diagnostic tests in which specific antibodies from the patient's blood are detected and identified. Such tests are called *serologic* tests. Sometimes they are carried out in a separate laboratory known as the serologic laboratory. All states, most larger cities, and some health districts in more rural areas maintain diagnostic laboratories. These laboratories are mainly concerned with the diagnosis of diseases dangerous to the public health. Their services are free to registered physicians. There are also private laboratories that perform diagnostic tests for a fee, and some physicians and private clinics have their own laboratories.

Laboratories of the Public Health Service, special reference laboratories, and WHO laboratories in other parts of the world all cooperate with our local laboratories.

All such laboratories should be under the direction of trained bacteriologists and serologists and staffed by trained medical technologists. Only competently staffed laboratories are approved by organizations such as the American Medical Association and licensed in the more progressive states. A course in microbiology or training as a nurse is not adequate preparation for such laboratory work. The graduate nurse working as a doctor's assistant may sometimes do routine tests under the doctor's supervision, but specifically trained technologists are required in regular diagnostic laboratories.

In addition to aiding in the diagnosis of cases of infectious disease, diagnostic laboratories carry out other related tests. Among these are detection of carriers; detection of pathogenic organisms in milk, foods, etc.; tests indicating the progress of the disease in the patient; tests to detect possible persistence of the carrier state in convalescents ready for discharge; and postmortem tests for microorganisms.

The Collection of Specimens for the Laboratory. The materials most frequently collected for laboratory examination are pus, sputum, feces, urine, blood, peritoneal fluid, pleural fluid, spinal fluid, and swabbed material from such locations as the throat, nose, nasopharynx, and vagina.

The nurse is frequently responsible for the collection of specimens to be sent to the laboratory and for the labeling and delivery of those collected by the physician. The laboratory cannot do reliable work unless it receives good specimens. If the specimen is unsatisfactory, valuable time may be lost and the patient's life endangered. The exact methods to be used in collecting specimens are not given here, since the technique varies in different hospitals, but there are certain general rules which should be followed.

1. Obtain the correct specimen. If a specimen of sputum is required, be sure to collect material expectorated from the lungs—not saliva or nasal secretions that run down into the throat from the nose. Throat swab specimens should be swabs wiped carefully over inflamed areas of the throat, not swabs of the back of the tongue. Follow carefully all directions as to method of collection. Never add disinfectant to a specimen unless specifically directed to do so.

2. Obtain an uncontaminated specimen. A sterile container must be used for any specimen from which microorganisms are to be cultivated. The specimen must be protected from all contamination.

3. Handle with care to avoid infection. Any materials such as swabs which are contaminated in collecting the specimen must be disposed of with care. Care must be taken to avoid any contamination of the outside of the container.

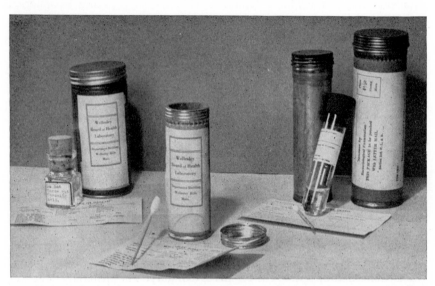

FIG. 22·1   Collection kits for diagnostic specimens. Left—bottle for sputum for diagnosis of tuberculosis. Center—slide and swab for diagnosis of malaria and gonorrhea. Right—bottle of buffered glycerine solution for fecal specimen for diagnosis of typhoid and similar infections. The double mailing containers are required by law. (*Institute of Laboratories, Massachusetts State Department of Health.*)

4. Label specimen correctly and fully. Mistakes in labeling may lead to serious errors of diagnosis and treatment. Incomplete labeling may cause the laboratory to perform unnecessary and time-consuming tests.

5. See that the specimen reaches the laboratory promptly. The fresher the specimen when it reaches the laboratory, the more satisfactory it is. In some diseases specimens only a few hours old may be practically useless. Unless there are other definite orders, culture specimens in culture media should be left in the incubator and all other specimens in the refrigerator when there is no technician present in the laboratory to take charge of them. Public health laboratories provide special mailing outfits for the collection of specimens (Figs. 22·1 and 22·2).

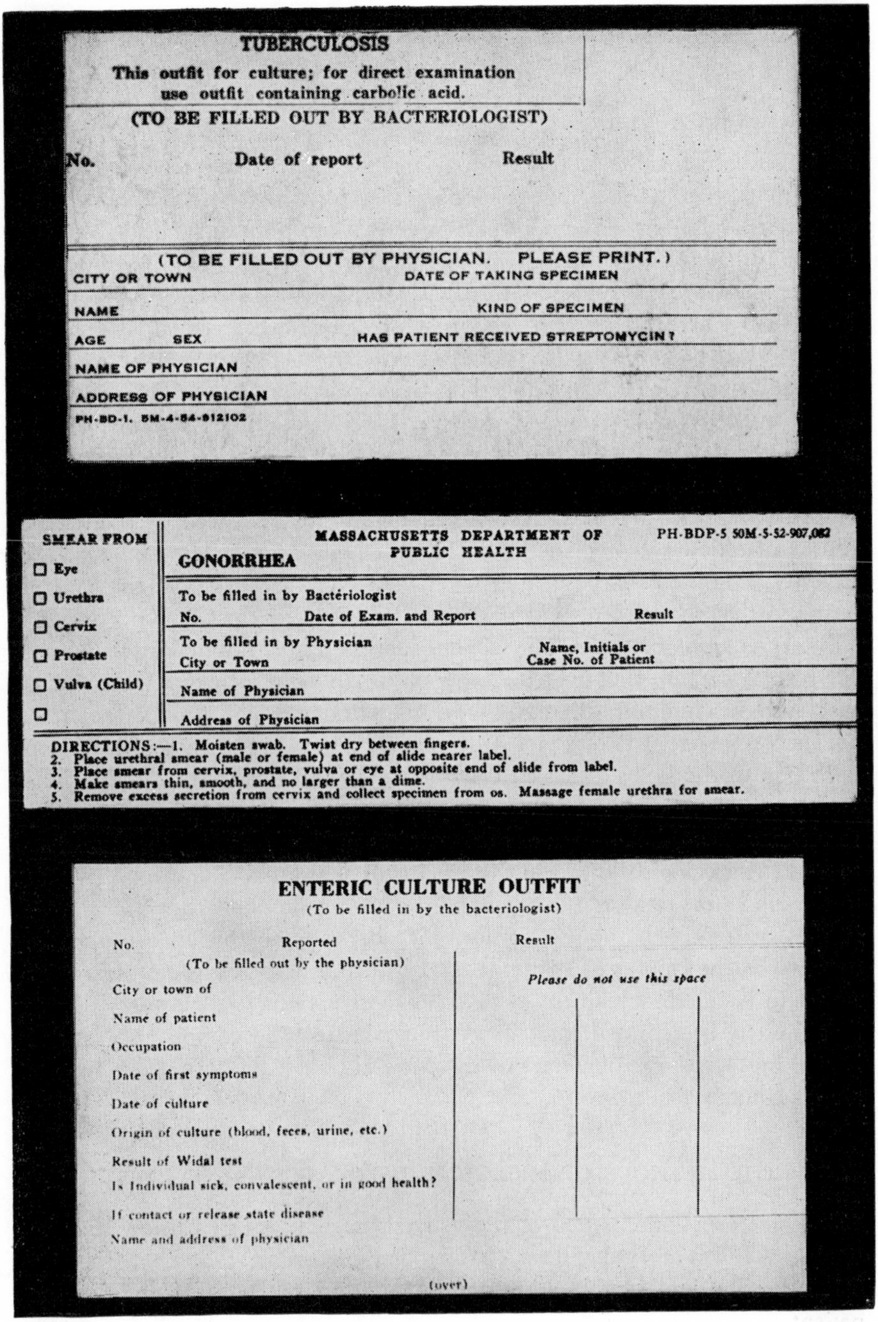

TUBERCULOSIS

This outfit for culture; for direct examination
use outfit containing carbolic acid.

(TO BE FILLED OUT BY BACTERIOLOGIST)

No.   Date of report   Result

(TO BE FILLED OUT BY PHYSICIAN.   PLEASE PRINT.)
CITY OR TOWN   DATE OF TAKING SPECIMEN

NAME   KIND OF SPECIMEN

AGE   SEX   HAS PATIENT RECEIVED STREPTOMYCIN?

NAME OF PHYSICIAN

ADDRESS OF PHYSICIAN

PH-BD-1. 5M-4-54-912102

| SMEAR FROM | MASSACHUSETTS DEPARTMENT OF PUBLIC HEALTH | PH-BDP-5 50M-5-52-907,082 |

GONORRHEA

☐ Eye
☐ Urethra
☐ Cervix
☐ Prostate
☐ Vulva (Child)
☐

To be filled in by Bactériologist
No.   Date of Exam. and Report   Result

To be filled in by Physician   Name, Initials or
City or Town   Case No. of Patient

Name of Physician

Address of Physician

DIRECTIONS:—1. Moisten swab. Twist dry between fingers.
2. Place urethral smear (male or female) at end of slide nearer label.
3. Place smear from cervix, prostate, vulva or eye at opposite end of slide from label.
4. Make smears thin, smooth, and no larger than a dime.
5. Remove excess secretion from cervix and collect specimen from os. Massage female urethra for smear.

ENTERIC CULTURE OUTFIT

(To be filled in by the bacteriologist)

No.   Reported   Result
(To be filled out by the physician)
City or town of   *Please do not use this space*

Name of patient

Occupation

Date of first symptoms

Date of culture

Origin of culture (blood, feces, urine, etc.)

Result of Widal test

Is Individual sick, convalescent, or in good health?

If contact or release state disease

Name and address of physician

(over)

FIG. 22·2 Cards to accompany specimens sent to the diagnostic laboratory. (*Institute of Laboratories, Massachusetts State Department of Health.*)

Choice of Techniques in Laboratory Diagnosis. The laboratory worker chooses the test or series of tests that will give a reliable result in the shortest time. In diseases where prompt diagnosis is of great importance in determining treatment, the laboratory may make a preliminary report based on a presumptive test, following it as soon as possible with a further report based on confirmatory tests. The clinical type of the infection and the stage of the infection may influence the choice of test.

There are no officially sponsored "standard tests" for the diagnosis of infections. There are certain tests that are generally accepted as reliable, but the exact techniques vary greatly in different laboratories. Two manuals published by the American Public Health Association, *Diagnostic Procedures and Reagents* and *Diagnostic Procedures for Virus and Rickettsial Diseases,* include the methods used in most American laboratories. Progressive laboratories continually strive to develop better methods and try out new ones reported by other workers. New methods are always checked against the results of older, accepted methods. The methods described in this text are necessarily limited to those in general use. They are described in general terms so that the student will understand their techniques and purposes.

Interpretation of Results. The laboratory worker does not make a diagnosis. He reports the results of his tests to the physician, who correlates these results with his other findings. Generally speaking, positive results of diagnostic tests are more significant than negative results. The proved presence of a known pathogen in the body of a sick person is definite evidence of disease; in a well person it is evidence of a carrier state. On the other hand, a negative result may mean the absence of the organism or the failure of the laboratory to find the specific pathogen in the specimens submitted. The specimen sent to the laboratory may not contain the organisms although they are present in the patient's body, or the number may be so small that they cannot be detected by the laboratory methods used. When a negative laboratory report seems to be in disagreement with other observations, the doctor will ask that the test be repeated. Not infrequently he may be completely justified in making a positive diagnosis of infection although the laboratory reports are continuously negative.

THE METHODS OF MICROBIAL LABORATORY DIAGNOSIS

Any one or a combination of the general procedures listed below may be used in the laboratory diagnosis of microbial disease.

1. Detection and identification of the causative microorganism from the patient

    a. By direct microscopic examination

b. By cultivation in artificial media

c. By cultivation in laboratory animals, tissue cultures, or fertile eggs

d. By reaction with known specific antisera (serologic tests in which the antigen is the unknown)

2. Detection and identification of specific antibody in the patient's serum by reaction with known specific microorganisms or their products (serologic tests in which the antibody is the unknown).

The general techniques of these methods and their uses are discussed in the rest of this chapter. More detailed descriptions of the tests used in the important communicable diseases will be found in the chapters on the pathogenic microorganisms. Certain tests that are used in the diagnosis of virus diseases are described in detail in the chapters on the viruses. See page 467 for a discussion of virus neutralization tests and page 468 for a diagram of hemagglutination-inhibition tests.

Detection and Identification of Pathogenic Organisms. *Direct microscopic examination.* Some microorganisms can be readily recognized by their appearance under the microscope. Special staining methods may help. Sometimes the material is concentrated by some method such as centrifuging before examination. Laboratory diagnosis of worm and protozoan infections such as hookworm and malaria is almost always done by direct examination. Many fungous diseases can be tentatively diagnosed by observing hyphae and spores in sputum or skin scrapings. Direct microscopic examination is useful in some bacterial diseases. It may enable the laboratory to make a tentative diagnosis which is then confirmed by other methods. Among the bacteria that can be tentatively identified by their distinctive morphologic and staining characteristics are *Mycobacterium tuberculosis, Neisseria gonorrhoeae,* and several of the spirochetes.

Cultivation in artificial media. Cultivation may be done to detect organisms that are present in numbers too small to be found by microscopic methods or to study the cultural characteristics of an organism in order to identify it.

The techniques followed may include any or all of the following: (1) cultivation in selective enrichment media, (2) isolation in pure culture, (3) systematic study by inoculation of sugar media, gelatin, etc.

Inoculation of laboratory animals, tissue cultures, or fertile eggs. As has already been noted, laboratory workers do not use animals when other methods are successful and reliable, but animal inoculation is required in the diagnosis of some infections. Animal inoculation may be necessary to (1) cultivate organisms that cannot be grown in artificial media, (2) obtain pure cultures of organisms that cannot be isolated in artificial media, and (3) test the virulence of suspected pathogens. The techniques of cultivation

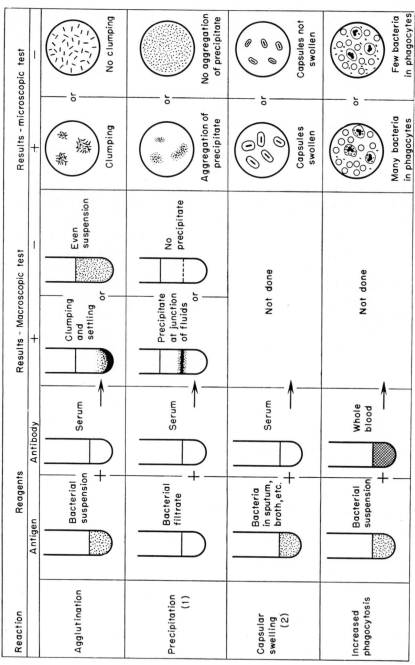

FIG. 22·3 Serologic (antigen-antibody) reactions. (1) Microscopic test represents flocculation test for syphilis. In this case a special tissue extract is used as the antigen. (2) Methylene blue solution is added to make capsules more visible.

of viruses and rickettsiae in the fertilized egg and in tissue cultures will be considered in the chapters on these microorganisms.

Reaction with known specific antisera. The exact species or type of bacterium obtained from the patient may be determined by its reactions with specific antisera. These sera are obtained from animals that have been repeatedly injected with pure cultures of specific types of the bacteria. The sera are kept on hand by the laboratory for these tests.

The three most commonly used tests are described here. The nature of such antigen-antibody reactions was discussed in Chap. 18, page 226. The reactions of these tests are illustrated diagrammatically in Fig. 22·3.

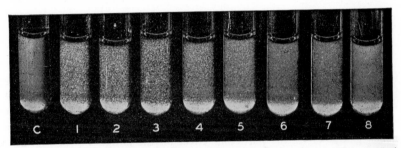

FIG. 22·4 Macroscopic agglutination test. Control tube *C* contains bacterial suspension only. Numbered tubes contain bacterial suspension plus the following dilutions of serum: 1:100, 1:200, 1:500, 1:1,000, 1:2,000, 1:5,000, 1:10,000, and 1:20,000. Agglutination is evident in dilutions 1:100 to 1:10,000 (tubes 1 through 7) but not in 1:20,000 (tube 8). The titer of the serum is therefore 1:10,000. (*From Burrows, "Textbook of Microbiology," Saunders.*)

1. Agglutination test. The clumping of bacteria by homologous serum may be observed with the naked eye when the organisms and sera are combined in test tubes. Clumping in drops placed on a glass slide can be observed with the naked eye or with the low dry power of the microscope. A third method, the microscopic agglutination test, is done by mixing loopfuls of the bacteria and the serum in a hanging drop, which is then examined with the high dry lens. (See Figs. 22·3 and 22·4.)

2. Precipitation test. The antigen used in precipitation tests is a filtrate of a broth culture of the organisms rather than the bacteria themselves. The test may be carried out in a test tube or on a slide. In the test tube the serum is layered over the bacterial filtrate, and if the test is positive a cloudy layer of precipitate develops between the two. The same reaction may be observed with the microscope when drops of the two liquids are placed side by side on a slide. If the resulting precipitate is flaky (flocculent), the test is called a *flocculation test*. (See Figs. 22·3 and 22·5.)

3. Capsular-swelling test. Specific antiserum will cause the swelling of bacterial capsules. The test is usually done by making a liquid mount of

the organisms, specific antiserum, and a suitable stain and examining it with the oil immersion lens. (See Figs. 22·3 and 27·1.)

Detection and Identification of Specific Antibodies. The specific antibodies developed in the patient's body as the result of his infection may be identified by their reactions with known organisms. In these tests the patient's serum provides the unknown antibodies to be studied and the antigens are preparations of stock cultures of microorganisms. The laboratory keeps a supply of known stock cultures for these tests. The agglutination and precipitation techniques described above may be used for this purpose, employing the patient's serum and known cultures of organisms or filtrates of known cultures. These tests are often done quantitatively to determine the *antibody*

FIG. 22·5 Tube precipitation test, positive result. ×4. Cloudy ring developed between antigen and serum indicates presence of specific antibody in the serum. ("*Medichrome,*" *Clay-Adams Co., Inc., Dr. Gregory Shwartzman, Mt. Sinai Hospital.*)

titer, the highest dilution of the serum that will cause the particular effect on the antigen. (See Fig. 22·4.)

Specific antibody of virus disease is often identified by neutralization tests in which the patient's serum is shown to have the ability to protect animals, tissue cultures, or fertile eggs from infective doses of a known virus. Hemagglutination-inhibition tests are also used to identify and measure viral antibodies.

The presence of specific antibody may result from a past infection or artificial immunization. Therefore it is usually necessary to do quantitative tests on two samples of the patient's serum and show that the antibody titer has increased during the course of a suspected infection. One sample is taken when the patient is first seen by the doctor, and a second sample is taken a week or more later. A definite increase in antibody is substantial evidence that the patient is suffering from acute infection. The two serum specimens are referred to as *paired sera.* Only a single serum specimen need be examined in some diseases, notably syphilis, in which antibody lasts only during active infection and is never the result of active immunization.

Complement-fixation test. This is the most often used of all antibody identification tests. Complement (alexin) has been described in Chap. 18 as the substance that completes the lysis of the microorganisms when they are combined with lysin antibody. The term *fixation* refers to the combination or fastening of the complement so that it is no longer free to enter into any other reaction. A complement-fixation test is more complicated than

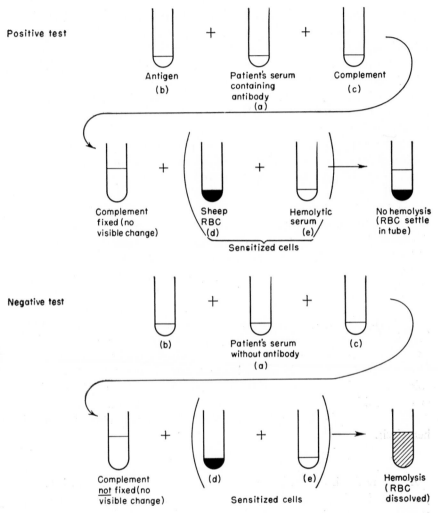

Fig. 22·6 Complement-fixation test. For small letters in parentheses see descriptions in text on this page and the next.

other antigen-antibody reactions and involves the use of five reagents. As you read this description, check each step on the diagram (Fig. 22·6).

(*a*) The patient's serum which may or may not contain the specific antibody. This is the unknown in the test.

(*b*) The antigen, a preparation of the organisms (or a substitute).

(*c*) Complement contained in carefully titrated pooled serum from normal guinea pigs.

(*d*) Red blood cells from a sheep or other mammal. These have been freed from all serum and are suspended in normal salt solution. This material is called *hemolytic antigen.*

(*e*) Serum from a rabbit or other animal that has been repeatedly injected with hemolytic antigen until its serum has a high titer of specific hemolysin.

The patient's serum (*a*) and the animal serum (*e*) are heated at 56°C. for 30 minutes to destroy the complement in them. The suspension of red blood cells (*d*) and the hemolytic antiserum (*e*) are combined. This mixture is called *sensitized cells.* The erythrocytes will not hemolyze in this mixture because there is no complement present. Carefully measured amounts of the patient's serum (*a*), the antigen (*b*), and the complement (*c*) are placed in small test tubes and allowed to stand for a short time. If the patient's serum is positive (contains the specific antibody) the complement will be fixed when the three substances combine; if the serum is negative (without the antibody) the complement will remain uncombined. There will be no *visible* change in either case. The sensitized cell mixture (*d* plus *e*) is added and the tubes are held at 37°C. for a short time. If the complement has already been fixed by combination with the patient's antibody, there will be none present to complete the hemolytic reaction and the red blood cells will not be hemolyzed. If the complement is unfixed because there was no antibody in the patient's serum, it can now combine with the hemolytic antibody and will cause the hemolysis of the red cells. The hemolysis is easily observed. Unhemolyzed cells settle in a layer at the bottom of the tube, leaving the fluid colorless and clear. If the red cells are hemolyzed there will be no sediment and the fluid will be clear red. Partial fixation of the complement due to small amounts of antibody in the patient's serum will result in a partial hemolysis.

STUDY SUGGESTIONS

As you read this chapter make a list of the topics you need to review. Have you clearly in mind the material covered so far in your course on the topics listed on page 275 under the heading Essential Information Concerning Each Pathogenic Microorganism? If not, review the chapters dealing with the topics on which you are weak. Methods of laboratory diagnosis include many techniques already studied. If they are not clear in your mind, review the material in Chaps. 5, 6, and 18 and your laboratory notes.

SUGGESTED READING

General References on Communicable Disease

AMERICAN ACADEMY OF PEDIATRICS: "Report of the Committee on Immunization and Therapeutic Procedures for the Acute Infectious Diseases." Evanston, 1955.
AMERICAN PUBLIC HEALTH ASSOCIATION: "The Control of Communicable Disease." 8th ed., New York, 1955.
ANDERSON, G. W., and M. G. ARNSTEIN: "Communicable Disease Control." 3d ed., Macmillan, New York, 1953.
BOWERS, A. G., and E. B. PILANT: "Communicable Diseases." 7th ed., Saunders, Philadelphia, 1953.
GREENBERG, M., and A. V. MATZ: "Modern Concepts of Communicable Disease." Putnam, New York, 1953.
PULLEN, R. L.: "Communicable Diseases." Lea & Febiger, Philadelphia, 1950.

Functions and Usefulness of the Diagnostic Laboratory

FROBISHER, M., JR.: Reference diagnostic service. *C. D. C. Bull.* (June, 1949).
PHAIR, J. J.: The diagnostic laboratory in the civil defense for biological warfare. *Am. J. Pub. Health* **44**:43 (1954).
VONDELEHR, R. A.: The public health laboratory of the future. *C. D. C. Bull.* **10**:1 (1951).

Diagnostic Methods

AMERICAN PUBLIC HEALTH ASSOCIATION: "Diagnostic Methods and Reagents." 4th ed., New York, 1955.
———: "Diagnostic Methods for Virus and Rickettsial Disease." New York, 1948.
AYRES, J. C., and R. F. FEEMSTER: Medical progress: Serologic tests in the diagnosis of infectious diseases. *New England J. Med.* **243**:996, 1034 (1950).
KALZ, G. G., and E. G. D. MURRAY: Applied Medical Bacteriology, in R. J. Dubos's "Bacterial and Mycotic Infections of Man." 2d ed., Lippincott, Philadelphia, 1952.
SIMMONS, J. S., and C. J. GENTZKOW: "Medical and Public Health Laboratory Methods." 6th ed., Lea & Febiger, 1955.
SMITH, D. F., and N. C. CONANT: "Zinsser's Textbook of Bacteriology." 10th ed., Appleton-Century-Crofts, New York, 1952.
STITT, E. R., *et al.*: "Practical Bacteriology, Hematology, and Parasitology." 10th ed., rev., Blakiston, New York, 1952.

PART SIX

The Pathogenic Bacteria

Salmonella typhosa

This chapter is devoted to the study of a single species of bacteria, *Salmonella typhosa,* the cause of typhoid fever. This organism has been chosen as the first pathogen to be studied intensively because it is an excellent example of a bacterium that causes a specific infection. Moreover, this organism is one whose nature is quite well understood, and the practical applications of this knowledge have effectively controlled the disease.

THE ORGANISM

Salmonella typhosa is the most completely studied and the best known of the large group of nonsporing rods causing enteric disease. These organisms compose the tribe *Salmonelleae* and are closely related to the nonpathogenic members of the family *Enterobacteriaceae,* such as *Escherichia coli, Proteus vulgaris,* and *Aerobacter aerogenes* (see Appendix B, Section 1). The tribe *Salmonelleae* is divided into two genera, *Salmonella* and *Shigella.*

The other important species of the genus *Salmonella* and the species of the genus *Shigella* will be described in the next chapter.

Morphology and Staining. *S. typhosa* is often called *Eberthella typhosa* or *Bacterium typhosa* (or *typhi*). The organism is a short gram-negative rod that does not form spores. It has a dozen or more flagella and is actively motile (Fig. 23·1). Agar colonies are smooth, glistening, and grayish white.

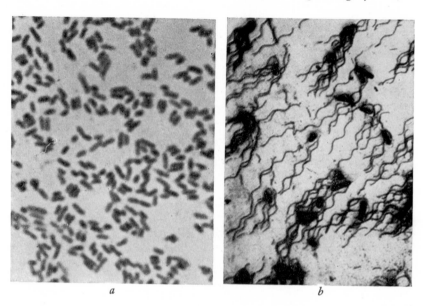

a   b

FIG. 23·1 *Salmonella typhosa.* (*a*) Methylene blue stain. ×2,000. (*b*) Flagella stain. ×4,000. [(*a*) *Copyright by General Biological Supply House, Inc.; (b) "Medichrome," Clay-Adams Co., Inc., Dr. Gregory Shwartzman, Mt. Sinai Hospital.*)

Their characteristic maple-leaf shape is clearly shown in Fig. 23·2. The appearance of *S. typhosa* under the microscope and in standard culture media is so similar to that of the other pathogenic and nonpathogenic members of the enteric group that further testing is always required for identification (Fig. 6·5).

Physiology and Cultivation. The typhoid bacillus grows readily in all standard culture media. Its optimum temperature is 37°C., and it prefers a neutral reaction. It is a facultative anaerobe. The physiologic characteristics that differentiate *S. typhosa* from the other enteric bacteria are summarized in Table 23·1, page 298. The student will note that ability to form acid but not gas from dextrose, inability to ferment lactose, and inability to liquefy gelatin differentiate the typhoid organism from all *Enterobacteriaceae* except those of the genus *Shigella*. Like all other salmonellas, *S. typhosa* is motile, while the dysentery bacteria of the genus *Shigella* are nonmotile.

Effect of Physical and Chemical Agents. The survival of the organism in nature is extremely variable, depending on conditions of moisture, light, and pH. In general the enteric bacteria survive longer than most nonsporing pathogens. *S. typhosa* has been recorded as remaining alive in infected ice for 3 months, in polluted water for 3 weeks, and in moist fecal matter for

FIG. 23·2   Colonies of *Salmonella typhosa* on nutrient agar. ×6. (*From Burrows, "Textbook of Microbiology," Saunders.*)

2 months. In certain types of prepared foods and in milk kept at warm temperatures the typhoid organisms can grow outside the host's body.

The thermal death point of the organism is 65°C. It is destroyed by the accepted methods of pasteurization. Ten minutes' boiling of contaminated articles is the most practical method of disinfection.

Typhoid bacilli are more resistant to most chemical disinfectants than some of the more fragile pathogens but are more easily destroyed by chemicals than the staphylococci. Since they are usually embedded in protein-containing body excretions, the chemicals used must be those that are not inhibited by proteins. Chlorine compounds, coal tar disinfectants, and formaldehyde are all effective. Chlorination of sewage and of water effectively destroys all the enteric pathogens.

Antigenic Structure. *S. typhosa* does not produce exotoxin, but various endotoxic substances have been extracted from the organism. Its antigenic complex is expressed as IX, XII, Vi: d, indicating that it contains somatic antigens IX and XII and the specific flagella antigen d (see page 217). As can be seen in Table 24·1, this indicates that *S. typhosa* is closely related to many of the other salmonellas, notably *S. enteritidis*. The presence of these O and H antigens is of great importance in the agglutination reactions that aid in the diagnosis of the disease. The Vi antigen is found in freshly isolated cultures but may disappear in laboratory cultures. Cultures possessing Vi antigen are used to prepare vaccines for active immunization. Several distinct types of *S. typhosa* are recognized according to their susceptibility to the action of specific bacteriophages (page 474).

TYPHOID FEVER

In a paper published in 1856 the English physician Budd showed that typhoid fever is spread by polluted water. The organism was first described in 1880 by Carl Eberth, who found it in tissues from persons dead from the disease. Gaffky, one of Koch's associates, grew it in culture media in 1884. Sir Almroth Wright of England developed the use of typhoid vaccine during the years 1896 to 1905.

Character of the Infection. Typhoid fever is usually thought of as an intestinal infection, because the organisms enter through the intestinal tract and leave the body in the feces and because many of the severe symptoms of the disease are intestinal. The organisms of typhoid fever, however, actually spread through the whole body by the blood stream and lymphatics. They are present in large numbers in the spleen and the lymph nodes and also in the *rose spots,* which appear in the skin on the abdomen. Infected lymph nodes of the intestinal wall, particularly the Peyer's patches of the ileum, break down and form large areas of ulceration in the lining of the gut. Hemorrhage from these ulcers and perforations of the intestinal wall, giving rise to severe peritonitis, are serious complications of the disease. Typhoid fever has an insidious onset. The disease lasts for several weeks and convalescence is slow.

The Spread of Typhoid Fever. Typhoid fever was a very common disease in the past. Now it is uncommon in those parts of the world where there are pure water and milk supplies and sanitary disposal of sewage. It is also practically unknown in our armed forces because they are effectively protected by vaccination. The disease is still common in areas where sanitation is poor and in armies, concentration camps, and refugee populations where immunization has not been provided.

Sources of Infection. Typhoid fever has a long incubation period, from 7 to 21 days or more. This makes the identification of sources of infection difficult. Animals do not have typhoid. The possible sources of infection are recognized cases, missed cases, convalescent carriers, and chronic carriers.

Where public health and medical practice are poor, their importance is in the order listed. In up-to-date communities practically all cases are correctly diagnosed and patients are isolated and not released until they cease to harbor the organisms. In these communities the sources of the small infrequent epidemics that still occur are unrecognized permanent carriers, particularly those who are employed as food handlers.

Persons suffering from typhoid discharge the organisms in feces. They may also discharge them in urine and in vomitus. Their hands, mouths, clothing, and bedding become contaminated with these discharges. Carriers generally discharge the organisms intermittently in their feces. About 10 per cent of recovered cases remain convalescent carriers for as long as 2 months, and 2 to 5 per cent become chronic carriers. Older persons, particularly women, are most likely to become chronic carriers. In these persons the organisms are frequently localized in the chronically inflamed gallbladder. Some carriers are cured by cholecystectomy.

Water-, Milk-, and Food-borne Epidemics. Where public water supplies are unprotected, water-borne epidemics may attack large numbers of the population of all ages and classes. Small water-borne epidemics in rural areas are traced to well water or surface water polluted from nearby privies. Polluted ice may spread the infection. Milk-borne typhoid is practically unknown where pasteurization laws are enforced. Foods that may be implicated in typhoid include shellfish taken from polluted waters, raw fruits and vegetables grown in polluted soil or irrigated with polluted water, and cheese and ice cream made from infected raw milk. If carriers are employed as food handlers they may infect foods. Such foods as milk, creamed dishes, hash, croquettes, casserole dishes, and sandwich fillings, which the organisms can use as culture media, are particularly dangerous when they are kept in warm places before serving. Where human excreta are exposed in unsanitary privies, flies may carry the organisms to food and milk.

Direct Transfer of Typhoid Infection. Typhoid may be spread by direct contact. This fact is often forgotten because the indirect modes of infection give rise to the large epidemics of the disease. The healthy carrier or missed case may be the source of infection for small numbers of cases in homes and institutions. At least one epidemic in a hospital has been traced to a patient who was an unrecognized carrier. In this instance it was suggested that improperly disinfected enema tubes might have spread the disease to the other patients.

Treatment. Sera from animals or convalescents are not effective in the treatment of typhoid. Chloramphenicol (Chloromycetin) is generally agreed to be the most useful antibiotic. It definitely shortens the duration of the disease, eliminates the salmonella from the feces, decreases the intestinal complications, and in some epidemics has cut the fatality from the usual 10 per cent to 2 per cent. The drug must be continued for some time after symptoms disappear in order to prevent relapses.

Prevention and Control. In regions with complete public health services typhoid cases are very rare. In poorly sanitated regions the individual can be protected by repeated vaccinations.

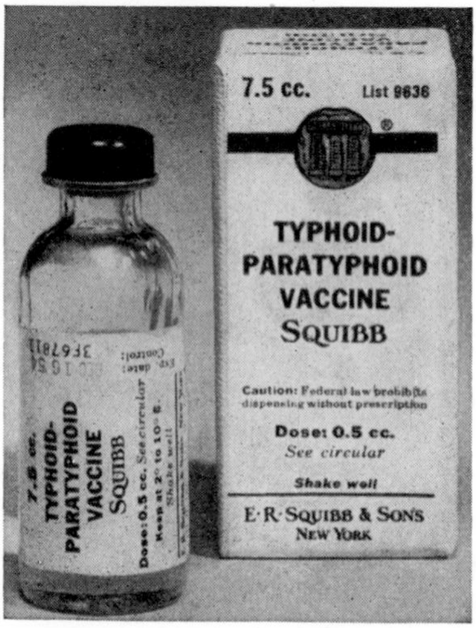

FIG. 23·3 Vaccine for immunization against typhoid fever and the paratyphoid fevers, A and B. This package, containing 7.5 ml., will vaccinate five persons. (*E. R. Squibb and Sons.*)

Sanitation and Other Public Health Measures. Public health control depends on the following measures:

1. Prompt diagnosis and reporting of all cases.

2. Isolation of all cases in adequately equipped hospitals until the patient no longer discharges the typhoid bacillus.

3. Provision of vaccine and facilities for vaccination whenever needed.

4. Epidemiologic investigation of all cases of typhoid to determine the source and modes of infection. Detection of previously unrecognized carriers is particularly important.

5. Continued supervision and education of persons known to be carriers.

6. Provision of a pure water supply.

7. Sanitary disposal of public and private sewage.

8. Pasteurization of milk and milk products.

9. Sanitary control of the sale of shellfish such as oysters.

10. Sanitary supervision of food supplies, food handlers, and food establishments.

11. Provision of adequate public health laboratory facilities to implement the measures listed above.

Active Immunization. The value of vaccination has been most strikingly proved by the disappearance of the disease from the American and British armies even in war times when troops were exposed to heavy infection in the native populations and in war prisoners.

The vaccine is prepared from a virulent, smooth strain of *S. typhosa.* A suspension of the organism in sterile salt solution is killed by formalin, alcohol, or ultraviolet light. It is diluted so that it contains a standard number of bacilli per milliliter. A preservative such as phenol is added to prevent the growth of any contaminating organisms. Sometimes killed cultures of the salmonellas of paratyphoid fevers are combined with typhoid vaccine to make a "triple vaccine." (See Fig. 23·3.)

Typhoid vaccine is given in three doses of 0.5 ml., 1 ml., and 1 ml., respectively, at weekly intervals. It is ordinarily introduced into the body by subcutaneous injection. However intracutaneous injection is just as efficient and is recommended for those who show signs of hypersensitivity to the vaccine. Medical personnel, including nurses and laboratory workers, should be immunized. Immunization is required for all members of the armed forces and for persons traveling to many places where the disease is endemic. It is now widely practiced on the children in countries with poor sanitation. A single intracutaneous booster dose at intervals of 1 to 3 years keeps immunity at a high level.

Laboratory Diagnosis. A case of enteric disease is definitely diagnosed as typhoid fever if *S. typhosa* is found in specimens of blood, feces, or urine. The identification of agglutinins in the blood of a person in the later stages of the disease may be useful but is not as conclusive as the finding of the specific organisms.

During the first 10 days of the infection the bacteria may be cultivated from blood specimens. After that time they may be found in the feces and sometimes in the urine.

Cases are not released from quarantine until the fecal cultures have been negative for *S. typhosa* for 3 or more successive days. Many health departments require the released patients to submit fecal and urine specimens at intervals for a year before the case is taken from their files. Those who become persistent carriers are kept permanently under the supervision of the public health authorities. Duodenal drainage specimens are particularly valuable in the detection of carriers. Bile is collected by a special tube passed through the mouth into the duodenum. Isolation and identification of typhoid organisms from such materials as water, milk, and foods are impracticable. But standard bacteriologic tests may provide valuable evidence of fecal pollution of these materials and so confirm epidemiologic evidence of the mode of infection in an epidemic (Chaps. 14 and 15). The techniques used in the isolation and identification of the typhoid bacillus are the same as those used for the study of the other enteric pathogens. These techniques will be described in the next chapter.

Nursing Considerations in the Care of Enteric Diseases. The nurse must prevent the spread of enteric infection from patients with enteric disease to other patients and to the community; she must protect all patients from enteric infection from all sources; and she must protect herself from such infection.

Table 23·1. Characteristics

Genera	Morphology	Motility *	Action on sugars †	
			Dextrose	Lactose
Proteus.................	Gram-negative nonsporing rods	+	AG	O
Escherichia and *Aerobacter*...	Gram-negative nonsporing rods	±	AG	AG
Salmonella typhosa.........	Gram-negative nonsporing rods	+	A	O
Salmonella other than *S. typhosa*	Gram-negative nonsporing rods	+	AG	O
Shigella.................	Gram-negative nonsporing rods	−	A	O ‡

* +, motile; −, nonmotile; ±, some species motile.   † AG, acid and gas; A, acid formed;

Care of the Patient on Enteric Precautions. The term *enteric precautions* refers to the special care given a patient with known or suspected enteric disease. Its purpose is to prevent the infectious organisms from leaving the patient's unit. Organisms of enteric disease pass from the patient's body in feces, urine, and vomitus. They contaminate his clothing, bedding, hands, dishes, bedpan, and any other objects with which he comes in contact. They may be carried from the patient's unit by such objects, by the nurse or doctor, or by flies. There is no reason to believe that they are commonly air-borne, though where there has been widespread contamination with fecal material there is always a possibility that they may be dust-borne. The nursing procedures formulated by hospitals for the care of enteric disease will accomplish their purpose only if every nurse follows them with thoughtfulness and comprehension of the principles involved.

Protection of All Patients against Enteric Infection. The hospital administration provides safe water, milk, and food supplies for the patients. The housekeeping and nursing staff must see that these supplies are completely protected against contamination after they reach the hospital.

Routine ward procedures in the care of enema tubes, dishes, bedding, bedpans, urinals, clinical thermometers, and other objects are designed to prevent intestinal organisms from one patient from reaching any other patient. In a hundred-bed hospital the chances are that there will be several unsuspected carriers of enteric organisms, including probably at least one carrier of typhoid or amebic dysentery. The nurse who keeps this in mind will not slight her routine nursing techniques.

of Enteric Bacteria

Utiliza-tion of urea	Cultural characteristics	Pathogenicity
+	Spreading colonies; putrefactive odor	See page 313
−	Dark, lustrous colonies on Endo's agar and eosin methylene blue agar	See page 313
−	Black colonies on bismuth sulfite agar	Cause of typhoid fever
−	Smooth translucent colonies on SS agar	Cause of paratyphoid fevers, salmonella food poisonings, etc.
−	Smooth translucent colonies on SS agar	Cause of bacterial dysenteries

O, no fermentation; O ‡, slow fermentation in some species.

Protection of the Nurse. Student nurses are immunized against typhoid fever. The nurse should not let her immunization lapse after graduation but should continue to have a booster dose each year. Nurses should remember that they are not necessarily immune to other intestinal infections of their patients. Careful attention to prescribed nursing techniques in the disposal of dejecta from all patients is their best protection against such diseases.

STUDY SUGGESTIONS

Review your knowledge of sources and modes of infection (Part Three of this text). Why is the residual typhoid fever in modern communities due to carriers who are food handlers? What other sources of infection and modes of infection are important in other communities? Does your home community adequately protect its citizens against typhoid fever?

Why should the nurse be protected against typhoid even though she may not care for any cases diagnosed as that disease? How does your hospital protect you from typhoid fever? What part might the nurse play in the spread of typhoid fever from cases of the disease?

Can you describe the morphology and physiology of *S. typhosa*? How does it differ from the other organisms of the genus *Salmonella* and from those of the genus *Shigella*?

How is typhoid vaccine prepared? How is it administered? Who should be immunized?

Make a summary of this organism and the disease it causes, using the headings suggested in Chap. 22 (or fill in outlines provided by your instructor).

SUGGESTED READING

(See also page 314.)

The Organism

BEARD, P. J.: Longevity of *Eberthella typhosa* in various soils. *Am. J. Pub. Health* **30:**1077 (1940).

HAVENS, L. C.: "The Bacteriology of Typhoid." Commonwealth Fund, New York, 1935.

Carriers

AMES, W. R., and M. ROBBINS: Age and sex factors in the development of the typhoid carrier state and a method of estimating carrier prevalence. *Am. J. Pub. Health* **33:**221 (1943).

FEEMSTER, R. F., *et al.:* "The Control of Typhoid Carriers." American Public Health Association Yearbook **39:**71 (1949).

FOWLER, R. P.: Even with the law on our side. *Am. J. Pub. Health* **38:**1569 (1948). The tale of a persistent carrier who evaded the law for years.

LITTMAN, A.: The chronic typhoid carrier. 1. The natural course of the carrier state. *Am. J. Pub. Health* **38:**1675 (1948).

Typhoid Epidemiology

ADKERSON, J.: A typhoid epidemic. *Am. J. Nursing* **44:**239 (1944).

ROUECHÉ, B.: A Game of Wild Indians, in "Eleven Blue Men." Little, Brown, Boston, 1954.

RUBENSTEIN, A. D.: Certain aspects of present-day typhoid epidemiology. *New York State J. Med.* **43:**1736 (1943).

Immunization and Treatment

BATSON, H. C.: Typhoid Fever Prophylaxis by Active Immunization. *Pub. Health Rep. Supp.* **212,** 1949.

COLLINS, H. S., and M. FINLAND: Treatment of typhoid fever with chloromycetin. *New England J. Med.* **241:**556 (1949).

SMADEL, J. E., T. E. WOODWARD, and C. A. BAILEY: Relation of relapses in typhoid fever to duration of chloramphenicol treatment. *J.A.M.A.* **141:**129 (1949).

SYVERTON, J. T., *et al.:* Typhoid and paratyphoid A in immunized military personnel. *J.A.M.A.* **131:**507 (1946).

Other Bacteria of Enteric Infections

Salmonella typhosa, the cause of typhoid fever, was discussed in the last chapter. In this chapter the closely related organisms of the genus *Salmonella* and the genus *Shigella* are described, as well as certain other bacteria causing specific and nonspecific enteric infections.

THE GENUS SALMONELLA

The genus *Salmonella* was named for Dr. Daniel E. Salmon, who was at one time head of the U.S. Public Health Service. All salmonellas are parasites of man, mammals, or birds. Over 150 types have been described, and more are continually being added to the list. Many have been given species names based on the place where they were first found or the animal that they parasitize. Examples are *S. typhimurium* (the salmonella of mouse typhoid), *S. newport,* and *S. london.* As relationships of these organisms have been more fully investigated it has been recognized that they belong to a limited number of groups, each including a number of closely related species.

Characteristics of the Genus Salmonella. The other salmonellas are indistinguishable from *S. typhosa* in morphology and staining and in their growth on standard agar and broth media. Their inability to ferment lactose and to utilize urea differentiates them from the nonpathogenic genera. (See Table 23·1, page 298.) Their motility and their ability to form gas as well as acid from dextrose and certain other sugars differentiates them from the shigellas. The groups of salmonellas are identified by serologic tests. The antigenic formulas of some of the more important salmonellas are given in Table 24·1.

Table 24·1

The Genus Salmonella

Species	Disease	Antigenic structure
Salmonella typhosa.....	Typhoid fever	IX, XII, Vi; d
S. paratyphi...........	Paratyphoid A fever	I, II, XII; a
S. schottmuelleri.......	Paratyphoid B fever	I, IV, V, XII; b; 1, 2
S. typhimurium........	Salmonella food poisoning	I, IV, V, XII; i; 1, 2, 3
S. choleraesuis........	Salmonella food poisoning	VI, VII; c; 1, 5
S. enteritidis.........	Salmonella food poisoning	I, IX, XII; g, m

The Diseases Caused by the Salmonellas. Salmonella organisms other than *S. typhosa* cause three types of infection, which may all be called *salmonelloses* (sing. *salmonellosis*).

The Paratyphoid Infections of Man. Two typhoidlike infections of man, paratyphoid A fever and paratyphoid B fever (also called *alpha* and *beta*), are due to two species of salmonellas, *S. paratyphi* and *S. schottmuelleri,* respectively. The clinical picture resembles that of typhoid, but the incubation periods are much shorter and the diseases are milder than typhoid. Paratyphoid B is quite common in the United States.

Paratyphoid is a strictly human disease. The source of infection is always a human case or carrier. The modes of infection and methods of sanitary control are the same as for typhoid fever. In areas where paratyphoid fever is common, the triple vaccine, containing killed *S. paratyphi* and *S. schott-muelleri* as well as *S. typhosa* (known as *TAB*), is used for immunization against all three infections.

Salmonella Food Poisoning. As was noted in Chap. 15, one common type of food poisoning is caused by members of this genus. The names *gastro-enteritis* and *salmonellosis* are also used for these infections. The characteristics of food-borne salmonellosis were summarized in Table 15·2.

The salmonellas of food poisoning are frequently from swine, dogs, eggs, and poultry. Both human and animal cases and carriers may be sources of infection. Before the days of sanitary inspection of meat, epidemics of gastro-enteritis resulted from the slaughtering and eating of cattle ill with salmonella infection. The cause was *S. enteritidis* (also known as *Gaertner's bacillus*). This infection was sometimes so severe as to be confused with Asiatic cholera.

Although there are minor differences in cultural and physiologic characteristics, satisfactory differentiation of the salmonella types requires serologic tests with highly specific sera.

S. typhimurium (synonym, *S. aertrycke*) is the commonest cause of salmonellosis in this country. Other types frequently found are *S. choleraesuis* (from pigs), *S. anatis* (from ducks), and the types designated as *newport, oranienburg,* and *montevideo.*

Salmonelloses of Animals. A number of important infections of domestic animals are due to salmonella infections. Among them are the white diarrhea of chickens and the fowl typhoid of older poultry, as well as contagious abortion of horses and sheep.

THE GENUS SHIGELLA

The name of the genus *Shigella* is derived from the name of Shiga, the Japanese bacteriologist who first discovered one of the important members of the genus.

Characteristics of the Shigellas. These organisms resemble those of the genus *Salmonella* in morphology and staining. The character of their growth on agar and in broth is like that of the other genus but is usually more scanty. They resemble the typhoid bacteria in their inability to ferment most sugars. Their most striking difference from the salmonellas is their lack of flagella. These differential characteristics were summarized in Table 23·1.

Like the salmonellas, the genus consists of groups of closely related organisms which have not yet been satisfactorily classified. The various recognized species of the genus *Shigella* are differentiated on the basis of the fermentation of several sugars and the production of indol. Table 24·2 summarizes these characteristics.

Table 24·2

The Genus Shigella

Group	Type species	Fermentation		Indol formation	Type of dysentery
		Of mannitol	Of lactose		
A.......	Shigella dysenteriae	−	−	− *	Shiga
B.......	S. flexneri	+	−	+ †	Flexner
C.......	S. boydii	+	−	− *	Boyd
D.......	S. sonnei	+	(slow)	−	Sonné

* One or two types are +.
† One type is −.

Serologic Types of Shigellas. The organisms of the genus *Shigella* are placed in four groups, A, B, C, and D. The types within the groups are designated by letters. The characteristics of these groups are summarized in Table 24·2. *S. dysenteriae* of Group A produces a very potent toxic substance which is one factor in the severity of Shiga-type dysentery. *S. dysenteriae* is uncommon in North America but prevalent in Asia and in other parts of the world.

Flexner-type dysentery due to *S. flexneri* (*S. paradysenteriae*), the Group B organism, is more common in this country. So is the Sonné type caused by *S. sonnei,* the Group D organism. Infections with these shigellas are seldom fatal, and many are very mild. The bacteria of Group C, commonly called the Boyd types (*S. boydii*), were first described in India but are now known to have world-wide distribution. They are closely related to the Flexner organisms.

The alkalescens-dispar group of *Enterobacteriaceae* are sometimes found in cases of dysentery. They are considered to be intermediate between the genus *Escherichia* and the genus *Shigella*. Like the shigellas they are nonmotile and do not ferment lactose, but serologically they are closer to *E. coli*.

Bacillary Dysentery. *Dysentery* is a general clinical term. A case of dysentery is characterized by inflammation of the lower bowel resulting in diarrhea, abdominal pain, and sometimes blood in the stools. There are two distinct types of infectious dysentery, *amebic dysentery,* due to the pathogenic protozoan *Endamoeba histolytica,* and *bacillary dysentery,* due to members of the genus *Shigella*. Bacillary dysentery is also called *shigellosis*.

Epidemiology of Bacillary Dysentery. Cases and epidemics of dysentery vary greatly in severity. In this country most cases are relatively mild. In

Oriental countries, in tropical regions, and in refugee populations the epidemics are generally larger and more severe. Even in communities with advanced sanitation the infection may be persistent and severe in hospitals for the insane.

The disease may be water-borne, milk-borne, or fly-borne. Epidemics spread by polluted food are still more common. Missed cases and healthy human carriers are the sources of dysentery. Animals do not ordinarily suffer from shigella infection and are not important in the spread of the disease.

Treatment and Prevention. Sulfa drugs and tetracycline are the chemotherapeutic drugs most useful in bacillary dysentery. Antitoxic serum has been used to treat cases of *S. dysenteriae* infection. To date, it has been impossible to produce an effective, nontoxic shigella vaccine. All measures that contribute to sanitary living in the community lower the incidence of dysentery. Food sanitation and fly control are the most important factors.

LABORATORY DIAGNOSIS OF SALMONELLA AND SHIGELLA INFECTIONS

Laboratory tests are made to diagnose suspected cases, to identify carriers, and to determine when convalescents may be safely released from isolation. The most valuable and conclusive evidence comes from the isolation and identification of specific members of the enteric bacteria. When this cannot be successfully accomplished, serologic tests establishing the presence of specific antibodies in the blood give useful information.

The Identification of the Causative Organism. Specimens of the patient's feces are the most common materials sent to the laboratory for examination. Specimens of blood, urine, duodenal drainage, and occasionally excised gallbladders are also examined for the enteric bacteria. If the examination is to be delayed for more than 2 hours, the specimen is placed in a tube of buffered 30 per cent glycerin solution. The essential steps for isolation and identification are the same in all laboratories, though the details of technique vary considerably. These steps are indicated in Fig. 24·1.

The Isolation of Suspected Organisms. A carefully collected blood specimen will contain a pure culture if any organisms are present, but in specimens of feces the pathogens will often be outnumbered by coliform bacteria. The specimen is streaked on one or more plates of selective media such as bismuth sulfite agar, SS agar (salmonella-shigella agar, a bile-citrate medium), and Endo's agar. At the same time some of the specimen is inoculated into an enrichment broth. Tetrathionate broth and glycerol bile broth are most commonly used. After suitable incubation, the broth culture is streaked on one or more plates of the selective agars. The colonies of *Salmonella typhosa,*

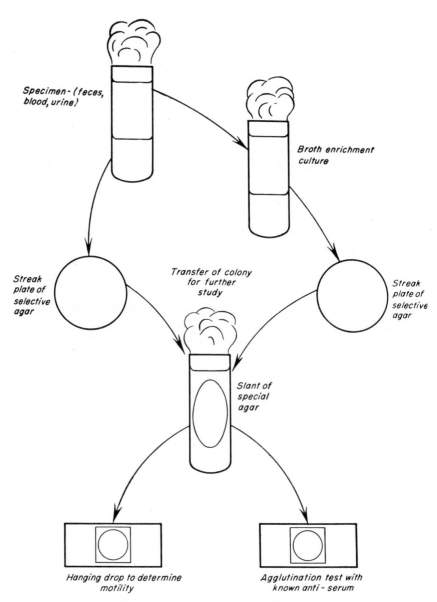

Specimen - (feces, blood, urine)

Broth enrichment culture

Streak plate of selective agar

Transfer of colony for further study

Streak plate of selective agar

Slant of special agar

Hanging drop to determine motility

Agglutination test with known anti - serum

Fig. 24·1 Laboratory procedure for diagnosis of enteric infection.

other important species of salmonellas, and shigella organisms can usually be recognized by the experienced laboratory worker after 18 to 24 hours' incubation. Characteristic colonies are shown in Figs. 24·2 and 24·3.

Identification of Genus. Several of the chosen colonies are transferred to tubes of differential media for preliminary testing. The tube medium is usually a slant containing two or three sugars (Fig. 24·4) or a broth containing two sugars. Cultures showing the fermentation reactions characteristic

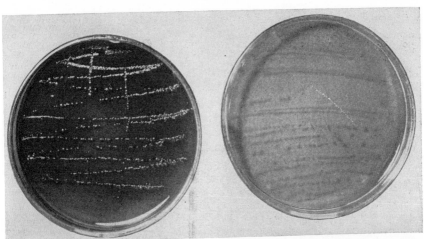

Fig. 24·2   Growth of enteric bacteria on Endo agar. Left—*Escherichia coli,* medium darkened, colonies deep red with metallic surface luster. Right—*Salmonella typhosa,* colorless colonies.

of the nonpathogenic enterobacteria are discarded; those showing reactions characteristic of salmonellas or shigellas are tested further. A urea-containing medium may also be used at this time. The utilization of the urea indicates that the isolated bacterium is a member of the genus *Proteus.* A hanging drop is made to differentiate the nonmotile shigella organisms from the motile genera. Macroscopic slide agglutination tests with suspensions of the bacteria mixed with pooled salmonella antiserum, pooled shigella antiserum, and typhoid antiserum serve as a check on the bacteriologist's identification of the genus. Further cultural tests and agglutination tests with various dilutions of specific antiserum will be made to confirm the tentative diagnosis. These will generally be sufficient to identify *Salmonella typhosa* and the salmonellas of the paratyphoid fevers (*S. paratyphi* and *S. schottmuelleri*) but will not conclusively differentiate other species of salmonellas or shigellas. The doctor will be sent a report of the results of these tests.

Identification of Species and Types. For many reasons physicians and public health workers may wish to know the exact type of salmonella or shigella involved in a case or an epidemic. The necessary serologic tests with specially

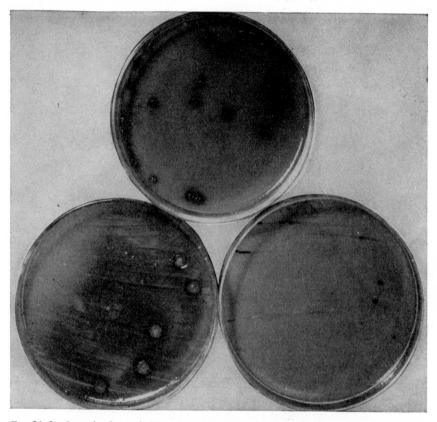

FIG. 24·3 Growth of enteric bacteria on bismuth sulfite agar. Lower right—*Escherichia coli*, poor growth, occasional small green-to-brown colony. Upper—*Salmonella typhosa*, black colonies with black halos. Lower left—*Salmonella schottmuelleri*, dark colonies with black halos.

prepared type-specific sera are done in the United States at laboratories designated as *typing centers*. There are also typing centers authorized to determine the bacteriophage types of *S. typhosa* cultures. (See Fig. 33·13 on page 475 and the accompanying discussion.)

Tests for Specific Antibodies in the Patient's Blood. These tests are useful in the later stages of a suspected case of typhoid from which it has been impossible to isolate *S. typhosa*. They are seldom used in diagnosis of other salmonella or shigella infections. The patient's serum in a dilution of 1:10 to 1:160 or higher is placed in test tubes. A killed suspension of *S. typhosa* is added to each tube. After being held for 15 to 18 hours, the tubes are

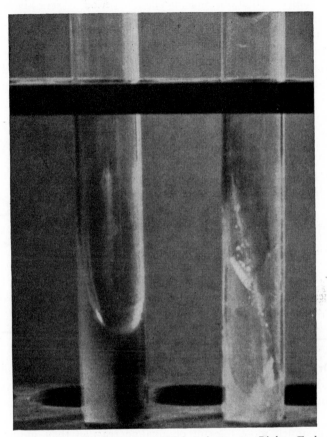

FIG. 24·4   Growth of enteric bacteria on Kligler's iron agar. Right—*Escherichia coli*, acid throughout (yellow), gas bubbles in agar, no hydrogen sulfide. Left—*Salmonella typhosa*, acid butt (yellow), no acid in slant (red), no gas, blackening along stab due to hydrogen sulfide production.

examined for the appearance of definite clumping. Agglutination of O and H antigen preparations (see page 217) by dilutions of 1:80 or higher is considered evidence of active typhoid infection. The diluted sera of chronic typhoid carriers agglutinates Vi antigen. The name *Widal test* is used for these agglutination techniques, although the original test devised by Widal was a much simpler one.

VIBRIO COMMA, THE CAUSE OF ASIATIC CHOLERA

Cholera is an acute intestinal infection characterized by profuse diarrhea, vomiting, and dehydration. The incubation period is very short, onset is sudden, and a fatal outcome within 2 or 3 days is common. Cholera is endemic and epidemic in India and other countries of southern Asia. During the nineteenth century it frequently spread to Europe and to North America. It still flourishes in Asia but is kept out of other parts of the world by strict quarantine enforcement. An alarming epidemic occurred in Egypt in 1947.

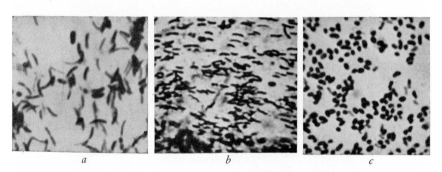

FIG. 24·5 *Vibrio comma.* ×1,200. (*a*) Cholera vibrios with other intestinal bacteria in a fecal smear. (*b*) Vibrios in shred of mucus from feces. (*c*) Rod and coccoid forms from pure culture on agar. (*SAB print 282, from Reimann, G. C. T., et al. Am. J. Trop. Med. 26:631.*)

The Organism. *Vibrio comma* is also known as *Vibrio cholerae*. It was discovered by Robert Koch in India in 1883. The organism is a very short curved rod with a single polar flagellum. It is nonsporing and gram-negative. (See Fig. 24·5.) *V. comma* grows well in ordinary media at body temperature. It is much more tolerant of alkaline reaction than most intestinal bacteria and will grow in media with a pH as high as 9.5. It prefers to grow aerobically and forms a film on the surface of liquid media. Most authorities consider it less resistant to conditions outside the human body than the other enteric bacteria. Ordinarily it dies out in soil and water in a very few days. It is killed by pasteurization and by the usual chemical disinfectants.

The vibrio does not form an exotoxin, but endotoxin substances liberated from the disintegrating organisms cause rapid desquamation of the intestinal mucosa. As a result a large amount of body fluid is lost through the intestinal wall. The patient becomes severely dehydrated and also suffers from loss of blood proteins. The organism does not invade other tissues. It is a strictly human parasite.

Laboratory Diagnosis. During epidemics the diagnosis is made by detection of the typical vibrios in stained smears of the mucous flakes in the watery stools. Diagnosis of sporadic cases, detection of carriers, and examination of fecal specimens from convalescents involve the cultivation of the organisms. Specimens are inoculated into an enrichment medium, an alkaline peptone water, in which the vibrios grow much more quickly than other intestinal bacteria. This liquid culture is streaked on alkaline nutrient agar. Bacteria from typical colonies are checked by slide agglutination tests using cholera antiserum, and inoculated into other media to confirm cultural reactions. *V. comma* liquefies gelatin, produces indol, reduces nitrates, and forms acid from certain sugars.

Epidemiology, Prevention, and Treatment. Cholera is spread in much the same way as typhoid fever. Chronic carriers are not known, but convalescent carriers and missed cases are common. Adequate sanitation eliminates cholera. Quarantine regulations including laboratory examinations of persons from endemic areas prevent the introduction of the disease into other countries.

Vaccination against cholera is done with a phenol-killed suspension of virulent *V. comma*. Two inoculations are given, followed by frequent booster doses. The experience of the Allied armies in Asiatic countries during the Second World War has amply proved the effectiveness of this immunization. Passive immunization is not useful.

Modern treatment of cholera is very effective. The extreme loss of proteins and water from the body due to the profuse diarrhea and vomiting are combated by drugs that reduce peristalsis and by intravenous therapy with saline solution and blood plasma. The vibrios disappear within 2 days in 99 per cent of cases treated with sulfaguanidine and streptomycin, or with terramycin.

DIARRHEAL DISEASES OF INFANTS

Wherever infant mortality rates are high, a large portion of infant illness and death is due to diarrheal disease. Pure water, pure milk and foods, elimination of flies, and education of mothers in sanitation have greatly decreased the incidence of such infections in the privileged areas of the world.

The shigellas are the most important cause of infant diarrheas. All the organisms of adult intestinal disease may infect infants. In addition the infant intestinal tract is susceptible to infection with various species of *Proteus,* with *Clostridium perfringens,* and members of the coliform group.

Epidemic Diarrhea of the Newborn. Infants under one month of age are particularly susceptible to diarrheal infection. Epidemics are alarmingly common in lying-in and infant hospitals. Fatality is often as high as 25 per cent among full-term babies and 50 per cent among premature infants.

The shigellas and salmonellas are found only rarely. Some investigators have reported evidence of virus etiology. In the last few years evidence has accumulated that certain strains of *Escherichia coli* (strains 0111 and 055) are the causative organisms in many epidemics. Neomycin is effective in the treatment of these cases.

Epidemics are much more likely to occur in poorly equipped and badly run hospitals than in well-equipped and well-run institutions. Nurses are

FIG. 24·6 Modern milk formula room, Elizabeth Steel Magee Hospital, Pittsburgh. The nurse is taking formula bottles from sterilizer and placing them on rack for transportation to the refrigerator. Note paper covers protecting nipples, and gloves and mask worn by nurse. (*American Sterilizer Company.*)

often irked at what seem to be unnecessary regulations and details of technique required in a modern infants' ward, but all procedures must be carried out faultlessly if infections of the newborn are to be successfully avoided. (See Fig. 24·6.)

NONSPECIFIC INFECTIONS OF THE DIGESTIVE TRACT

All parts of the digestive system are subject to nonspecific infections. These diseases are commonly named for the part affected—gastritis, ileitis, appendicitis, etc. Predisposing factors such as vitamin deficiencies, mechanical injury, and abnormal or deficient secretions are important in the development of these conditions. It is usually impossible to implicate any one species of pathogenic organism as the etiologic agent. Mixtures of opportunist bacteria are usually found. Ulcers of the stomach and duodenum are the result of hypersecretion of acid which erodes the epithelium. Opportunist bacteria may play a part in the extension of these ulcers, but there is no evidence that they cause the lesions. Four important conditions involving nonspecific infections are briefly described here.

Appendicitis. Acute and recurrent inflammations of the vermiform appendix are common forms of intestinal infection. No one etiologic agent has been discovered. Bacteriologic examination of the removed appendix always reveals a mixture of organisms. Among those found are streptococci, staphylococci, members of the *Salmonella* and *Proteus* genera, spore-forming anaerobes such as *Cl. perfringens,* and certain nonsporing anaerobes belonging to the *Bacteroides* and *Fusobacterium* genera.

Cholecystitis. Inflammation of the gallbladder may occur with or without the formation of gallstones. *Escherichia coli,* staphylococci, and streptococci are often found in these infections. Cholecystitis due to the typhoid bacillus may persist for years after an attack of typhoid fever.

Peritonitis. The peritoneal cavity becomes infected with bacteria when the wall of the intestine is perforated or injured, so that organisms pass through it. The organisms most commonly responsible are *E. coli* and streptococci.

Chronic Ulcerative Colitis. Nonsporing anaerobes have been so frequently found in this disease that some bacteriologists believe they are the specific cause, though others consider them to be opportunist invaders.

STUDY SUGGESTIONS

How does *Salmonella typhosa* differ from the other salmonellas in morphology, physiology, and pathogenicity? What three types of disease, besides typhoid fever, are caused by salmonellas? Which species are involved in the salmonelloses affecting man? Are students of your training school immunized against paratyphoid fevers? If an epidemic of salmonella infection developed in your institution, what possible sources of infection would be investigated?

How do the shigellas differ from the salmonellas? What are the important groups of the genus *Shigella*? What names are given to the forms of bacillary dysentery caused by these groups?

What specimens would be sent to the laboratory for diagnosis of enteric infections? Outline the steps the laboratory workers would use and the results they might obtain that would justify a report that *S. typhosa* was present in the specimen? that a shigella of undetermined species was present? What further tests for identification might be desirable? Would a reported positive Widal test be the equivalent of a positive report of the identification of *S. typhosa* from a fecal specimen?

Compare Asiatic cholera with typhoid fever as to causative organism, course of the infection, epidemiology, treatment, and prevention.

What measures in the home care of infants should successfully prevent diarrheal disease? What measures are carried out in the care of premature and full-term babies in hospitals?

SUGGESTED READING

Salmonellas and the Salmonelloses (See also page 300.)

DACK, G. M.: "Food Poisoning." Rev. ed., University of Chicago Press, Chicago, 1949.

FEIG, M.: Diarrhea, dysentery, food poisoning, and gastroenteritis. *Am. J. Pub. Health* **40:**1372 (1950).

MORGAN, H. R.: The Salmonella, in R. J. Dubos's, "Bacterial and Mycotic Infections of Man." 2d ed., Lippincott, Philadelphia, 1952.

Shigellas and Shigelloses

CHEEVER, F. S.: Bacillary Dysentery and the Shigellas, in R. J. Dubos's, "Bacterial and Mycotic Infections of Man." 2d ed., Lippincott, Philadelphia, 1952.

DUBOS, R. J., and J. W. GEIGER: Preparation and properties of *Shigella* toxin and toxoid. *J. Exper. Med.* **84:**143 (1946).

HALPERN, S. R.: Bacillary dysentery in children. *Am. J. Nursing* **50:**320 (1950).

HARDY, A. V., and J. WATT: The acute diarrheal diseases. *J.A.M.A.* **124:**1173 (1944).

KINNAMAN, C. H., and F. C. BELLMAN: An epidemic of 300 cases of bacillary dysentery involving a war industry and members of the armed forces. *Am. J. Pub. Health* **34:**94 (1944).

KUHNS, C. M., and T. G. ANDERSON: A fly-borne bacillary dysentery epidemic in a large military establishment. *Am. J. Pub. Health* **34:**750 (1944).

WATT, A. A., and D. R. LINDSAY: Diarrheal control studies. I. Effect of fly control in a high morbidity area. *Pub. Health Rep.* **63:**1319 (1948).

WHEELER, K. M., and C. A. STUART: The mannitol-negative *Shigella* group. *J. Bact.* **51:**317 (1946).

Laboratory Diagnosis of Enteric Infections

COLEMAN, M. B.: Salmonella and Shigella, in "Diagnostic Procedures and Reagents." 3d ed., American Public Health Association, New York, 1950.

EDWARDS, P. R., and W. H. EWING: "A Manual for Enteric Bacteriology." Federal Security Agency, Communicable Disease Center, Atlanta, 1951.

Vibrio comma and Asiatic Cholera

BURROWS, W., *et al.:* The O and H antigenic structure of the cholera and related vibrios. *J. Infect. Dis.* **79:**168 (1946).

SEASTONE, C. V.: The Cholera Vibrio, in "Diagnostic Procedures and Reagents." 3d ed., American Public Health Association, New York, 1950.

Infant Diarrhea

ABRAMSON, H.: Acute diarrheal disorders of newborn infants. *Am. J. Dis. Child.* **79**:698 (1950).

CHILDREN'S BUREAU, U.S. Printing Office: "Standards and Recommendations for Hospital Care of Newborn Infants, Fullterm and Premature." Publication 292, Washington, D.C., 1947.

LIGHT, J. S., and H. L. HODES: Isolation from cases of infantile diarrhea of a filterable agent causing diarrhea in calves. *J. Exper. Med.* **90**:113 (1949).

NETER, E. W., *et al.:* Study of the etiology, epidemiology, and antibiotic therapy of infant diarrhea with particular reference to certain serotypes of *E. coli. Am. J. Pub. Health* **41**:1490 (1951).

WEYMULLER, C. A., and A. C. BECK: Measures for protection of newborn infants. *J.A.M.A.* **133**:78 (1947).

The *Parvobacteriaceae*

In addition to the enteric organisms discussed in the last chapters, there are many other nonsporing rods that cause disease. The most important belong to the family *Parvobacteriaceae* (little bacteria) and the family *Corynebacteriaceae* (clubbed rods). The *Parvobacteriaceae* are described in this chapter; the *Corynebacteriaceae* and a few others in the next chapter. All the "little bacteria" are gram-negative nonmotile rods.

THE GENUS BRUCELLA

Three species of this genus cause infections in man and domestic animals. All these infections may be referred to as *brucelloses* (sing. *brucellosis*). They are also known by various popular names. The disease resulting from *Brucella melitensis* infection from goats is called *Malta fever*. *B. abortus* infection of cattle is called *contagious abortion* or *Bang's disease*. The third species, *B. suis*, attacks both pigs and cattle. All three infections may be

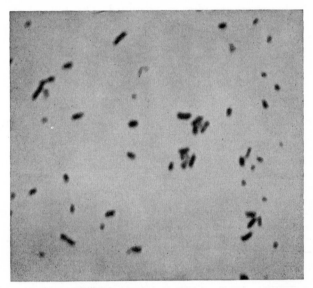

FIG. 25·1   *Brucella melitensis.* ×2,000. Note bacillary and coccoid forms. ("*Medichrome*," *Clay-Adams Co., Inc., Dr. Gregory Shwartzman, Mt. Sinai Hospital.*)

acquired by man, in whom the disease is popularly called *undulant fever*.

The Organisms. In 1887 a British Army commission headed by Colonel David Bruce announced that it had discovered the cause of the intermittent fever common on the Mediterranean island of Malta. They mistook the organism for a coccus and named it *Micrococcus melitensis*. In 1897, in Denmark, Bang isolated the organism associated with contagious abortion of cattle. This was called *Bacillus abortus*. In 1918 the American bacteriologist Alice Evans proved that the two organisms are very closely related types. The name *Brucella* was given to the genus in honor of Colonel Bruce. The porcine (pig) species had been isolated by another American, Traum, in 1914.

All brucellas are gram-negative rods, often so short as to appear coccoid (Fig. 25·1). They are nonmotile and nonsporing. They are present in the blood and tissues of infected animals and persons. These organisms are readily destroyed by all the usual methods of physical and chemical disinfection and by sunlight. They can survive for several days in sweet milk, for weeks in cheese and butter, and for long periods in soil, dust, and in the discarded afterbirth of animals.

Brucellas are cultivated in enriched media. Newly isolated cultures, particularly *B. abortus,* prefer an atmosphere of increased carbon dioxide, as in a candle jar. The colonies on solid media are small, white, and translucent.

Differentiation of Species. There are no morphologic or staining characteristics by which the species may be identified. The cultural characteristics useful for this purpose are summarized in Table 25·1. *B. abortus* and *B.*

Table 25·1

Characteristics of the Species of Brucella

Characteristics	*B. melitensis*	*B. abortus*	*B. suis*
Principal animal hosts.....	Goats	Cattle	Swine, cattle
Carbon dioxide requirements for isolation......	None	10 per cent	None
Hydrogen sulfide production	None or only trace in 4 days	Moderate or marked for 2 days	Moderate or marked for 4 days
Growth in tryptone agar containing:			
1:100,000 basic fuchsin..	+	+	−
1:100,000 thionin.......	+	−	+

melitensis have two antigens in common but present in markedly different concentrations, so that each can be identified by an agglutination test with a special serum from which the specific antibody of lesser concentration has been removed. *B. suis* is so similar antigenically to *B. abortus* that no simple serologic reaction is available for its identification.

The Disease. Brucellosis of domestic animals causes premature birth and death of the young, and marked decrease in milk production. In man the illness may be acute and self-limited, or so mild as to escape detection, or chronic and debilitating over many years. The few fatal cases are due to bacterial endocarditis or meningoencephalitis.

Epidemiology. While it is theoretically possible for brucellosis to pass from person to person, such transfer has never been recorded. Therefore no isolation precautions are required. It is certain that in the vast majority of instances the infection is acquired from animals. The organisms enter the body through the digestive tract or the skin. Man commonly is infected by ingesting raw milk or milk products, or by handling infected animals or their carcasses.

Prevention. The public can be protected from brucellosis by the elimination of the disease from domestic animals. The U.S. Department of Agriculture has carried on a campaign against the disease since 1934. A more intensive program was started in 1949 with the backing of farmers' organizations. The usual state-administered program includes detection of infected herds and individual cows, sale of infected animals for slaughter, and vaccination of calves. Pasteurization of milk and milk products is, of course, an important safeguard against the disease.

No satisfactory vaccine for man is known. Sera are not used for treatment. Patients with chronic infections whose symptoms are considered to be due to allergy are treated with antigenic substances. Combined therapy using two of the following drugs—sulfadiazine, streptomycin, and Aureomycin— is particularly effective in acute cases.

Laboratory Diagnosis. The laboratory is called on to detect brucella infections in both man and animals. Because of the nonspecificity of the clinical manifestations of the disease the laboratory tests are particularly important.

Isolation of the Organism. The brucellas can be isolated from fresh venous blood of cases in the acute stage or in febrile periods of chronic infection. Enriched broth is inoculated and incubated at increased carbon dioxide tension. The broth culture is streaked over enriched agar. Occasionally cultures are made from tissues, urine, feces, and dairy products. Agglutination tests, dye tests, etc., identify the species (see Table 25·1).

Serologic Methods. Various agglutination tests are the chief methods of diagnosing brucellosis in animals and in chronic cases of man. Dilutions of the patient's serum are tested for their effect on killed brucella antigens. Plate agglutination tests are used more often than tube tests. Titers of over 1:100 are considered significant evidence of infection in sick persons. A simple agglutination test, the *ring test,* is used to detect infected herds of milking cows. A suspension of killed stained brucella cells is added to a tube of the pooled milk. If there is infection in the herd, antibody in the milk will clump the dyed bacteria, and they will rise with the cream to form a colored ring above the skim milk. Identification of the individual infected cows is done by agglutination tests of their blood sera.

PASTEURELLA PESTIS, THE CAUSE OF PLAGUE

The genus *Pasteurella* is made up of small, gram-negative, nonsporing, nonmotile rods that show deeply staining granules at both ends (bipolar

Table 25·2. Important Diseases

Disease	The causative organism		
	Name	Morphology	Cultivation
Plague.....	*Pasteurella pestis*	Small rod with bipolar staining; pleomorphic in salt media	Good growth in standard media
Tularemia..	*P. tularensis*	Pleomorphic, coccoid to rod-shaped	Requires enriched media
Pertussis ...	*Hemophilus pertussis*	Minute oval capsulated rod	Requires enriched media
Brucellosis .	*Brucella melitensis, B. abortus, B. suis*	Small rod, often coccoid	Grows on standard media, *B. abortus* needs 10 per cent carbon dioxide for isolation

staining) (Fig. 25·2). They are usually parasites of mammals and birds. In these animals they cause severe infections characterized by bacteremia and multiple hemorrhages in internal organs and mucous membranes. These infections are called *hemorrhagic septicemias.* Two of these infections may spread from animals to man. Plague is caused by *P. pestis,* tularemia by *P. tularensis.*

The Organism. When *P. pestis* is cultivated on 3 per cent salt agar it forms an extraordinary variety of involution forms. Colonies on nutrient agar are small and granular with irregular margins. In broth the growth is granular, hanging in threads from the surface, adhering to the sides of the tube, and forming a granular sediment.

P. pestis is readily destroyed by the usual chemical and physical methods of disinfection. Ordinarily it succumbs quickly to conditions outside its living hosts, but if expelled in droplets of sputum into very moist cool air, it may remain alive for some time.

The Disease. Plague (*the black death*) spread over Europe in the Middle Ages, sometimes killing as many as 50 per cent of the population of whole countries. During the last 60 years there has been another pandemic of the disease with thousands of cases in Asia and smaller outbreaks in all parts of the world.

Types of Infection. Bubonic plague is the usual form of the disease, characterized by *buboes* (suppurating lymph nodes) in the axillae and groin. In *septicemic plague* the lymph nodes are not affected and the rapidly fatal infection spreads through the blood stream. Inhalation of plague organisms results in *primary pneumonic plague.*

Caused by the "Little Bacteria"

Sources of infection	Modes of infection	Immunization
Rodents; human cases of pneumonic plague	Fleas; air-borne if pneumonic	Vaccination by killed culture
Rabbits, squirrels, and other rodents	Biting insects; contact with infected animals	None
Human cases	Droplets, contact, infected articles	Vaccination with killed cultures
Goats, cattle, swine	Raw milk; contact with infected animals	None

Epidemiology. Plague persists in many areas of the world as an infection of wild rodents. It is spread from animal to animal by insect ectoparasites and is a mild chronic infection. Domestic rats from time to time acquire the infection from the wild rodents. In them the infection is severe and fatal.

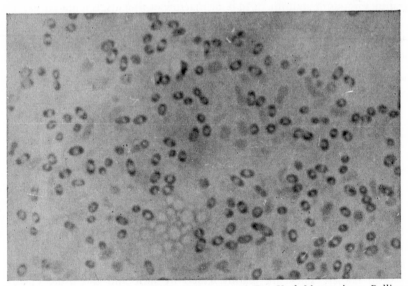

FIG. 25·2 *Pasteurella pestis.* ×3,000. (*Courtesy of Dr. Karl Meyer, from Pollitzer, "Plague," World Health Organization.*)

Man usually is infected by fleas that have fed on infected rats. Contact infection is possible through the skin while handling infected animals or via the alimentary canal. (See Fig. 25·3.) Human-to-human infection occurs in epidemics of primary pneumonic plague.

Control, Prevention, and Treatment. It is obvious that epidemic plague depends on the existence of infected rodent reservoirs parasitized by insects that also attack man. Suppression of domestic rats and fleas is possible, but control of the wild rodent reservoirs is very difficult. It follows that while it is possible to prevent epidemics of plague, sporadic cases of plague in areas inhabited by infected wild rodents will still occur.

Effective vaccines of either heat-killed or living avirulent bacteria are used extensively. Sulfadiazine in daily doses will protect persons temporarily exposed.

The fatality of septicemic and pneumonic attacks was as high as 100 per cent in the past. Serum therapy was of moderate effectiveness in *bubonic* infections. Sulfadiazine is very effective in the bubonic disease. In the last few years it has been shown that streptomycin and the wide-range antibiotics are definitely curative in septicemic and pneumonic infections.

Laboratory Diagnosis. During epidemics of plague the clinical signs are usually sufficient for diagnosis. Laboratory tests are required for the diagnosis of sporadic cases in man and for the identification of the infection in wild rodent and rat populations. The discovery of gram-negative rods with bipolar granules in pus or sputum, or in bone marrow of rodents, is tentative evidence of the infection. The characteristic appearance of the organisms from salt agar cultures, the type of growth in media, the lesion developing in guinea pigs, and agglutination by homologous serum confirm the identification.

PASTEURELLA TULARENSIS, THE CAUSE OF TULAREMIA

Tularemia is also known as *rabbit fever*. The causative organism is *P. tularensis.* The disease, both in animals and man, resembles plague.

The Organism. *P. tularensis* appears as coccoid cells in body tissues. In cultures it is extremely pleomorphic. It is not a typical bacterium, for it reproduces by budding rather than by fission. It does not grow on standard media but can be cultivated on egg media or on blood-glucose-cystine agar.

Although the organism has no capsule, it does produce a soluble specific polysaccharide which acts as a precipitin-producing antigen. Some of its protein antigens are shared by brucellas. The bacteria die off rapidly in cultures, but they have been found to survive for some time in water and in dead bodies. They are readily killed by heat and the usual chemical disinfectants.

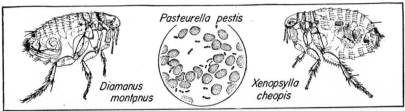

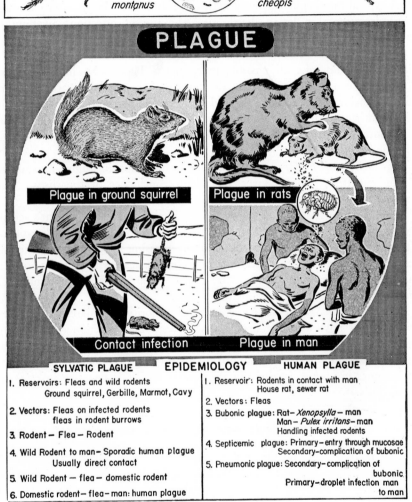

FIG. 25·3   Epidemiology of plague. (*From Mackie, Hunter, and Worth, "A Manual of Tropical Medicine," Saunders.*)

The Disease. *P. tularensis* infects rabbits and many other wild rodents, game birds, and man. Man acquires the infection accidentally. The most common method of infection is through the skin while handling infected animals. In addition tularemia may be acquired by the bites of infected ticks, deer flies, and other insects, and by the ingestion of incompletely cooked infected meat.

A typical case begins abruptly with chills and fever 3 days after exposure. An ulcerative skin lesion develops at the site of infection. Swelling of adjacent lymph nodes follows.

Prevention and Treatment. Persons who handle animals that may be infected should take all possible precautions. Those who have to do so frequently can be vaccinated, but the efficacy of the available vaccines is not finally established. Streptomycin and Aureomycin are both very effective in the treatment of tularemia. Without antibiotic therapy 5 per cent of cases die.

Laboratory Diagnosis. Three types of tests are used in the diagnosis of this disease.

Cultivation of the Organisms. Although cultivation in guinea pigs of the organisms from patients gives very definite evidence of the disease, the method is not often used because of the danger to laboratory workers.

Agglutination Test. After the first week of the disease the patient's serum will give positive agglutination tests with an antigen made from a formalin-killed suspension of an avirulent strain. A rising titer of agglutinins is conclusive evidence of the infection. Simultaneous tests with brucella antigen are done because of the clinical similarity of tularemia and undulant fever and because cross agglutinations may occur.

The Bacterial Skin Test. An American authority on tularemia, Dr. Lee Foshay, has advocated the use of a skin test. The injection of a minute amount of an extract of *P. tularensis* causes the formation of a definite wheal within 48 hours in cases of tularemia. This test has two definite advantages: it becomes positive very early in the disease and it is negative in cases of brucellosis.

HEMOPHILUS PERTUSSIS, THE CAUSE OF PERTUSSIS

The members of the genus *Hemophilus* are very small gram-negative bacteria without spores or flagella. All are fastidious in their cultivation, often growing most abundantly in blood media. Hence the name *Hemophilus* (blood-loving). They usually attack the mucous membranes of the respiratory tract or eye.

Hemophilus pertussis, the cause of whooping cough, is also known as the *Bordet-Gengou bacillus* after its two discoverers. *Pertussis* is the scientific name for whooping cough.

The Organism. *H. pertussis* is a very small ovoid rod (Fig. 25·4). When first isolated it requires blood for growth, but after repeated transfers it will grow in ordinary nutrient media. Newly isolated cultures are smooth and capsulated. They are called *Phase I* organisms. On further cultivation the bacteria become rough and less virulent. *H. pertussis* produces a thermolabile exotoxin.

Under natural conditions animals are not infected. Mice succumb rapidly to intravenous or intracerebral inoculation and are used to test virulence of cultures and effectiveness of vaccines.

Two other bacteria, *Brucella bronchiseptica* and *Hemophilus parapertussis,* are occasionally found in pertussislike infections.

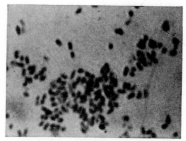

The Disease. Whooping cough is a form of acute bronchitis. The bacteria are present in enormous numbers in the ciliated lining of the bronchi and trachea. Their mucoid secretion prevents the normal action of the cilia, and their endotoxins cause irritation of the tissues. The incubation period is 7 to 10 days, and the early signs resemble those of the common cold. The characteristic cough develops a week or 10 days later. Each paroxysm of coughing is followed by a violent inspiration, which is the "whoop." The cough persists for several weeks, but *H. pertussis* disappears by the end of the third week.

Fig. 25·4 *Hemophilus pertussis.* ×2,000. ("*Medichrome,*" Clay-Adams Co., Inc., Dr. Gregory Shwartzman, Mt. Sinai Hospital.)

Many people think that whooping cough is a mild and unimportant infection. In North America and Europe it causes three times as many deaths as all other "children's diseases" combined! Ninety per cent of the deaths are of children under three years of age and in cases complicated by bronchopneumonia.

Undiagnosed early cases and atypical cases are the chief sources of infection. Spread of the organisms is by droplets and articles freshly contaminated with bronchial discharges. Infants and preschool children should be kept from contact with the disease. Children with whooping cough should be kept from school and from public places, but strict isolation is unworkable and is no longer generally recommended.

Immunization. Alum-precipitated pertussis vaccine is combined with diphtheria and tetanus toxoid to make the so-called *combined vaccine* (Fig. 19·1*a*). Authorities recommend that the vaccine be given in three monthly doses beginning at three months of age. Single booster doses should then be given at the ages of eighteen and thirty months, and thereafter every 3 years (at the ages of five and eight). Pertussis vaccine is made from killed cultures of Phase I bacteria. The preparation is sometimes called Sauer's vaccine after the American doctor who was largely responsible for its development. (See Fig. 25·5.)

Vaccination of pregnant women who have no history of whooping cough is sometimes advocated. Its purpose is to protect newborn infants who would otherwise not obtain any congenital antibodies. Hyperimmune human serum may be used in an emergency to protect exposed susceptible infants. The wide-range antibiotics, especially Aureomycin, are very useful in the treatment of whooping cough.

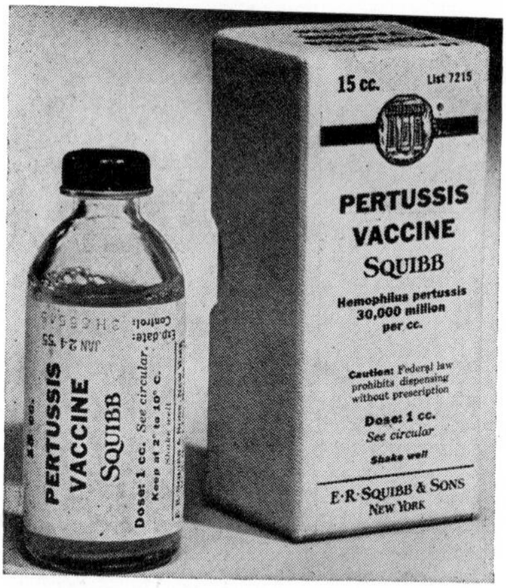

FIG. 25·5 Pertussis vaccine. (*E. R. Squibb and Sons.*)

Laboratory Diagnosis. The isolation and identification of *H. pertussis* are used to a limited extent in the diagnosis of early and atypical cases. The medium used is glycerin-potato agar with added rabbit or human blood. Penicillin may be added to the medium to prevent the growth of other respiratory bacteria. Two methods of inoculation are used. The first is the cough plate. An open plate of fresh medium is held 4 or 5 inches from the patient's mouth during several paroxysms of coughing. The other is the nasal swab method, which is useful in collection of material from infants and others who do not cough explosively. A small cotton swab on a thin wire is passed very gently through one nostril into the nasopharynx and held there while the child coughs. The swab is withdrawn and streaked on the medium. Small hemolytic colonies appear after several days' incubation. Identification is based on colony appearance, morphology of the organism in stained smears, and slide or tube agglutination tests with specific agglutinating serum. Serologic tests are seldom used.

HEMOPHILUS INFLUENZAE

In 1892 Pfeiffer discovered this organism and thought it to be the cause of influenza. It is now well established that influenza is a virus infection. However, *H. influenzae* is responsible for important infections of infants. It is also known as the *influenza bacillus* and as *Pfeiffer's bacillus*.

The Organism. The cells of *H. influenzae* are very small capsulated rods when seen in materials obtained from the body and in young cultures. In older cultures varied coccoid and filamentous forms may appear. Unlike *H. pertussis,* this organism never becomes adjusted to growth in ordinary media.

Pathogenicity. *H. influenzae* is present in the upper respiratory tracts of normal adults. It may become an opportunist invader during attacks of viral infections. Infants are particularly susceptible to infection with the B type of the organism. Presumably they acquire the infection from healthy adult contacts. In some infants the influenza bacillus causes severe illnesses including endocarditis and obstructive laryngotracheitis. *H. influenzae* meningitis is the commonest type of meningitis in babies. In the past it was almost invariably fatal. Now many cases are saved by chemotherapy (streptomycin and sulfadiazine, or chloramphenicol). Type-specific rabbit antiserum is used in cases that do not respond promptly to chemical treatment.

Laboratory Diagnosis. The discovery of tiny gram-negative rods in spinal fluid or from blood cultures from sick infants is presumptive evidence of this infection. The organisms in spinal fluid or from blood cultures will give a capsular-swelling reaction with specific antiserum.

OTHER MEDICALLY IMPORTANT ORGANISMS OF THE PARVOBACTERIACEAE

The Bacteria of Conjunctivitis. *Acute epidemic conjunctivitis,* popularly called pink eye, is caused by *Hemophilus aegyptius* (the Koch-Weeks bacillus). (See also the discussion of infectious inclusion blennorrhea and trachoma in Chap. 32 and of acute infectious conjunctivitis of the newborn in Chap. 27.)

Hemophilus ducreyi, the Cause of Chancroid. *Chancroid* (soft chancre) is an infection of the external genitals. It is a venereal disease. See Chap. 31, page 427. *H. ducreyi* (Ducrey's bacillus) can be seen in direct smears from the lesions and cultivated on blood media or in the fertile egg. A skin test, the *Ito-Reenstierna reaction,* is positive in active and recovered cases. The antigen is a suspension of the dead bacteria and is injected intradermally. Chemotherapy is effective.

Streptobacillus moniliformis, the Cause of Ratbite Fever. This actinomycetelike organism is a natural parasite of rats. Sporadic cases in man are the result of rat bite. At least two epidemics have been traced to raw milk, presumably infected by rats. This infection is very similar to the ratbite fever caused by the *Spirillum minus,* which is discussed in Chap. 31.

Anaerobic cultures in enriched media are used to isolate the organism from pus, blood, and joint fluid. Diagnosis is confirmed by mouse inoculation.

Malleomyces mallei, the Cause of Glanders. The organisms of the genus *Malleomyces* resemble the pasteurellas. *M. mallei* causes severe infections of horses known as *glanders* and *farcy*. Infection may be acquired by veterinarians, stablemen, and others who handle sick horses.

Another species, *M. pseudomallei* (also known as *M. whitmori*), is the cause of a similar infection, *melioidosis,* transmitted from rodents to man. Most of the cases have been reported from southeast Asia. This organism has been suggested as an effective weapon of bacteriologic warfare.

The Anaerobic Genera: Bacteroides and Fusobacterium. Members of the genus *Bacteroides* are common in feces. Several species are found in suppurating lesions of the mouth, lungs, and digestive tract.

The spindle-shaped members of the genus *Fusobacterium* are found on the gums and tonsils of normal persons. They are often associated with certain spirochetes in the mixed infections of *fusospirochetal* disease. These infections, including the stomatitis known as *trench mouth* and other lesions of the respiratory and genital organs, are discussed in Chap. 31.

STUDY SUGGESTIONS

You should study Tables 25·1 and 25·2 before reading the text of the chapter. Then study and master the section on each of these diseases before going on to the next. If you will make a simple table listing the other bacteria described in the last section of the chapter, their important characteristics, and the diseases with which they are connected, you will be more likely to remember them and will have a handy reference table.

Which of the diseases described in this chapter is present in every community? Which are occasionally present in your state? Which one is very rare in the United States? What measures do the public health authorities take to protect us against each of the diseases discussed in detail? What measures can the individual take to protect himself? Describe cases of any of these infections of which you have personal knowledge.

What specific nursing precautions would be reasonable in each of these infections?

SUGGESTED READING

(See also appropriate chapters or sections of medical texts listed in Appendix A, page 572.)

The Brucellas and Brucellosis

AMERICAN PUBLIC HEALTH ASSOCIATION: "Standard Methods for the Examination of Dairy Products." 10th ed., New York, 1953.

BORMAN, E. K., and D. E. WEST: Brucellosis (Undulant Fever), in "Diagnostic Procedures and Reagents." American Public Health Association, New York, 1950.

EVANS, A. C.: Brucellosis in the United States. *Am. J. Pub. Health* **37**:139 (1947).

FEIG, M.: Some epidemiological aspects of brucellosis in the midwest. *Am. J. Pub. Health* 42:1253 (1952).

KEILHOLZ, F. J.: They're clamping a ban on brucellosis. *Country Gentleman,* October, 1951.

SPINK, W. W., *et al.:* Control of brucellosis. *J.A.M.A.* 141:326 (1950).

Pasteurella pestis and Plague

LINK, V. B.: Plague. *Am. J. Trop. Med.* 31:452 (1951).

MACKIE, T. T., G. W. HUNTER, and C. B. WORTH: "A Manual of Tropical Medicine." 2d ed., Saunders, Philadelphia, 1954. Page 174.

Pasteurella tularensis and Tularemia

AYRES, J. C., and R. F. FEEMSTER: Epidemiology of tularemia in Massachusetts with a review of the literature. *New England J. Med.* 238:187 (1948).

BRIGHAM, G. D.: Tularemia (*Pasteurella tularensis*) in "Diagnostic Procedures and Reagents." 3d ed., American Public Health Association, New York, 1950.

HESSELBROCK, W., and L. FOSHAY: The morphology of *Bacterium tularense.* *J. Bact.* 49:209 (1945).

LINDEKE, H. L., and S. D. MAIDEN: Tularemia treated with aureomycin. *J.A.M.A.* 142:99 (1950).

TILLMAN, S. G.: Nursing care in tularemia. *Am. J. Nursing* 48:389 (1948).

Hemophilus pertussis and Whooping Cough

AMERICAN ACADEMY OF PEDIATRICS: "Report of the Committee on Immunization and Therapeutic Procedures for Acute Infectious Diseases." Evanston, 1952.

BELL, J. A.: Pertussis immunization. *J.A.M.A.* 137:1276 (1948).

COHEN, S. M., and M. W. WHEELER: Pertussis vaccine prepared with Phase I cultures grown in fluid medium. *Am. J. Pub. Health* 36:371 (1946).

KENDRICK, P. A., E. M. LAWSON, and J. J. MILLER: *Hemophilus pertussis,* in "Diagnostic Methods and Reagents." 3d ed., American Public Health Association, New York, 1950.

Hemophilus influenzae

ALEXANDER, H. E., and G. LEIDY: *Hemophilus influenzae* meningitis treated with streptomycin. *J.A.M.A.* 132:434 (1946).

GRANKE, J.: Influenza meningitis. *Am. J. Nursing* 45:568 (1945).

Other Important Parvobacteriaceae

DACK, G. M.: Non-sporing anaerobic bacteria of medical importance. *Bact. Rev.* 4:227 (1940).

HAYMAN, A., P. B. BEESON, and W. H. SHELDON: Diagnosis of chancroid. *J.A.M.A.* 129:935 (1945).

HINE, M. K., and G. P. BERRY: Morphological and cultural studies of the genus *Fusiformis.* *J. Bact.* 34:517 (1937).

CHAPTER 26

Corynebacterium diphtheriae and Other Nonsporing Rods of Medical Importance

Gram-positive rods that tend to be pleomorphic and have granules and bars belong to the family *Corynebacteriaceae*. They are usually but not always aerobic and nonmotile. The most important member of this family is *Corynebacterium diphtheriae*, the cause of diphtheria. Two other species are described here. In addition three other genera of nonsporing bacilli are included in this chapter.

CORYNEBACTERIUM DIPHTHERIAE, THE CAUSE OF DIPHTHERIA

In the United States deaths from diphtheria have decreased from 40 per 100,000 in 1900 to 0.6 per 100,000 in 1950. The conquest of diphtheria is the

330

result of our very complete knowledge of the bacteriology and immunology of the disease. The organism can be found and identified with great accuracy. Methods of active and passive immunization, specific serum therapy, and detection of susceptible persons have all been perfected. In American communities where this knowledge has been effectively utilized, diphtheria has practically disappeared. On the other hand, during the Second World War there was a great increase in the incidence of diphtheria in Europe and an increased fatality that seemed to be associated with the spread of unusually virulent strains.

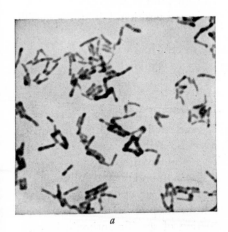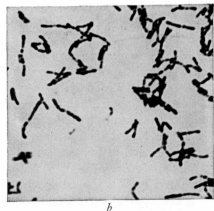

a   *b*

FIG. 26·1 *Corynebacterium diphtheriae* stained with methylene blue. ×1,200. (*a*) Gravis strain; (*b*) intermedius strain. (*From Burrows, "Textbook of Microbiology,"* *Saunders.*)

The Organism. The diphtheria bacillus was first recognized by Klebs in 1883 and cultured by Loeffler in 1884. It is frequently called the *Klebs-Loeffler bacillus* (sometimes shortened to *K.L. bacillus*). The correct scientific name is *Corynebacterium diphtheriae.*

Morphology and Staining. *C. diphtheriae* is a slender pleomorphic rod. It is nonmotile and has neither capsule nor spores. Slightly curved, club-shaped, and wedge-shaped cells are common. Branching forms are sometimes seen. Many cells stain evenly, particularly in young cultures, but most cells contain metachromatic material in the form of granules or bars (Fig. 26·1). Corynebacteria are gram-positive but are usually stained with methylene blue, which colors the granules dark blue and the rest of the cell light blue. Other differential stains such as Neisser's may be used to show the granules.

Physiology. The organisms are essentially aerobic, though they will grow slowly under anaerobic conditions. They prefer body temperature and a slightly alkaline reaction. Proteins are not digested, but typical cultures form acid from dextrose and maltose. Their most important physiologic characteristic, their ability to form exotoxin, is discussed below.

Resistance. Diphtheria bacilli are readily killed by heat and the usual chemical disinfectants. They may survive long periods of drying if they are embedded in pieces of the diphtheritic pseudomembrane.

Cultivation. The organism will grow on all ordinary media, but three special kinds are commonly used.

1. Loeffler's medium. This is a mixture of three parts of fresh animal serum and one part of glucose broth. The medium is coagulated in slants by heating the medium in tubes held in a slanted position. Diphtheria bacilli grow very rapidly on the surface of this medium.

2. Tellurite agar. This is a plating medium enriched with blood or serum to which a small amount of potassium tellurite is added. This salt inhibits many bacteria and causes the diphtheria organisms to form characteristic dark colonies (Fig. 26·2).

3. Special liquid medium for toxin production. Diphtheria toxin is produced commercially by cultivating a specially selected strain of *C. diphtheriae* in a liquid medium containing amino acids, maltose, accessory growth substances, and a very small but definite amount of iron.

Diphtheria Toxin. In 1888 Roux and Yersin found that cultures of the diphtheria bacillus formed filtrable toxin. It is a true exotoxin (page 213). It is destroyed by exposure to moderate heat. Its properties are altered by the action of formalin. It causes the formation of specific antitoxin in man and animals and is neutralized quantitatively by antitoxic serum.

The toxin is a very strong poison. One milliliter of a toxic filtrate may contain enough toxin to kill more than 1,000 guinea pigs. The simplest unit of toxin is an *MLD* (*minimum lethal dose*). It is the amount that will kill a 250-gram guinea pig on the fourth day. An *L+ dose* (*lethal plus dose*) is the amount of toxin that, when mixed with a unit of diphtheria antitoxin, will kill the guinea pig in 4 days. An L+ dose is much larger than an MLD.

Other Corynebacteria. There are many species of the genus *Corynebacterium* in addition to the diphtheria organism. Several species have been found responsible for diseases of farm animals and mice. Two species, *C. pseudodiphtheriticum* (*Hofmann's bacillus*) and *C. xerose,* are nonpathogenic inhabitants of the human nose and throat. *C. acnes* (page 378) and others are common on the skin. These bacteria are often called *diphtheroids.*

Types of C. diphtheriae. Avirulent strains of the diphtheria organism undoubtedly exist, but their relation to virulent (toxigenic) strains is not clear. All toxigenic strains produce the same exotoxin, but the amounts produced may differ.

Types of *C. diphtheriae* also differ in colony morphology, cultural charac-

a

b

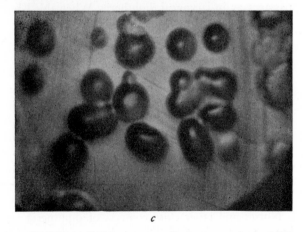

c

FIG. 26·2 Colonies of *Corynebacterium diphtheriae* on tellurite agar plates. ×15. (*a*) Gravis type; (*b*) mitis type; (*c*) intermedius type. (*Courtesy of Dr. Martin Frobisher, Jr*)

teristics, and antigenic composition. Three main types are generally recognized. They are the *mitis,* the *intermedius,* and the *gravis* types. From the point of view of phase variation these types are respectively S, sR, and SR, indicating variation from smooth to predominantly rough forms. These types also correspond to serologic types as determined by agglutination tests. A fourth type, *minimus,* characterized by very small colonies has also been described. In the laboratory, the types are differentiated by the character of the colony on tellurite agar (Fig. 26·2), pellicle formation in broth, fermentation of starch and glycogen, and hemolytic action on human erythrocytes.

The Disease. Diphtheria is an acute specific infection due to *C. diphtheriae.* Natural infection occurs only in man, but many animals are susceptible to the action of diphtheria toxin.

Local Infection and Toxemia. Diphtheria organisms localize in some one region of the infected body, but the toxin they produce spreads in the blood to all parts of the body. The most common place of local infection is the pharynx in the region of the tonsils. Next most common are the nares and the larynx. Laryngeal infection is common in small children and is sometimes called *membranous croup.* Occasionally the infection localizes in the vagina or in the eye. Wound infections and ulcers due to the organism are quite common in the tropics. The affected tissues become swollen, undergo degenerative changes, and form large amounts of fibrous exudate. This exudate collects on the surface and becomes the characteristic *diphtheritic membrane* (or *pseudomembrane*). It is gray in color and adherent to the underlying tissues. The membrane is composed of fibrin, tissue debris, leukocytes, and bacteria. The membrane may completely block the respiratory passageway in laryngeal diphtheria. When this happens it may be necessary to place a small tube in the larynx (*intubation*) or cut an artificial opening into the trachea below the larynx (*tracheotomy*) to allow the patient to breathe.

The absorbed toxin causes a degeneration of nerve and cardiac muscle tissue. It affects the kidneys and other organs. Some of these systemic effects are apparent early in the disease, but others such as heart failure and paralysis of the muscles of swallowing may be delayed for a week or more.

Diphtheria Carriers. Most diphtheria convalescents become noninfectious within 3 weeks, but a small percentage become convalescent carriers. They are usually persons having some abnormal condition of the nose or throat. Diphtheria cases are not discharged from isolation until at least two nose and throat cultures taken on successive days are negative.

Nurses and other close contacts of diphtheria patients are very likely to become contact carriers. The condition seldom persists for more than 2 weeks. No nurse should be transferred from the care of diphtheria cases to other duty unless she has negative nose and throat cultures.

In communities where diphtheria is common the organisms are passed continually from person to person. It has been estimated on the basis of carrier surveys that 75 per cent of the people in such communities become infected at least once in every 5 years and that each person is infected on the average at least two and a half times every 10 years. These infections may result in active disease. More frequently they result in a temporary carrier state and in an increased resistance to the disease. These infected persons are termed *casual carriers*. Adolescents and adults who have negative Schick tests without a history of clinical infection or immunization have presumably been casual carriers at some time in their past. In communities where diphtheria is well controlled, immunization by means of the casual carrier state is less likely and adults may give positive Schick tests showing that they remain susceptible to the disease.

Sources and Modes of Infection. Clinical cases, missed cases, and carriers are all sources of diphtheria infection. The organisms are discharged from the respiratory tract. They are spread by air-borne infection, by freshly contaminated objects, and by milk and milk products.

Immunity. Immunity to diphtheria is primarily due to the presence of an adequate level of diphtheria antitoxin in the body. Immunity acquired from a clinical attack or from a previous carrier state is quite lasting. Artificial immunization creates a less durable immunity. Repetitions of the carrier state fortify immunity in communities where diphtheria is prevalent. Wherever diphtheria is rare, booster doses are needed to fortify and reestablish immunity in those likely to be exposed to infection.

Treatment. Diphtheria antitoxin from immunized horses has been used in this country since 1895. It is prepared as described on page 235. The potency is expressed in units based on its ability to protect guinea pigs against the lethal effect of the toxin. In the past, exposed susceptible persons were passively immunized with an injection of 1,000 units of antitoxin. Now they are given penicillin and a recall dose of fluid toxoid.

Antitoxin is still the most important treatment in cases of diphtheria. A single dose of from 10,000 to 40,000 units is given intramuscularly as soon as the case is diagnosed by the doctor. Larger doses, often given intravenously, are needed if the patient has been ill for more than 24 hours or if there is severe toxemia. (See Fig. 26·3.)

Penicillin is very effective in stopping the growth of the diphtheria bacteria. It markedly decreases the incidence and duration of the convalescent carrier state. It does not neutralize the toxin. Therefore it is given in combination with antitoxin therapy.

The Shick Test. One-fiftieth of an MLD of highly purified diphtheria toxin is injected into the superficial skin of the forearm. Persons with sufficient antitoxin to be immune to diphtheria fail to react because the

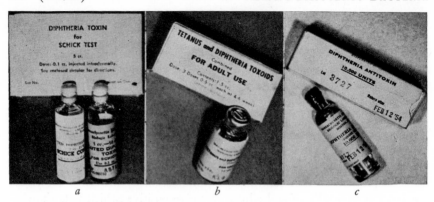

Fig. 26·3 Biologicals used in the control of diphtheria. (*a*) Toxin preparations for the Schick test. Right vial contains test toxin; left vial contains diluted toxoid for the Moloney control. (*b*) Diphtheria toxoid combined with tetanus toxoid. Used for the immunization of adults. (See Fig. 19·2 for the material used to immunize infants.) (*c*) Antitoxin for treatment. (*Institute of Laboratories, Massachusetts State Department of Health.*)

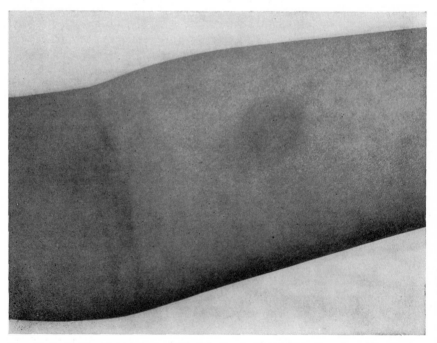

Fig. 26·4 Positive Schick test. (*"Medichrome," Clay-Adams Co., Inc., Dr. Gregory Shwartzman, Mt. Sinai Hospital.*)

injected toxin is promptly neutralized by their antitoxin. Those who have little or no antitoxin develop an area of redness which is most marked on the fourth to seventh days and fades slowly, leaving a brownish pigmentation. (See Fig. 26·4.) The Schick test is used to detect those who need active immunization for future protection or in the presence of an epidemic. It also serves to check the development of antibody after immunization.

Infants and young children who have not been previously immunized are assumed to be susceptible and are actively immunized without previous Schick-testing. Three to six months after immunization they are Schick-tested to be sure that the vaccination has "taken."

Schick-testing is done routinely on adults and older children before immunization is undertaken. Many of them will have already gained immunity by previous vaccination or by recognized or subclinical diphtheria infections and do not need immunization. Some adults and older children are hypersensitive to toxoid. When they are Schick-tested, a control test (the *Moloney test*) is done simultaneously on the other arm. The Moloney test material is a small amount of diluted toxoid. (See Fig. 26·3.) In hypersensitive individuals redness and swelling develop in this control test area in 48 hours and disappear within a week. (As noted above, reaction to the toxin of the

Table 26·1

The Schick Test

Age group	Schick test	Moloney test	Results and recommendations
Newborn to 6 years (not previously immunized)	Not done	Not done	Immunize with combined vaccine
Up to 10 years (have not been routinely immunized)	Negative	Not done	No immunization needed
	Positive	Not done	Immunize
Older children and adults	Negative	Negative	No immunization needed
	Negative	Positive	No immunization needed
	Positive	Negative	Immunize
	Positive	Positive (mild)	Immunize with 4 small doses of fluid toxoid
		Positive (severe)	No immunization needed (tests serve as recall doses)

Schick test develops slowly and persists.) Schick-positive persons who are also markedly Moloney-positive have been shown to have a considerable degree of immunity. In them the tests act as booster doses and no further immunization is needed. Table 26·1 summarizes information concerning the use of the Shick test.

Active Immunization. The purified and modified toxin of *C. diphtheriae* is used for active immunization. Toxoid is prepared by formalin treatment of the toxin. This is known as fluid toxoid (also called FT). Toxoid precipitated by aluminum phosphate (alum-precipitated toxoid, or APT) is used most commonly. Toxoid may also be precipitated by adsorption with aluminum hydroxide. Fluid toxoid stimulates antitoxin formation more rapidly than APT and is used during epidemics. As has already been noted, diphtheria toxoid is usually combined with tetanus toxoid and pertussis vaccine for infant immunization (page 325). Three doses at monthly intervals is the usual procedure. A Schick test 3 to 6 months later is desirable to be sure that sufficient antitoxin has developed.

Recall (booster) doses of toxoid are needed to maintain satisfactory immunity in persons living in communities relatively free from the disease (Fig. 26·3b). A single small dose of the combined vaccine is given again at eighteen months, three to four years, six to seven years, and eight to ten years. A single dose of dilute fluid toxoid is given to previously immunized older children and adults who are exposed to infection. Exposed persons are also given penicillin as a prophylactic measure.

Control of Diphtheria. Diphtheria is definitely diminished in communities when the majority of school children is immunized. It practically disappears when the majority of infants is immunized and recall immunization is routinely practiced. The modern attack on this disease is based on early immunization and reimmunization. Other methods of control such as isolation of cases, quarantine of contacts, and pasteurization of milk are important factors in places where immunization is incomplete.

Laboratory Diagnosis. The laboratory examines specimens from suspected cases, from convalescents ready for discharge, and from suspected contact carriers. The procedures used are (1) microscopic examination of a crude culture for the presence of morphologically typical organisms, and (2) isolation and testing of virulence (toxin production). Microscopic examination alone may be sufficient for a preliminary report when the specimen is from a person ill with the typical symptoms of diphtheria. The virulence test is required to differentiate toxin-producing organisms from harmless diphtheroids when the specimen is from a case of longer than 3 weeks' duration or from a healthy carrier. Laboratories should carry out the virulence test on all specimens. Cultural tests and tests differentiating between the *gravis, intermedius,* and *mitis* strains are done in special studies.

Specimens. Nose and throat swabs are taken from suspected cases and suspected carriers. Swabs from the larynx, the vagina, wounds, or the eye are taken when the infection is localized in those sites. The swab is rubbed gently but thoroughly over the inflamed area. Swabbing should never be done after the use of an antiseptic gargle, mouthwash, or spray. The swabs are rolled over the surface of slants of Loeffler's medium. Both slants and swabs are immediately dispatched to the laboratory. (See Fig. 26·5.)

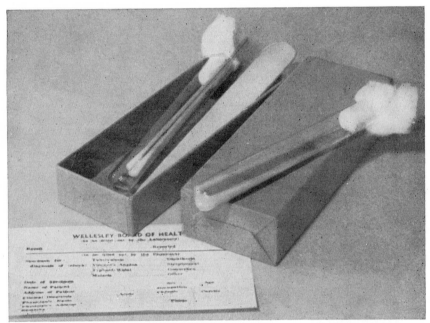

Fig. 26·5   Collection kit for diphtheria diagnosis. Sterile swabs, tongue depressor, and tube of slanted Loeffler's medium. (*Wellesley, Massachusetts, Board of Health.*)

Microscopic Examination of Cultures. After 10 to 18 hours' incubation smears are made from the Loeffler slants. If morphologically typical bacteria are seen, a report to that effect is sent to the doctor. Many bacteriologists make tellurite agar plates from the swabs. These enable them to discover corynebacteria that might have been overgrown in the less selective Loeffler's medium.

Virulence Test. A pure culture of the suspected organism is obtained by fishing a typical colony from a tellurite agar plate. Its ability to produce true diphtheria toxin is tested on a rabbit, guinea pig, or week-old chick. The exact technique used varies. The intracutaneous test on the rabbit will be described here.

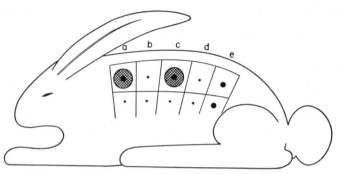

Fig. 26·6 Virulence test in rabbit (in vitro test). Culture *a* is control of known virulent diphtheria bacterium. Culture *c* is also a virulent culture of *Corynebacterium diphtheriae*. Cultures *b* and *d* are nonvirulent cultures. Culture *e* is slightly injurious to rabbit's skin but is not *C. diphtheriae*. Upper row of squares was inoculated first. Five hours later the rabbit was given a dose of diphtheria antitoxin. Then the lower row of squares was inoculated with the same cultures.

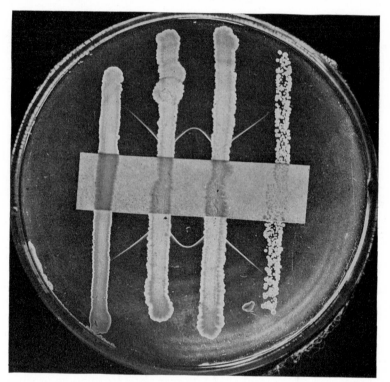

Fig. 26·7 In vitro virulence test. The lines of flocculation radiating from the two central streaks show that these two organisms are toxin-producing *Corynebacterium diphtheriae*. The two outer streaks are of organisms that do not produce toxin. (*From M. Frobisher, "Fundamentals of Bacteriology," Saunders.*)

Heavy suspensions of the pure cultures to be tested are inoculated into marked squares on the skin of the back. One square is injected with a control —a known virulent culture of *C. diphtheriae*. Five hours later 1,000 units of antitoxin are injected intravenously into the animal, and this is immediately followed by the injection of the same pure cultures into a corresponding series of marked squares on this same animal. Two days later necrotic lesions will have developed in the areas where the control culture and any other toxigenic culture were inoculated but not in the corresponding areas injected after the administration of antitoxin. Avirulent cultures will cause no lesions. Atypical lesions alike in both test areas will be due to organisms pathogenic for rabbits that are not virulent *C. diphtheriae*. (See Fig. 26·6.)

An in vitro virulence test is also used. A strip of filter paper saturated with antitoxin is placed in an agar plate. Parallel streaks of the cultures are made, each crossing the paper strip at right angles. White lines, formed by the flocculation of the toxin with the antitoxin, develop, bisecting the angles where the virulent cultures cross the paper. No lines are found at the junction of the paper and the avirulent cultures. (See Fig. 26·7.)

OTHER NONSPORING RODS OF MEDICAL IMPORTANCE

Certain other non-spore-forming rods are described here to complete our discussion of this group.

Erysipelothrix rhusiopathiae, the Cause of Erysipeloid. These bacteria cause a disease known as *swine erysipelas* in hogs. Fish that feed on animal wastes may become infected. Human infection occurs in persons who handle infected animals or meat, infected fish, manure, or other animal products. In man the infection is an erysipelaslike inflammation of the skin of the fingers and hand. Only rarely does generalized infection develop.

Erysipelothrix rhusiopathiae exists in the form of long filaments and short bacilli. They are gram-positive, nonmotile, and nonsporing. They may be found in bits of skin excised from the hand lesions. They can be cultivated in blood agar and their pathogenicity tested by inoculation into mice.

The Genus Lactobacillus. Important nonmedical activities of this group of gram-positive, acid-forming rods were described in Chap. 7. Their presence in the normal vagina and in the stools of infants has been noted. Lactobacilli of the mouth are considered important in the production of dental caries. Lactobacilli are found in the stomach in some pathologic conditions.

The Genus Pseudomonas. Gram-negative nonsporing rods that form soluble blue-green pigment in cultures are placed in the genus *Pseudomonas*. Most of them are inhabitants of soil and water. Sometimes they grow in milk and turn it blue. One species, *Pseudomonas aeruginosa*, is associated with the formation of greenish pus in chronic infections of wounds, the middle ear, nasal sinuses, and other locations. Pseudomonas intestinal infections of infants and pseudomonas bronchopneumonias have also been reported.

The Genus Klebsiella. Although the klebsiellas inhabit the respiratory rather than the digestive system, they are otherwise very closely related to the genus *Escherichia*. They are heavily capsulated, gram-negative, and non-motile. They make a viscid growth on standard agar media and ferment

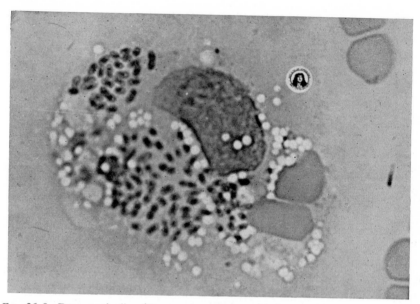

FIG. 26·8 Donovan bodies (*Donovania granulomatis*) in cytoplasm of large monocyte. ×2,000. Tissue smear from case of granuloma inguinale. (*SAB print 292, from Greenblatt, Dienst, and West, Am. J. Syph. 35:291.*)

many sugars with gas formation. They can be divided on the basis of varied O and K (capsular) antigens into several groups.

K. pneumoniae was first described by Friedländer and is often called *Friedländer's bacillus*. It causes rare but serious cases of pneumonia and has been increasingly common in mixed infections in persons treated with penicillin.

Klebsiellas with somewhat different antigenic structure have been found in two chronic infections of the nose in man: *ozena*, characterized by suppuration and crusting; and *rhinoscleroma*, a tumorlike hypertrophy of the nasal mucosa.

An organism commonly called *Donovania granulomatis* is the cause of the venereal disease granuloma inguinale (see Table 31·1 on page 428). The small capsulated rods, called *Donovan bodies*, can be seen in material from the characteristic ulcers (Fig. 26·8). They have been cultivated in the chick yolk sac but not on artificial media. Morphologically and serologically they seem to be members of the genus *Klebsiella*.

All klebsiella infections are susceptible to streptomycin.

The Pleuropneumonia Group. Very minute microorganisms that stain with difficulty and form tiny delicate colonies on enriched agar belong to

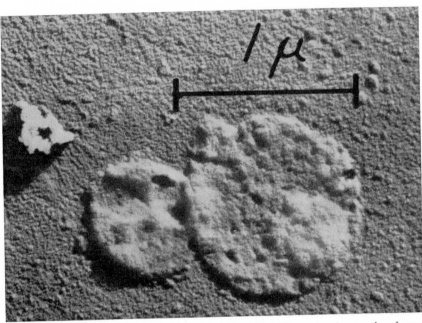

Fig. 26·9 Pleuropneumonialike organisms (PPLO). Electron micrograph of two chromium-shadowed cells from a case of urethritis. The collapsed and broken appearance of the cells is attributed to the absence of a rigid cell wall. (*From Morton et al., J. Bact. 68:697.*)

this group. The first one to be described was the causative organism of pleuropneumonia, a disease of cattle. Similar forms referred to as *pleuropneumonialike organisms* (or *PPLO*) have been found in soil, in animals, and in man. They have frequently been isolated from the male and female genital tracts and may be associated with nonspecific urethritis and other pelvic inflammatory conditions. In cultures of some species of bacteria, variants appear that are very similar to PPLO. They are known as the *L forms* of these species. (See Fig. 26·9.)

STUDY SUGGESTIONS

What are the characteristics of the family *Corynebacteriaceae?* of the genus *Corynebacterium?* Are all diphtheria organisms alike? How is an organism proved to be a truly virulent diphtheria bacillus? Describe a typical case of the disease. What types of carriers are found in this disease? Have you any evidence that would indicate that you have or have not been a carrier?

Explain the use of the Schick test and active immunization in the control of diphtheria. Check on your understanding of the Schick test and its control test. What personal experience have you had with the Schick test and with active immunization in your own community and in the hospital? How is the nursing personnel in your institution protected from diphtheria? What measures in your hospital prevent the spread of the infection among patients and other persons?

What technique is used in your institution for the collection of specimens from the respiratory tract? How is such material sent to the laboratory? What is the importance and the significance of the virulence test in diphtheria diagnosis?

Make a table listing the other organisms described in this chapter, their characteristics and the diseases they cause. Have you known of any cases of these other infections?

SUGGESTED READING

Corynebacterium diphtheriae and Diphtheria

AMERICAN ACADEMY OF PEDIATRICS: "Report of the Committee on Immunization and Therapeutic Procedures for Acute Infectious Diseases." Evanston, 1952.

CRAWFORD, J. D.: Penicillin in the treatment of diphtheria and the diphtheria-carrier state. *New England J. Med.* **239:**220 (1948).

FROBISHER, M., JR.: The Diphtheria Bacillus (*Corynebacterium diphtheriae*), in "Diagnostic Procedures and Reagents." 3d ed., American Public Health Association, New York, 1950.

———, E. I. PARSONS, and E. UPDYKE: The correlation of laboratory and clinical evidence of virulence of *Corynebacterium diphtheriae. Am. J. Pub. Health* **37:**543 (1947).

KING, E. O., M. FROBISHER, JR., and E. I. PARSONS: The *in vitro* test for virulence of *Corynebacterium diphtheriae. Am. J. Pub. Health* **39:**1314 (1949).

McCOMB, J. A.: The use of biological products in the control and treatment of diphtheria in Massachusetts. *New England J. Med.* **249:**120 (1953).

McLEOD, J. W.: The types mitis, intermedius, and gravis of *Corynebacterium diphtheriae. Bact. Rev.* **7:**1 (1947).

MEULLER, J. H.: The Diphtheria Bacillus and the Diphtheroids, in R. J. Dubos's, "Bacterial and Mycotic Infections of Man." 2d ed., Lippincott, Philadelphia, 1952.

Pappenheimer, A. M., and H. S. Lawrence: Immunization of adults with diphtheria toxoid. *Am. J. Hyg.* **36:**795 (1948).

Sauer, L. W., and W. H. Tucker: Simultaneous immunization of young children against diphtheria, tetanus, and pertussis. *Am. J. Pub. Health* **40:**781 (1950).

Other Pathogenic Nonsporing Rods

Anderson, K., W. A. DeMenbruen, and E. W. Goodpasture: An etiological consideration of *Donovania granulomatis* cultivated from granuloma inguinale (three cases) in embryonic yolk. *J. Exper. Med.* **81:**25 (1945).

Dienes, L.: Morphology and nature of the pleuropneumonia group of organisms. *J. Bact.* **50:**441 (1945).

Osterman, E., and L. G. Rettger: A comparison of the organisms of Friedländer's and coli-aerogenes groups. *J. Bact.* **42:**699, 721 (1941).

Solomon, S.: *Bacillus friedländer* wound infections and meningitis. *New England J. Med.* **237:**149 (1947).

Woodbine, M.: *Erysipelothrix rhusiopathiae,* bacteriology and chemotherapy. *Bact. Rev.* **14:**161 (1950).

The Diplococci and the Neisseriae

Three important species of spherical bacteria will be discussed in this chapter, *Diplococcus pneumoniae, Neisseria meningitidis,* and *Neisseria gonorrhoeae.* These organisms are the causes of acute lobar pneumonia, epidemic meningitis, and gonorrhea, respectively. They are all paired cocci. The two other groups of medically important cocci, the streptococci and the staphylococci, will be the subject of the next chapter. A summary of the important facts about these pathogenic spherical bacteria will be found in Table 27·1.

Table 27·1

Characteristics of Important Genera of Cocci

Genus	Morphology and staining	Important distinguishing characteristics	Diseases caused
Neisseria......	Bean-shaped paired cocci; gram-negative	Positive oxidase test; no hemolysis of blood media	Gonorrhea, vulvovaginitis, infectious conjunctivitis
Diplococcus....	Lance-shaped paired cocci; gram-positive	Bile-soluble; ferment inulin; alpha hemolysis of blood media	Lobar pneumonia, bronchopneumonia, pneumococcal meningitis, etc.
Streptococcus...	Cocci in chains; gram-positive	Not bile-soluble; do not ferment inulin; beta or alpha hemolysis of blood media	Streptococcal pharyngitis, scarlet fever, erysipelas, wound infections, etc.
Micrococcus....	Cocci in irregular groups; gram-positive	Abundant growth on standard media	Staphylococcal infections of skin, respiratory tract, etc.; staphylococcal food poisoning

DIPLOCOCCUS PNEUMONIAE AND PNEUMONIA

A preliminary note is necessary concerning the forms and causes of pneumonias. The term *pneumonia* designates any inflammation of the alveoli of the lungs with exudate filling the alveolar spaces. There are three commonly recognized forms of pneumonia.

1. Acute lobar pneumonia. This is an acute infectious disease with sudden onset and termination by crisis. It is a primary infection attacking persons of all ages and involving one or more whole lobes of the lungs. Bacteremia occurs in a considerable proportion of the cases. Well over 90 per cent are caused by *D. pneumoniae.* The remainder are due to infection by streptococci, *Klebsiella pneumoniae, Hemophilus influenzae,* and other pyogenic bacteria.

2. Bronchopneumonia. This is a secondary infection usually developing as an extension of a preexisting upper respiratory tract infection. The organisms spread by way of the bronchi and involve scattered areas of lung tissue. The respiratory opportunists, the streptococci, staphylococci, and *H. influenzae* cause many cases. Still more are due to *D. pneumoniae.*

3. Primary atypical pneumonia (virus pneumonia). Discussed in Chap. 32.

The Organism. Although the scientific name of this organism is *Diplococcus pneumoniae,* it is usually referred to as the *pneumococcus.* Fränkel in 1884 proved the association of this organism with human disease.

Morphology. Pneumococci are small, gram-positive cocci, nonmotile and nonsporing. They are seldom perfectly spherical, but rather somewhat elongated with one pointed end. They are often described as lance-shaped. All are capsulated (Fig. 27·1). They form short chains when they grow in liquid media. In this and other ways they are very like the streptococci. English bacteriologists classify them as *Streptococcus pneumoniae*.

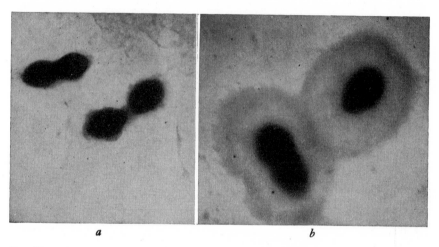

a   b

FIG. 27·1 *Diplococcus pneumoniae*—Neufeld capsular-swelling reaction. ×10,000. (*a*) Negative result. Type 3 organisms in type 1 serum. (*b*) Positive result. Type 1 organisms in type 1 serum. (*Electron micrographs courtesy of Dr. Stuart Mudd.*)

Physiology. Pneumococci are aerobes and facultative anaerobes. They need enriched media for growth. On blood agar they form characteristic granular colonies surrounded by a narrow zone of greenish discoloration. Like the related streptococci, they ferment many sugars with the formation of acid but no gas. Two characteristics distinguish them from the streptococci: (1) nearly all pneumococci ferment inulin, a starchlike polysaccharide, which is not attacked by streptococci; (2) the cells of the pneumococci are lysed (dissolved) by substances that lower surface tension, such as bile, sodium lauryl sulfate (Dreft), and other surface-tension depressants, including soap solutions. Streptococci do not undergo such lysis.

Pneumococci are readily killed by heat and chemicals. They are much more susceptible to soaps and detergents than most other bacteria. On the other hand they are resistant to drying when embedded in bits of sputum and remain alive for days in dust.

Antigens and Types. The somatic antigens are the same in all pneumococci, but a great variety of specific polysaccharides are present in their capsules.

On the basis of these polysaccharides the organisms are divided into many types. These capsular substances are also called *specific soluble substances,* and the term is often shortened to SSS. They act as haptens.

During the last 20 years American bacteriologists, led by Dr. Gladys Cooper of the New York City Health Laboratories, have differentiated 75 types of pneumococci on the basis of immunologic specificity due to the capsular material. Sera are available for the laboratory identification of some 30 types, including all that are common in this country. These types are usually indicated by Roman numerals, but some authorities prefer to use Arabic numerals. Thus the commonest type of all the pneumococci is referred to either as Type I or as Type 1. Small letters following the type number indicate subtypes, e.g., VIIa (or 7a). Type 3 is differentiated from all others by its much heavier capsule. It is sometimes called *D. mucosus.* One type or growth phase of a pneumococcus can be transformed into another type or phase by growing it in contact with killed organisms of the second type or their extracts. The materials responsible for this transformation are desoxy-ribonucleic acids and presumably are specific genetic materials from the organism causing the transformations.

Acute Lobar Pneumonia. The pneumococci are strictly parasitic organisms. All types have been found in the mouths and throats of healthy persons, but the incidence of this carrier state is intermittent and irregular. More people carry more pneumococci in cold weather and when respiratory infections are prevalent. Although the more virulent types, particularly Type 3, may frequently be found in healthy persons, carriers of the less virulent types are more common. The types concerned in clinical cases of pneumonia vary greatly in different regions and in different epidemics. Type I is most common, causing over 25 per cent of all cases. Types II, III, VII, and VIII are also often encountered. Certain other types are more common in pneumonias of infants. The high-numbered types (XXV and above) are seldom the cause of clinical disease.

Spread. Pneumococci are passed from person to person by air-borne infection (including infection by dust), by direct contact as in kissing, and by objects freshly contaminated with respiratory secretions. Man has considerable natural resistance to pneumococcal infection. Healthy carriers may develop pneumonia when cold, fatigue, dietary deficiencies, or existing infections enable organisms already present in the upper respiratory tract to invade the blood stream and the lung tissue.

Treatment. Type-specific antipneumococcal serum from immunized horses was previously used in pneumonia therapy. The routine treatment at present is penicillin. Chlortetracycline and other broad-range antibiotics are also used. The fatality without chemotherapy is over 30 per cent; with adequate penicillin it is below 5 per cent.

Immunization. Mixtures of the specific polysaccharides of the prevalent types of pneumococci have been used successfully to immunize special groups against pneumonia. The immunity was short-lived, however, and at present no vaccine is available for general use. The efficiency of penicillin in treatment makes it unlikely that there will be a demand for such immunization in the civilian population in peacetime.

Prevention. Prophylactic doses of penicillin may be given to groups of persons in institutions or military establishments when an epidemic threatens. The value of isolation and quarantine in the general population is debatable.

Other D. pneumoniae *Infections.* Sinus infections are frequently due to pneumococci. The diplococci also cause otitis media. In young children the pneumococci may cause meningitis, peritonitis, and septicemia.

Laboratory Diagnosis. The clinical symptoms of lobar pneumonia are not difficult to recognize in the majority of cases. Most physicians will, at the present time, prescribe penicillin or chlortetracycline therapy on the basis of these symptoms. Laboratory diagnosis is, however, very helpful in atypical cases of lobar pneumonia and also in pneumococcal infections of other parts of the body. It also serves to differentiate lobar pneumonia due to pneumococci from cases caused by other bacteria.

Collection of Specimens. The material most often examined is fresh sputum expectorated directly into a wide-mouthed bottle. The nurse should make sure that the specimen is sputum expectorated from the lungs, not saliva or nasopharyngeal discharge. Other specimens that may be sent to the laboratory are blood, spinal fluid, and pleural exudate. Pus from cases of otitis media and mastoiditis may also be sent. It is very desirable that all such specimens be collected before chemotherapy has commenced. If the patient has already received an antibiotic, a note to that effect should accompany the specimen.

Recognition of the Pneumococcus. If pneumococci are present in sufficient numbers, they can be readily demonstrated by a Neufeld capsular-swelling test done directly on the specimen. The technique of the test is described below. If the bacteria are scanty, the material is inoculated into an enriched broth or into a white mouse. After as short a time as 3 hours it may be possible to use the broth culture or the peritoneal fluid of the mouse for the Neufeld test. Many laboratories make blood agar plate cultures. From these not only pneumococci but other pathogenic bacteria can be isolated for further study. Inulin fermentation and lysis by bile will help to distinguish pneumococci from streptococci.

Neufeld Reaction (Quellung Reaction, Capsular-swelling Reaction). The capsule of a pneumococcus will become granular and visible when the bacterium is mixed with serum containing type-specific antibody. One or more loopfuls of the purulent portion of fresh sputum or organisms from cultures are placed on a clean glass slide. Loopfuls of appropriate typing sera and of methylene blue are added. The mixture is covered with a coverslip and examined with the oil immersion lens and a very strong light. In a positive test the deep-blue diplococci are surrounded by a granular grayish-green capsule with a definite outline. In a negative test the capsule will be nongranular and indefinite. (See Fig. 27·1.) Since it would be impractical to test each specimen with 31 different sera, it is customary to do a preliminary series of tests with Type 1 serum and six pooled sera. Pool B serum, for example, is a mixture of Types 3, 4, 5, 6, and 8 serum. If it causes a positive test, the specimen is then tested with each of these five sera to determine the exact type.

NONSPECIFIC INFECTIONS OF THE RESPIRATORY TRACT

Many specific respiratory diseases are discussed in other parts of this text. Among them are tuberculosis, influenza, measles, mumps, the common cold, diphtheria, scarlet fever, and whooping cough. Nonspecific infections of the upper respiratory tract are very common. The names given these infections usually indicate the region attacked. Sinusitis, tonsillitis, pharyngitis, and laryngitis are examples. Such infections may become chronic or recurrent. They are frequently sequelae of the common cold or associated with allergic conditions. The opportunist bacteria of the nose and throat multiply in these conditions. Among those often found are various streptococci and staphylococci, pneumococci, *Pseudomonas aeruginosa, Hemophilus influenzae,* and *Klebsiella pneumoniae.*

Bronchitis is a common complication of respiratory disease. It is likely to become chronic in elderly persons. *Bronchiectasis* is a condition that develops as a result of chronic bronchitis. The dilated walls of the bronchi form cavities in which microorganisms grow. Lung abscesses develop when foreign material such as saliva or bits of food are inhaled into the lungs. This is most likely to happen when the person is under anesthesia, in a coma, or intoxicated. Anaerobic streptococci, spirochetes, fusiform bacteria, and actinomycetes are common in bronchiectasis and lung abscesses. They impart a very foul odor to the expectorated pus.

NURSING CONSIDERATIONS IN RESPIRATORY DISEASE

The nurse must prevent the spread of primary respiratory infections among those under her care. She must prevent the development of secondary nonspecific infections in her patients. She must avoid acquiring respiratory infections herself.

The measures effective against the spread of respiratory infections include all types of routine sanitization and concurrent disinfection and the special measures taken against air-borne infection. The susceptibility of pneumococci to soaps and detergents provides an effective means of destroying these bacteria. The nurse must remember that she herself may be a very important source of opportunist mouth, nose, and throat bacteria.

A considerable proportion of the persons who are in contact with cases of pneumonia and other respiratory diseases become carriers of the causative organisms. Only by careful technique can the nurse avoid acquiring such organisms from her patients and spreading them to others or developing these diseases herself.

PATHOGENIC ORGANISMS OF THE GENUS NEISSERIA

This genus is named after Albert Neisser, who discovered in 1879 the organism causing gonorrhea. All neisseriae are gram-negative paired cocci with flattened adjacent sides. All are parasitic. Two species, *N. gonorrhoeae* and *N. meningitidis,* are important pathogens. A chromogenic species, *N. flavescens,* is an occasional incitant of meningitis. *N. catarrhalis* and several other nonpathogenic species are common inhabitants of the mouth, throat, and nose. Table 27·2 summarizes the characteristics of the commoner species.

The Oxidase Test. All neisseria colonies produce an enzyme known as *oxidase.* When the colonies are flooded with a special reagent (1 per cent dimethyl-para-phenylene-diamine hydrochloride), they turn first pink, then

Table 27·2. Important

Species	*Pathogenicity*	*Organisms found in*
N. *gonorrhoeae*	Cause of gonorrhea, vulvovaginitis, infectious conjunctivitis	Discharges of infected genital tract and eyes
N. *meningitidis* ...	Cause of epidemic meningitis, meningococcemia	Nasopharynx of sick persons and carriers; blood and spinal fluid of sick persons
N. *flavescens*	Cause of occasional case of meningitis	Nasopharynx and spinal fluid
N. *catarrhalis*	Nonpathogenic	Upper respiratory tract
Neisseria—other species	Nonpathogenic	Upper respiratory tract

maroon, then black. There are some other bacteria that give this reaction, but their colonies are readily differentiated from those of neisseriae. If the colony is fished before it becomes dark-colored, the neisseriae will still be alive and will grow in subculture. This test is a valuable aid in detecting these organisms in mixed culture. (See Fig. 27·2.)

NEISSERIA MENINGITIDIS, THE CAUSE OF EPIDEMIC MENINGITIS

The term *meningitis* indicates an inflammatory condition of the meninges, the membranes that envelop the brain and spinal cord. The plural of this word is *meningitides*. Epidemic meningitis is caused by *Neisseria meningitidis*. Sporadic meningitides are due to a great variety of organisms, including pneumococci, *Hemophilus influenzae,* and various members of the genus *Salmonella*. Meningitis resulting from an extension of mastoiditis or from head injuries is generally caused by streptococci or micrococci. Meningitides caused by the organism of tuberculosis and the organism of syphilis also occur, and some forms are caused by filtrable viruses.

The Organism. *N. meningitidis* is also called *N. intracellularis* and is popularly known as the *meningococcus*. Its morphology and staining are typical of the genus (Fig. 27·3). The organism is a strict parasite. It is found in the nasopharynx, blood, spinal fluid, and skin petechiae in cases of infection and in the nasopharynx of healthy carriers. It is a fragile organism that is readily destroyed by drying and by changes in temperature. It is killed by all the usual methods of disinfection.

Species of Neisseria

Cultivation	Pigment on agar	Acid produced from			
		Dextrose	Lactose	Sucrose	Maltose
Good growth only on enriched media with increased carbon dioxide pressure at 35–37 °C.	None	+	−	−	−
Same	None	+	−	−	+
Good growth on standard media in air at 27–37 °C.	Yellow	−	−	−	−
Same	None	−	−	−	−
Same	Often yellow (often rough)	±	±	±	±

The colonies on blood agar are white and smooth. A white pellicle is formed on semisolid agar. Dextrose and maltose are fermented, but not sucrose. There are capsules on Group A organisms, but not on those of Group B.

Groups of Meningococci. The meningococci found in this country belong to serologic Groups A, B, and C. Group A organisms are responsible for all major epidemics. The noncapsulated organisms of Group B are constantly

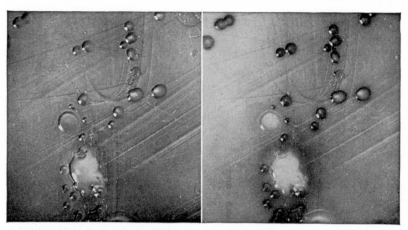

FIG. 27·2 The oxidase test. Colonies of *Neisseria meningitidis* and other bacteria on an agar plate. Left—before adding oxidase reagent. Right—after adding oxidase reagent. Note darkened colonies of *Neisseria*. (*From Burrows, "Textbook of Microbiology," Saunders.*)

present in the population. They include many different types and cause small epidemics and sporadic cases. The virulent Group C bacteria have been found in a very few small epidemics.

Meningococcal Infections. There are three forms of meningococcal infection.

1. *Infection of the Nasopharynx.* In nonepidemic periods 2 to 4 per cent of the population are carriers of meningococci. During an epidemic in an army camp 90 per cent of the men sooner or later became carriers. Such carriers may develop mild respiratory infection which confers immunity against the type of meningococcus that they carry. Others, particularly those carrying the Group A neisseria, may develop more extensive infection.

2. *Meningococcemia (infection of the blood stream).* Meningococcemia may be a transient phase in the development of cases of meningitis. A rash, called "spotted fever," may be present at this stage. Some Group B organisms cause chronic or intermittent fevers not diagnosed until the organisms in the blood stream are identified. In a few cases the bacteria invade the adrenal

glands, causing rapid collapse and death (Waterhouse-Friderichsen syndrome).

3. *Meningococcal Meningitis* (*cerebrospinal fever, "brain fever"*). Meningitis results when the organisms in the blood reach the meninges and localize there. The spinal fluid becomes loaded with pus containing the organisms and very large numbers of polymorphonuclear leukocytes. The disease has a sudden onset. It is characterized by delirium, high fever, and severe headache.

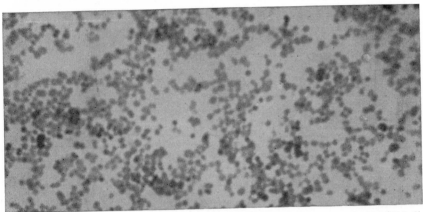

FIG. 27·3 *Neisseria meningitidis.* ×1,000. Stained smear of a pure culture. ("*Medichrome*," *Clay-Adams Co., Inc., Dr. Gregory Shwartzman, Mt. Sinai Hospital.*)

Epidemiology. It is seldom possible to trace the spread of infection from one recognized case of meningitis to another. Direct transfer by droplets and by freshly contaminated objects spreads the organisms from carriers and subclinical cases to healthy persons. Epidemics seem to be most common in army camps and refugee populations where people are crowded together and fatigued. Epidemics in the general population of this country involve relatively small numbers of cases but are alarming because of the potential high fatality.

Treatment. Before the use of antimeningococcal serum up to 90 per cent of cases died in epidemics. The use of polyvalent serum in army hospitals in the First World War brought the fatality down to 35 per cent. Serum treatment has now been supplanted by chemotherapy with still greater saving of lives. In the Second World War only 3.8 per cent of army cases died, though meningococcal meningitis still caused more deaths than any other infectious disease. Sulfadiazine is the usual treatment. Penicillin is equally effective in meningococcemia but does not penetrate the meninges so well. Sometimes both drugs are used.

Prevention. There is no effective method of active or passive immunization against meningococcal infection. The detection and quarantine of carriers are useful measures in institutions and military establishments but are impractical in the general population. Prophylactic doses of sulfa drugs have been used by the U.S. Army when an epidemic threatened, and penicillin is being used prophylactically in the Sudan, where meningitis is a principal cause of death.

Laboratory Diagnosis. The specimens used for laboratory diagnosis in meningococcal infections include swabbings from the nasopharynx, blood, and spinal fluid. The nasopharynx may be swabbed through the mouth with a bent swab, taking care not to collect mouth secretions, or through the nose by passing a swab on a flexible wire to the back of the nasopharynx. Blood is collected with sterile precautions by intravenous puncture. Spinal fluid is collected by lumbar puncture.

Because of the susceptibility of the meningococcus to drying and cold, the specimens must be examined as soon as possible. Media are best inoculated at the bedside. Specimens taken to the laboratory must be delivered directly to laboratory personnel. They should never be placed in the refrigerator. If the specimens have been taken after the administration of sulfa drugs or penicillin, the laboratory should be notified of this fact.

Direct Microscopic Examination. Gram-stained smears of spinal fluid are examined for the presence of gram-negative neisseriae. The presence of such organisms in cases with typical symptoms justifies a tentative diagnosis of epidemic meningitis. Some laboratories check the identification of the meningococci by performing a capsular-swelling test with polyvalent anti-meningococcus serum.

Cultivation. Cultivation is required for the discovery of the organisms in blood or nasopharyngeal swabs. It is also needed to confirm the tentative diagnosis based on direct smears. The media most commonly used are blood agar and semisolid agar. The colonies are gray, translucent, and nonhemolytic. On the nasopharyngeal plates they will be the only smooth colonies that give the typical oxidase test. Suspected colonies will be examined by gram-staining and fished for further testing in pure culture.

Identification of Isolated Organisms. The laboratory diagnosis will be confirmed by growth on agar to detect pigment production, fermentation tests in selected carbohydrate media, slide or tube agglutination tests, and quellung tests. The serologic groups of *N. meningitidis* may be determined by agglutination or quellung tests using specific antisera.

Differential Diagnosis of the Meningitides. When the laboratory worker makes his preliminary direct smear examination of the spinal fluid, he never looks for neisseriae alone but rather for any type of bacteria. He may find streptococci, micrococci, gram-negative rods that might be *Hemophilus in-*

fluenzae or salmonellas, or the gram-positive diplococci, *Diplococcus pneumoniae*. Appropriate methods of cultivation and further testing will be used to make the identification of the organisms certain. If no bacteria are seen but the smear shows many polymorphonuclear leukocytes, the specimen will be cultivated on blood agar. Special cultures for the organism of tuberculosis or serologic tests for syphilis will be done when the clinical picture and the appearance of the spinal fluid smears suggest these infections. If all such tests are negative, virus infection may be suspected and tested for by animal inoculation or other techniques. The microbiologic methods used in all these cases are discussed in the sections on the specific organisms.

NEISSERIA GONORRHOEAE, THE CAUSE OF GONORRHEA

N. gonorrhoeae is a strictly human pathogen. It causes the disease known as *gonorrhea* and is also the principal cause of acute infectious conjunctivitis in newborn infants and of many cases of vaginitis in female children.

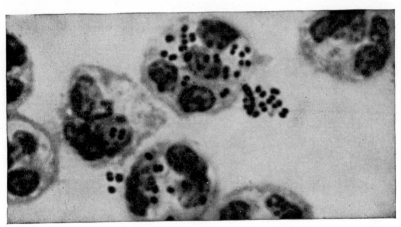

Fig. 27·4 *Neisseria gonorrhoeae* in an urethral smear. ×2,400. (*From Burrows, "Textbook of Microbiology," Saunders.*)

The Organism. *N. gonorrhoeae* is also called the *gonococcus*. The bacteria are large, paired, gram-negative cocci. In exudates they are found typically within the cytoplasm of polymorphonuclear leukocytes. (See Fig. 27·4.)

The gonococci survive longer in the refrigerator than at higher temperatures. The thermal death point is very low—50 to 55°C. They die quickly when exposed to air and dryness. They are readily killed by the usual chemical disinfectants.

Growth is best on plates of chocolate agar incubated in increased carbon dioxide tension. Colonies of gonococci are smooth and gray-white, with undulating margins. They are smaller than colonies of most other neisseriae. (See Fig. 27·5.) They give the typical oxidase reaction.

Gonococcal Infections. Reliable estimates indicate that over 1 million new gonorrheal infections come to the attention of the medical profession each year. It is estimated that another million receive no medical treatment. Three forms of the disease are described here.

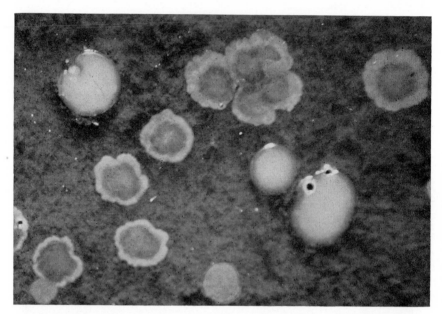

FIG. 27·5 Colonies of *Neisseria gonorrhoeae* (gray) and *Neisseria catarrhalis* (white) on chocolate agar. ×5. (*Courtesy of Dr. Charles M. Carpenter, from "Diagnostic Procedures and Reagents," American Public Health Association.*)

Gonorrhea of Adults. This disease is primarily an acute infection of the urogenital system in adults. Three to five days after exposure there is an acute inflammation of the mucosa of the urethra and of the vagina in the female, with an abundant purulent discharge. The acute stage may regress spontaneously or with appropriate treatment. Alcoholism, menstruation, sexual intercourse, heavy exercise, or other factors that alter the blood supply of the parts involved may cause the spread of the infection to other parts of the urogenital tract and the development of a chronic gonococcal infection. Scar tissue forming in infected genital tubes may prevent the passage of ova or sperm and so make the patient physiologically sterile. Often conditions necessitating major operations result from such infections. In an appreciable number of cases the organisms spread to still other parts of the body, causing gonococcal arthritis, endocarditis, and conjunctivitis.

There is no natural immunity to gonorrhea, and one attack confers no lasting immunity, though reinfection does not occur during the disease. Chronic unsuspected cases are important sources of infection. Careless and ignorant persons may spread the disease at all stages. There are no healthy carriers in the strict sense of the term. Sexual intercourse is the principal method of spread, but infections may be acquired in other ways. The spread of all genitoinfectious diseases and measures of control are discussed more fully in Chap. 31.

Acute Infectious Conjunctivitis. The most serious cases of gonorrheal conjunctivitis occur in the newborn. The infection is called *ophthalmia neonatorum*. When a baby is delivered from a mother with gonorrhea, its eyes become infected during its passage through the vagina. Other bacteria and the virus of inclusion conjunctivitis (page 451) cause less frequent and less severe forms of ophthalmia in infants. Gonococcal conjunctivitis has been one of the leading causes of blindness in early life. The number of cases has been greatly reduced by the prophylactic use of silver nitrate (Credé method) or penicillin in the eyes of babies immediately after birth. This procedure is required by law. Infants may also contract gonococcal infection of the vulva at the time of birth.

Gonorrheal conjunctivitis of older infants and children may be acquired from infected adults, and adult cases of conjunctivitis may be the result of transfer of infection from genitals to eyes by the patient's own hands. Nurses and doctors have sometimes infected their own eyes.

Gonorrheal Vulvovaginitis of Preadolescent Girls. Leukorrheal discharge and inflammation of the vagina in young girls may be due to a variety of causes. Less than half such cases are due to gonorrheal infection. In most cases of gonorrheal vulvovaginitis the infection is believed to have been acquired by sexual contact. Spread by the common use of towels and washcloths in the home is a possibility but an unlikely one. Rectal infection has been spread in hospitals by the use of improperly disinfected rectal thermometers. There is no scientific support for the theory that the infection is spread by school toilet seats. The infection in preadolescents has little tendency to spread and generally clears up within 6 months.

Treatment. One or two 10-day courses of sulfathiazole treatment were found in 1940 to be effective in nearly all cases. But as this treatment became common, sulfa-resistant strains developed in incompletely treated persons and were passed on to others. By 1945 the drug was effective in less than 50 per cent of cases. Fortunately at that time the effectiveness of penicillin was proved by extensive clinical tests. One to three doses of a slowly absorbable preparation of penicillin cures practically all cases of gonorrhea. The broad-range antibiotics are also effective. A single dose of penicillin by mouth will effectively prevent the development of gonorrhea in a person who is exposed to the disease. Fortunately there seems to be little or no tendency for gonococci to develop penicillin-resistant strains. Occasionally cases of syphilis and of nonspecific urethritis appear in persons who have received prophylactic or therapeutic treatment with penicillin. The dosage used may not have been great enough to suppress syphilitic infection acquired at the same time; the bacteria or viruses causing the urethritis may not be penicillin-sensitive.

Laboratory Diagnosis. The materials most frequently examined for the presence of *N. gonorrhoeae* are the purulent discharges from the urogenital system and eyes. Blood and joint fluid are sometimes examined. Because the gonococci are so fragile, special precautions are needed in taking and caring for specimens. Sterile swabs are used to collect the discharges. Special instructions for the collection of such specimens as those from the uterine cervix of the female or the prostate gland of the male must be followed carefully. Ideally, plates of chocolate agar are inoculated at the bedside or in the clinic as soon as the specimens are taken. When specimens for culture have to be transported to distant laboratories, the swab may be rubbed over a slant of enriched agar or placed in a tube of broth provided with the collection kit. Some public health laboratories supply a tube of dilute defibrinated blood containing crystal violet for this purpose. The dye inhibits the growth of gram-positive cocci that may be present and increases the likelihood that the gonococci will be alive when they reach the laboratory.

The Direct Smear. Two or more clean glass slides are usually provided with the collection kit. The person taking the specimens makes smears by rolling the freshly infected swabs across the slides. He allows the smears to dry in the air, fixes them by passing them through the flame, and sends them to the laboratory. The laboratory worker stains the smears by the Gram method and examines them for the typical intracellular, gram-negative, bean-shaped diplococci. When they are found he cannot be absolutely sure that they are gonococci, so his report reads, "Intracellular diplococci resembling gonococci were found." He will also report the types and relative numbers of pus cells present and may note the presence of other significant microorganisms.

Cultivation. It is generally agreed that cultivation reveals a larger number of infections than does the direct microscopic examination alone, particularly in chronic cases. Present methods of cultivation and identification are not difficult for the trained technician, especially if fresh specimens are provided. The organisms then grow quite readily on the chocolate agar plates, incubated in an atmosphere of increased carbon dioxide. The oxidase test helps the technician to select colonies for further study. Organisms are examined by gram-staining and by fermentation tests. *N. gonorrhoeae* should form acid in dextrose but not in other common sugars. Agglutination and capsular-swelling tests are not used.

Interpretation of Laboratory Reports. The diagnosis of gonorrhea must take into consideration the social history and habits of the patient as well as the clinical picture and laboratory results. A positive report from a direct smear is seldom questioned in the typical acute case. Confirmation by culture is needed in cases of vaginitis and in atypical cases. When a reliable laboratory reports repeated negative results in an acute case of urogenital disease, the condition is most certainly due to some other cause than neisserian infection.

The interpretation of results in chronic cases is much more difficult. Negative reports on smears should never be the sole criteria of cure or absence of infection. Cultures should always be made and will often be positive. Repeatedly negative cultures are sometimes reported from cases that show persistent clinical evidences of infection. In summary it may be said that while acute infections can be diagnosed with comparative ease and certainty, the question of the persistence or cure of a chronic infection is often very difficult to answer.

STUDY SUGGESTIONS

Table 27·1 provides a useful summary of the organisms discussed in this chapter and the next. It will pay you to study it carefully. Do not neglect the other table or the illustrations.

Can you summarize the morphologic and physiologic differences between the organisms of the genus *Diplococcus* and those of the genus *Neisseria?* between the typical diplococci and the typical streptococci?

What are the differences between a typical case of acute lobar pneumonia and a typical case of bronchopneumonia? In what other infections may a pneumococcus be the causative organism?

How do the types of pneumococci differ? When may it be desirable to determine the type of pneumococcus? How is this done?

List at least six organisms that may cause meningitis. How does epidemic meningitis differ from other meningitides? Does everyone who acquires *N. meningitidis* develop meningitis? Explain.

Why is the chronic stage of gonorrhea of such great importance? What forms of gonorrheal infection are found in immature individuals? How are these infections contracted?

Describe the collection and care of specimens for the laboratory diagnosis of acute lobar pneumonia, gonorrhea, and epidemic meningitis. Describe the laboratory tests and results that would lead to the following diagnoses: chronic gonorrheal salpyngitis (inflammation of the ovarian tubes), Type 3 pneumococcal pleuritis, meningococcemia, acute meningitis due to infection with a salmonella.

SUGGESTED READING

(Consult also the medical texts listed in Appendix A, page 572.)

Pneumococci and Pneumonia

COOPER, G. M., and A. W. WALTER: Application of Neufeld reaction to identification of types of pneumococci. Use of antiserum for 32 types. *Am. J. Pub. Health* **25**:469 (1935).

GOODNER, K.: The Pneumococcus, in "Diagnostic Procedures and Reagents." 3d ed., American Public Health Association, New York, 1950.

HEIDELBERGER, M., *et al.:* Antibody formation in volunteers following injection of pneumococci or their type-specific polysaccharides. *J. Exper. Med.* **83**:303 (1946).

HODGES, R. G., *et al.:* Epidemic pneumococcal pneumonia. *Am. J. Hyg.* **44**:183 (1946).

WHITE, B.: "The Biology of the Pneumococci." Commonwealth Fund, New York, 1938.

Meningococci and Meningitis

BRANHAM, S. E.: Serological relationships among meningococci. *Bact. Rev.* **17**:175 (1953).

———: The Meningococcus (*Neisseria meningitidis*), in "Diagnostic Procedures and Reagents." 3d ed., American Public Health Association, New York, 1950.

HEDRICH, A. W.: Recent trends in meningococcal disease. *Pub. Health Rep.* **67**:411 (1952).

KUHNS, D. M., *et al.:* The prophylactic value of sulfadiazine in the control of meningococcic meningitis. *J.A.M.A.* **123**:134 (1943).

PHAIR, J. J., and E. B. SCHOENBACH: The dynamics of meningococcal infections and the effect of chemotherapy. *Am. J. Hyg.* **40**:318 (1944).

ROSENBERG, D. H., and P. A. ARLING: Penicillin in the treatment of meningitis. *J.A.M.A.* **125**:1011 (1944).

SARTWELL, P. E., and W. M. SMITH: Epidemiological notes on meningococcal meningitis in the Army. *Am. J. Pub. Health* **34**:40 (1944).

Gonococci and Gonorrhea (See also references on venereal disease on page 435.)

ALLEN, J. H., and L. E. BARRERE: Prophylaxis of gonorrheal ophthalmia of the newborn. *J.A.M.A.* **141**:552 (1950).

BUCCA, M. A.: The effect of germicides on the viability and on the respiratory enzyme activity of gonococci. *J. Bact.* **46**:151 (1943).

Carpenter, C. M.: The Gonococcus (*Neisseria gonorrhoeae*), in "Diagnostic Procedures and Reagents." 3d ed., American Public Health Association, New York, 1950.

Eldering, G., and E. Palser: Gonococcus examinations: a comparison of slides, mailed slants, and immediate plates. *Am. J. Pub. Health* **36**:1022 (1946).

Heller, J. R.: The adequate treatment of gonorrhea. *J.A.M.A.* **131**:1480 (1946).

Laboratory Section of the American Public Health Association: Diagnostic procedures for gonococcal infection. *Am. J. Pub. Health* **36**:1461 (1946).

Welch, H., *et al.*: Penicillin X: successful treatment of gonorrhea with single intravenous injection. *J.A.M.A.* **126**:1024 (1944).

The Streptococci and the Micrococci

In addition to the organisms discussed in the last chapter there are two other important groups of pathogenic cocci, the streptococci and the micrococci (staphylococci).

THE STREPTOCOCCI

The streptococci are the most important of all pyogenic organisms. They were seen in pus by many early investigators, but not until 1884 were they proved to be the cause of pus formation. The great diversity of the conditions with which they are associated and the complexity of their relationships make them among the most fascinating of the commonly encountered pathogenic bacteria.

The Organisms. Streptococci are gram-positive and grow typically in chains. They are nonsporing. Capsules are not prominent. The cells are seldom perfectly spherical; some appear as diplococci and others are distinctly elongated. The chains may be short or long. In stained smears made from growth on solid media, the cells may be in clumps. (See Fig. 28·1.)

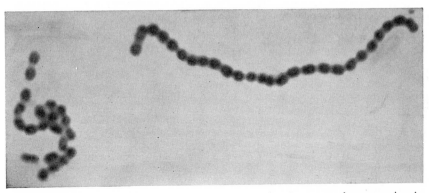

Fig. 28·1 *Streptococcus pyogenes.* ×3,000. Gram's stain of a pure culture growing in broth. (*"Medichrome," Clay-Adams Co., Inc., Dr. Gregory Shwartzman, Mt. Sinai Hospital.*)

Media made from meat infusion or containing blood or serum are needed for good growth. Many kinds of streptococci prefer diminished oxygen tension and increased carbon dioxide. Some are strict anaerobes. Sugars are fermented with the production of considerable amounts of lactic acid. Gas is seldom formed. Fermentation of special sugars helps to distinguish specific types of streptococci (Table 28·1). Streptococci differ from closely related pneumococci in their lack of bile-solubility and in their inability to ferment inulin.

Except for species that grow in milk and milk products, the streptococci are parasitic organisms of man and animals. But they are capable of survival outside their hosts. Their persistence and dissemination in dusts are important factors in the spread of streptococcal infections. They are readily killed by boiling and by pasteurization. Both the sulfonamides and penicillin are effective against them. Their growth in laboratory media is readily inhibited by the use of penicillin.

A number of important extracellular toxic substances are produced by the streptococci. One or more of these substances are found in each pathogenic type, but the nonpathogenic strains lack them all. The *erythrogenic toxin* acts on the skin, producing *erythema* (redness) followed by desquamation. It is responsible for the rashes of scarlet fever, erysipelas, and other streptococcal infections. It also causes generalized symptoms such as nausea, fever, and headache.

The streptococci vary in their ability to produce hemolysins. The hemolysins of the streptococci are called *streptolysins.* Virulent streptococci usually produce both streptolysin-S (stable in the presence of oxygen) and streptolysin-O (unstable in the presence of oxygen).

Several toxic substances elaborated by the streptococci are enzymes that destroy various components of tissues. These include streptokinase which is a fibrinolysin; streptodornase capable of attacking the desoxyribonucleic acid of cell nuclei; hyaluronidase; and proteinase.

Classification. Early bacteriologists named the streptococci according to the disease from which they were isolated or, in the case of nonpathogenic types, from the animal or food in which they were found. So such names as *Streptococcus scarlatinae, S. erysipelas, S. epidemicus* (the organism found in epidemic sore throat), *S. equi,* and *S. lactis* were commonly used. However, careful study demonstrated that identical organisms might be isolated from dissimilar clinical infections. Streptococci from a case of scarlet fever, from a case of puerperal sepsis, and from the throat of a healthy person might all be alike.

Dr. J. Howard Brown of Baltimore and others showed that streptococci could be divided into three groups on the basis of their effects on blood agar. Those that produced a green discoloration and partial hemolysis of the medium were placed in the alpha (α) group and named *S. viridans.* Those that formed zones of complete hemolysis around the colonies were placed in the beta (β) group and called *S. hemolyticus,* and those that did not affect the erythrocytes in the blood agar were included in the gamma (γ) group and called *S. anhemolyticus.* These reactions are shown in Fig. 28·2.

During the last 20 years, bacteriologists, following the lead of Griffith in England and Rebecca Lancefield in this country, have investigated the antigenic content of the streptococci. The typing methods that are now used are based principally on precipitation tests. The technique is usually referred to as *Lancefield typing.* They have been divided into Lancefield groups designated as A, B, C, D, etc. Each group is subdivided into types that are given numbers. Group A organisms have been found in 95 per cent of human infections due to beta-hemolytic streptococci. When the organism associated with a human infection is designated by number alone, it can generally be assumed that it belongs to Group A. Group B organisms are usually associated with infections of cattle. Group C organisms are generally of animal origin but are occasionally found in human disease. Groups D, E, etc., include bacteria from milk, from feces, and from other sources.

The Important Groups and Their Relation to Disease. Table 28·1 summarizes the important facts concerning the chief kinds of streptococci.

Beta-hemolytic Streptococci. Group A beta-hemolytic streptococci are by far the most important in diseases of man. They cause scarlet fever and the closely related streptococcal infections of the throat, tonsillitis, peritonsillar

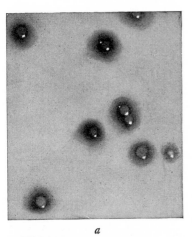
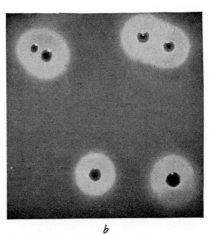

a	*b*

FIG. 28·2 Colonies of hemolytic cocci on blood agar. (*a*) Alpha-type hemolysis. Colonies of *Diplococcus pneumoniae.* ×3. (*b*) Beta-type hemolysis. Colonies of *Streptococcus pyogenes.* ×5. (*From Burrows, "Textbook of Microbiology," Saunders.*)

abscesses, and the epidemic milk-borne septic sore throat. These organisms are the most dreaded secondary invaders in diseases of the respiratory tract, causing many cases of mastoiditis, bronchopneumonia, empyema, and pulmonary abscess. They have extraordinary ability to invade cutaneous and subcutaneous tissues, causing cellulitis and suppuration. They spread to muscle tissue, causing myositis, and to the bones, causing osteomyelitis. There is always danger that they may spread to the general circulation, with resulting septicemia and pyemia. They also cause *puerperal fever* (infection of the female reproductive tract at parturition). Group A beta-hemolytic streptococci are classified as *S. pyogenes.*

Alpha-hemolytic Streptococci. The green-producing streptococci lack many of the toxic substances formed by the beta-hemolytic types. On the other hand they are constantly present in the upper respiratory tract of normal persons and always ready to invade the tissues. They are usually referred to as *S. viridans,* though the name *S. salivarius* is preferred. These organisms

Table 28·1

Distinguishing Characteristics of the Important Streptococci

Group	Type of hemolysis	Important species	Lance-field group	Hydrolysis of sodium hippurate	Fermentation of		Found in
					Trehalose	Sorbitol	
Hemolytic *......	Beta	S. pyogenes	A	−	+	−	Human disease
		S. agalactiae	B	+	+	−	Bovine mastitis
		S. equi	C	−	−	−	Disease of horses †
Green-producing..	Alpha	S. salivarius (viridans)	‡	−	±	−	Human disease
Enterococci.......	Variable	S. faecalis	D	−	+	+	Human feces
Lactic acid streptococci	Gamma	S. lactis	N	−	−	−	Milk and milk products

* Beta-hemolytic is a better term but is less often used.
† Some C group organisms other than *S. equi* may cause human infection.
‡ Have no Lancefield antigens.

are found in some cases of middle ear infection and meningitis, and they are common in diseased tonsils and tooth abscesses. After tonsillectomy or tooth extraction they may be found at least temporarily in the blood stream. They spread to the lungs to cause secondary bronchopneumonias. They and their antigenic products may repeatedly enter the blood from known or unsuspected foci of infection. Severe chronic illnesses such as bacterial endocarditis, rheumatic fever and the associated conditions of heart disease and chorea, and some forms of arthritis may result from infections and reinfections with these streptococci.

Other Important Streptococci. The other important streptococci may be divided into three groups.

1. Animal pathogens. Two specific infections of domestic animals are due to beta-hemolytic streptococci: strangles in horses, caused by the Group C organism *S. equi,* and the predominant form of mastitis in cattle, caused by the Group B organism *S. agalactiae.* These organisms are considered nonpathogenic for humans. However, it should be remembered that animals may become infected with human strains and then become sources of

infection for human beings. The most striking example is the infection of the cow's udder with Group A streptococci, which may result in large epidemics of septic sore throat in those who drink the milk raw.

2. Intestinal types. The feces of man and other mammals contain green-producing and anhemolytic streptococci. They are called *enterococci*. The best-known species is *S. faecalis*.

3. Types found in milk and milk products. Certain nonpathogenic strepto-cocci are very common in milk and its products. They form lactic acid from milk sugar and so initiate the souring of milk. *S. lactis* is the best-known species.

The Respiratory Group of Streptococcus Infections. The most important forms of streptococcal infection enter and leave the body by the upper respiratory tract. When a virulent streptococcus spreads through a group of people, many of them develop a carrier state, with the streptococci persist-ing in the nares or pharynx for varying periods. Some develop active strepto-coccal disease. The clinical picture is most often that of a pharyngitis, usually referred to as streptococcal sore throat. If the organisms produce erythrogenic toxin, many of the younger people infected develop typical cases of scarlet fever, but many infected older individuals fail to show any rash, since they are immune to the toxin. Streptococcal pneumonia, middle ear infection, nephritis, and other complications develop in some of the infected persons. Later development of subacute bacterial endocarditis and rheumatic fever can be expected in a small portion of infected persons. These respiratory cases and carriers are the usual sources of wound infections, cases of puerperal sepsis, and erysipelas. If they are food handlers or dairy farmers they may be responsible for related epidemics of streptococcal food poisoning or epi-demic septic sore throat. Figure 28·3 illustrates the possible spread of strepto-coccal infection in a community.

The spread of the organisms is from the upper respiratory tract, mainly from the nares. Both fresh and dried secretions may contain the streptococci. Dust arising from infected bedding and clothing is an important factor. Transfer by infected hands, dressings, and instruments is important in some circumstances.

Scarlet Fever. The classical case of scarlet fever (scarletina) is a severe streptococcal sore throat accompanied by a characteristic skin rash. The rash is due to the susceptibility of the patient to the erythrogenic toxin. The streptococci are not present in the rash nor in the desquamating skin.

Susceptibility to the erythrogenic toxin can be detected by the Dick test (see Chap. 19, page 239). A negative Dick test indicates only immunity to the specific toxin; it does not give any evidence concerning immunity to infection by the cocci themselves. It is possible to immunize against the toxin, but not against the cocci, by repeated doses of streptococcal toxoid or precipitated toxin. This active immunization is no longer recommended by pediatricians.

Penicillin and the tetracycline antibiotics are very effective in scarlet fever,

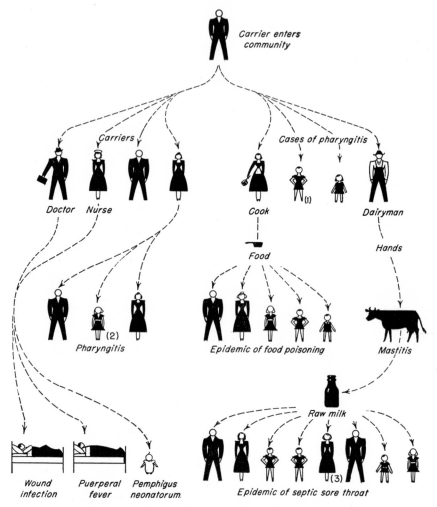

FIG. 28·3 Spread of streptococcal infection. (1) Develops middle ear infection; (2) develops rheumatic fever; (3) develops subacute bacterial endocarditis.

as in all streptococcal infections. In cases with severe toxic symptoms, convalescent human serum or horse antitoxic serum may also be used. Penicillin is now preferred to antitoxin for prophylaxis in exposed susceptible persons.

Other Streptococcal Infections. Many streptococcal infections are discussed in other portions of this text: streptococcal pneumonias were noted in Chap. 27, impetigo and pemphigus are discussed in a later section of this chapter, and wound infections in Chap. 29. Streptococcal food poisoning and milk-borne septic sore throat were described in Chap. 15.

Erysipelas. Several types of group A streptococci may cause this local, spreading skin infection, which is accompanied by generalized symptoms of toxemia. The lesions are most commonly on the face and legs. The aged and infants are most often attacked, and recurrences are frequent. Penicillin therapy is very effective. Erysipelas is contagious, particularly among debilitated babies. Cases are isolated, and strict precautions are practiced.

Puerperal Infection. When the fetus and its membranes are separated from the uterus at the time of childbirth, the entire inner surface of that organ is open to infection. Unsterile instruments and hands of doctors, nurses, or midwives may introduce dangerous organisms before, during, or after delivery. The infection may be endogenous, caused by organisms from the mother's vagina. From 1 to 3 days after infection there is a sudden onset of fever and pain. A fatal septicemia often follows. The causative organisms are most often Group A beta-hemolytic streptococci. If the organisms are toxin producers, the patient may develop a typical "scarlet fever" rash. The infection is also known as *childbed fever*. In the past it was tragically common in obstetric wards. Most cases that occur in the United States at the present time result from deliveries by unclean midwives or from illegal abortions.

Rheumatic Fever. This important disease of children and young adults is believed to be essentially an allergic reaction to streptococcal infection. An acute attack of polyarthritis and fever may develop suddenly in persons who have recently had streptococcal infections. Recurrences of the infection initiate new attacks of the rheumatic fever. In many persons who have rheumatic fever heart lesions develop. Ninety per cent of deaths from heart disease in persons between the ages of four and twenty are due to rheumatic fever.

Cases of rheumatic fever have a high anti-streptolysin-O level in their blood serum. Penicillin treatment of initial streptococcal infections diminishes the incidence of rheumatic fever. Children who have already had one or more attacks of rheumatic fever are protected from further attacks by long-continued penicillin therapy.

Subacute Bacterial Endocarditis. Persons with heart lesions due either to early attacks of rheumatic fever or to congenital malformations are the victims of this relatively rare but very severe illness. The causative organism is usually an alpha-hemolytic streptococcus. It localizes on the free edges of the heart valves, forming masses called *vegetations*. From these vegetations streptococci are constantly escaping into the general circulation. Penicillin is effective in treatment.

Control of Streptococcal Infection. Specific public health control is limited to the isolation of clinical cases for at least 7 days or until all signs of infections have disappeared. Medical and nursing service in schools to detect early infections, pasteurization of milk, and other public health practices diminish the spread of streptococcal infections in the community.

Antibiotic therapy of streptococcal infections not only cures the diseases but also results in the prompt disappearance of the organisms from the body. Penicillin for prevention of infections is employed wherever there is a definite danger of the spread of streptococci. The drug is used in this way when infected teeth are extracted, and before operations of many kinds.

Laboratory Diagnosis. Examination of suitable specimens in the laboratory confirms the doctor's diagnosis in active cases, determines when convalescents may be safely discharged, and detects healthy carriers. Studies that involve the exact typing of organisms from cases and carriers are of great importance in tracing the spread of infection. The methods used include preliminary direct microscopic examination, identification by culture on blood agar, isolation, and identification by cultural methods and by precipitation and agglutination tests.

Cultivation. Blood, spinal fluid, pus, nose and throat swabs, and environmental materials such as milk, foods, and dust may be sent to the laboratory. Some are streaked directly on blood agar. Others may be first cultivated in an enrichment broth containing sodium azide and dilute crystal violet to discourage the growth of staphylococci and other unwanted bacteria. Colonies typical of the alpha- or beta-hemolytic streptococci can usually be recognized without difficulty. The morphology of the organism may be checked by stained smears. Further testing of effects on various sugars, ability to grow at various temperatures and pHs, production of fibrinolysin, etc., aid in determining the species.

Typing. *Lancefield grouping* is done very commonly in epidemiologic and research studies. The specific antigens of the streptococcus under study are extracted by treatment with hydrochloric acid. The test is done in a series of capillary tubes, each containing a little of the extract (antigen) and a little of one group-specific antiserum (antibody). In the tube containing the homologous antiserum a ring of precipitate will form where the antigen and antibody come together, thus identifying the group to which the streptococcus belongs.

THE MICROCOCCI

Micrococci are found in large numbers not only on the skin and mucous membranes of man and animals but also in the soil, in water, and in decomposing organic material. Formerly the parasitic species were placed in the genus *Staphylococcus* and the saprophytic species in the genus *Micrococcus*. Actually there is no sharp differentiation between the groups, but rather a graded series of organisms ranging from virulent obligate parasites to completely harmless free-living types. Therefore all are now included in the genus *Micrococcus*. Table 28·2 summarizes the most frequently noted characteristics of virulent and nonvirulent forms, but it must be understood that there are many intermediate types. The terms *staphylococcus* and *micrococcus* are interchangeable.

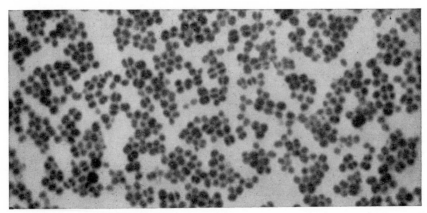

FIG. 28·4   Pure culture of micrococci. ×2,000. (*Courtesy of Dr. A. C. Lonert and General Biological Supply House, Inc.*)

Morphology and Physiology. Staphylococci are gram-positive cocci found in irregular groupings. They are nonmotile and do not form spores. No capsules are found, though the closely related organism *Gaffkya tetragena,* the common tetracoccus of the upper respiratory tract, is capsulated. Staphyloccus cells are spherical except when they are in the process of cell division. They are much less pleomorphic than the streptococci. Clumps of irregularly arranged cells predominate, but single cells, pairs, tetrads, and short chains may be seen in microscopic preparations (Fig. 28·4). In older cultures the cells may become gram-negative.

Although there are some obligate anaerobes among the staphylococci, the majority are aerobes and facultative anaerobes. They grow well over a wide range of temperatures and hydrogen ion concentrations. Growth is good on simple media, but strictly parasitic forms grow more quickly and abundantly on enriched media. The typical colony is round, smooth, and raised. Staphylococci isolated from pathologic conditions usually produce a golden-yellow pigment and are known as *Micrococcus aureus,* or more correctly as *M. pyogenes* var. *aureus.* (The term *var.* means variety.) Non-

pigmented strains from minor lesions and from the environment are called
M. albus (*M. pyogenes* var. *albus*). Lemon-yellow, brick-yellow, and red
strains are rarely associated with disease. Pathogenic strains typically digest
gelatin and serum protein and ferment lactose and mannitol (Table 28·2).

Table 28·2

Differentiation of Pathogenic and Nonpathogenic Staphylococci

Characteristics	*Pathogenic strains*	*Nonpathogenic strains*
Habitat......................	Skin and upper respiratory tract, purulent discharges	Soil and water, decomposing organic materials
Pigment production............	Golden-yellow or none	None, lemon-yellow, brick-yellow, or red
Digestion of gelatin...........	+	−
Digestion of serum protein......	+	−
Fermentation of lactose........	+	−
Fermentation of mannitol......	+	−
Coagulase test................	+	−
Hemolysis of blood media......	+	−
Production of enterotoxin......	+	−
Names of common species......	*Micrococcus pyogenes* var. *aureus* *M. pyogenes* var. *albus*	*Micrococcus citreus* *M. epidermidis*

Staphylococci produce no gas and only moderate amounts of acid when
they ferment sugars. They cause so little obvious change when they grow
in such foods as meat and custards that the presence of millions of bacteria
may produce no detectable alteration of odor or taste.

Resistance. The micrococci are among the most resistant of the nonsporing
bacteria. Some strains survive a temperature of 80°C. for 30 minutes. However, boiling for 10 minutes kills even the hardiest. They survive for weeks
and months in a dried state on articles and in dust. They are more resistant
to chemical disinfection than most other bacteria. They will grow in high
concentrations of salt.

Ten years ago practically all strains of micrococci were susceptible to
penicillin. At the present time over 50 per cent of cultures isolated from
hospital patients are penicillin-resistant. The widespread use of penicillin
has favored the development of these resistant strains. Now it is routine
practice to test all micrococcus cultures against a number of antibiotics and
use the one most effective in the tests for the treatment of the patient.

Penicillin-resistant micrococci may be responsible for secondary infections,
particularly in children. A type of severe staphylococcal enteritis appears

sometimes in persons who have had a great deal of antibiotic therapy. It may occur postoperatively in patients who have been given antibiotics pre-operatively.

Toxic Products. Virulent strains of staphylococci produce one or more toxic products such as hemolysins, leukocidins, fibrinolysin, and the spreading factor (Chap. 17, page 215). Two factors, one lethal to rabbits and one producing skin necrosis in these animals, can be found in some cultures. Cultures associated with cases of food poisoning produce *enterotoxin*. The ability to coagulate human plasma is such a common characteristic of virulent strains that the *coagulase test* is the accepted method of rapid identification of such cultures. Staphylococci seem to be able to penetrate the unbroken skin and are the most active of all bacteria in causing pus formation.

Infections Due to Staphylococci. M. *albus* is an almost invariable inhabitant of the normal skin and mucous membranes and so gives rise to frequent endogenous infections. M. *aureus* is not commonly found in normal persons. It may come from a case of infection, but the ability of the organism to survive in the environment makes its source very difficult to determine. Infections caused by micrococci can be conveniently divided into three groups: (1) infections of the skin and subcutaneous tissues, (2) infections of internal tissues, and (3) staphylococcus food poisoning.

Infections of the Skin and Subcutaneous Tissues. Minor staphylococcal infections of the skin are probably the commonest of all human infections. Examples are pimples, *stitch abscesses* that develop at points where sutures pierce the skin, and minor infections of small cuts and scratches. *Paronychia* (inflammation of the tissues around the finger or toe nail) is another. Localized but more serious infections include some cases of conjunctivitis, the localized abscesses of the eyelids called "styes," furuncles, and carbuncles. A *furuncle* or boil is a localized skin abscess. The term *furunculosis* is used when there is a series of such abscesses. A *carbuncle* is a similar involvement of deeper subcutaneous tissues with more than one pocket of pus. Both furuncles and carbuncles develop most frequently in areas where staphylococci are rubbed into the skin. The back of the neck, especially in men who wear stiff collars, and the buttocks are common sites.

Infections of Internal Tissues. Staphylococci spread from the upper respiratory tract to cause bronchopneumonias and mastoiditis. Meningitis due to staphylococci may result from head injuries or from the extension of head infections such as mastoiditis. *Cystitis* (inflammation of the urinary bladder) and *pyelitis* (inflammation of the kidney pelvis) are often due to staphylococci. They also cause chronic inflammation of bony tissue, *osteomyelitis* and *periostitis*. They are the causative organisms in some cases of puerperal fever. Generalized infection is more often due to streptococci, but staphylococcal septicemia is frequently fatal in infants. In older persons staphylococci spreading in the circulation tend to localize, giving rise to such lesions as osteomyelitis and abscesses in internal organs and between layers of fascia.

Food Poisoning. Enterotoxin-forming staphylococci may grow rapidly in suitable foods. Persons consuming the food will become ill within a few hours from the effects of the toxin. The origin of the organisms responsible is difficult to trace, but in a few instances infections on the hands of bakery

FIG. 28·5 Coagulase test. Left tube negative; right tube shows coagulation of serum due to action of staphylococcus coagulase. (*"Medichrome," Clay-Adams Co., Inc., Dr. Gregory Shwartzman, Mt. Sinai Hospital.*)

workers have been considered responsible. Refrigeration of bakery products and meat dishes prevents this type of food poisoning. (See discussion and Table 15·2 on page 192.)

Laboratory Diagnosis. The micrococci are detected by stained smears of pus or cultivation from specimens of urine, blood, foods, and other materials. The organisms form large, soft, and often hemolytic colonies on blood agar, which are readily recognized by experienced bacteriologists. The identification of the colony will be checked by a stained smear and its pigment production tested on agar or serum medium.

The original specimen, or organisms, from selected colonies is tested on antibiotic disk plates or by other means in order to determine the best therapeutic agent.

The discovery that micrococci can be typed by means of specific phages permits epidemiologic studies tracing the spread of the organisms. (See Chap. 33.)

Cultural characteristics such as those listed in Table 28·2 help to distinguish the type of organism. The coagulase test is considered the most useful test for distinguishing virulent from nonvirulent strains. It is done by mixing small amounts of a saline suspension of the organisms with citrated human blood or rabbit plasma in a test tube or on a slide. If the blood or plasma is coagulated, the test is positive and the strain is considered virulent. (See Fig. 28·5.)

Enterotoxin production is tested by intraperitoneal or intravenous injection into kittens or by feeding to human volunteers. These tests are not entirely satisfactory, since the kittens may become ill from the effects of nonbacterial substances in the culture medium and the human volunteers may be immune to the enterotoxin.

SKIN INFECTIONS

The skin is involved in many ways in many different infections. In some, such as ringworm and chickenpox, it is the principal site of the disease. In others, *e.g.*, typhoid fever and epidemic meningitis, there are transitory lesions containing the organisms. In some, such as scarlet fever, skin lesions result from toxins carried to the skin. Diseases spread by insects may begin with an initial lesion in the skin, and some bacterial diseases have similar initial lesions. The primary lesions of rickettsial diseases and the chancre of syphilis are examples. The most prevalent mycotic infections are those of the skin. One form of tuberculosis, *lupus,* is a skin disease. Streptococcal and staphylococcal infections of the skin have already been discussed in this chapter. Allergic conditions of the skin may be complicated by secondary infection with bacteria, and bacterial infections may give rise to allergic conditions. For more detailed discussion of all these skin conditions the student should consult the index.

Four Important Skin Conditions. Four skin conditions that are not discussed elsewhere in this text are impetigo contagiosa, pemphigus neonatorum, acne, and decubital ulcers.

Impetigo Contagiosa. This purulent inflammation of the skin occurs most frequently as an epidemic disease of school children. The lesions are generally on the face and hands. The causative organisms are considered to be staphylococci and streptococci. The infection is spread by direct contact and by such articles as pillowcases. All measures that make for cleanliness discourage the infection. Control involves complete concurrent disinfection of all articles coming in contact with the patient's skin.

Pemphigus Neonatorum. Infants from the age of four to ten days are the victims of this disease, which is also known as *pyoderma* and *impetigo of the newborn.* The lesions are scattered swellings that later rupture and form crusts. This and other skin infections of the newborn are avoided by postponing soap and water baths until the infant is ten to fourteen days old. Instead the skin is given daily care with sterile oil. Sterile clothing and bedding are provided. Attendants of newborn infants must wear masks. Their hands must be properly cleaned, and they must wear sterile gloves. Under no circumstances should a person with skin lesions of any sort be allowed to handle newborn infants. The fatal pemphigus of adults is a different disease entity and is not of infectious origin.

Acne. The persistent and recurrent skin disease with pitting and scarring on healing that is so common in adolescents is named *acne.* The primary causes are believed to be physiologic and related to the hormones that are responsible for the development of secondary sex characteristics. Dietary and allergic conditions may play a part in some cases. Bacterial infection invariably complicates cases of acne. Streptococci and staphylococci are frequently found in the lesions. A small granular rod, *Corynebacterium acnes,* has been isolated from the pustules but is not considered the specific cause of the disease.

Decubital Ulcers. The common names for the decubital ulcers that develop in bedridden persons are *bedsore* and *pressure sore.* They develop on the buttocks and similar areas in debilitated patients. The primary cause is the diminution of the blood supply to the affected area. The prevention and care of these sores will be fully covered in the courses on nursing arts. Bacteria play an important secondary role, complicating the care and delaying the healing of the ulcers.

Nursing Considerations. The nurse has an important role in the prevention and care of skin infections. Her failure to observe signs of skin infection and to carry out prescribed techniques may have very serious results, particularly in infants.

1. The nurse must always call the attention of her supervisor to any previously unnoted abnormal skin condition observed in her patients.

2. Any skin rash or lesion must be considered as infectious until the nurse has received definite instructions as to its care. Then the instructions must be followed without any deviation.

3. The nurse must protect the skin of her patients at all times by keeping them and all the materials with which they come in contact scrupulously clean. She must avoid inflicting any mechanical or chemical injury to their skin.

4. The nurse must immediately report to the proper authority any rash or other skin lesion that develops on any part of her own body. She should

call the attention of the supervisor to skin lesions or rashes on any visitor or ward attendant.

STUDY SUGGESTIONS

Make a table comparing the streptococci and the staphylococci. Use the following headings: *Morphology, Toxicity, Important physiologic characteristics, Important species, Diseases caused.*

Streptococci are subdivided according to their effects on blood agar and according to their antigenic content. What are these groups? How are they determined?

Suppose three cases of streptococcal puerperal fever appear on a maternity ward. How would the authorities proceed to investigate the possible sources and method of infection? What laboratory evidence might point to an individual nurse as the almost certain source of the infection?

Explain how it might be possible to have cases of scarlet fever, streptococcal sore throat, erysipelas, and food poisoning all occurring in one epidemic.

What general and specific measures carried out in your hospital prevent and control the possible spread of streptococcal infection?

List the important kinds of staphylococcal infections. What are the probable sources of infection in each? What laboratory tests would lead to a report that "*Micrococcus* var. *aureus*, coagulase-positive but probably not forming enterotoxin" had been isolated from a specimen?

A check list of skin infections and the cause of each might well be begun at this time to become a part of your permanent records. It should have the following headings: *Name of disease, Causative organism, Clinical picture, Methods of control.*

Both erysipelas and scarlet fever are caused by streptococci. Will the same precautions be taken in the care of the skin lesions of these two diseases? What experience or instruction have you had in the care of impetigo, pemphigus neonatorum, and decubital ulcer?

SUGGESTED READING

Streptococci and Streptococcal Infections

BLOOMFIELD, A. L., and R. M. HALPERN: The penicillin treatment of subacute bacterial endocarditis. *J.A.M.A.* **129**:1135 (1945).

COMMISSION ON ACUTE RESPIRATORY DISEASE: Role of beta hemolytic streptococci in common respiratory disease. *Am. J. Pub. Health* **35**:675 (1945).

EVANS, A.: Distribution of types of hemolytic streptococci of group A. *J. Infect. Dis.* **78**:18 (1946).

————: The enterococci—with special reference to their association with human disease. *J. Bact.* **54**:495 (1947).

HARRIS, T. N., and S. HARRIS: Studies in the relation of the hemolytic streptococci to rheumatic fever. *Am. J. M. Sc.* **217**:174 (1949).

LANCEFIELD, R. C.: Specific relationship of cell compounds to biological activity of hemolytic streptococci. *Harvey Lect.* **36**:251 (1940–1941).

LEMON, H. M.: The nasal carrier of beta-hemolytic streptococci. *New England J. Med.* **237**:26 (1947).

MACKENZIE, G. M.: Hemolytic Streptococci, in "Diagnostic Procedures and Reagents." 3d ed., American Public Health Association, New York, 1950.

MASSELL, B. F., J. W. Dow, and T. D. JONES: Penicillin in rheumatic fever. *J.A.M.A.* **138**:1030 (1948).

RAMMELKAMP, C. H., and J. H. DINGLE: Pathogenic Streptococci, in "Annual Review of Microbiology." Vol. 2, Annual Reviews, Inc., Stanford, 1948.

SMITH, M. A.: Rheumatic fever prophylaxis: a community program through the private physician. *J.A.M.A.* **149**:636 (1952).

SWIFT, H. F., A. T. WILSON, and R. C. LANCEFIELD: Typing group A hemolytic streptococci by M precipiten reaction in capillary pipettes. *J. Exper. Med.* **78**:127 (1943).

WANAMAKER, L. W., *et al.:* The effect of penicillin prophylaxis on streptococcal disease rates and the carrier state. *New England J. Med.* **249**:1 (1953).

WEINSTEIN, L., and T. S. PERRIN: Treatment of scarlet fever with penicillin administered three times a day. *J.A.M.A.* **145**:1011 (1951).

Micrococci and Micrococcal (Staphylococcal) Infections

BLAIR, J. E., and M. C. CARR: The bacteriophage typing of staphylococci. *J. Infect. Dis.* **93**:1 (1953).

DOWLING, H. F., M. H. LEPPER, and G. G. JACKSON: Observations on the epidemiological spread of antibiotic-resistant staphylococci, with measurements of the changes in sensitivity to penicillin and aureomycin. *Am. J. Pub. Health* **43**:860 (1953).

Skin Infections

COHEN, S. R.: Common skin diseases in the schools. *Pub. Health Nursing* **30**:120 (1938).

PILLSBURY, D. M.: The management of bacterial infections of the skin. *J.A.M.A.* **132**:692 (1946).

The Pathogenic Spore-forming Bacilli

The general nature of the spore-forming bacilli and the process of spore formation have already been discussed (Chap. 2). The classification of the family *Bacillaceae* into two genera, genus *Bacillus* composed of aerobic forms and genus *Clostridium* composed of obligate anaerobic forms, has been described (Chap. 2, also Appendix B, page 582). Fortunately there are very few pathogenic members of these genera. Only one, *Bacillus anthracis*, the cause of anthrax, is aerobic. One anaerobe, *Clostridium botulinum*, causes botulinus poisoning. Another, *Cl. tetani,* is the cause of tetanus. The other pathogenic clostridia, *Cl. perfringens, Cl. novyi, Cl. septicum, Cl. histolyticum, Cl. sporogenes,* etc., are all associated with wound infection.

BACILLUS ANTHRACIS, THE CAUSE OF ANTHRAX

This organism was seen one hundred years ago in the blood of animals ill with anthrax. In 1877 Robert Koch was able to isolate it and prove it to be the true cause of the disease by inoculating his pure cultures into susceptible cattle.

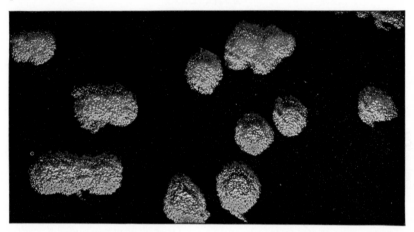

FIG. 29·1   Colonies of *Bacillus anthracis* on nutrient agar. ×3. (*From Burrows, "Textbook of Microbiology," Saunders.*)

The Organism. The anthrax bacillus is a large, gram-positive rod. It tends to form long chains. It is not motile. The oval spores are centrally located in the cells and are no larger than the diameter of the rod. Spores are not formed in the infected animal, but they are abundant in agar cultures. The organism grows readily in standard media. The bacilli have capsules in the animal body but lose them when they are grown in artificial culture. Agar plate colonies are large, white, and rough and have "curled hair" edges (Fig. 29·1).

The vegetative cells are readily destroyed by chemical and physical agents of disinfection, but the spores can survive for years in dust or soil and on contaminated objects. The spores survive 5 minutes' boiling and the action of the ordinary chemical disinfectants. Incineration and steam sterilization are the only methods that can be relied on to kill the spores.

The Disease. Anthrax is primarily a disease of sheep, cattle, and pigs. Animals acquire intestinal anthrax by ingesting the spores on fodder from soil infected by excreta or carcasses of diseased animals. Man acquires the infection through the skin from handling infected animals or their products such as hides, wool, hair, and bristles. Pulmonary anthrax sometimes develops in workers who inhale spores from wool or hair.

In this country recent epidemics among animals have been traced to infected imported bone meal. A few human cases have resulted from contact with animals in these epidemics. Most human cases in North America are among employees of factories using wool and hair from Asia to make rugs. Leather workers acquire anthrax from infected hides. Facial pustules have been caused by infected bristles of shaving brushes.

Intestinal and pulmonary infection in man and animals is rapidly fatal unless immediately treated with antibiotics. The skin infection, commoner in man, is often limited to a *malignant pustule,* located where the organism entered the skin. The pustule may heal spontaneously or the bacteria may spread to cause a generalized bacteremia. In the past anthrax antiserum was used for treatment. Now the usual therapy is the use of penicillin or other antibiotics.

Control. The disease in animals is controlled by the use of a vaccine of avirulent spores and by regulations that require safe disposal of the bodies of animals dead from anthrax. Where the disease is not prevalent in animals, the sources of infection are imported animal products such as leather and wool. Disinfection of such materials from countries where the disease is common is attempted but is difficult in the case of hides. Immunization of man against anthrax is not considered practicable. Sera of immunized animals and penicillin are used in treatment of all cases.

Laboratory Diagnosis. A diagnosis of anthrax is made immediately if large, gram-positive rods are found in smears of pus from a typical malignant pustule. Other specimens or pus that may have been contaminated in transit to the laboratory require further testing by cultivation, isolation, and inoculation into white mice or guinea pigs.

When decomposed tissues or hides are examined, the *Ascoli test* is used. Heat-resistant antigens are extracted from the material by grinding and heating in salt solution. The extract is layered over special antianthrax serum. A ring of precipitate between the two fluids indicates the presence of the anthrax organisms in the specimen.

CLOSTRIDIUM BOTULINUM, THE CAUSE OF BOTULINUS POISONING

This type of food poisoning has already been mentioned briefly in Chap. 15. See page 190 and Table 15·2.

The Organism and Its Toxin. *Cl. botulinum* is a large, gram-positive, motile rod. Its subterminal spores are wider than the vegetative cells (Fig.

29·2). These spores are extremely resistant. Some have been reported to withstand boiling for over 20 hours. They are killed by steam pressure sterilization. The time and temperature needed vary with the number present and the material in which they are contained. The organism is a strict anaerobe. It attacks both proteins and carbohydrates. The botulinus clostridia found in America do not digest protein. They have been designated *Cl. parabotulinum*.

Both *Cl. botulinum* and *Cl. parabotulinum* produce very powerful toxin. Five types of toxin are recognized. Organisms designated A and B, because

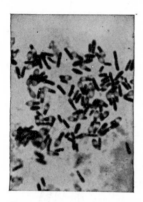

they form toxin A and toxin B respectively, are found in this country. These types are widely distributed in the soil. Very powerful toxin is formed when these organisms grow in cultures or in anaerobic conditions in suitable foods. The organisms are essentially saprophytic and are unable to grow in the body. But the ingestion of food containing already formed toxin causes a toxemia that is often fatal.

The Disease. Within a day or two of the ingestion of the toxin-containing food the patient shows disturbances of vision, intestinal symptoms, and paralysis. Death is due to respiratory paralysis.

FIG. 29·2   Bacilli and spores of *Clostridium botulinum* ×1,200. (*From Salle, "Fundamental Principles of Bacteriology," 4th ed., McGraw-Hill.*)

Most cases in this country have been traced to home-canned nonacid vegetables. Sausage and brined meats and fish have been implicated in epidemics in Europe.

Antitoxin can be produced in horses, but by the time diagnosis is established it may be too late for serum treatment to be effective. Since the relatively few cases of this disease cannot be anticipated, no method of immunization is practicable. Laboratory workers can be immunized with toxoid.

Prevention. The measures useful in the prevention of botulism are

1. Governmental regulation and inspection of commercial canneries.

2. Use of the pressure cooker in home canning of nonacid vegetables.

3. Boiling of all home-canned vegetables for at least 5 minutes before they are served and thorough cooking of sausage, hams, and corned beef. This cooking is not expected to kill the bacilli or spores but is sufficient to destroy the preformed toxin.

Laboratory Diagnosis. Whenever possible, samples of suspected foods are sent to the bacteriologic laboratory. Vomitus, stomach washings, and autopsy specimens of intestine may also be examined. Small amounts of the specimens are injected into mice to detect the presence of toxin. Anaerobic cultures are made and studied.

CLOSTRIDIUM TETANI, THE CAUSE OF TETANUS

In 1889 Kitasato proved that tetanus is caused by an anaerobic bacillus. He was able to cultivate the organism and demonstrate its power to form exotoxin. Working with von Behring he developed tetanus antitoxic serum and showed that it is useful for prevention of the disease.

The Organism and Its Toxin. *Cl. tetani* is a slender, gram-positive rod. It is motile in young cultures and does not form capsules. The large round spores are formed at the ends of the rods, giving them their typical drumstick appearance. The organism is strictly anaerobic. It does not attack carbohydrates and is only weakly proteolytic. Mature spores are very resistant to drying and chemicals but can be destroyed by steam sterilization at 15 lb. for 15 minutes.

Tetanus Exotoxin. The organism produces a substance called *tetanospasmin* that causes the contraction of skeletal muscle. It acts through the motor nerve supply, but its methods of action and dissemination to the tissues are not completely understood. This toxin is one of the most powerful poisons known. It is said that 0.00025 gram of purified toxin would be enough to kill a man. Like all true toxins it is destroyed by heat. It deteriorates at room temperature and in the light. Precipitated, purified toxin can be kept for a considerable time in the refrigerator. The toxin is destroyed by proteolytic enzymes and is therefore not poisonous when swallowed or when formed in the normal alimentary canal.

Cl. tetani is a common inhabitant of the intestines of the horse. It is often found in the feces of healthy humans and other animals. Spores are common in soil and dust and on dirty objects, particularly in areas where the soil has been manured.

The Disease. Tetanus is a disease of horses and other animals as well as man. The organism enters from dirt through wounds. Because the clostridia cannot grow and form toxin unless conditions are anaerobic, puncture wounds are most liable to develop tetanus. The local inflammation may be so slight that the doctor is not consulted. The toxin spreads rapidly and immediately unites with nerve tissue. Muscles of the head and neck are affected first. The name "lockjaw" arises from the characteristic contraction of the muscles of mastication. Once the disease is established, treatment is often tragically ineffectual.

In the past tetanus was a fatal complication of many war wounds and civilian accidents. It sometimes became epidemic in hospital wards. Tetanus of the umbilical wound (*neonatal tetanus*) still occurs where midwives are uneducated and unclean. Unsterilized catgut and contaminated smallpox vaccine have given rise to cases of tetanus. In civilian life in this country most cases of tetanus are from small puncture wounds, such as result from stepping on a nail, that are not seen by a physician until generalized symptoms have developed.

Treatment. Once the symptoms of tetanus have developed, intensive therapy is required to save the patient's life. Tetanus antitoxic serum is given intravenously and also by intramuscular injection around the region of the wound. In addition the wound itself is cleaned surgically, and penicillin is given to control infection with symbiotic bacteria.

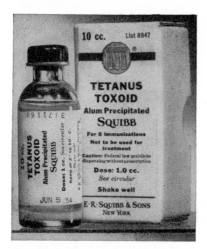

FIG. 29·3 Tetanus toxoid. (*E. R. Squibb and Sons.*)

Immunization. Active immunization by the use of toxoid is the most effective method for the prevention of tetanus. Passive immunization by antitoxin can be used to protect injured persons who have not already received active immunization.

Active Immunization. Active immunity is conferred by two or three doses at monthly intervals of alum-precipitated toxoid or aluminum hydroxide-adsorbed toxoid (Fig. 29·3). In infancy this immunization is combined with immunization against diphtheria and whooping cough (see page 325). The inoculated person is considered immune to tetanus a few weeks after the last dose. The level of immunity declines rapidly in the months that follow. For this reason booster doses of APT or FT are given at 1-year and then 3-year intervals if the person continues to be exposed to the disease. All members of the armed services are immunized in this way. Authorities recommend that persons who are in contact with presumably infected soil, such as farmers, should be immunized. Children living on farms or attending summer camps should be immunized. When a person who has been previously immunized with toxoid receives a dangerous wound, he is given a booster dose of fluid toxoid. This results in a sharp rise in the amount of antitoxin in his blood.

Passive Immunization by Antitoxin. When a person who has not been immunized by toxoid receives a dangerous wound he is passively immunized with a large dose of antitoxic serum. If the wound shows any signs of continued infection the dose must be repeated at intervals of a week or 10 days, since the passive immunization is not lasting.

Laboratory Diagnosis. Diagnosis of the active disease depends on the characteristic symptoms. Laboratory examinations are of little importance in the care of the usual case. When for some reason the physician desires confirmatory evidence, pus or material excised from the wound is examined for the presence of slender gram-positive rods, cultivated anaerobically, and tested by inoculation into susceptible and immunized guinea pigs.

THE CLOSTRIDIA OF GAS GANGRENE

Gas gangrene (or *gaseous gangrene*) is a serious form of infection developing most commonly in improperly cared-for lacerated wounds. The wound and surrounding tissues are infected by one or more species of clostridia. The organisms produce marked local effects and general toxemia.

The Organisms. The clostridia of gas gangrene are all gram-positive, spore-forming rods. All can be cultivated without difficulty under anaerobic conditions. They are widely distributed in the soil and are also found in human and animal feces. Their ability to produce disease depends on their enzymatic action on local tissues and on their exotoxin production. Two physiologically different groups are recognized.

The Saccharolytic Group. The most important members of this group are *Cl. perfringens* (*Cl. welchii*), *Cl. novyi* (*Cl. oedematiens*), and *Cl. septicum* (*Vibrion septique*). These organisms ferment most sugars. They cause the formation of gas in infected tissues. The tissues swell and become *crepitant* (crackle when palpated). This effect is most marked when the principal invading organism is *Cl. perfringens*. Edema may be the most prominent local sign when *Cl. novyi* or *Cl. septicum* is present. All three organisms form toxins which spread through the body, causing general symptoms. These toxins are less specific, less powerful, and slower acting than the toxin of *Cl. tetani*.

The Proteolytic Group. The two outstanding members of this group are *Cl. histolyticum* and *Cl. sporogenes*. They attack few sugars but rapidly digest all types of protein. A pure culture of *Cl. histolyticum* inoculated into the gluteus muscle of the guinea pig completely digests the muscle and surrounding tissue so that within 2 days the femur is exposed. The formation of peptones, amino acids, and other products by the proteolytic species accelerates the growth of the saccharolytic species with which they are almost always associated. The proteolytic species do not form exotoxins.

Other Medically Important Clostridia. Other species are sometimes found in mixed infections of man. Blackleg, a serious disease of cattle, is caused by a clostridium that resembles *Cl. septicum* very closely. Clostridia related to

Table 29·1. Important Characteristics

Scientific name	Synonyms	Sporulation	Motility	Capsules
Cl. tetani..........	....	Spherical, terminal	+	—
Cl. perfringens........	Cl. welchii, Bacillus aerogenes capsulatus, Fraenkel's bacillus	Oval, central	—	+
Cl. novyi...........	Cl. oedematiens	Oval, subterminal	+	—
Cl. septicum..........	Vibrion septique, Cl. oedematiens	Oval, subterminal	+	—
Cl. histolyticum.......	....	Oval, subterminal	+	—
Cl. sporogenes.........	....	Oval, subterminal	+	—

Cl. perfringens cause intestinal infections in lambs and sheep. These animal pathogens are not found in human infections.

Infections Caused by the Gas Gangrene Clostridia. The pathogenic clostridia have little invasive power. They grow chiefly in the traumatized tissue and accumulated secretions of deep wounds.

Infection of Wounds. The typical case of gas gangrene develops in a deep, dirty wound which is not properly treated within 6 hours of the time it is received. In practically all cases the infection is mixed, with both saccharolytic, toxin-forming species and proteolytic species present. *Cl. perfringens* is present in over three-quarters of the cases. The incidence of other species varies greatly.

In contrast to tetanus infection, the local picture is usually much more striking than the signs of general toxemia. As the infection progresses, more and more of the nearby tissues are involved. Crepitation, swelling, edema, and *serosanguineous* (thin and bloody) discharge are characteristic.

Other Infections. *Cl. perfringens* has been implicated in cases of food poisoning, infant diarrhea, in frothy diarrhea of adults, and in uterine and other genitourinary infections. It has been suggested that it and other clostridia contribute to the general toxemia and disintegration of the intestinal wall following complete obstruction of the lumen of the intestine. The clostridia are the causative or secondary invading organisms in cases of gangrenous appendicitis and in some cases of puerperal sepsis. They may grow in the necrotic areas of the feet in diabetic gangrene. Food poisonings due to clostridia were discussed in Chap. 15.

Sources and Modes of Infection. These clostridia are present in soil and feces. The organisms enter wounds in bits of soil or dirty clothing. Before of the Clostridia of Wound Infections

Action on carbohydrates	Action on proteins	Local tissue reaction	Toxemia
None	Weak	Very slight	Very marked
Very strong	Very weak	Crepitation, swelling, edema	Moderate
Strong	Very weak	Edema	Marked
Strong	Very weak	Edema	Moderate
None	Very strong	Softening of tissues	Very weak or absent
Weak	Strong	Softening of tissues	None

the development of aseptic surgery and midwifery, gas gangrene spread in epidemics through surgical and maternity wards carried by unsterilized instruments and dressings and by the hands of the doctors and nurses. Sporadic cases still occur in modern hospitals. Development of gas gangrene in a surgical case may be due to contamination of the surgical wound with intestinal contents during the operation. Irresponsible patients may contaminate their fingers with their own feces and then infect their own wounds when they pull away the dressings. The development of secondary cases of gas gangrene in modern hospitals is not unknown. It must be the result of some break in aseptic procedures. Resterilization of all supplies and rechecking of all techniques are immediately instituted.

Treatment. Although penicillin and other antibiotics are definitely effective against these microorganisms, they do not neutralize the clostridial exotoxins. Therefore polyvalent gas gangrene antitoxic serum is used in conjunction with antibiotic therapy. Neither serum nor antibody treatment is as important as the prompt surgical treatment of the wound.

Laboratory Diagnosis. The presence of large, gram-positive rods in exudate from typical lesions is presumptive evidence of infection with gas gangrene organisms. Anaerobic cultivation is required to rule out contaminating aerobic bacilli. Evidence of the presence of *Cl. perfringens* is obtained by the "stormy fermentation" of a tube of milk inoculated with a specimen (Fig. 29·4). The milk proteins are coagulated by acid and then the curd is torn apart by the gas produced in the fermentation of the lactose. Identification of species requires isolation of pure cultures, inoculation into animals, and cultivation in sugar agars, iron milk medium, and protein media.

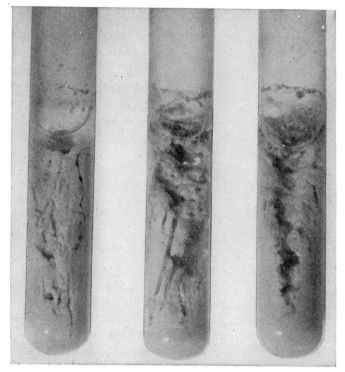

FIG. 29·4   Stormy fermentation of milk by *Clostridium perfringens*. (*Courtesy of Dr. Martin Frobisher, Jr.*)

WOUND INFECTIONS AND SEPTICEMIA

The body is normally enveloped with a complete and unbroken covering of skin. Any break in that covering, no matter how small, opens a path for potentially dangerous microorganisms. If the lower layers of the skin and the tissues beneath are healthy they are able to deal with most types of invading organisms. If dead tissue is present in the wound, if blood and lymph accumulate there, if irritating foreign materials such as soil and bits of clothing are present, microorganisms are able to multiply. Anaerobic conditions in the wound favor the growth of dangerous types.

Types of Wounds. Wounds may be divided into *surgical wounds* and *accidental wounds*. Surgical wounds are classed as either clean or septic. A *clean wound* is one that involves uninfected tissues. The excision of a fatty tumor and the transplantation of a tendon are examples. A *septic surgical wound* is one that involves infected tissues. The removal of an infected appendix or of infected tonsils is an example. Surgical wounds involving any part of the intestine are septic wounds.

Accidental wounds must all be regarded as infected. Insect bites may be considered as a special sort of accidental wound. They may be infected directly with organisms carried by the insect or secondarily by scratching.

Wounds are also classified as abrasions, incised wounds, puncture wounds, and lacerated wounds.

An *abrasion* results from the removal or injury of the outer layer of the skin. The "skinned knees" so common in childhood are typical abrasions. Anaerobic bacteria are unlikely to find conditions for growth in an abrasion, but the large open surface allows the entrance and growth of aerobic and microaerophilic types such as the staphylococci. Burns and chemical injuries produce similar conditions.

The *incised wound* is a cut such as the housewife suffers when she slices her finger with the bread knife. Since there is little cell destruction and plenty of opportunity for drainage, the incised wound is the least likely of all types to develop serious infection. Surgical wounds are usually incised wounds.

The *puncture wound* results from a stab with a sharp instrument. Typical puncture wounds are those received from stepping on a nail or being stabbed with a knife or needle. Gunshot wounds are puncture wounds. Anaerobic conditions are present at the bottom of such wounds, and rapid healing or scab formation at the surface prevents adequate drainage. Tetanus organisms are likely to find conditions ideal for their growth in such wounds. Hypodermic injections result, or should result, in clean puncture wounds.

The *lacerated wound* is one in which the tissues are torn or crushed. Lacerated wounds result from traffic accidents and from various explosives such as shrapnel. These wounds contain masses of necrotic tissue; blood and secretions accumulate in deep pockets without proper drainage; and anaerobic conditions develop rapidly. Organisms of the gas gangrene group are favored by such conditions.

The Organisms of Infected Wounds. The species and numbers of bacteria to be found in an infected wound depend on the types that have gained entrance there and the conditions in the wound. Most infected wounds harbor a mixed flora of bacteria, and this flora changes during the course of the infection. Bacteriophage typing of staphylococci and coliforms and the Lancefield typing of streptococci show that secondary invaders are often from the skin or respiratory flora of nurses or from dust. An extraordinary variety of bacteria have been found in wounds. In one study of 36 wounds, 214 different bacteria were isolated. Wound organisms may be divided somewhat arbitrarily into four groups.

Invasive Types. There are surprisingly few organisms that are capable of growth in wounds free from necrotic tissue, accumulated secretions, and foreign matter (the so-called "clean" wounds). Beta-hemolytic Group A streptococci are the outstanding exceptions. They possess unusual power to invade living tissue. Certain bacteria spread by insects, such as the organisms of tularemia and bubonic plague, might also be considered as belonging to this group.

Toxigenic Types. The toxin-producing clostridia are the outstanding examples of this type. It also includes the organism of diphtheria and the toxin-producing streptococci.

Proteolytic Types. These include the proteolytic clostridia such as *Cl. histolyticum* and also aerobic organisms such as the members of the genus *Proteus*. These bacteria increase the growth and hasten the invasion of toxigenic types. It is also possible that some produce toxic compounds by their decomposition of tissue proteins.

Nonpathogenic Types. Many organisms that are essentially nonpathogenic are found in mixed infections. They are sometimes found in wounds that appear to be free from infection. Some play an important part in mixed infections because they stimulate the growth of the more virulent species. Organisms of this group include *Pseudomonas aeruginosa* and *Aerobacter aerogenes*.

Prevention and Control of Wound Infection. Infection of wounds is prevented in two ways: (1) by preventing the entrance of organisms into the wound, and (2) by preventing conditions that allow any organisms that do gain entrance to grow or spread.

Aseptic procedures at the time of operation and in the dressing of wounds are aimed at eliminating all contamination of surgical wounds with outside organisms. Little can be done to control the original contamination of accidental wounds, but all further infection can be avoided by proper first aid, surgical, and nursing techniques. The nurse must remember that wounds may be readily *superinfected* by the entrance of organisms from dust, droplet nuclei, and other environmental sources. She must keep in mind that commensal types that are common in the environment may play an important part in wound infections.

Treatment of Major Wounds. Earlier methods of treating wounds emphasized the use of strong disinfectants. These substances killed invading organisms, but they so injured the tissues that reinfection was encouraged and healing delayed. This subject has already been discussed in Chaps. 8 and 11. The present-day methods of wound management result from the development of antibacterial agents that inhibit bacterial growth without causing tissue injury and from the knowledge that wound organisms are generally unable to grow in "clean" wounds. The measures used in the management of major wounds may be summarized as follows:

1. Immunization against tetanus. Active immunization with toxoid and the use of the booster dose on wounded persons are the only measures that can be relied on to prevent tetanus wound infection.

2. Prompt and complete surgical treatment of the wound. The term *precise surgical toilet* has been used to describe such treatment. The wound is cleaned of all foreign material, all dead and dying tissue is removed (this is *debridement*), and adequate drainage is established. The surgical toilet may have to be repeated if suppuration develops. Pressure dressings, drains, and splinting may help to prevent the accumulation of secretions in the wound.

3. Chemotherapy. Penicillin and other antibiotics are effective against organisms that have spread from the site of the wound through the blood or lymph. They also prevent any further spread. They are less effective in destroying organisms at the site of infection. A recent article states, "No available antibiotic can completely sterilize an open wound."

4. Stimulation of defensive mechanisms. General therapy that is aimed to improve the defensive activities of the tissues includes high protein and vitamin diets and replacement of lost blood and serum proteins by transfusion.

5. Surgical closure. When the patient's general condition, the state of healing in the wound, and the reports from the laboratory are satisfactory, the physician closes the wound. This is done as soon as possible, for only a closed wound will remain sterile. A clean surgical wound is, of course, closed at the end of the operation.

Treatment of Minor Wounds. The home care of cuts and scratches should consist of cleaning with clean water and cloth (or paper) and protection from further infection by a sterile but not airproof covering. All puncture and lacerated wounds and all wounds that show signs of inflammation should be cared for by a doctor. Application of moist heat is the only method that can be safely recommended for the home treatment of infections.

Septicemia. The terms *septicemia, bacteremia,* and *pyemia* have been defined on page 219. Certain specific communicable diseases such as those caused by pasteurellas are essentially septicemias. There is really no clear dividing line between septicemias and the bacteremias that occur in many infections with *Neisseria meningitidis* and *Diplococcus pneumoniae*. Septicemias also develop from known or unsuspected internal infections in which the bacteria gain access to the blood through the mucous membranes. Septicemia as the result of puerperal infection of the uterus is an example. They may also be the result of the spread of infection from wounds.

Group A beta-hemolytic streptococci are the organisms most often found in typical septicemias. Staphylococci are less frequent, but the infections are difficult to treat, since these organisms are more resistant to antibiotics. The wound clostridia have little tendency to spread from the site of infection until just before or at the time of the patient's death. The exception is *Cl. septicum,* which may spread from wounds to cause a generalized *malignant edema.* Septicemias due to organisms of the salmonella group, to *Escherichia coli, Hemophilus influenzae,* and a great variety of other bacteria occur, usually in infants.

Diagnosis and Treatment. Diagnosis depends on the cultivation and identification of the causative organism from a freshly drawn specimen of venous blood. The specimen must be obtained by an experienced person, using the strictest aseptic technique. Contaminants may suppress or outgrow the more delicate pathogens and make it impossible for the laboratory to give a correct report on the specimen. Both aerobic and anaerobic cultures are made in enriched media. The organisms are identified by microscopic study, cultivation in special media, and animal inoculation. If the patient has already been treated with penicillin or sulfa drugs, the concentration of the drug in the blood may be sufficient to suppress growth in the first culture medium. In that case a substance that will neutralize the antibiotic is added to the medium.

The organism isolated from the patient is tested to determine its susceptibility to antibiotics (see page 139). The test will also indicate roughly the dosage of the drug necessary to give an effective antibacterial concentration in the blood. The identity of the organism will help determine the antibiotic to be used. In some infections specific antisera may be used for treatment.

STUDY SUGGESTIONS

Check your knowledge of spores and spore formation and of the classification of the spore-forming bacteria.

How does the organism of anthrax differ from the others discussed in this chapter? What are the three clinical types of anthrax? Which is commonest in this country and why?

Review the food poisonings. How does botulinus poisoning differ from each of the others? How would you explain the dangers of botulinus poisoning to an intelligent housewife and tell her how such dangers can be avoided?

Compare *Cl. tetani* with the clostridia of gas gangrene. Compare their toxins. What are the chief differences between a typical case of tetanus and a typical case of gas gangrene? Why is toxoid immunization against tetanus better than antitoxin immunization? Who should be immunized against tetanus?

Describe the nature and activities of the chief organisms of the gas gangrene group.

When and how may cases of gas gangrene appear in modern hospitals? What measures do you think will be taken to deal with this emergency?

What are the chief types of wounds? Give examples. Why are serious wound infections less common and less fatal than they used to be? What procedures have you read about or seen carried out in the hospital that minimize the possibility of infection of wounds? What procedures have you seen carried out in the case of infected or potentially infected wounds? Why must wounds be protected not just from infection from other wounds but from all organisms?

How may cases of septicemia arise? What bacteria are responsible? What methods developed within the last 20 years have decreased the incidence and severity of septicemias?

Which characteristic(s) of each of the important pathogenic spore-forming bacteria is an important aid in its identification in the laboratory? Why must special care be exercised in the collection and transportation of specimens for blood cultures?

SUGGESTED READING

(See also appropriate chapters in the medical bacteriology texts listed on page 572.)

Bacillus anthracis and Anthrax

CROMARTIE, W. J., *et al.*: Studies on infection with *Bacillus anthracis*. *J. Infect. Dis.* **80**:1 (1947).

ELLINGTON, H. V., *et al.*: Cutaneous anthrax: report of 26 cases. *J.A.M.A.* **131**:1105 (1946).

HAGAN, W. A.: The Laboratory Diagnosis of Anthrax, in "Diagnostic Procedures and Reagents." 3d ed., American Public Health Association, New York, 1950.

SIMPSON, R. C.: Anthrax. *Am. J. Nursing* **48**:795 (1948).

SMYTH, H. F.: Check anthrax—a warning and a plea. *Am. J. Pub. Health* **33**:854 (1948).

STEELE, J. H., and R. J. HELVIG: Anthrax in the United States. *Pub. Health Rep.* **68**:615 (1953).

Clostridium botulinum and Botulinus Poisoning (See also page 194.)

DACK, G. M.: Bacterial Food Poisoning, in "Diagnostic Procedures and Reagents." 3d ed., American Public Health Association, New York, 1950.

————: "Food Poisoning." Rev. ed., University of Chicago Press, Chicago, 1949.

HALL, J. C.: The danger of botulism. *Am. J. Pub. Health* **33**:818 (1943).

ROUECHÉ, B.: Family Reunion, in "Eleven Blue Men." Little, Brown, Boston, 1954.

Clostridium tetani and Tetanus

AMERICAN ACADEMY OF PEDIATRICS: "Report of the Committee on Immunization and Therapeutic Procedures for Acute Infectious Diseases." Evanston, 1952.

BIGLER, J. A.: Tetanus immunization. *Am. J. Dis. Child.*, **81**:226 (1951).

Diaz-Rivera, R. S., L. R. Deliz, and J. Berio-Suarez: Penicillin in tetanus. *J.A.M.A.* **138:**191 (1948).

Long, A. P.: Tetanus toxoid: its use in the United States Army. *Am. J. Pub. Health* **33:**53 (1943).

Mueller, J. H., and P. A. Miller: Growth requirements of *Clostridium tetani. J. Bact.* **43:**763 (1942).

Pickett, M. J., P. D. Hedrich, and R. C. Germain: Purification of high titer toxin. *J. Bact.* **49:**515 (1945).

Pratt, E. L.: Clinical tetanus. *J.A.M.A.* **129:**1243 (1948).

Roueché, B.: A Pinch of Dust, in "Eleven Blue Men." Little, Brown, Boston, 1954.

Clostridium perfringens, Other Clostridia, and Gas Gangrene

Orr, J. H., and G. B. Reed: Serological types of *Clostridium perfringens. J. Bact.* **40:**441 (1940).

Smith, L. D.: Clostridia in gas gangrene. *Bact. Rev.* **13:**233 (1949).

Wound Infection and Septicemia

Burns, C. G.: Blood Cultures, in "Diagnostic Procedures and Reagents." 3d ed., American Public Health Association, New York, 1950.

Lyons, C.: Chemotherapy in the management of wounds. *J.A.M.A.* **133:**215 (1947).

Meleney, F. L.: "Treatise on Surgical Infection." Oxford, New York, 1948.

Pulaski, E. J.: Medical progress: War wounds. *New England J. Med.* **249:**890, 932 (1953).

Rustigan, R., and A. Cipriani: The bacteriology of open wounds. *J.A.M.A.* **133:**224 (1947).

Walter, C. W.: "The Aseptic Treatment of Wounds." Macmillan, New York, 1948.

CHAPTER 30

Mycobacterium tuberculosis and *Mycobacterium leprae*

The characteristics of the moldlike higher bacteria, the members of the order *Actinomycetales,* have been described in Chap. 2. Their classification into families and genera is outlined in Appendix B. *Mycobacterium tuberculosis,* the cause of tuberculosis, and *M. leprae,* the cause of leprosy, are described in this chapter. The more moldlike members of the order, the actinomycetes, will be discussed in Chap. 36.

MYCOBACTERIUM TUBERCULOSIS, THE CAUSE OF TUBERCULOSIS

Despite steadily declining death rates, tuberculosis is still one of the most important diseases of man. In the United States over 25,000 people died of tuberculosis in 1952. There are half a million known cases of the disease in this country, and each year there are more than 100,000 new cases. Tuberculosis is the leading cause of death in young adults. The incidence of the disease in Negroes, Indians, and Eskimos is many times that in the rest of the population. Tuberculosis is the chief cause of illness and death in newly industrialized areas in many backward countries.

The Organism. The tuberculosis bacillus was first isolated by Robert Koch in 1882. He was able to grow the organism in pure culture and reproduce the disease with these cultures. In 1895 the American bacteriologist Theobald Smith differentiated between the human and bovine varieties.

Morphology and Staining. Mycobacterium tuberculosis var. *hominis* is a nonsporing, nonmotile rod. The typical bacillus is of medium length, slender, and frequently curved (Fig. 30·1). The bacteria are found in small groups

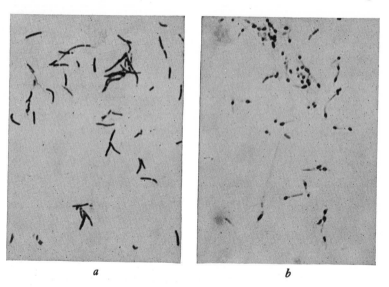

a *b*

Fig. 30·1 *Mycobacterium tuberculosis.* ×1,200. Acid-fast stain. (*a*) Appearance when correctly stained; (*b*) granular appearance due to faulty staining. (*Courtesy of Dr. Diran Yegian, from J. Bact. 44:667.*)

but never in chains. In older cultures filamentous and branching forms are found. Nuclei, granules, and vacuoles can be seen when the bacteria are examined by electron micrography.

The tubercle bacilli are gram-positive and strongly acid-fast. The acid-fast staining technique (Ziehl-Neelsen stain) is described on page 413. The acid-fastness is due to the character of the cell wall which prevents the dye from escaping from the cell. When the cell walls are broken, the bacteria are no longer acid-fast. The beaded appearance often seen in stained smears is due to the collection of the intracellular dye into distinct globules. Figures 30·1*a* and *b* show the effect of varying stain techniques.

Cultivation. Tuberculosis organisms grow very slowly in cultures. Several weeks is needed to obtain maximum growth even on the most favorable media. The organisms are strictly aerobic and prefer a temperature close to 37°C. Egg-glycerin media are most commonly used. They contain egg yolk, serum, and potato for enrichment; glycerin, which is a growth stimulant for human-type mycobacteria; and dyes that inhibit the growth of contaminants. The Löwenstein-Jensen medium, considered the best for the isolation of the bacteria, contains potato flour, malachite green dye, glycerol, asparagine, and essential salts, together with a very large amount of homogenized whole fresh eggs. The egg albumin coagulates the medium. The mixed ingredients are heated in slanted tubes. On this and similar media the bacteria grow in clumps resembling heaped-up granular paraffin (Fig. 30·2). Human strains are white but may become yellow or orange in old cultures. In broth cultures a wrinkled pellicle covers the surface, leaving the rest of the medium clear (Fig. 30·3). There is no obvious digestion of proteins or fermentation of sugars.

Fig. 30·2 *Mycobacterium tuberculosis* var. *hominis* on a slant of coagulated egg medium. ("*Medichrome,*" Clay-Adams Co., Inc., Dr. Gregory Shwartzman, Mt. Sinai Hospital.)

Dr. René Dubos and his coworkers have recently introduced a different type of medium. The basal medium is a carefully balanced solution of essential minerals with asparagine and partially digested casein. To this is added a small amount of the anionic detergent *Tween 80* and a little albumin. The Tween 80 alters the surface tension of the broth so that the mycobacteria are wetted by the medium. Dubos's oleic acid–albumin agar for isolation has the same basic ingredients plus agar, oleic acid, albumin, and penicillin.

Survival and Resistance to Disinfectants. M. tuberculosis is an obligate parasite and there is no reason to believe that it ever multiplies in the environment. But it is capable of long survival outside its hosts, particularly when embedded in sputum or pus. Even when sputum is so dry that it is blown about as dust, the living organism can still be recovered from it. Ordinary chemical disinfectants such as 5 per cent phenol take many hours to kill the organism. Hypochlorite solutions have practically no effect on it. It sur-

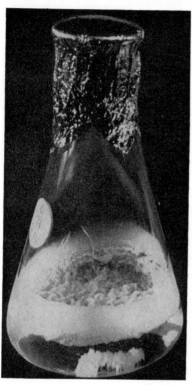

vives the action of strong acids and alkalies that destroy other bacteria rapidly. The one agent that is reliably effective against it is heat. Five minutes' boiling or 30 minutes at pasteurizing temperature kills all tuberculosis organisms.

Types of Tuberculosis Bacteria. Virulent tuberculosis strains grow as *R* colonies. Avirulent strains, sometimes *S* in form, develop rather readily. Cultures used for research purposes, vaccine production, etc., are given numbers, followed by the designation of the colony form and then by subletters—*v* if virulent and *a* if avirulent. The final test of virulence is, of course, animal inoculation. There are, however, simple laboratory tests that distinguish *v* and *a* strains. In egg-free media, virulent strains grow in cords and form spreading colonies, while avirulent strains make a more amorphous growth and form more compact colonies. These characteristics are shown in Fig. 30·4. Phagocytes which take up virulent bacteria show a decrease in mobility as compared with those that have ingested avirulent forms. Avirulent bacteria reduce methylene blue more rapidly than virulent strains.

FIG. 30·3 *Mycobacterium tuberculosis* growing on a synthetic liquid medium free from toxic substances. (*Courtesy of Dr. W. F. Drea, from J. Bact. 44: 154.*)

The bovine tuberculosis bacterium, *Tuberculosis* var. *bovis,* is also pathogenic for man. There are avian and "cold-blooded" varieties pathogenic for birds and amphibians. A nonpathogenic acid-fast bacillus, *M. smegmatis,* is found on human skin, especially around the external genitals. Several species of saprophytic mycobacteria are common in soil, hay, and dairy products. The tests by which human and bovine varieties are recognized are discussed in the section on laboratory diagnosis and are summarized in Table 30·1, page 415.

The Disease. The pulmonary form of tuberculosis is by far the most common and causes 90 per cent of tuberculosis deaths in this country. Tuberculosis of other parts of the body, usually designated *nonpulmonary tuberculosis,* is responsible for the other 10 per cent of deaths. Pulmonary tuberculosis is caused by the human variety of the organism, while nonpulmonary tuberculosis is often due to organisms of the bovine type. *Phthisis* and *consumption* are two other names for tuberculosis. The adjectives *phthisical* and *consumptive* mean tuberculous. The student should note that

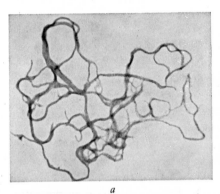
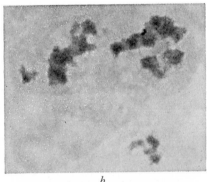

a   *b*

FIG. 30·4 Typical growth of variants of human strains of *M. tuberculosis*. (*a*) "Cord" growth of virulent human strain (H37Rv); (*b*) loose, amorphous growth of avirulent human strain (R1Ra). (*Courtesy of Dr. Diran Yegian, from Yegian and Kurung, J. Bact. 65:181.*)

the adjective *tubercular* means pertaining to the tubercle (page 402), while *tuberculous* means pertaining to tuberculosis infection.

Sources and Modes of Infection. By far the most important source of infection is the person with active pulmonary disease, for he constantly discharges organisms into his environment. Particularly dangerous are undiagnosed cases in parents, teachers, and food handlers. The disease is often unsuspected in elderly persons, and they are frequently the sources of infection for children living in the same home. Nonpulmonary cases are much less likely to spread the infection. In countries where tuberculosis in cattle is not controlled, the infected cow is a very important source of childhood nonpulmonary tuberculosis. Organisms from human cases are spread by droplets, droplet nuclei, dust, and contaminated objects. Bovine-type tuberculosis is spread by raw milk and milk products.

Portals of Infection. Most infections result from the inhalation of air-borne organisms. Many nonpulmonary infections result from the ingestion of food-borne organisms. The bacteria make their way through the walls of the upper respiratory tract or through the lymphoid tissue of the nasopharynx or intestine to nearby lymph nodes. They may be carried all the way to the alveoli of the lungs. Infection through breaks in the skin is known to occur. Infection through the urogenital system or the conjunctiva is also possible.

Primary Tuberculosis. The first time tuberculosis bacteria enter the body the tissues show no immediate reaction. The bacteria spread rapidly, most of them localizing in nearby lymph nodes. There a cellular reaction takes place, and in a month or 6 weeks the bacteria are enclosed in a wall of cells. This is the *primary tubercle.*

The only outward sign of this process in most cases is a temporary low-grade fever, which usually passes unnoticed. In some infants this primary infection may spread. There may be a benign tuberculous infiltration of the lung tissue, or more extensive involvement of the lymph nodes in the hila of the lungs or in the abdominal mesenteries. Even these more extensive infections do not cause notable or distinctive symptoms. In only 15 to 20 per cent of the cases are the processes of fibrosis and of calcification sufficiently extensive to be seen by x-ray.

The only definite sign in 80 per cent of cases of primary infection is the development of hypersensitiveness to the tuberculin test. Until about one month after this first infection the person shows no reaction to the intracutaneous injection of a minute amount of *M. tuberculosis* antigen (tuberculin). At the end of this time and for a long time thereafter the person is tuberculin-positive and will have a local area of edema whenever tuberculin is introduced into his skin.

There is considerable evidence to show that the primary infection process creates a relative resistance to subsequent tuberculosis infection. Experiments on susceptible laboratory animals show that whereas the tubercle bacteria of the first inoculation tend to spread rapidly from the site of injection, those inoculated subsequently are quickly immobilized and the resulting local lesion heals promptly. Statistical studies of tuberculin-positive and tuberculin-negative persons who are later exposed to tuberculosis show that those who have had a primary infection and become hypersensitive (the tuberculin-positive ones) are only about one-quarter as likely to develop active tuberculosis as those who have never been infected (the tuberculin-negative ones).

Where tuberculosis is prevalent, practically everyone will acquire primary infection during childhood. For this reason primary infection has often been called *childhood-type infection.* At the present time in most of the United States infection before school age occurs in less than one-fifth of our children.

Many people do not have their primary infections until adult life, and more and more escape tuberculosis infection entirely.

Reinfection Tuberculosis. The active clinical illnesses due to *M. tuberculosis* result from reinfection of persons who have had the primary infection. The reinfection may be delayed for many years. Or primary infection, particularly in infants, may be followed so closely by reinfection disease that it is impossible to separate the two conditions. The organisms responsible for the reinfection may be endogenous or exogenous in origin; they may be living bacteria that have survived in the primary tubercles, or they may be introduced from the environment. Over 90 per cent of active tuberculosis is chronic pulmonary disease. Nonpulmonary tuberculosis accounts for less than 10 per cent of cases, most of them in children.

Wherever the organism localizes, it tends to cause the breakdown of surrounding cells, leading to the formation of accumulations of *caseous* (cheesy) pus. If the pus drains away, as it does in the lungs and kidneys, cavities are formed. These processes of tissue destruction are combated by defense mechanisms of the body. Fibrosis and calcification wall off the infected areas successfully if the case improves.

Pulmonary Tuberculosis. This type of infection begins with fibrous infiltration of the apex of the lung. If the disease progresses, cavities are formed there and in other parts of the lung. Loss of weight, fatigue, cough and expectoration, and sometimes hemoptysis are the characteristic symptoms. Minimal infection is most readily recognized by chest x-ray. The importance of the pulmonary case as the source of tuberculosis in the community has already been pointed out.

Nonpulmonary Tuberculosis. Certain forms of nonpulmonary infection are characteristic of childhood and are often due to bovine-type organisms. These forms are rare in areas where the milk supply is good. They include bone and joint tuberculosis and *cervical adenitis* (*scrofula*). *Miliary tuberculosis* (acute disseminated tuberculosis) is a rapidly developing, generalized form of the disease in which thousands of small tubercles are formed throughout the body. Infants are often the victims of *tuberculous meningitis*. Tuberculous infection of the kidney or the adrenal glands (*Addison's disease*) may occur. Infection in the lungs may spread to the larynx, the pleura, or even to the pericardium.

Predisposing Factors. It is obvious that of the large number of persons who are infected with *M. tuberculosis* one or more times during their lives, only a small proportion develop the active disease. The factors that are believed to predispose to the development of active disease are (1) hereditary and racial susceptibility, (2) massive and repeated infection, and (3) lowered levels of general health and resistance.

1. Heredity and racial susceptibility. No person inherits tuberculosis, but

there may be inheritance of resistance or susceptibility to the infection. Races and nations in which tuberculosis has been prevalent appear to become increasingly resistant to the disease. Individuals do not inherit an acquired resistance to the disease, but the more susceptible individuals may die before they produce children and the succeeding generations will be the descendants of the resistant portion of the population. Tuberculosis becomes an epidemic disease when introduced into a previously unexposed population. The high incidence of the disease among the Eskimos and that among Negro peoples in Africa are modern examples.

2. Massive and repeated infection. The incidence of active tuberculosis is much higher among those who have been in intimate, continued contact with cases of pulmonary tuberculosis than among those whose contact has been only temporary and casual. Tuberculosis is primarily a family disease. Children brought up in homes where they are in daily contact with infectious cases receive repeated doses of infection. Their natural resistance to tuberculosis is broken down by this constantly repeated reinfection.

3. Low levels of general health and resistance. The relatively effective natural defenses of the body against tuberculosis are dependent on good health. Any factor that lowers the general level of well-being predisposes to active disease. Malnutrition, particularly a low or poor protein intake, is a very important factor. After the Second World War, as after the First World War, tuberculosis increased at an alarming rate in all places where the diet was deficient. Continued fatigue or strain, including the strain of pregnancy, predispose to active tuberculosis. The lowering of general resistance due to other infections is important. Tuberculosis frequently develops in persons convalescing from other illnesses. Workers in quarries and other dusty trades inhale silicate dust and develop a fibrosis of the lungs called *silicosis*. This condition predisposes to a rapid development of pulmonary tuberculosis.

Status of the Individual in Relation to Tuberculosis Infection. Every living person can be classified in one of the following groups:

1. Persons without active tuberculosis—tuberculin-negative
a. Persons who have never been infected
2. Persons without active tuberculosis—tuberculin-positive
a. Persons who have had primary-infection tuberculosis
b. Persons who have been successfully vaccinated with BCG (see page 407)
3. Persons with reinfection tuberculosis—tuberculin-positive
a. Persons with active cases of reinfection tuberculosis
b. Persons with arrested cases of reinfection tuberculosis

Immunity. The healthy human body has great powers of resistance to tuberculosis infection, but there is no reason to believe that anyone possesses a complete natural or acquired immunity to the disease. Neither primary-infection tuberculosis nor reinfection tuberculosis can make the victim completely immune to the disease. Years of research have failed to develop any certain method of artificial immunization. Sera from animals and humans are not useful for passive immunization or treatment.

Tuberculin and the Tuberculin Test. Robert Koch prepared an extract of old culture of tubercle bacilli which he called *tuberculin.* It did not prove useful for treatment as he had hoped. However, tests on animals showed that it provoked a reaction in previously infected animals, while noninfected animals failed to react to it. Tuberculin testing of man and animals may

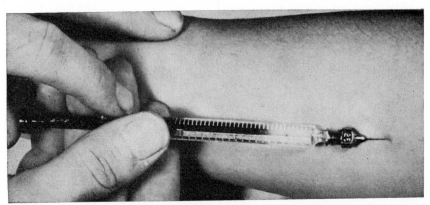

FIG. 30·5   Mantoux tuberculin test. Intracutaneous introduction of tuberculin. (*"Medichrome," Clay-Adams Co., Inc., National Tuberculosis Association.*)

be done with material prepared by Koch's method, *tuberculin OT* (old type), or with a highly stable and purified preparation called *PPD* (purified protein derivative).

The tuberculin test may be done in various ways. The three most commonly used are the Mantoux test, the von Pirquet test, and the Vollmer patch test. Local redness, edema, and papule formation appearing in 24 to 48 hours are signs of positive reactions in all three tests. (See Figs. 30·5, 30·6, 30·7, and 30·8.)

1. Mantoux test. This is the most useful and accurate test. Two strengths of PPD or OT are used. The stronger dose is assumed to detect all those who have become hypersensitive because of previous infection. It may, however, give rise to a severe reaction in cases of active infection.

2. von Pirquet test. Tuberculin is rubbed into the scarified skin. This is an older method which is seldom used.

3. Vollmer patch test. A small square of filter paper impregnated with concentrated tuberculin is taped on the cleaned skin of the forearm. This is a convenient method of testing large groups such as school children.

Usefulness of the Tuberculin Test. The principal uses of the tuberculin test may be summarized as follows (see also Chap. 15 for discussion of tuberculin testing of cattle):

1. As an aid to epidemiologic studies. The incidence of positive tuberculin tests in various age groups and other divisions of the population gives valuable information about prevalence of primary tuberculosis infection in a community and helps evaluate measures of tuberculosis control. In areas

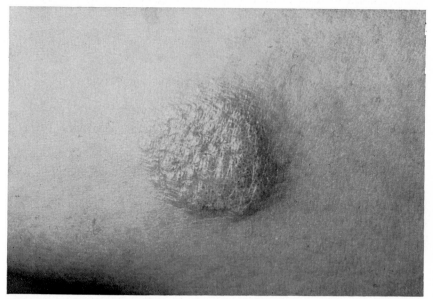

FIG. 30·6 Positive result of Mantoux test. (*"Medichrome," Clay-Adams Co., Inc., National Tuberculosis Association.*)

where certain pulmonary mycoses are prevalent, the test indicates whether lesions seen in x-ray pictures are the results of fungous infection or the results of primary tuberculosis infection.

2. As an aid to the diagnosis of reinfection tuberculosis. A negative tuberculin test rules out the possibility of tuberculosis. It is therefore useful when differential diagnosis between tuberculosis and other disease is difficult.

3. As an aid to the diagnosis of primary infection tuberculosis. The development of a positive tuberculin test (tuberculin *conversion*) in persons who have been previously tuberculin-negative indicates exposure to tuberculosis during the interval since the last test. Reversal of a previously negative tuberculin test may help the physician to identify an otherwise obscure illness as primary tuberculosis and to trace the spread of the bacteria in a family or institution.

4. To determine the need for special protection of those likely to be exposed
to infection. It is now generally recommended that persons with negative
tuberculin tests should not be employed in the care of tuberculous patients.
Nurses and other hospital personnel, children in families where adults have
the active disease, and persons living in environments where the disease is

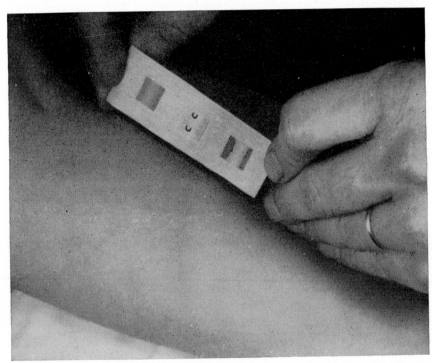

FIG. 30·7 Vollmer patch tuberculin test. Adhesive strip being applied to skin of arm.
Gauze at each end contains tuberculin; spot in center is control. (*"Medichrome," Clay-
Adams Co., Inc., National Tuberculosis Association.*)

common are tuberculin tested and given BCG vaccine if they are found
to be tuberculin-negative.

BCG and Protection against Active Tuberculosis. The French bacteriologist Calmette grew a culture of bovine-type organisms for 13 years on a bile
medium. At the end of that time the organism had become nonpathogenic
for calves. The preparation made from this organism is called *BCG.* This
term stands for *Bacille-Calmette-Guérin* (the bacillus of Calmette and
Guérin). After the First World War it was used extensively in an attempt
to decrease the high incidence of childhood tuberculosis in France. Large-
scale, controlled tests of this vaccine in Scandinavian countries and in North

America indicated that it does confer a considerable degree of protection. The Tuberculosis Recording Office of WHO, our Public Health Service, and many other agencies are now studying the results of very large-scale trials of the vaccine.

BCG vaccine is prepared from carefully grown cultures of the stock organism. The growth is homogenized in a special solution and is tested

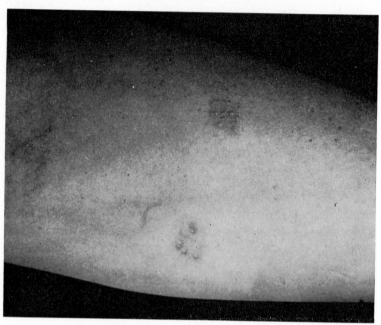

Fig. 30·8   Positive result of Vollmer test. (*"Medichrome," Clay-Adams Co., Inc., National Tuberculosis Association.*)

for viability, lack of virulence, and ability to convert the tuberculin reaction in guinea pigs. The vaccine is distributed in liquid form for immediate use, and as a freeze-dried powder (Fig. 30·9). The freeze-dried preparation remains effective for periods up to 10 months. Multiple puncture into the superficial skin is the recommended method of vaccination. One instrument devised for the purpose is shown in Fig. 30·10. Tiny papules form in 1 to 3 weeks at the points where the skin was infected. Figure 30·11 shows a typical reaction. No permanent scar is formed. Eight weeks after vaccination a tuberculin test is administered. The test should be positive, as evidenced by a definite area of induration at the site of injection. Revaccination should be done if the tuberculin test is negative (i.e., if there has been no conversion).

There is now general agreement among authorities on tuberculosis that

BCG vaccination is a safe procedure and that it provides considerable, though not absolute, protection against active tuberculosis. There is some evidence that when the disease does occur in vaccinated individuals it is relatively mild. In countries where tuberculosis is common, vaccination of children by the millions has been carried out under the auspices of international health organizations. In some Scandinavian countries all tuberculin-negative school children are vaccinated. In the United States and in other countries where most individuals live in environments free from the tubercle bacilli, vaccination is generally limited to those in special situations where tuberculosis infection is likely. The persons needing vaccination include (1) doctors, nurses, and medical students; (2) hospital and laboratory personnel whose work exposes them to tuberculosis; (3) individuals, particularly infants and small children, in whose homes there are cases of open pulmonary infection; (4) patients and employees of mental hospitals and other institutions where the incidence of tuberculosis is high; (5) children living in communities where the incidence of tuberculosis is unusually high (Indians on reservations, certain racial groups in crowded city areas, etc.) and adults who have contact with these groups. In all these groups vaccination is done only on the tuberculin-negative individuals.

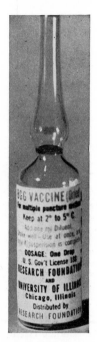

Other forms of tuberculosis vaccine have been developed and used experimentally. It is very likely that a more stable and effective vaccine will eventually replace BCG.

Fig. 30·9 BCG vaccine. This ampule contains material for the vaccination of 14 persons. (*Courtesy of Dr. S. R. Rosenthal and the Research Foundation.*)

Treatment of Active Tuberculosis. For many years tuberculosis has been treated by giving the patient optimum conditions for the development of his general resistance to the disease. Rest and diet have been the factors most stressed. Surgery has been used to immobilize infected areas. *Phrenectomy* (the cutting of the phrenic nerve) and *thoracoplasty* (the excision of sections of ribs), both of which immobilize portions of infected lungs, are examples of such operations.

In the last few years methods of treatment which attack the tuberculosis organism in the tissues have been developed. The new emphasis in treatment is on the elimination or suppression of the mycobacteria. Improved thoracic surgery now enables the surgeon to remove single infected lobes of lung (*lobectomy*) or a whole lung (*pneumonectomy*) in cases where the tuberculosis lesions are definitely localized. The major factor in the change in tuberculosis therapy has been the discovery of drugs specifically antagonistic to *M. tuberculosis,* effective in vivo, and relatively nontoxic to human tissue. Streptomycin was the first of these drugs to be used extensively. Combined therapy with para-aminosalicylic acid (PASA) and streptomycin has been the chief method of treating tuberculosis in this country for the last 5 years. Other antibiotics including dihydrostreptomycin, viomycin, neomycin, and

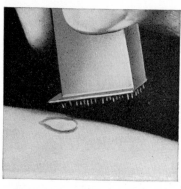 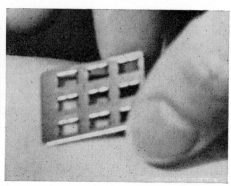

a   *b*

FIG. 30·10 BCG vaccination by the multiple-puncture technique. (*a*) The drop of vaccine is spread with the wide edge of the metal plate. The plate is then pressed into the skin to make many small punctures. (*b*) The edge of the plate is used to redistribute the vaccine so that it will enter the punctures. (*Courtesy of Dr. S. R. Rosenthal and the Research Foundation.*)

oxytetracycline have all been used with some success but have no advantage over streptomycin.

Three groups of synthetic drugs are now used for treatment of tuberculosis. They are PASA and its derivatives, the thiosemicarbazones, and the derivatives of pyridine carboxylic acid. PASA and similar drugs interfere with the normal respiration of mycobacteria. They are effective in tuberculosis of the lungs and mucous membranes. *Tibione (Tb I)*, a thiosemicarbazone, is widely used in Europe but is considered undesirably toxic by American authorities. The third group of drugs is represented in present chemotherapy by *isoniazide, pyrazinamide,* and closely related *isonicotinyl hydrazines. Rimifon* and *Marsilid* are two commonly used commercial preparations of these drugs. Prompt subjective improvement results from their use but is not always paralleled by equal clinical improvement.

The toxicity of many of the newer compounds seems to be very low, and their tuberculostatic activity against the usual infection is efficient. The isonicotinyl hydrazines have the advantages of small molecular size and diffusibility. A so-far unsolved problem of the chemotherapy of tuberculosis is the rapidity with which *M. tuberculosis* organisms in the body develop strains resistant to whatever drug is used. It is to be hoped that in the future some type of chemical may be found against which the organism is genetically incapable of developing resistance. In the meantime prompt treatment with combined drugs in the highest tolerated dosages and selective surgical pro-

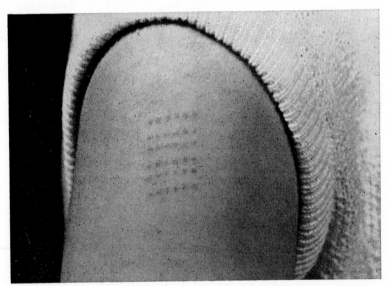

FIG. 30·11   BCG vaccination reaction after 13 days. (*Courtesy of Dr. S. R. Rosenthal and the Research Foundation.*)

cedures have caused a marked drop in the fatality of most forms of tuberculosis.

Prevention and Control. Important measures for the control of tuberculosis are summarized below.

1. Measures that decrease liability to active infection

a. Optimum diet for all

b. Adequate rest and recreation for all

c. Maximum protection against all diseases and adequate treatment of all illnesses

d. Protection of workers from silicate dusts

e. Protection of selected groups by BCG vaccination

2. Measures that prevent the spread of *M. tuberculosis*

a. Prompt detection and diagnosis of early cases

b. Hospital care for all cases with open pulmonary lesions *c.* Education of the patient and his family in the dangers of spread of the infection

d. Pasteurization of all milk supplies; eradication of tuberculosis in dairy cattle

e. Separation of infants and children from families with adult cases of tuberculosis until a tuberculin test done 8 weeks after BCG vaccination is positive

Tuberculosis in Hospital Personnel. The incidence of active tuberculosis is greater among student nurses, medical students, and interns than it is among persons of the same age groups in the general population. It varies considerably in different institutions.

Nursing students are of an age group especially susceptible to tuberculosis, and they are much more likely to be exposed to infection than they would be in other occupations. Investigations have shown that as many as 10 per cent of the patients admitted to general hospitals have undiagnosed active tuberculosis. The hard work and study involved in the nurse's training may lower her natural resistance to infection.

No one measure can prevent development of tuberculosis among nurses. All the following measures should be part of the planned program of every hospital and affiliated school of nursing.

1. Preadmission and periodic chest x-rays should be made on all nursing-school students and other personnel.

2. Patients with known or suspected tuberculosis should be cared for only by persons with positive tuberculin tests.

3. Chest x-rays should be taken of all patients admitted to the hospital or its clinics.

4. Special units with carefully worked out procedures must be provided for the care of all known and suspected cases of tuberculosis.

5. Hospital procedures and nursing techniques for the care of all cases with respiratory discharges must be carefully developed and carried out. Such procedures must not be neglected during the process of admitting the patient.

6. The staff should be provided with good food, good living quarters, and adequate recreation facilities. Hours of duty and nursing load must be designed to avoid undue fatigue. All illnesses must be prevented as far as possible and properly cared for when they do occur.

7. The staff must be taught personal hygiene in an effective manner. It must realize that no other measures can compensate for own indifference and carelessness in matters of health. An important part of nursing education is the learning of good habits of nutrition, rest, and recreation.

8. All hospital personnel who are found to be tuberculin-negative should be offered and urged to accept BCG vaccination.

Laboratory Diagnosis. The bacteriologic tests used in the diagnosis of tuberculosis are aimed at the discovery and definite identification of the causative organism. Serologic tests are not commonly used. The role of the tuberculin test in diagnosis has already been discussed (page 406). Roentgenologic examinations of persons exhibiting the physical signs of the disease or known to have been in contact with open cases disclose those who are presumptive victims of active tuberculosis. The demonstration of typical *M. tuberculosis* in the sputum or other body material is the only absolute proof that the disease is active tuberculosis. Repeated thorough laboratory examination of carefully collected specimens seldom fails to reveal the organisms.

Collection of Specimens. The materials commonly examined for the presence of *M. tuberculosis* are

1. Sputum. At least 90 per cent of all examinations are done on sputum specimens. The sputum must be material expectorated from the lungs and is best collected when the patient first wakes in the morning. It should be coughed directly into a wide-mouthed specimen bottle fitted with a tight stopper.

2. Gastric washings. Gastric lavage with normal saline solution is used to collect stomach contents when the patient wakens. The acid washings are neutralized if examination of the specimen is to be delayed. Gastric washings are needed for diagnosis in infants and small children who swallow their sputum, and in adults with positive chest x-rays who fail to show mycobacteria in their sputum.

3. Other body material. Specimens to be examined in nonpulmonary cases include urine in cases of suspected renal tuberculosis, spinal fluid when meningitis is suspected, pleural and peritoneal fluids, pus aspirated from infected lymph nodes and bone lesions, and tissues excised at necropsy.

4. Milk and milk products.

Direct Microscopic Examination. Sputum is examined in a petri dish placed on a black background. Bits of caseous material are smeared over three-quarters of the surface of a slide and stained by the Ziehl-Neelsen technique. The smear is stained with hot carbol fuchsin, decolorized with acid alcohol, and counterstained with methylene blue. The acid-fast mycobacteria appear as red rods against a blue background. Pus and caseous matter from autopsy specimens are also stained directly. Urine, body fluids, milk serum, and digested specimens of sputum (see below) are centrifuged, and the sediment is smeared and stained. Using a mechanical clamp which moves the slide evenly across the microscope stage, the technician examines all fields in three lines across the slide. She may indicate roughly the numbers of acid-fast bacteria seen. The scale recommended by the American Trudeau Society is:

Numerous (3+)—10 or more acid-fast bacilli per field
Few (2+)—10 or more bacilli in entire smear
Rare (1+)—3 to 9 acid-fast bacilli in entire smear
1 or 2 bacilli per smear to be so recorded.

Acid-fast bacteria seen in smears from patients constitute presumptive evidence that the disease is tuberculosis. In most laboratories direct microscopic examination is followed by an attempt to cultivate the mycobacteria. Specimens of sputum from cases already conclusively shown to be tuberculosis do not need cultural confirmation.

Cultivation. Although the ideal medium for discovery of **M.** *tuberculosis* is still to be found, modern media and methods enable the bacteriologist to detect the tuberculosis organism even when it is present in very small numbers. Characteristic growth in selective media (Fig. 30·2) allows the laboratory worker to state with confidence that the patient is discharging living **M.** *tuberculosis.* The isolated organism can be subjected to further tests if they are needed.

Specimens are prepared for cultivation by chemical and mechanical treatments designed to free the bacteria from tissue substances in which they are embedded, to destroy other bacteria, and to concentrate the mycobacteria in a small volume of fluid. One commonly used procedure consists of adding an equal volume of dilute sodium hydroxide to the specimen and shaking the mixture until it is homogeneous. The mixture is then centrifuged and the sediment neutralized with hydrochloric acid. The neutralized sediment is spread over the surface of a slant of Löwenstein-Jensen or other glycerin-egg medium. The character of the resulting growth tells the expert whether the organism is a human or bovine variety or a saprophytic species. (See Table 30·1.) On Dubos medium the type of colony will indicate presumptively the virulence of the mycobacterium.

Animal Inoculation. In the past guinea pig inoculation was commonly used as a means of culturing the tuberculosis organism. Sometimes the mycobacteria can be recovered from guinea pigs when cultures in artificial media have failed repeatedly because of heavy bacterial contamination of the specimen. The concentrated specimen is injected into the skin of the groin. After 3 weeks the animal is tuberculin-tested. If the tuberculin test is positive, the animal is killed and autopsied. If the test is negative, the autopsy is done at the end of 6 to 8 weeks. Smears are made from any organs showing lesions, stained by the acid-fast method, and examined for mycobacteria. The presence of acid-fast bacteria in typical lesions is definite evidence of the virulence of the bacteria.

Animals are also used for the "typing" of cultures. *Typing* in the case of **M.** *tuberculosis* means the determination of the variety of the bacterium. The bovine organisms are more virulent for rabbits than are the human

Table 30·1

Characteristics of Important Mycobacteria

Organism	Culture in egg-glycerin medium	Results of rabbit inoculation	Pathogenicity for man
M. *tuberculosis* var. *hominis*	Growth in 12–25 days; dry, rough, good-sized colonies (*eugonic*)	Few, small tubercles in lung and kidneys	Cause of all cases of pulmonary tuberculosis and of many nonpulmonary infections
M. *tuberculosis* var. *bovis*	Growth in 25–40 days; smooth, small colonies (*dysgonic*)	Generalized infection; death within 3 weeks	Cause of many cases of nonpulmonary tuberculoses in children
Saprophytic mycobacteria	Growth in 7 days; growth at 25°C.; soft, smooth, chromogenic colonies	Occasional local lesions at site of injection	No infection
M. *leprae*.........	No growth in culture media	No infection in any animal	Cause of leprosy

strains. Tuberculin-negative rabbits are inoculated with serial dilutions of the culture. The animals are killed and examined at the end of 2 to 3 months. The reactions characteristic of the principal varieties of mycobacteria are summarized in Table 30·1.

Serologic Tests. The sera of patients with active tuberculosis agglutinate red blood cells that have adsorbed antigens of *M. tuberculosis* (from cultures or from tuberculin). This is the *Middlebrook-Dubos test.* The titer of the hemagglutinating antibody is said to increase as the active disease progresses and to decrease as the disease is controlled. If complement is added to the test, the erythrocytes are lysed. These tests are not yet sufficiently standardized to be used routinely by diagnostic laboratories.

MYCOBACTERIUM LEPRAE: THE CAUSE OF LEPROSY

The Organism. *Mycobacterium leprae* (*Hansen's bacillus*) was first identified by Hansen in 1872. Leprosy bacilli look and stain like the tuberculosis bacilli (Fig. 30·12). In tissue smears they lie in packets of parallel rods within epithelioid cells. They also resemble the tuberculosis bacteria in their chemical composition. They grow only within the cells of human tissue. It has been suggested that they are dependent on the enzymes of the host cells for their respiratory functions. *M. leprae* cannot be cultivated in artificial media, nor will it grow in any animal but man. A very similar mycobacterium, the rat leprosy bacillus (*M. lepraemurium*), is frequently used in laboratory studies. It can be grown in tissue cultures as well as in the rodent hosts.

The Disease. Leprosy is an uncommon infection in the United States. American cases include migrants from countries where leprosy is endemic; native Americans from foci in Louisiana, Texas, and Florida; and a small number of persons infected during foreign service. In many areas of Africa and southern Asia leprosy is very common. In parts of Nigeria and India several persons out of every hundred have the disease. It is estimated that each year over 15,000 children are infected in India.

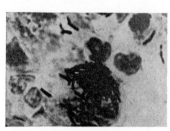

FIG. 30·12 *Mycobacterium leprae* in smear stained by acid-fast method. ×2,000. (*Armed Forces Institute of Pathology print 38988.*)

Clinical Types. Four types of leprosy are recognized. *Neural* leprosy lesions develop along the peripheral nerves. Sensation is lost in parts of the hands or feet, and mutilating lesions develop there. The nodules of the *lepromatous* disease are most marked in the nose and on the face but also occur in other areas of the skin and in internal organs. The nodules undergo necrotic changes and are subject to secondary bacterial infection. *Tuberculoid* leprosy is a mild chronic form characterized by reddened areas on the skin. *Mixed*-type cases show both neural and lepromatous lesions.

Transmission and Infection. Contrary to the usual conception, leprosy is the "least communicable of all communicable diseases." In nontropical countries the disease shows little tendency to spread. Even in tropical areas where sanitation is poor, only a limited number of exposed persons, more often children than adults, acquire the disease. The lepromatous types with open lesions are believed to be the usual source of the infection. The bacteria may both leave and enter via the nares. However infection through the skin and other mucous membranes is possible.

It is likely that leprosy infection may be very much more common than the active disease in those countries where the disease is endemic. *Lepromin,* a filtrate of disintegrated material from leprous nodules, produces a skin reaction in sensitized persons comparable to the tuberculin reaction. A strongly positive lepromin reaction found in many tuberculoid cases appears to indicate an active defense reaction. Active acute lepromatous cases may be lepromin-negative, indicating a failure of defensive mechanisms.

Treatment. For centuries leprosy has been considered an incurable disease. Only within the last few years has any specific remedy been used. Now the sulfone drugs are known to be definitely effective. The compound *DADPS* (diaminodiphenylsulfone) and its derivatives *promin* and *diazone* arrest many cases of the disease. Small doses prevent relapses in arrested cases. A less toxic compound, *Promacetin,* is now used in this country. Good general medical care and antibiotics that prevent secondary bacterial infections are also important in the treatment of leprosy. Figure 30·13 shows the effect of treatment with sulfones.

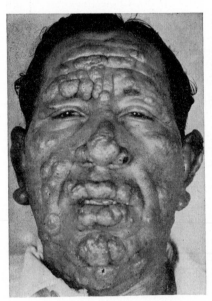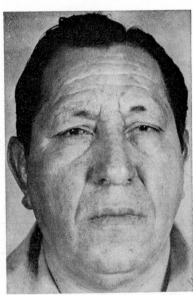

FIG. 30·13   Case of advanced lepromatous leprosy before and after 6 years' treatment with sulfones. (*Courtesy of Dr. R. R. Wolcott, U.S. Public Health Service Hospital, Carville, Louisiana.*)

Prevention. Segregation of lepers in leprosariums was long considered the all-important measure in leprosy control. But experts no longer believe the prisonlike detention that used to be practiced is necessary or even useful. Our National Leprosy Hospital in Carville, Louisiana, is a true hospital for the expert treatment of cases. In many parts of the United States cases not needing hospital treatment and having no dangerous active lesions are treated at home. Arrested cases must, however, be registered by the health departments and have repeated examinations.

On theoretic grounds it has been thought that BCG vaccination might prevent the development of active leprosy in the same way that it prevents the development of active reinfection tuberculosis. So BCG vaccination is being tried in some areas where the incidence of leprosy is very high. It is too early to evaluate the results.

Laboratory Diagnosis. The observation of typical intracellular acid-fast bacteria in scrapings from skin lesions is important in the diagnosis of the disease. The number of organisms is often small, so great care must be taken in selecting the skin area to be tested. The advancing edge of a skin lesion should be chosen. The skin is pinched between the fingers and a short cut is made deep enough to go through the whole thickness of skin. As the razor blade or scalpel is taken out of the cut, it is turned sideways so that one surface of the incision is thoroughly scraped. A smear is made using all the scraped material and stained by a modification of the Ziehl-Neelsen technique. In a positive specimen there will be clumps of epithelioid cells containing the acid-fast rods. If there is any chance that the mycobacteria might be tubercle bacilli, a guinea pig is inoculated. Tuberculosis bacteria will cause characteristic lesions and death; leprosy bacteria will not infect the animal.

Several serologic tests may be used in leprosy. Sera from advanced cases give a positive complement-fixation test with any mycobacterial antigen.

STUDY SUGGESTIONS

Review the characteristics and classification of the mycobacteria. Describe the morphology of *M. tuberculosis*. Explain the acid-fast stain technique. What two strains of the organism are pathogenic for man? Which is more important? Why has there been a great decrease in cases due to the bovine variety?

What have you learned about the resistance of the tubercle bacillus to physical and chemical agents? Give specific examples of the relation of these facts to the modes of infection of this organism and to methods of disinfection in the disease.

Compose a history of a typical case of tuberculosis. Include source and mode of the primary infection and tell how the organisms spread and were dealt with in the tissues. Give the source and modes of the reinfection. How did the organisms enter the body and where did they localize? What circumstances predisposed this individual to the development of an active infection? This case may be based on a true history which you know about.

Compare the tuberculin test with the Dick test as to material used, methods, and significance of positive and negative results. What experience have you had in your own community or in the hospital with the tuberculin test? To what group as outlined on page 404 do you belong? Explain the reasons for your answer.

What is BCG? What do its advocates claim that it accomplishes? Under what conditions should it be used?

How are the nurses and other members of your hospital's staff protected against tuberculosis? Give examples of nursing technique and hospital regulations that protect you and others against the infection. Who are the most likely sources of infection for hospital personnel? Have you any bad habits of personal hygiene that you should take pains to correct?

What is the procedure in your hospital for the collection of sputum and other specimens for tuberculosis diagnosis? What are the basic methods of laboratory diagnosis? What methods of preliminary treatment of specimens are used? What do they accomplish? Why is a positive report from the laboratory conclusive evidence of the existence of tuberculosis? Why is a negative report inconclusive? What other evidence may lead the doctor to diagnose the case as tuberculosis even though laboratory reports are repeatedly negative? Does a negative report from the bacteriologic laboratory mean that an active case has been cured?

Compare *M. leprae* with *M. tuberculosis* as to morphology, cultivation, and pathogenicity for animals. In what respects does leprosy resemble tuberculosis? In what respects is it different? The discovery of a case of leprosy in a community or an institution often gives rise to a condition of general panic. Is this alarm justified? Explain.

SUGGESTED READING

Mycobacterium tuberculosis and Tuberculosis Infection (See also recent volumes of *American Review of Tuberculosis.*)

General References

Aᴍᴇʀɪᴄᴀɴ Assᴏᴄɪᴀᴛɪᴏɴ ғᴏʀ ᴛʜᴇ Aᴅᴠᴀɴᴄᴇᴍᴇɴᴛ ᴏғ Sᴄɪᴇɴᴄᴇ: "Tuberculosis and Leprosy, the Mycobacterial Diseases." Washington, D.C., 1938.

Cᴀᴅʏ, L. L.: "Nursing in Tuberculosis." Saunders, Philadelphia, 1948.

Fʀᴇᴜɴᴅ, J., and G. Mɪᴅᴅʟᴇʙʀᴏᴏᴋ: The Mycobacteria, in R. J. Dubos's, "Bacterial and Mycotic Infections of Man." 2d ed., Lippincott, Philadelphia, 1952.

Hᴇᴛʜᴇʀɪɴɢᴛᴏɴ, H. W., and F. Esᴄʜʟᴇᴍᴀɴ: "Nursing in Prevention and Control of Tuberculosis." Lea & Febiger, Philadelphia, 1946.

Kɪɴɢ, D. S.: Medical progress: Tuberculosis. *New England J. Med.* **243:**530, 565 (1950).

Mᴇʏᴇʀs, J.: "Tuberculosis among Children and Adults." 3d ed., Charles C Thomas. Springfield, Ill., 1951.

Yᴀɴ, I., and C. E. Pᴀʟᴍᴇʀ: The WHO Tuberculosis Record Office. *Pub. Health Rep.* **68:**678 (1951).

The Organism and Laboratory Diagnosis

Bʟᴏᴄʜ, H.: The Acid-fast Bacteria, in "Annual Review of Microbiology." Vol. 7, Annual Reviews, Inc., Stanford, 1953.

Cᴜᴍᴍɪɴɢs, M. M.: The Tubercle Bacilli (*Mycobacterium tuberculosis*), in "Diagnostic Procedures and Reagents." 3d ed., American Public Health Association, New York, 1950.

Kɴᴀʏsɪ, G.: The structure, division and fusion of nuclei observed in living cells of Mycobacterium thamnopheos. *J. Bact.* **64:**859 (1952).

MAILLARD, E. R.: Further studies of a new serological test for tuberculosis. *Am. J. Pub. Health* **42**:175 (1952).

MIDDLEBROOK, G., R. J. DUBOS, and C. PIERCE: Virulence and morphological characteristics of mammalian tubercle bacilli. *J. Exper. Med.* **86**:175 (1947).

RICHMOND, L., and M. M. CUMMINGS: An evaluation of methods of testing the virulence of acid-fast bacilli. *Am. Rev. Tuberc.* **62**:632 (1950).

The Disease

DIGGS, A. D.: The primary complex of pulmonary tuberculosis. *Am. J. Dis. Child.* **80**:566 (1950).

RICH, A. R.: "The Pathogenesis of Tuberculosis." Charles C Thomas, Springfield, Ill., 1951.

STONE, M. G., and P. DUFAULT: "The Diagnosis and Treatment of Tuberculosis." Lea & Febiger, Philadelphia, 1946.

Treatment: Chemotherapy

AMBERSON, J. B.: Treatment of tuberculosis. *Pub. Health Rep.* **68**:10 (1953).

D'ESOPO, N.: Chemotherapy of tuberculosis in man. *J.A.M.A.* **154**:52 (1954).

FOX, H. H.: The chemical approach to the control of tuberculosis. *Science* **116**:129 (1952).

ISRAEL, H. L.: Modern treatment of tuberculosis. *Am. J. Pub. Health* **43**:965 (1953).

WAKSMAN, S. A.: Antibiotics and tuberculosis. *J.A.M.A.* **135**:478 (1947).

Control of Tuberculosis

Administrative judgment in the control of tuberculosis. *Am. J. Pub. Health* **38**:557 (1948). Editorial. A comparison of the methods advocated in the references by Myers and Weber below.

CHADWICK, H. D., and A. S. POPE: "Modern Attack on Tuberculosis." Rev. ed., Commonwealth Fund, New York, 1946.

MYERS, A. J.: Eradication of tuberculosis by epidemiological methods. *Am. J. Pub. Health* **38**:516 (1949).

PARRAN, T.: Tuberculosis: a time for decision. *Pub. Health Rep.* **68**:921 (1953).

WEBER, F. J., and R. J. ANDERSON: Summary of tuberculosis control activities. *Am. J. Pub. Health* **38**:516 (1948).

Tuberculin and BCG

AMERICAN TRUDEAU SOCIETY: "Statement on BCG." American Tuberculosis Association, New York, 1949.

ANDERSON, R. J., and C. E. PALMER: BCG. *J.A.M.A.* **143**:1048 (1950).

BIRKHAUG, C.: Experiments in BCG standardization. *Bull. WHO* **5**:227 (1952).

BRAHDY, L.: Immunity and positive tuberculin reaction. *Am. J. Pub. Health* **31**:1040 (1941).

Partenheimer, R. C.: Medical progress: Tuberculosis. *New England J. Med.* **245**:496 (1951).

Research Foundation: "BCG Vaccination." Chicago, 1953.

Rosenthal, S. R., E. I. Leslie, and E. Loewensohn: BCG vaccination in all age groups. *J.A.M.A.* **136**:73 (1948).

UNICEF: "Mass BCG Vaccination Campaign. A Practical Guide." Geneva, 1952.

Tuberculosis and Nursing Personnel

Bates, R. C., and W. N. Davey: Tuberculosis in medical and nursing students. *Am. Rev. Tuberc.* **63**:332 (1951).

Connolly, E. R.: "Tuberculosis among Hospital Personnel." National Tuberculosis Association, New York, 1950.

Edwards, L. B., I. Lewis, and C. E. Palmer: Studies on pulmonary findings and antigen sensitivity among student nurses. *Pub. Health Rep.* **63**:1569 (1948).

National Tuberculosis Association: "Safer Ways in Nursing To Protect against Tuberculosis." Rev. ed., New York, 1948.

South, J.: "Tuberculosis Handbook for Public Health Nurses." National Tuberculosis Association, New York, 1950.

Mycobacterium leprae and Leprosy

Carrol, D. L.: The role of the local public health nurse in Hansen's disease control. *C.D.C. Bull.* **10**:48 (1951).

Hopkins, R., and G. H. Faget: Recent trends of leprosy in the United States. *J.A.M.A.* **126**:937 (1944).

Johansen, F., and P. Erickson: Leprosy: current status of therapy. *J.A.M.A.* **144**:12 (1950).

McCoy, G. W.: Modern public health methods in leprosy. *Pub. Health Nursing* **41**:28 (1949).

Pardo-Castello, V., and F. R. Tiant: Leprosy: the correlation of its clinical, pathologic, immunologic, and bacteriologic aspects. *J.A.M.A.* **121**:1264 (1943).

The Pathogenic Spirochetes

The spirochetes are the members of the order *Spirochaetales,* the spiral, protozoalike bacteria. Three genera, *Treponema, Borrelia,* and *Leptospira,* include organisms pathogenic for man. The other genera consist entirely of saprophytic species and parasites of lower animals. The morphologic charac- teristics of the important genera are shown in Fig. 2·12. The motions of these organisms as seen under the microscope also help to differentiate them.

For many years the treponeme of syphilis has been thought of as the only one of great importance. We are now beginning to realize the importance of other spirochetoses of both man and animals.

TREPONEMA PALLIDUM, THE CAUSE OF SYPHILIS

Syphilis is the most dreaded of all the venereal diseases. Although the effectiveness of penicillin in curing early cases has markedly decreased the incidence and deaths from the disease in the last 15 years, syphilis still causes several thousand deaths in this country every year. Moreover, it is estimated that over 2 millions of Americans with syphilis have been inadequately treated. Of the probable 200,000 new cases here each year, less than half are promptly diagnosed and treated.

The Organism. The name *Treponema pallidum* means "pale thread." The organism was first recognized as the cause of the disease by Schaudinn and Hoffman in 1905. Any organism of the genus *Treponema* may be called

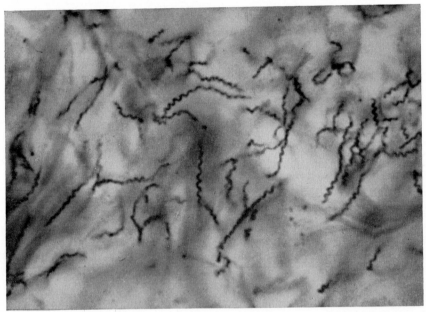

Fig. 31·1   *Treponema pallidum.* ×1,200. (*Courtesy of Dr. A. C. Lonert and General Biological Supply House, Inc.*)

a *treponema* (pl. *treponemata*) or a *treponeme* (pl. *treponemes*), but the term *spirochete* is often used.

Morphology. T. pallidum is a slender, tightly coiled spiral. The spirals form 6 to 14 even turns. (See Fig. 31·1.) The pointed ends of the cells terminate in long filaments. Although flagellalike structures have been seen in some electron microscope preparations, the bacteria are considered nonflagellated. The organisms are relatively rigid and move with a slow, corkscrew motion.

Staining and Microscopic Demonstration. The spirochetes do not stain well with the usual bacterial stains. *T. pallidum* in tissue sections can be stained with special silver preparations. It is most clearly seen when slides of fresh, moist material are examined with the dark-field microscope.

Cultivation. Virulent strains of *T. pallidum* have never been cultivated in artificial media. Avirulent treponemes can be grown under anaerobic condi tions in enriched media and fertile eggs. Although under natural conditions syphilis infection is limited to man, the virulent treponemes will grow readily when they are inoculated into the testicles of rabbits.

Effects of Antibacterial Agents. T. pallidum is probably the least resistant of all pathogenic bacteria. The organisms die rapidly if exposed to air, drying, or water. Cold acts as a preservative, but high temperatures kill them within a few minutes, as does 1 hour's exposure at 41.5°C. Substances that lower surface tension, such as soap and bile, kill them quickly. In the tissues they are susceptible to metallic compounds containing arsenic, bismuth, and mercury. Penicillin and several other antibiotics are very effective against the treponemes.

The Disease. Syphilitic infection has been recognized in Europe since the end of the fifteenth century, when severe epidemics spread through Italy and France. There is evidence that the disease existed in the Western hemisphere before that time, and it has been suggested that it was taken to Europe by sailors of Columbus's crew. The name *syphilis* comes from that of *Syphilus,* the infected hero of a poem written in 1530 by Fracastorius. Syphilis is also called *lues,* and the adjective *luetic* means syphilitic.

Stages of Syphilis. The disease is a chronic infection that develops in three distinct stages.

1. Primary syphilis. A primary lesion called the *chancre* appears after 3 weeks at the place where the organisms enter the skin or mucous membrane. The chancre is a single ulcer with a hard (indurated) base. It is not painful and heals without treatment, leaving a typical scar. The chancre is most commonly formed on the penis in the male and on the labia or uterine cervix in the female. The chancre may also develop on the lip or the hand if these spots are the sites of the primary infection. Although there are no generalized symptoms at this time, the organisms spread quickly from the chancre through the blood stream.

2. Secondary syphilis. Symptoms of generalized infection begin to appear 1 or 2 months later, though they may be delayed for a longer time. They may be transitory or they may be recurrent over a period of several years. The most obvious symptoms are lesions of the skin and the mucous membranes of the genitalia and mouth. There is also inflammation of lymph nodes, joint pains, and fever.

3. Tertiary syphilis. The third stage may follow the second immediately or may be delayed for years. In this third stage, the organisms localize in various tissues. The typical local lesion is a soft, gelatinous area of necrosis. It is called a *gumma* (pl. *gummata*). The clinical picture is very varied, for the lesions may be in the skeletal system, the aorta, the liver, the stomach, or other organs. Symptoms of tertiary syphilis may resemble those of almost any other chronic disease.

Neurosyphilis. The infection may attack the nervous system during the third stage. Destructive lesions of the brain and spinal cord result in general paralysis (general paresis) and tabes dorsalis. Insanity is a frequent result of neurosyphilis.

Congenital Syphilis. As was explained in Chap. 13, syphilis is not a truly inherited disease, but it may be a congenitally acquired infection. *T. pallidum* can spread from the blood stream of an infected pregnant woman to her developing child. This prenatal infection can result in the death and expulsion of the fetus (stillbirth) or in the premature or full-term birth of an infected infant. In many cases the baby may appear normal at birth but develop the disease after months or years. Congenital syphilis is a generalized infection. Infected infants frequently have skin and mucous membrane involvement and can be sources of infection for others.

Infants and children may be infected by diseased parents or nurses. If this happens they will develop the typical disease, beginning with a chancre.

Immunity. There is no natural immunity to syphilis. Every untreated person who has acquired the infection develops the disease. A person who already has the disease is resistant to typical primary reinfection, but his immunity is not strong enough to cure him. Cases that are cured by chemotherapy can be reinfected, for no persistent immunity results from an aborted attack of the disease. There is no method of immunization against syphilis. Serum is not used for treatment.

Treatment. Untreated syphilis is seldom cured spontaneously. The only effective treatment is chemotherapy. In 1909 Ehrlich announced that arsphenamine, an organic compound of arsenic commonly called *salvarsan,* was effective in the treatment of the disease. Other compounds of arsenic and compounds of mercury and bismuth have also been used.

The repository penicillin compounds, benzathine penicillin and procaine penicillin in oil with aluminum monostearate, are now the preferred treatment for all stages of syphilis. Fifteen daily doses totaling 10 million units are commonly used. With the development of long-acting penicillin compounds, semiweekly or weekly doses are employed. An allergic effect, the *Herxheimer reaction,* occurs in the early part of penicillin therapy in a considerable number of cases of late syphilis. It is due to the antigens released from the bacteria that are destroyed, not to the drug itself.

Transmission. People with primary and secondary syphilis are the sources of the infection. The organisms are discharged from the chancre in the first stage and from the skin and mucous membrane lesions in the second stage. Because of their extreme fragility the treponemata must be transferred directly from person to person or by means of objects contaminated with fresh, moist discharges. Sexual intercourse or other sexual contact is the most common mode of transfer. Transfer by kissing gives rise to primary lesions on the lips. Syphilis may be transferred by transfusions of fresh blood. Congenital transfer has already been discussed.

Laboratory Diagnosis. There are two principal methods of diagnosis of syphilis. The first is by the demonstration of the spirochetes in material from the chancre. The second is by serologic tests of the patient's blood or spinal fluid.

Dark-field Demonstration of T. pallidum. The clear serum expressed from the chancre or aspirated from enlarged adjacent lymph nodes is examined with the dark-field microscope. The spirochetes are readily recognized by their morphology and characteristic motion.

Serodiagnosis. For many years the *Wassermann test,* a complement-fixation test, has been used to diagnose syphilis. The technique of the complement-fixation test has been discussed on page 284. (See also Fig. 22·6.) The complexity of this test led many investigators to attempt to develop simpler methods. It was found that the serum of persons with syphilis would cause precipitation or flocculation of Wassermann antigens. The *Kahn,* the *Hinton,* and the *Eagle* tests are tube tests. The *Kline* and the *Mazzini* tests are slide flocculation tests. The Venereal Disease Research Laboratory of the Public Health Service has developed both a tube and a slide *VDRL* test. Modifications of these tests using small amounts of serum or even dried blood have been suggested. The antigens and antibodies used in these tests are not strictly specific. Wassermann originally used an extract of liver tissue from stillborn syphilitic infants as the antigen. Later it was found that tissue extracts of normal animals would serve equally well. Extensive research has identified the nature of the compound that reacts with the antibody in syphilitic serum. Now a purified antigen called *cardiolipin* is used. The material in the patient's serum that reacts with the antigen is called *reagin.*

Suspensions of virulent living or killed whole *T. pallidum* prepared by recently discovered techniques can be used as antigens. Reactions of serum antibodies and these antigens are more specific than the reactions between cardiolipid antigens and reagin. The *TPI* (*T. pallidum* immobilization) test is performed with the living spirochetes. They remain motile in nonsyphilitic serum but lose their motility in serum from an active case. A test involving the agglutination of heat-killed *T. pallidum* has also been described.

Interpretation of Tests. All these tests will give positive results with sera from cases of yaws and other treponema infections. The complement-fixation and flocculation tests may give false positive reactions in cases of malaria, leprosy, and other chronic diseases in which there is considerable tissue destruction. Contrary to the popular belief, pregnancy does not cause false positive tests for syphilis.

Rapid and hypersensitive complement-fixation and precipitation tests may be used as screening tests. Sera giving negative reactions can be safely designated as nonsyphilitic. Sera giving positive results must be tested further by more exact methods to determine which are syphilitic. Such screening tests are used as time-saving procedures in large clinics, mass surveys, and the examination of bloods for blood banks.

All the serologic tests may be falsely negative in the first few weeks of the disease. Tests may become negative temporarily after a course of specific treatment. Some cases continue to give positive complement-fixation and precipitation tests even though they have been treated and no longer show any clinical symptoms. Such cases are said to be *seroresistant* or, more specifically, *Wassermann-fast* or *Hinton-fast,* etc. The chief use of the TPI test at present is to determine which adequately treated, seroresistant cases are actually still harboring the infection.

VENEREAL DISEASE

The term *venereal disease* is applied to those infections that are frequently spread by sexual intercourse. This term is somewhat objectionable because it ignores the fact that many persons with these diseases have been infected by other means. Moreover, the term has come to convey an implication of moral guilt which is frequently unjustified and which has no place in the professional relationship between the patient and the doctor or nurse. The term *genitoinfectious disease* is preferred by many people.

Table 31·1 lists these diseases and gives their causes, their general clinical pictures, and page references to this text.

Prevention of Venereal Transmission of Disease. Control of the transmission of venereal disease presents special problems. No methods of immunization are known. The infectious hosts cannot be isolated except in exceptional situations. No readily available public health measures such as insect or rodent control, or sanitation of water, milk, or food have any effect on the spread of the infections. The two effective objectives of modern venereal disease control programs are early diagnosis and prompt, adequate treatment. Now that effective antibiotic therapy is available for all the major venereal infections the picture is much brighter than it was even a few years ago. Early diagnosis is also more likely, for the ignorance and prejudice that formerly hampered public health authorities have lessened appreciably. Therefore infected people are more willing to consult physicians when they suspect they may have venereal disease and more willing to divulge the identity of their sexual partners.

For the prompt detection of cases the community must have adequate facilities for clinical and laboratory diagnosis. Trained workers must be available to interview patients and trace contacts. Compulsory blood tests for syphilis are required of certain groups including service personnel, applicants

Table 31·1

Venereal Diseases *

Disease	Causative organism	Clinical characteristics	Text reference
Syphilis...........	*Treponema pallidum*—spirochete	Primary: chancre at site of infection Secondary: skin, mucous membranes, and other lesions Tertiary: gummata of internal organs, neurosyphilis	424
Gonorrhea.........	*Neisseria gonorrhoeae*—gram-negative, paired coccus	Acute: inflammation and purulent discharge of genital organs Chronic: infection of genital organs, etc.	358
Chancroid.........	*Hemophilus ducreyi*—gram-negative, nonsporing rod	Ulcer on genital organs with inflammation of adjacent lymph nodes	327
Granuloma inguinale	*Donovania granulomatis*—capsulated, gram-negative, nonsporing rods	Chronic spreading ulceration of skin and mucous membranes of genitalia	342
Lymphogranuloma venereum	*Miyagawanealla lymphogranulomatis*—rickettsialike microorganism	Small initial genital lesion, then massive inflammation and suppuration of adjacent lymph nodes	451
Trichomoniasis.....	*Trichomonas vaginalis*—flagellated protozoan	Persistent vaginal or urethral discharge and inflammation	540

* The fungus of moniliasis (page 526), the bacteria of the fusospirochetal infection (page 431), the rickettsialike organisms of inclusion conjunctivitis (page 451), and the PPL organisms of nonspecific urethritis (page 343) may also be considered as causes of genitoinfectious disease.

for marriage licenses, and pregnant women. To ensure adequate treatment there must be adequate free hospital and clinic facilities. Free drugs for treatment are provided by many states. Social measures include the control of prostitution, the provision of adequate and properly supervised recreation facilities, and education in the nature and dangers of venereal disease. It has been shown repeatedly that socially maladjusted persons are most prone to acquire venereal disease. All measures that lead to the development of socially mature and responsible men and women decrease the possibility of the spread of venereal disease.

Nursing Considerations. Careful technique in clinic and ward care of cases of these diseases will prevent any spread of infection to other patients or to the nursing or other hospital personnel. Student nurses are often surprised to encounter cases of syphilis on general wards. It should be remembered that cases of latent and tertiary syphilis are noninfectious, since no spirochetes are discharged from the internal lesions. The nurse should report any signs of genital organ infection in any patient if they have not been previously noted, including signs of inflammation of adjacent lymph nodes.

The student nurse must conscientiously discard all prejudices and misconceptions that she has about genitoinfectious diseases and just as conscientiously learn the scientific facts about these infections. Her attitude toward all cases of these diseases must be completely professional. The nurse must pass on accurate information about these infections to her patients and other contacts.

TREPONEMATA AND NONVENEREAL TREPONEMATOSES

Over 20 million persons in rural areas of the tropics and semitropics suffer from nonvenereal treponematoses. The causative organisms resemble *T. pallidum* so closely that it is likely they are all variants of the spirochete. The infections are acquired in childhood. Lesions of the skin are more widespread and persistent than in syphilis. In later stages the infection also involves underlying tissues and often results in crippling deformities of the hands and feet and disfigurement of the face. Infection is spread by direct contact and by insects that are attracted to the suppurating sores. Foreigners and persons of higher economic status often escape infection since the daily use of soap and water is usually sufficient to destroy any treponemes that may be on the skin.

The sera of persons with these treponema diseases react with the antigens used in the blood tests for syphilis. In the last few years the WHO has tested millions of persons in Haiti, Indonesia, Thailand, and the Philippines. In Haiti alone over 1½ million cases of yaws were discovered and treated. One or two large doses of penicillin are sufficient for cure (Fig. 31·2).

The nonvenereal treponematoses are summarized in Table 31·2.

LEPTOSPIRAS AND THE LEPTOSPIROSES

The spirochetes belonging to the genus *Leptospira* are tightly coiled and have hooked ends (Fig. 5·3). They are aerobic and can be grown in enriched media, in the fertile egg, and in rodents. Leptospiras normally infect a great variety of animal hosts. Rodents are the animal reservoirs of most types. From them the organisms are spread to wild and domestic animals and to man. The best-known species of rodent origin is *Leptospira icterohaemor-*

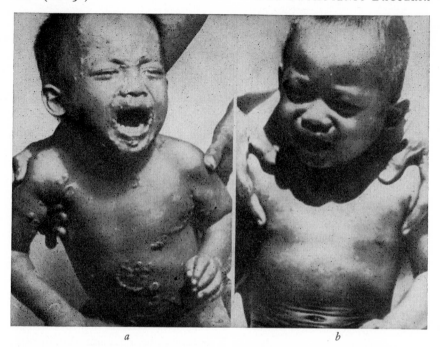

a   *b*

FIG. 31·2   Indonesian child with yaws. (*a*) Before treatment; (*b*) 2 weeks after single injection of penicillin. (*World Health Organization, United Nations.*)

Table 31·2

Nonvenereal Treponematoses

Disease	Cause	Geographic distribution	Characteristics
Epidemic syphilis..	*T. pallidum*	Balkans, Tahiti, parts of India, etc.	True syphilis, spread by contact infection
Bejel...............	*T. pallidum*(?)	Syria, Iraq (among nomadic tribes)	Resembles both yaws and syphilis
Njovera...........	*T. pallidum*(?)	South Africa	Similar to bejel
Yaws.............	*T. pertenue*	Rural tropical and semi-tropical areas	"Mother yaw" followed by generalized skin and subcutaneous lesions
Pinta.............	*T. carateum*	Mexico, Central and South America	Superficial skin infection with loss of pigmentation

rhagiae. Among the types not found in rodents are *L. canicola* of dogs and *L. pomona* of swine, cattle, and horses. The economic losses caused by leptospiroses of animals in this country as well as in other parts of the world are just beginning to be appreciated.

Most infected rodents show few symptoms and often become chronic carriers. The infection is more severe in man and domestic animals. Cases and carriers discharge large numbers of the spirochetes in their urine. Infection is acquired by direct contact or by the ingestion of foods contaminated by urine. The bacteria in infected water and soil penetrate the skin, probably through abrasions. In man leptospirosis epidemics occur among persons whose occupations expose them to infected animals or to water or soil infected by animal urine. Sporadic cases in this country are often due to contact with infected pet dogs. The disease in man varies from severe febrile jaundice terminating in death to brief benign infection. The severe form is known as *Weil's disease.* The mild form in this country is referred to as *Fort Bragg fever* because of an epidemic occurring in that army camp in 1944. Oxytetracycline is said to be the most effective antibiotic.

Leptospiras are found by culturing the blood, spinal fluid, or urine in the active stage of the disease. The cultures can be typed by complement-fixation or agglutination tests. Paired sera can also be sent to laboratories if cultures cannot be obtained. Specialists in many countries are now studying the problems of leptospira classification. Most of them believe it is best to consider all leptospiras as serotypes of one species rather than as separate species.

BORRELIAS AND THE BORRELIA INFECTIONS

Borrelia Species and Relapsing Fevers. There are two general types of relapsing fever. One is the epidemic type spread by lice from man to man and caused by *Borrelia recurrentis.* The other is endemic in many areas of the world where the various species of borrelia are spread from infected rodents to man by ticks. All cases of relapsing fever are characterized by a febrile period lasting several days. The fever disappears but almost always recurs, causing one to ten relapses.

The borrelias are loosely coiled, flexuous spirochetes. Their morphology is shown in Figs. 31·3 and 31·4. They cannot be maintained in artificial media but grow well in inoculated rodents and in the chick embryo. The organisms are seen by dark-field examination of blood taken at the beginning of a febrile period. Rodents may be inoculated and their blood examined in the same way.

Borrelia vincentii and the Fusospirochetal Infections. Loosely coiled spirochetes are common in the mouth, and so are the anaerobic spindle-shaped rods of the genus *Fusobacterium*. In certain infections of the mouth and throat, in some cases of pulmonary abscess, in occasional infections of deep

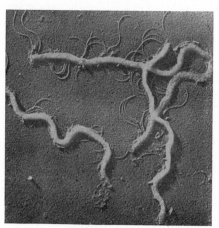

wounds, and in ulcers on the genitalia (Table 31·1) these same types occur in large numbers. These infections are the *fusospirochetal infections*. The most striking and best known of these infections is *Vincent's angina,* an ulcerated condition of the throat. More common and milder are infections of the mouth (*Vincent's stomatitis*) and of the gums (*Vincent's gingivitis*). The term *trench mouth* is often used because of the common occurrence of these infections in soldiers in the First World War. These infections are not readily communicable. All forms of Vincent's infection are commoner in those suffering from malnutrion or from con-

FIG. 31·3 *Borrelia vincentii.* ×15,000. Electron micrograph showing granules and flagellalike structures. (*Courtesy of Dr. E. C. Hamp, from J. Bact. 55:762.*)

current infectious disease than in healthy persons. The organisms should be regarded as secondary invaders of tissues whose resistance is already low.

The bacteria found in these infections are called *Borrelia vincentii* and *Fusobacterium plauti-vincenti.* Their cultivation is difficult. Smears from the ulcers disclose the two organisms readily (Fig. 31·5) and serve to dif-

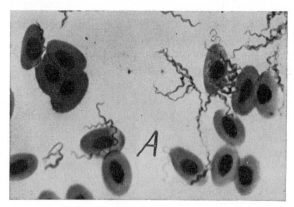

FIG. 31·4 *Borrelia anserina* in the blood of an infected turkey. (Erythrocytes of birds are oval and nucleated.) (*SAB print 243, courtesy of Dr. Ethel McNeil, from J. Bact. 57:191.*)

ferentiate these infections from those due to the organisms of diphtheria, the organisms of syphilis, and the hemolytic streptococci.

Spirillum minus, the Cause of Ratbite Fever. A small, rigid, spiral organism, *Spirillum minus,* infects man from the bite of an infected rat or other

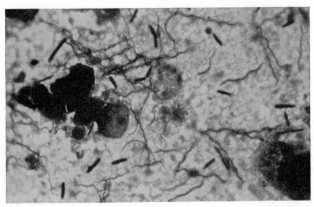

Fɪɢ. 31·5 Borrelias and fusiform bacteria in smear from fusospirochetal infection. ×3,000. (*Courtesy of Miss Stella Zimmer.*)

animal. The infection resembles the spirochetoses in its clinical course and can be treated by arsenicals and similar drugs. Some bacteriologists consider the organism a spirochete. This form of ratbite fever is less common in this country than that due to *Streptobacillus moniliformis* (page 327). It is very common in Japan, where it is known as *sodoku.*

STUDY SUGGESTIONS

How do the spirochetes differ from the spirilla and the vibrios? Why are they considered "higher bacteria"? What three genera include pathogens? Give examples. Describe a typical organism of each genus.

In what ways is the *Treponema pallidum* an unusual bacterium? Describe the stages of a typical case of syphilis. What is congenital syphilis? What measures should be taken to prevent congenital syphilis?

When and how is the organism of syphilis discovered by direct microscopic examination? What serologic tests are done in your hospital for the diagnosis of syphilis? What groups of persons should be urged to submit to tests for syphilis? The U.S. Public Health Service recommends a serologic test for syphilis as a part of the preentrance physical examination for every student of nursing. Do you agree with this recommendation? Why?

What diseases besides syphilis may be spread by sexual intercourse? What erroneous ideas about these infections have you had or found among people you know? To answer any questions you may still have, consult the references in the reading list or your instructor.

What other diseases are caused by treponemes? How are they spread? Why are they not prevalent in the United States?

What are the diseases caused by borrelias? by leptospiras? Make yourself a reference table of these infections, giving the name of the disease, the name of the organism, the character of the infection, and its sources and modes of transfer.

SUGGESTED READING

The Spirochetes

DAVIS, G. E.: The Spirochetes, in "Annual Review of Microbiology." Vol. 2, Annual Reviews, Inc., Stanford, 1948.

EAGLE, H.: The Spirochetes, in R. J. Dubos's "Bacterial and Mycotic Infections of Man." 2d ed., Lippincott, Philadelphia, 1952.

GEIMAN, Q. M.: Metabolism of Spirochetes, in "Annual Review of Microbiology." Vol. 6, Annual Reviews, Inc., Stanford, 1952.

KNAYSI, G.: "Elements of Bacterial Cytology." 2d ed., Comstock, Ithaca, N.Y., 1951. Chap. XIV.

Treponema pallidum and Syphilis

General References

CRAWFORD, G. M.: Medical progress: Syphilis. *New England J. Med.* **243:**916, 955 (1950).

MORRIS, E. H.: "Public Health Nursing in Syphilis and Gonorrhea." Saunders, Philadelphia, 1947.

VONDELEHR, R. A., and R. J. HELLER: "The Control of Venereal Disease." Reynal & Hitchcock, New York, 1946.

Laboratory Investigation and Diagnosis

MAHONEY, J. F., and M. R. ZWALLY: Serodiagnosis of Syphilis, in "Diagnostic Methods and Reagents," 3d ed., American Public Health Association, New York, 1950.

McLEOD, C. P., and H. J. MAGNUSON: Agglutination of *Treponema pallidum* in syphilitic serums. *Pub. Health Rep.* **68:**747 (1953).

MILLER, J. L., *et al.:* Treponemal immobilization test. *J.A.M.A.* **149:**987 (1952).

NELSON, R. A., JR.: Factors affecting the survival of *Treponema pallidum* in vitro. *Am. J. Hyg.* **48:**120 (1948).

OLANSKY, S., *et al.:* Small-quantity blood tests for syphilis. *Pub. Health Rep.* **67:**563 (1952). Five articles.

Chemotherapy and Control

CURTIS, A. C., *et al.:* Penicillin treatment of syphilis. *J.A.M.A.* **145:**1223 (1951).

Control of Venereal Disease (See also bibliographies on pages 362 and 454, recent volumes of *Journal of Venereal Disease Information*, and texts by Morris and Vondelehr listed above.)

Clarke, C. W., *et al.*: Conquest of venereal disease. *Hygeia* **27**: (beginning with March issue) (1949). A series of four articles.

Cutler, J. C.: Venereal disease now—and looking into the future. *Pub. Health Nursing* **44**:613 (1952).

Wright, J. J.: Venereal disease control. *J.A.M.A.* **147**:1408 (1951).

Other Treponemata and Nonvenereal Treponematoses

Dwindelle, J. H., *et al.*: Evaluation of penicillin in the treatment of yaws. *Am. J. Trop. Med.* **27**:633 (1947).

First International Symposium on Yaws Control. *Bull. WHO* **8**:1 (1953).

The Leptospiras and Leptospirosis

Gochenour, W. S., *et al.*: Laboratory diagnosis of leptospirosis. *Am. J. Pub. Health* **43**:405 (1953).

———: Leptospiral etiology of Fort Bragg fever. *Pub. Health Rep.* **67**:811 (1952).

LaGrange, W. E., *et al.*: Leptospirosis in farm animals. *Pub. Health Rep.* **67**:977 (1952).

Schlossberger, H., and H. Brandis: Leptospira, in "Annual Review of Microbiology." Vol. 8, Annual Reviews, Inc., Stanford (1954).

Other Pathogenic Spirochetes

American Association for the Advancement of Science: "Relapsing Fever in the Americas." Washington, D.C., 1942.

Hampp, E. G.: Observations on the oral spirochetal flora presented in Vincent's infection. *Am. J. Pub. Health* **35**:41 (1945).

Taft, W. C., and J. B. Pike: Relapsing fever. *J.A.M.A.* **129**:1002 (1945).

PART SEVEN

Pathogenic Organisms Other than Bacteria

The Rickettsiae and the Large Viruses

The microorganisms of human disease other than bacteria will be surveyed in this section of the text. These include the bacterialike rickettsiae and large viruses, the true viruses, the pathogenic fungi of the plant kingdom, and the protozoa and helminths (worm parasites) of the animal kingdom.

In the 6th edition of *Bergey's Manual of Determinative Bacteriology* three families of microorganisms are placed in the tentative order *Rickettsiales*. The first family, the *Rickettsiaceae*, is made up of the typical rickettsiae. The second family, the *Bartonellaceae*, consists of forms similar to rickettsiae.

Most microbiologists think of the third family, the *Chlamydoaceae,* as "large viruses" and refer to them as the organisms of the *psittacosis-lymphogranuloma group.*

THE RICKETTSIAE

Nature of the Rickettsiae. In many ways the rickettsiae resemble gram-negative bacilli. They are tiny rods that multiply by fission. Their chemical composition and enzyme systems are similar to those of gram-negative bacteria. Like the *Parvobacteriaceae* they are susceptible to the action of the broad-range antibiotics. In certain respects they are unlike most bacteria. They are small—only a quarter to a half of a micron in length. They multiply most readily within the cells of their hosts, preferably within cells that have a low metabolic rate (often in mature or injured cells). All of them are natural parasites of arthropods.

Parasitism. With one known exception, the rickettsiae do not injure their arthropod hosts. In fact many rickettsiae are passed from one generation of ticks or mites to the next as the ova of infected female ticks grow into infected larvae and adults. At some stage in its life cycle the rickettsiae-bearing arthropod feeds on an animal or on man. In the host animal the rickettsiae cause disease. These *rickettsioses* vary all the way from subclinical to fatal infections. There is considerable evidence that many animals and man continue to harbor the rickettsiae within their cells after clinical recovery from the infection.

Morphology. The microorganisms are typically short rods, averaging 0.35 by 0.25μ. Coccoid forms are seen in rapidly growing cultures, and filamentous forms over 1μ in length are found in feces of infected arthropods. Although the various species of rickettsiae show some differences in morphology, they cannot be identified by morphology alone. Rickettsiae are nonsporing and nonmotile. A capsule is seen very readily in electron microscope pictures. The somatic portions of the cells often show areas of denser material. (See Figs. $32\cdot1$ and $32\cdot2$.)

Cultivation. The rickettsiae, unlike most bacteria, cannot be grown in artificial media. They can be cultivated in susceptible arthropods. Guinea pigs and white mice are the animals used most frequently in the laboratory. All species will grow very readily in the chick embryo yolk sac. They also grow well in tissue cultures (page 458). One simple tissue culture technique uses serum agar slants covered with a layer of chick embryo tissue.

Chemical Composition. The capsule contains soluble carbohydrate and protein materials that are not type-specific. The somatic antigens are specific for species and types within the species. Toxins are also produced by rickettsiae.

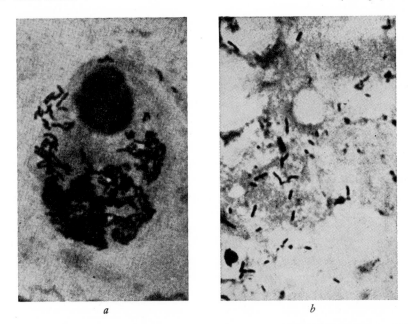

a   b

FIG. 32·1 Rickettsiae as seen in stained smears with the light microscope. ×4,000. (a) Rickettsiae of murine typhus in an epithelial cell of an inoculated guinea pig; (b) rickettsiae of epidemic typhus from yolk sac of a chick embryo. (*SAB print 26, from Plotz, J. Exper. Med. 77:355.*)

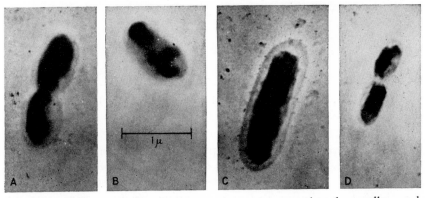

FIG. 32·2 Rickettsiae as seen in electron microscope preparations from yolk-sac cultures. ×20,000. (A) Rickettsiae of epidemic typhus; (B) rickettsia of murine typhus; (C) rickettsia of Rocky Mountain spotted fever; (D) rickettsiae of Q fever. (*SAB print 27 from Plotz, J. Exper. Med. 77:355.*)

Resistance. Rickettsiae are resistant to drying and may be dust-borne. They are readily killed by boiling and other forms of heat. However we know very little about their susceptibility to the usual chemical disinfectants. Heat should always be the method chosen for disinfection.

THE RICKETTSIOSES

Clinical Picture. The typical rickettsial disease follows a rather characteristic clinical pattern. After a variable incubation period averaging about twelve days, there is a prodromal stage in which the symptoms resemble those of severe influenza. At this time in some rickettsial diseases a primary ulcer can be found at the spot where the organism penetrated the skin (Fig. 32·3).

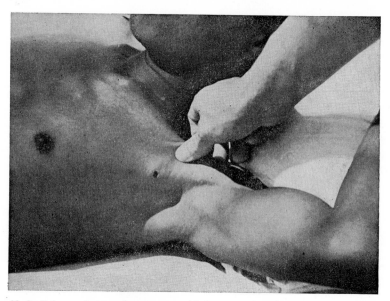

FIG. 32·3 Primary lesion of tsutsugamushi fever. Lesion (eschar) at point of introduction of the rickettsiae by bite of a mite. (*Courtesy of Dr. C. B. Philip.*)

After 3 to 5 days of generalized symptoms a rash develops which persists for at least a week. The patient shows a great degree of prostration, stupor, and delirium. Convalescence is relatively slow, but in most cases it is complete, leaving no sequelae. Rickettsial infections are much more severe in adults than in children. The fatality varies greatly in the different types of disease.

The forms of rickettsial disease are definitely related to specific types of insect vectors. They may be classified as

1. The flea-borne and louse-borne forms: classical typhus and murine typhus
2. The tick-borne forms: the spotted fevers, etc.
3. The mite-borne forms: tsutsugamushi fever, etc.

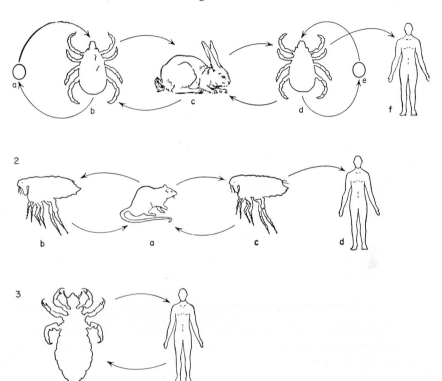

FIG. 32·4 Epidemiology of typical rickettsial diseases. 1. Rocky Mountain spotted fever. Transovarian infection (*a*) in rabbit tick (*b*); infected rabbit (*c*) is also bitten by wood tick (*d*) in which transovarian infection (*e*) may also take place; man (*f*) infected by wood tick. 2. Murine typhus. Disease spread in rodent host (*a*) by common rat flea (*b*); human flea or Indian rat flea (*c*) may transmit the disease to man (*d*). 3. Epidemic typhus. The body louse becomes infected by feeding on an infected man and can transmit the disease to another man.

The distinctive features of the important rickettsioses will be discussed in more detail in the next section of this chapter.

Epidemiology. The epidemiology of each rickettsial infection of man involves an arthropod host and an animal reservoir. Figure 32·4 pictures three typical epidemiologic cycles. The rickettsiae of Rocky Mountain spotted fever are natural intestinal parasites of ticks that feed mainly on rabbits. The infection is passed on from generation to generation by transovarian infection. The tick larvae may obtain their required blood feedings and transmit their rickettsiae to other animals or to man. In this cycle the tick is the reservoir of the infection.

Murine typhus is an example of a rickettsiosis in which a rodent has become the chief host to the microorganism. In many areas of the world rats and mice harbor rickettsiae which cause persistent but symptomless infections. The organisms are spread from rodent to rodent by lice, fleas, and mites which feed only on these animals. Occasionally a less discriminating species of flea—one willing to feed on either rodents or man—may feed on an infected rodent and later on man for whom the rickettsiae are much more virulent.

Epidemic typhus has an unusual epidemiology illustrated by the third diagram. The rickettsiae are passed from man to man by infected body lice. Both men and lice are made very ill by the infection, so it is assumed that the causative rickettsia is a recently developed variant to which the insect has not become adapted. No rodent or other animal reservoir of this disease is known but it is possible that one does exist. Since the infection is known to persist in man for years, he may be regarded as the chief reservoir of the disease.

The rickettsiae are usually plentiful in the alimentary canal of the arthropod. They may be introduced into the parasitized man or animal by the mouth parts of the arthropod or enter when the feces, vomitus, or the crushed parasite is rubbed or scratched into the skin. Dried infected material from the parasites may be inhaled. The organisms may also be transferred by blood transfusion from man to man.

Immunity and Treatment. One attack confers lasting immunity to future infections of the same type. Both species-specific and type-specific antibodies develop, and a rise of specific antibody can be detected within a week or two.

All the rickettsioses are treated with broad-range antibiotics. Chloramphenicol is considered the most effective. Para-aminobenzoic acid (PABA) is also useful. Late cases with marked toxic symptoms are benefited by the use of cortisone.

Control. The three most important methods of public health control are active immunization, destruction or repelling of arthropod hosts, and elimination of rodent reservoirs.

Effective vaccines for all the important infections except tsutsugamushi disease are made from formalized suspensions of infected yolk sac. (See Fig. 32·5.) General measures of insect and rodent control have been discussed in Chap. 16. The care of patients with rickettsial infections other than epidemic typhus involves no danger to the nurse and no isolation techniques are needed. The isolation techniques for epidemic typhus will be discussed in the section on that disease.

Laboratory Diagnosis. The detection of a definite increase in specific antibody in the patient's serum is the usual method of laboratory diagnosis. Two or more specimens must be sent to the laboratory, one collected as soon as the disease is suspected and the others at weekly or biweekly intervals. Three types of tests may be used.

The Weil-Felix Test. The simplest, but the least specific, is the *Weil-Felix test.* After about the tenth day of the disease the patient's serum will agglu-

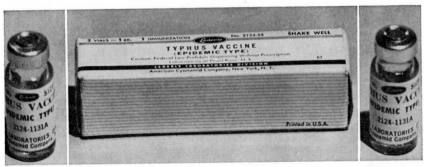

FIG. 32·5 Vaccine for epidemic typhus. Formalinized preparation of chick embryo yolk-sac culture. (*Lederle Laboratories Division, American Cyanamid Company.*)

tinate bacteria of the genus *Proteus.* The titer of agglutinins increases as the disease progresses but disappears rapidly within a few months. The *Proteus* culture originally used in the test, known as *Proteus OX19,* is agglutinated by sera from cases of both murine and epidemic typhus. This and other strains of *Proteus* are agglutinated by sera from cases of other rickettsioses. Experiments indicate that these cultures and the rickettsiae contain antigenically similar substances. Sera from cases of two infections, rickettsialpox and Q fever, do not agglutinate any known *Proteus* strains.

Other Serologic Tests. Complement-fixation and agglutination tests using species-specific and type-specific antigens prepared from yolk sac material give more definite evidence as to the exact infection involved. The complement-fixation test becomes positive early in the disease and the complement-fixing antibodies persist for years after recovery. The specific antigens are very expensive. Tests using very small amounts of antigen, such as slide complement-fixation tests and capillary tube agglutination tests, are proving useful (see Fig. 32·6). For careful study, the sera are usually sent to special reference laboratories.

Identification of Organisms. Direct microscopic detection of rickettsiae is possible and the organisms from patients, arthropods, or animals may be cultivated in laboratory animals, fertile eggs, or tissue cultures. However, work with the living microorganisms is difficult and dangerous. It is limited to research and reference laboratories.

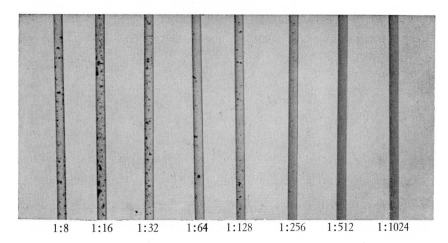

1:8   1:16   1:32   1:64   1:128   1:256   1:512   1:1024

FIG. 32·6 Capillary tube agglutination test for Q fever. ×3. *Coxiella burnetii* antigen with 1:8 to 1:1,024 dilutions of serum from infected cow. The antibody titer is 1:256, the last tube showing agglutination. (*Courtesy of Dr. L. Luoto, from J. Immunol. 71:226.*)

LOUSE-BORNE AND FLEA-BORNE RICKETTSIAE: THE TYPHUS FEVERS

Typhus fevers, rickettsial infections, must be clearly distinguished in the student's mind from typhoid fever, a bacterial disease. Typhoid and the related paratyphoids have been discussed in Chaps. 23 and 24.

Rickettsia prowazekii, the Cause of Epidemic Typhus (Louse-borne). This epidemic disease has been known in Europe since the 1400s. It is also referred to as *classic typhus* and *European typhus*. It is a disease of crowding and of filth. Epidemics in armies and refugee populations have changed the course of history. In peacetime it persists in slum areas, in unsanitary prisons and almshouses and asylums. One of the achievements of modern public health was the prompt control of typhus in the Mediterranean area, particularly in Naples, in the Second World War. The effectiveness of typhus vaccine was definitely proved by the almost complete absence of the disease in American troops. Prompt and thorough DDT dusting quickly controlled the epidemics among civilians. (See Fig. 16·3.)

As was stated above, epidemic typhus is the only rickettsial disease that may be dangerous for the nurse and may spread from the patient to others. All medical personnel in epidemic areas must be vaccinated. Two subcutaneous doses are given 14 days apart. Booster doses are recommended whenever exposure to typhus is likely. On admission to the hospital each patient must be received in a special delousing unit. Here he is given a complete bath and shampoo, followed by careful inspection to make sure that all insects have been removed. All nits (louse eggs) must be removed from the hairy parts of the body. Medical attendants wear insectproof clothing in this unit and when they work in outpatient clinics or in homes in infected areas.

Brill's Disease (Recrudescent Epidemic Typhus). Recovery from an attack of typhus may not always mean the complete disappearance of all the rickettsiae from the person's body. In this country a modified form of typhus, first described by Dr. Nathan Brill in New York City, occurs in immigrants who have had the disease in their country of origin. More recently it has been shown that the recrudescent infection also occurs in Central Europe in populations where typhus was previously epidemic. In the United States the patient with Brill's disease is unlikely to be the source of other cases since he is usually free from body lice. In countries where people are habitually infested with lice, the case of Brill's disease may start a new epidemic wave of typhus fever.

Trench Fever. In the First World War over a million cases of this louse-borne typhuslike infection occurred in the Allied and German Armies. It reappeared on the Russian-German front in the early part of the Second World War. The causative microorganism has been named *R. quintana.*

Rickettsia typhi, the Cause of Murine Typhus (Flea-borne). The flea-borne typhus which spreads from natural rodent hosts to man is also called *endemic typhus,* for it occurs sporadically in areas where the infected rodents are plentiful. It is often an occupational disease of granary and warehouse workers who are employed in rat-infested places. It has been common in the southern United States.

TICK-BORNE RICKETTSIAE

Rickettsia rickettsiae and Rocky Mountain Spotted Fever. Although Rocky Mountain spotted fever was first recognized in the northern Rocky Mountains, it has since been reported from nearly every state in the union and also from Canada and from many parts of South America. In the western United States the rabbit tick is believed to be the natural host of the microorganism. It does not feed on man. Other ticks, principally the wood tick (*Dermacentor variabilis*), become infected by feeding on infected animals and in turn may feed on man. (See Fig. 32·4.) The organism may enter by the tick bite or through the skin from tick feces or blood from crushed ticks. Vaccination is advised for persons with outdoor occupations in tick-infested areas. Special clothing and high boots prevent the ticks from attaching themselves. When a tick becomes attached to a person it should be immediately removed, for infection does not occur until the tick has fed for several hours.

Very similar spotted fevers are common in Africa. The two most important of these rickettsioses are *boutonneuse fever* of northern Africa and *South African tick-bite fever*. *R. conorii* is the name given to the causative organism. Other rickettsial infections of the spotted fever type have been reported from Australia, India, and Siberia.

Coxiella burnetii and Q Fever. The microorganisms causing Q fever are placed in the genus *Coxiella* because they are filtrable. They are more pleomorphic than other rickettsiae and grow well extracellularly. Their antigenic structure is quite different. *C. burnetii* resists drying and temperatures lethal to nonsporing bacteria.

Q fever is clinically unlike other rickettsioses. The disease resembles a mild pneumonia and there is no rash. *C. burnetii* is believed to be a natural parasite of certain ticks. Cattle, sheep, and other animals are infected by the ticks. The microorganism is present in milk and placental tissue of infected cows, sheep, and goats. Most human cases in this country are acquired by contact with infected animals or their products, the drinking of raw milk, or the inhalation of dust from infected barns. There is some question as to whether pasteurization temperatures are high enough to ensure the destruction of the Q fever organism.

Vaccination has proved very effective in protecting laboratory workers. It is increasingly used to immunize persons whose occupations expose them to the disease. Vaccination of farm animals has also been recommended.

MITE-BORNE RICKETTSIAE

Rickettsia tsutsugamushi and Tsutsugamushi Fever (Scrub Typhus). Scrub typhus is endemic in many areas of southeastern Asia, the Pacific Islands, and parts of Korea, China, and Japan. There are many antigenic types of *R. tsutsugamushi*. Since they undergo lysis in suspensions more quickly than other rickettsiae and stain differently, they are known to be different in chemical and physical structure. Despite extensive efforts, no satisfactory vaccine has been prepared for general use. Weekly doses of chloramphenicol have been used to protect soldiers in Malaya. A living vaccine accompanied by chemoprophylaxis with chloramphenicol has been used by the U.S. Army. Clothing impregnated with miticidal chemicals, and the clearing and spraying of brush areas that harbor mites, help to control the disease in military areas.

Rickettsia akari and Rickettsialpox. A mild rickettsiosis has recently been found to be endemic in New York City and in Boston. It is likely that it exists in other places. A species of mite that is common on the house mouse harbors the microorganism, *R. akari.* Clinically the disease is similar to chickenpox. Serologic tests readily diagnose the infection and distinguish it from other rickettsioses. Sanitation of basement areas, particularly the removal of trash that encourages the mouse population, quickly results in the local disappearance of the disease.

THE LARGE VIRUSES

The large viruses belong to the family *Chlamydoaceae.* Their characteristics indicate a close relationship to bacteria, but they also seem related to both the rickettsiae and the smaller, true viruses. The psittacosis-ornithosis group of infections of the human respiratory tract and the lympho-granuloma-trachoma infections of the genital and other mucous membranes, are all caused by these agents.

The Organisms. The large viruses are bacterialike in size, shape, and staining reactions. The coccoid cells are usually slightly less than 0.5μ in size. Like the *Parvobacteriaceae,* they are susceptible to the action of the broad-range antibiotics. Like the rickettsiae some of them are normally parasites of animals. However, none are arthropod-borne. Like the rickettsiae and viruses they cannot be cultivated on laboratory media, but are cultivatable in the cells of host animals, in tissue cultures, and in the chick embryo. The *Chlamydoaceae* have a definite life cycle in their host cells. The small *elementary* bodies within the cells grow into colonies called *inclusion bodies.* Multiplication of one large virus has been described as taking place on the surface of host cells as well as within the cells. The morphology of typical large viruses is shown in Fig. 32·7.

The Viruses of Psittacosis and Ornithosis. Organisms of the genus *Miyagawanella* are natural parasites of many birds. In the wild state the birds acquire the infection in the nest and show few if any symptoms. The infection persists throughout life. Infected birds kept in captivity suffer from recrudescences of the disease and discharge large numbers of organisms. The viruses are spread by the droppings and by dust from the birds' feathers. Human cases are most common in people who work in pet shops or have birds as pets. The disease acquired from parrots and related birds is named *psittacosis.* The term *ornithosis* is used for infections acquired from other birds.

Closely related microorganisms cause pneumonialike infections of kittens, rodents, and other animals. There is evidence that some of these infections may be passed on to man.

All the miyagawanellas are similar in morphology. They have a common complement-fixing antigen which indicates their close relationship. They are differentiated by other specific antigens and toxins. A rise in the complement-fixation titer of a patient's blood indicates that the person has a pneumonitis due to some organism of this group. Neutralization tests in mice give more specific information as to the identity of the causative organism.

Chlortetracycline is effective in all these infections. Since infection has been

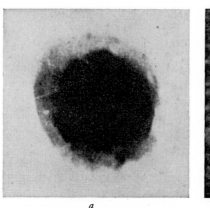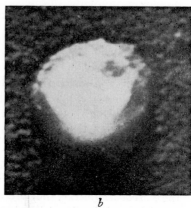

a   *b*

FIG. 32·7 Organisms of the psittacosis-lymphogranuloma group. Electron micrographs of chick embryo yolk-sac cultures. ×100,000. (*a*) The organism of psittacosis; (*b*) the organism of primary atypical pneumonia (gold-shadowed). (*SAB print 200 from Kurotchkin et al., J. Immunol. 55:283.*)

known to spread from patients to nurses and to other patients, isolation and respiratory precautions should be strictly observed. Public health control has been mainly aimed at preventing the import of infected parrots and other birds that harbor the virus.

Virus Pneumonia. There are also many cases of "virus pneumonia" of unknown etiology. The term *primary atypical pneumonia* (*PAP*) is the correct term. They are mild infections readily controlled by antibiotic therapy. Sera from patients with primary atypical pneumonia agglutinate human Group O erythrocytes at 4°C. This nonspecific reaction is known as the *cold hemagglutination test.*

Cat-scratch Fever. A virus similar to that of psittacosis and possibly related to feline pneumonitis is the cause of an infection that sometimes develops in persons who have been scratched or bitten by cats. It is characterized by local and general inflammation of the lymph nodes. The broad-range antibiotics are used for treatment. It is possible that the cat is only a passive carrier of the infection.

The Organism of Lymphogranuloma Venereum. Lymphogranuloma venereum is a genitoinfectious disease characterized by a very small primary sore on the genitals followed by marked inflammation and ulceration of inguinal and pelvic lymph nodes. Note that this is not the same disease as granuloma inguinale (see page 342). The organism (*Miyagawanella lymphogranulomatis*) can be found in lymphocytes in stained smears from the lesions. It is large and coccoid. It can be cultivated in the chick yolk sac.

The skin of an infected person reacts positively to the intradermal injection of a tiny amount of heated pus from a known lesion, the *Frei test. Lygranum,* an antigen made from infected chick yolk sac, is also used for diagnostic skin testing. The infection has been treated successfully by sulfa drugs, by penicillin, and by Aureomycin.

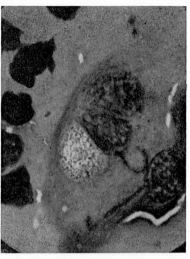

FIG. 32·8 Inclusion body of trachoma (light area) in an epithelial cell. ×1,500. (*Courtesy of Dr. Phillips Thygeson.*)

The Organisms of Trachoma and Inclusion Conjunctivitis. Large and small intracellular organisms are seen in stained smears from several forms of conjunctivitis (Fig. 32·8). Since these organisms have never been cultivated, their nature is in doubt and the various clinical types are difficult to differentiate. The most important of these infections is *trachoma,* a chronic infection often leading to blindness. Its cause has not been isolated but is believed to be an organism of this group (*Chlamydozoon trachomatis*). The disease is an important public health problem on Indian reservations and in rural areas in some Southern states. It is most common in children and is favored by malnutrition, exposure to sun and dust, and uncleanliness. The *inclusion conjunctivitis* of newborn infants is due to a similar organism acquired from the mother's urogenital organs during the birth process. The causative agent (*Chlamydozoon oculogenitale*) causes a very mild urogenital infection in adults.

Bartonella bacilliformis, the Cause of Oroya Fever and Verruga Peruana. The family *Bartonellaceae* is made up of insect-borne parasites of warm-blooded animals. The bacterialike rods are readily seen in (or on) the red cells in stained blood smears. They can be cultivated in enriched media. The bartonella of human infections is spread by bloodsucking sand flies. There are no known animal hosts. Other bartonellas cause apparent and inapparent infections of many rodents.

Human *bartonelliasis* occurs in two forms—Oroya fever, an often fatal acute anemia; and verruga peruana, a more chronic eruptive disease. The infection is limited to certain high valleys in the Andes Mountains in South America.

STUDY SUGGESTIONS

Subjects previously studied that are referred to in this chapter include the general nature of the rickettsiae; insect vectors, especially lice, fleas, ticks, and mites, and their control; the electron microscope; agglutination and complement fixation tests; tissue culture and fertile egg culture. Recheck your knowledge of these subjects.

Can you state in specific, scientific terms the likenesses and differences between bacteria and rickettsiae?

Make a table of the four principal rickettsial diseases—classic typhus, murine typhus, American spotted fever, and scrub typhus. List for each the synonyms for the name of the disease, cause, insect vector, and animal reservoirs. What rickettsial diseases are most likely to occur in your community? Why?

A blood specimen from a patient with an obscure and persistent fever is sent to the state laboratory. The Widal test, the Weil-Felix test, and the brucellosis agglutination test are all done on the specimen. Why? What would a positive test in each case indicate? What antigen would be used in each test?

What is the most commonly used method of cultivating rickettsiae? What advantages does this method have over other methods?

Why are cases of and deaths from rickettsial diseases so common among laboratory workers? What measures are taken by the modern laboratory to eliminate such infections?

What two methods of control of rickettsial disease, particularly typhus, are capable of completely eliminating them?

What are the characteristics of the lymphogranuloma-psittacosis group of microorganisms? Why are they classed with the rickettsiae? How do they differ from typical rickettsiae?

SUGGESTED READING

General References

AMERICAN ASSOCIATION FOR THE ADVANCEMENT OF SCIENCE: "Rickettsial Diseases of Man." Washington, D.C., 1948.

DYER, R. E.: The rickettsial diseases. *J.A.M.A.* **124**:1165 (1944).

LENNETTE, E. H.: Newer knowledge of the old rickettsial diseases. *Bact. Rev.* **14**:249 (1950).

LURIA, S. E.: "General Virology." Wiley, New York, 1953. Chap. 19.

RHODES, A. J., and C. E. VAN ROOYEN: "Textbook of Virology." 2d ed., Williams & Wilkins, Baltimore, 1953.

RIVERS, T. M.: "Viral and Rickettsial Infections of Man." 2d ed., Lippincott, Philadelphia, 1952. Chaps. 35–38.

SMADEL, J. E., *et al.*: Symposium on viral and rickettsial diseases. *Bact. Rev.* **14:** 195 (1950).

WOODWARD, T. E., and R. T. PARKER: Clinical Application and Mode of Action of Antibiotics in Rickettsial and Virus Diseases, in "Dynamics of Virus and Rickettsial Infections." Blakiston, New York, 1954.

Laboratory Diagnosis and Procedures

FELIX, A.: Standardization of serological tests for the diagnosis of the typhus group of fevers. *Bull. WHO* **2:**637 (1950).

LUOTO, L.: Capillary agglutination test for Q Fever. *J. Immunol.* **71:**226 (1953).

SHEPARD, C. G., and R. W. G. WYCKOFF: The nature of the soluble antigen from typhus rickettsiae. *Pub. Health Rep.* **61:**761 (1946).

Louse-borne and Flea-borne Rickettsioses: The Typhus Fevers

LEY, H. L., JR., T. E. WOODWARD, and J. E. SMADEL: Chloramphenicol (chloromycetin) in the treatment of murine typhus. *J.A.M.A.* **143:**217 (1950).

Murine Typhus. *C.D.C. Bull.* **9:**1 (1950).

MURRAY, E. S.: Brill's disease. I. Clinical and laboratory diagnosis. *J.A.M.A.* **142:**1059 (1950).

RAYMOND, A.: Now we can lick typhus. *Sat. Eve. Post,* April 22, 1944.

SADUSK, J. R., JR.: Typhus fever in the United States Army following immunization. *J.A.M.A.* **133:**1192 (1947).

Tick-borne Rickettsiae and the Spotted Fevers

PARKER, R. R., *et al.*: Isolation and characterization of Rocky Mountain spotted fever rickettsiae from the rabbit tick *Haemaphysalis leporis-palustris* Packard. *Pub. Health Rep.* **66:**455 (1951).

ROSS, S.: Aureomycin therapy in Rocky Mountain spotted fever. *J.A.M.A.* **138:** 1213 (1948).

WORLD HEALTH ORGANIZATION: "Report of Study-group on African Rickettsioses." WHO Tech. Rep. No. 23, Geneva, 1950.

Coxiella burnetii and Q Fever

BELL, J. A., M. D. BECK, and R. J. HUEBNER: Epidemiological studies of Q fever in southern California. *J.A.M.A.* **142:**868 (1950).

CLARK, W. H., E. H. LENNETTE, and M. S. ROMER: Q fever in California. XI. An epidemiologic summary of 350 cases occurring in northern California during 1948–1949. *Am. J. Hyg.* **54:**319 (1951).

DYER, R. E.: Q fever. History and present status. *Am. J. Pub. Health* **39:**471 (1949). First paper of a symposium.

MEIKLEJOHN, G., and E. H. LENNETTE: Q fever in California. I. Observations of vaccination of human beings. *Am. J. Hyg.* **52**:53 (1950).

RANSOM, S. E., and R. J. HUEBNER: Studies on the resistance of *Coxiella burnetii* to physical and chemical agents. *Am. J. Hyg.* **52**:110 (1950).

SIDKEY, M. M.: Epidemiology of Q fever. *Bull. WHO* **2**:563 (1950).

Rickettsia tsutsugamushi and Scrub Typhus

PHILIP, C. B.: Tsutsugamushi disease (scrub typhus) in World War II. *J. Parasitol.* **34**:169 (1948).

SMADEL, J. E., *et al.*: Chloramphenicol (Chloromycetin) in the chemoprophylaxis of scrub typhus. *Am. J. Hyg.* **50**:57 (1949).

————: Immunization against scrub typhus. I. Combined living vaccine and chemoprophylaxis in volunteers. *Am. J. Hyg.* **53**:317 (1951).

Rickettsia akari and Rickettsialpox

BARKER, L. P.: Rickettsialpox: clinical and laboratory study of twelve hospitalized cases. *J.A.M.A.* **141**:1119 (1949).

GREENBERG, M. O., L. J. PELLITERI, and W. L. JELLISON: Rickettsialpox—a newly recognized rickettsial disease. III. Epidemiology. *Am. J. Pub. Health* **37**:860 (1947).

ROUECHÉ, B.: The Alerting of Mr. Pomerantz, in "Eleven Blue Men." Little, Brown, Boston, 1954.

Organisms of the Psittacosis–Lymphogranuloma Group

BURNET, F. M.: "Virus as Organism." Harvard University Press, Cambridge, Mass., 1945.

COUTTS, W. E.:"Lymphogranuloma venereum: a general review." *Bull. WHO* **2**:545 (1950).

IRONS, J. V., T. D. Sullivan, and J. Brown: Outbreak of psittacosis from working with turkeys or chickens. *Am. J. Pub. Health* **41**:931 (1951).

MEYER, K. F.: Early Diagnosis of Infections by the Psittacosis–Lymphogranuloma Venereum Group, in "Dynamics of Virus and Rickettsial Infections." Blakiston, New York, 1954.

————: Psittacosis–Lymphogranuloma Group, in Rivers's "Viral and Rickettsial Infections of Man." 2d ed., Lippincott, Philadelphia, 1952.

————, and B. EDDIE: A review of psittacosis for the years 1948 to 1950. *Bull. Hyg.* **26**:1 (1951).

WEISS, E.: The extracellular development of agents of the psittacosis-lymphogranuloma group. *J. Infect. Dis.* **84**:125 (1949).

Other Large Viruses

EATON, M. D., and W. VAN HERICK: Serological and epidemiological studies on the primary atypical pneumonia and related upper respiratory disease. *Am. J. Hyg.* **45**:82 (1947).

SCHOENBACH, E. B., and M. G. BRYER: Treatment of atypical pneumonia with aureomycin. *J.A.M.A.* **139**:275 (1949).

THYGESON, R.: Trachoma and Inclusion Conjunctivitis, in Rivers's "Viral and Rickettsial Infections of Man." 2d ed., Lippincott, Philadelphia, 1952.

CHAPTER 33

The Filtrable Viruses:
General Characteristics

Our present-day knowledge of the true viruses will be summarized in this chapter. The two following chapters will describe the specific viruses causing disease in man.

HOW VIRUSES ARE STUDIED

The minute size of viruses and their inability to grow in culture media delayed their discovery until the 1890s (Chap. 21). All our knowledge of these organisms has been gained in the last 60 years, most of it in the last two decades. The development of electron microscopy, chick embryo culture

456

and tissue culture methods, and the application of new techniques of biochemistry and biophysics have provided tools with which scientists are now
able to study the viruses.

Detection of a Filtrable Virus. The presence of a virus is suspected when
thorough study of materials from cases of a clinically identified communicable infection fail to show any microorganisms that can be cultivated by

Fig. 33·1 Inoculation of fertile eggs for the commercial production of rickettsial or
viral vaccine. (*Parke, Davis & Co.*)

usual techniques or seen with the light microscope. If such materials, after
filtration through bacteriaproof filters (Fig. 6·10), are still capable of transmitting the disease to susceptible persons or animals, that is strong evidence
that the etiologic agent is a virus. The proof of the virus nature of the
infection is reasonably complete if similar filtrates from the experimentally
infected animals prove capable of transmitting the disease to others. Isolation,
characterization, and identification of the virus agent require its cultivation,
purification, and its study by electron microscopy, serology, and chemical
analysis.

Cultivation. Some viruses cannot be grown in laboratory animals. The
laboratory animal is not a readily controlled culture medium. The animal

may harbor latent viruses that cannot readily be separated from the virus being investigated. For these and other reasons, the chick embryo and tissue culture methods of cultivation are of great importance.

Cultivation in the Tissues of the Developing Chick Embryo. A fertilized hen's egg is incubated for 5 to 12 days to allow the embryo to commence its development. Through a small hole cut or drilled in the shell, a little virus-containing material is inserted with a needle or capillary pipet. The inocula-

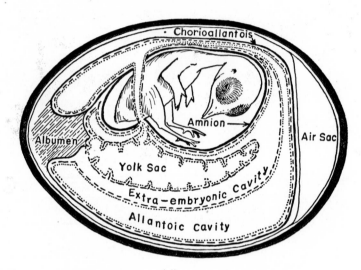

FIG. 33·2 Longitudinal section through fertile egg incubated 11 days, showing embryo and extraembryonic structures. (*Courtesy of Dr. G. J. Buddingh.*)

tion may be made on the chorioallantoic membrane, into the allantoic sac, in the amniotic sac, in the yolk sac, or into the embryo itself. (See Figs. 33·1 and 33·2.) The egg is reincubated. The embryo continues to grow and the virus multiplies in the growing cells. After a suitable interval the virus is harvested (Fig. 33·3). All procedures are carried out with sterile technique to avoid contamination with bacteria and fungi.

Cultivation in Tissue Culture. The cells of chick embryonic tissue and many tissues of animals including man can be grown outside the body in nutrient fluids. Tissue cultures have been used for many years to study the processes of cell growth. The successful growth of viruses in such cultures represents an important advance in virology technique. Addition of selected antibiotics in the tissue cultures prevents the growth of contaminating bacteria which plagued earlier virologists. Commercial firms now prepare the materials that are needed for the nutritive fluids. It has been found that cultures of human tissue (obtained from therapeutic abortions and operations

such as circumcision) will support the growth of viruses that cannot be
grown by other means. Strains of human cells that can be propagated serially
in pure culture have been found. The one most commonly used is a culture
of human cancer cells known as the *HeLa strain*.

F<small>IG</small>. 33·3 Harvesting of infected chick embryo for the commercial production of
rickettsial or viral vaccine. (*Parke, Davis & Co.*)

Types of Tissue Cultures. Suspended-cell cultures are made by placing
bits of minced tissue in the nutrient liquid in shallow flasks. *Fixed-cell
cultures* have the bits of tissue held in place in a thin layer of coagulated
plasma. In the *roller-tube method* the layer of fixed tissue in plasma is
deposited on the walls of test tubes or bottles. The nutrient fluid is added.
The cultures are placed in a rotating drum. By this means the tissues are
exposed alternately to the fluid and to air. (See Fig. 33·4.) To maintain prolonged growth the fluid may be replaced at intervals. When tissue growth
has reached the desired stage, the virus-containing material is introduced
and the tubes are returned to the incubator.

Detection of Virus Growth. The appearance of cloudiness, recognizable colonies, and detection of characteristic cells under the microscope are readily observable signs of growth in cultures of larger microorganisms. It is considerably more difficult to determine whether or not virus growth has taken

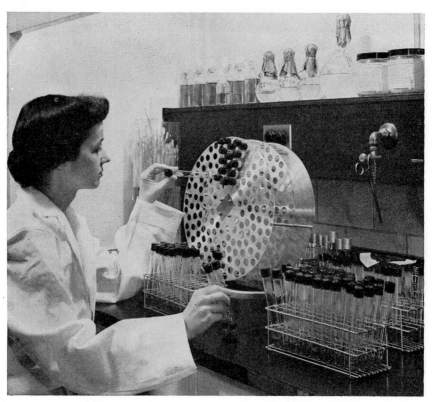

FIG. 33·4 Roller-tube technique of tissue culture. Poliomyelitis virus used in the preparation of vaccine is being tested in tissue cultures, which the virologist is placing in the roller-tube apparatus prior to incubation. (*Parke, Davis & Co.*)

place. In the chick embryo a few viruses cause the appearance of typical pocks (Fig. 33·5). The degenerative effect of some animal viruses on their host cells can be detected as plaques of degenerated cells when a limited number of virus particles are spread over the growth of a fixed-cell culture in a roller tube or in an agar plate (Fig. 33·6).

Examination of infected tissues under the microscope may show definite cell inclusions representing the localized proliferative area of the virus within the cell's nucleus or cytoplasm (Fig. 34·6). Low-power examination of roller-tube tissue cultures often reveals less clearly definable changes termed *cytopathic effects* (*cytopathogenic effects*). Figure 33·7 shows such an effect. Viruses which do not produce more definite morphologic changes can sometimes be detected by failure of host cells to spread (migrate) from the site of inoculation.

If facilities are available, the virus may be detected and sometimes identified by electron microscopy. Inoculation of susceptible animals may be

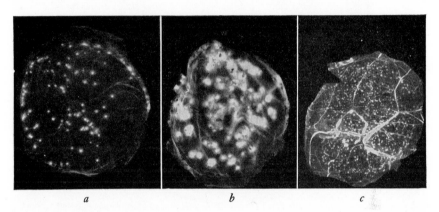

FIG. 33·5 Growth of viruses on chorioallantoic membranes of infected chick embryos. (*a*) Smallpox virus; (*b*) vaccine virus; (*c*) herpes simplex virus. (*Courtesy of Dr. A. W. Downie and Dr. F. O. MacCallum, from "Dynamics of Virus and Rickettsial Infections," McGraw-Hill, Blakiston Division.*)

required to make certain of the presence of the virus. Serologic tests in which the culture material is used as the antigen give the most specific identification. Serologic tests will be discussed in more detail later in the chapter.

Purification and Concentration. Any virus must be separated from its host cells if it is to be thoroughly studied. The actual amount of virus, even in heavily infected tissue, is very small. The usual process employed begins with low-speed centrifugation to remove noncellular material. The cellular residue is ground with an abrasive or repeatedly frozen and thawed to disintegrate the host cells and release the virus. Separation of the virus particles from the cellular debris is accomplished by selective centrifugation in the high-speed centrifuge. Sometimes substances that combine with the virus to form a precipitate are used to aid the centrifuge procedure. Some viruses are readily adsorbed to the surface of red blood cells and then can later be freed from the cells by appropriate methods. Proteolytic enzymes may help to separate

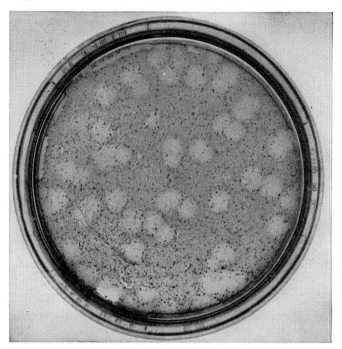

FIG. 33·6   Monolayer tissue culture in a petri dish (Dulbecco technique). In the single cell layer of chick embryonic cells that cover the bottom of the petri dish, units of Western equine encephalomyelitis virus have grown, destroying the chick cells and causing the clear plaques. (*Courtesy of Dr. R. Dulbecco; from S. E. Luria, "General Virology," Wiley.*)

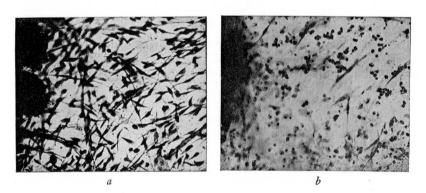

a   b

FIG. 33·7   Cytopathic effects of poliomyelitis virus in tissue culture. ×200. (*a*) Normal growth of human embryonic skin-muscle tissue culture before inoculation of the virus. (*b*) Cellular degeneration three days after inoculation of Type 1 poliomyelitis virus. (*Courtesy of Dr. T. M. Weller; from New England J. Med. 249:186.*)

the virus from closely associated proteins. This is possible because the viruses are resistant to the action of some digestive enzymes.

Microscopic Study. The size, shape, and in some instances some internal structure of the viruses are revealed in electron microscope preparations. Two methods are used, unshadowed preparations and metal-shadowed preparations. Figure 33·10 shows a virus prepared in each way. Rapid methods of freezing and drying the smear are best. They preserve the dimensions and structure of the particles. The collapse of virus particles prepared by other methods may alter their dimensions, but it also may reveal areas of greater density within the virus. (See Fig. 34·9.) The elementary bodies of some viruses can be detected with the light microscope (Fig. 34·2.)

Chemical and Physiologic Properties. Purified virus material can be subjected to the usual microchemical methods of analysis in order to determine its chemical composition. The physiology of a virus obviously cannot be studied by direct observation, nor is it possible to use the method of growth in artificial media to detect end products, etc. Often the effect of chemical or physical factors acting during the virus's growth in fertile eggs and tissue cultures cannot be differentiated from their effects on the host cells. However, the value of virustatic and virucidal agents can be determined by methods resembling those used in the study of bacteriostasis and disinfection. The inhibitory effects of chemotherapeutic agents, including antibiotics, can be studied by their ability to stop or slow the growth of the virus in the chick embryo or tissue culture. The protective effect of the drugs can also be tested on groups of infected laboratory animals. The virucidal effects of a chemical or physical agent can be measured by attempted cultivation of the virus after varied periods of exposure.

CHARACTERISTICS OF ANIMAL VIRUSES

Certain differences that distinguish viruses from other microorganisms have been recognized for a long time. Their small size and strict intracellular parasitism are accepted characteristics. Recent observations on a limited number of animal viruses, particularly the virus of influenza, and on the viruses that parasitize bacteria (see page 471) indicate that the fundamental differences between viruses and other microorganisms involve the special relationship the viruses have to their host cells.

Size and Morphology. The mature virus particle is measured by the metric unit called the *millimicron*. Each millimicron is 1/1,000 of a micron. The abbreviation for the millimicron is mμ. The largest of the viruses attacking man are those causing the pox diseases. The virus of smallpox is 150 mμ (or 0.15μ) in length. The viruses causing poliomyelitis and encephalitis are spheres 20 to 25 mμ in diameter. Other viruses are between these extremes. Most animal viruses have spherical or short rod shapes. Limiting membranes and capsules and areas of greater density have been detected in some viruses.

Chemical Composition. Even the smallest viruses have a complex chemical composition. As in all living material, the most important constituents are the proteins and the associated nucleic acids. The desoxyribonucleic acids (DNA) characteristic of nuclear material of higher organisms has been more often found in the animal viruses than has ribonucleic acid (RNA), which is characteristic of extranuclear cytoplasm. Fatty material (lipids) and carbohydrates are present in varying amounts. In general it is evident that viruses consist of forms of matter characteristic of living things.

THE NATURE OF ANIMAL VIRUSES

Life Cycle. The virus particle outside its host cell seems to be incapable of physiologic activity. It is, however, capable of initiating infection in a new, susceptible cell. The first step in infection is adsorption to the host-cell surface. Some larger viruses seem to be taken into the cell by the process of phagocytosis; in certain smaller viruses, notably the influenza viruses, an enzymatic action between a chemical portion of the virus particle and a receptive chemical group on the cell surface aids the infective process.

The infecting virus seems to disappear within the cell. It can no longer be seen, and for a matter of hours at least no infective virus can be obtained from the host cell. This is the stage of *"eclipse."* Then chemical substances —first the characteristic nucleic acids and later other substances—begin to appear within the host cell. Incomplete and noninfectious virus material, the *provirus,* can now be found in the cell. It can be identified by serologic tests, since it will react with antibodies specific for the virus. After a few more hours a considerable number (100 or more) of units of infectious virus can be found in the cell, and shortly thereafter they appear in the fluids outside the cell. The host cell is always damaged, and sometimes disintegrated, by this process. Some viruses are apparently capable of existing in a latent state in host cells for long periods. It is possible that such latent viruses may survive division of the host cells and thus be passed from one generation to the next.

Mutual Interference. When two different viruses are inoculated into animals, fertile eggs, or tissue cultures, one virus seems to prevent the other from infecting the cells. Presumably the first virus uses up the surface receptors of the cells or else changes the intracellular conditions so that the second virus cannot multiply. It is possible to protect an animal by introducing a virus of low virulence which will block another virulent virus. It has been suggested that the protective effect of some living-virus vaccines may be due to their persistence within susceptible host cells rather than to specific antibody formation.

Reproduction. It is evident that the virus particle does not reproduce by "growing to twice its former size and splitting in two," the usual concept of fission. Rather, it is now believed, the infecting virus provides pattern materials on which the metabolic processes of the host cell build many more identical units (*replicas*). These units are then combined to form the new crop of infective virus particles. To provide the building materials needed, the host cell has to utilize portions of its own substance and also material obtained from the surrounding medium. It has to divert these substances to the formation of virus instead of using them for its own growth, repair, and reproduction.

Genetics. The same mechanisms of genetics that have been discussed in relation to bacteria (page 45) operate in the natural history of the viruses. Changes in virulence and in many other characteristics have been observed under both natural and laboratory conditions. The best-known example is the modification of the virus of smallpox, which causes a generalized infection in man, to the virus of cowpox, which causes only a local skin lesion. This can be accomplished by growing the cowpox virus in the skin of cattle. Deliberately modified viruses provide the best means of active immunization against virus diseases. Yellow fever vaccine is made from virus that has been altered by growth in mouse nervous tissue and by prolonged cultivation in chick embryo tissue to a form that no longer causes the disease in man though it is still capable of arousing effective immunity. Both mutations and genetic recombinations (hybrids) have been demonstrated in laboratory experiments with purified strains of the influenza virus. Constant and wide variations occur in strains of influenza virus in nature.

Origin. There are two widely held theories of the origin of the viruses. The first, the *regression theory,* supposes that the viruses have evolved from intracellular bacterial and rickettsial forms that have become so dependent on the host cells that they have lost most of the functions and many of the structures characteristic of free-living organisms. Diminution in size is explained as resulting from the disappearance of unneeded portions of the organisms. The second theory, the *cell-component theory,* postulates that the viruses are derivatives of essential chemical structures of the cell, the nucleic acid compounds that are identified as the genes. Such genetic elements have developed ability to leave the cell, be transferred to other cells, and impose their patterns on the newly infected host cells. There is such wide variation among the viruses, especially if we include the viruses of bacteria and plants, that there is no reason to suppose that all viruses have arisen in the same fashion.

Shall we consider viruses to be living organisms? Probably not, since as

Luria says, "A virus is nothing but a part of the cell . . . independent enough to pass from cell to cell." Shall we consider viruses as living materials? Yes, for they possess the ability to reproduce as individuals and also the ability to develop modifications by mutation and adaptation.

VIRUS DISEASES

Most virus infections of man are acute diseases with a definite incubation period and a limited duration of active symptoms, followed by death or convalescence. The infected tissues undergo inflammatory and degenerative changes. New crops of viruses are released to invade other cells and to be spread from one animal or person to another. Some viruses of man may remain in the latent state within cells for long periods. Such a virus is that causing cold sores (page 486).

The specific viruses pathogenic for man will be described in more detail in Chaps. 34 and 35.

Viruses and Tumors. A number of viruses are known to cause transmissible tumors of animals, including both sarcomas and carcinomas. The common warts of man and animals are caused by viruses. The viruses of tumors and warts stimulate cells to excessive growth. These viruses are difficult to isolate, and the tumors and warts are not readily transmissible except by tissue transplant or injection of tissue filtrates. Presumably these viruses exist for the most part in noninfectious, provirus form within the cells. They do not destroy their host cells but remain in them as they multiply. The spontaneous cancers and sarcomas of man have no recognized relation to viruses, though there is a possibility that the cell proliferations may be due to latent viruses.

Immunity. Artificial immunization is successfully practiced against many, but not all, of the virus infections. Strains of attenuated virulence are used. Formerly all viruses for the preparation of vaccines were grown in susceptible animals (the vaccine virus in the cow, the rabies virus in the rabbit, and the yellow fever virus in the mouse). Now most virus vaccines are prepared from chick embryo cultures. Persons hypersensitive to egg protein may develop allergic reactions to the influenza vaccine and others prepared from the chick embryo. The American form of yellow fever vaccine and the Salk poliomyelitis vaccine are prepared from tissue culture. The preparation may be partially or completely inactivated by a chemical or by ultraviolet irradiation. The influenza and the Salk poliomyelitis vaccines contain no active virus. Complete inactivation of some other vaccines renders them ineffective as immunizing agents. Repeated doses and recall doses of virus vaccines are usually required to set up and maintain immunity.

Immune human sera and gamma globulin preparations are used for passive immunization against measles, infectious jaundice, and poliomyelitis. Immune animal serum is used for rabies prophylaxis. Skin tests to detect susceptibility or infection are not commonly used.

Serology. Serologic tests are very important in the detection, measurement, and identification of viruses in all types of virology research as well as in the laboratory diagnosis of virus diseases. The detection, identification, and measurement of antibodies from man and animals by their reactions with known virus antigens are also essential procedures in research and diagnosis.

The basic techniques of many virus antigen-antibody tests are the same as for similar tests in bacteriology. Complement-fixation tests are often used. Agglutination and precipitation tests are used occasionally. Since virus antigens are usually available only in small amounts (or are expensive if purchased) most of the tests are "micro" tests, done on slides or in capillary tubes.

Neutralization Test. A neutralization test is performed by inoculating mixtures of definite amounts of virus (antigen) and serum (antibody) into groups of 10 or more susceptible animals, fertile eggs, or suitable tissue cultures. Usually the virus antigen is a standardized preparation and the amount used is known to infect or kill the test animal or infect the fertile egg or tissue culture. Several dilutions of the serum are used. The titer of the dilution that protects 50 per cent of the animals, eggs, or tissue cultures from infection is noted and indicates the concentration of protective (neutralizing) antibodies in the serum sample.

Hemagglutination and Hemagglutination Inhibition. A number of viruses, including the influenza viruses and the virus of mumps, cause the agglutination of red blood cells in vitro. This is not an antigen-antibody reaction. The virus particles are adsorbed to the cell surface and cause changes in the surface membrane that result in the adhesion of the red cells to each other. The amount of virus in a preparation can be estimated by observing the greatest dilution that will cause the agglutination of a standard suspension of erythrocytes. Methods of virus inactivation can be studied by observing the extent to which the antiviral agent prevents hemagglutination.

Specific antiserum prevents a virus from causing hemagglutination. This is the basis of the *hemagglutination-inhibition test,* which can be used to identify a virus or to detect specific antibody in a serum. The diagrams in Fig. 33·8 illustrate the basic techniques of these tests.

Laboratory Diagnosis. An increasing number of public health and hospital laboratories now have facilities and personnel to carry out many diagnostic tests for virus infections. State and federal laboratories provide greater facilities for diagnosis. The basic methods are the same as for the diagnosis of other microbial infections: direct microscopic examination, cultivation, and serologic tests.

Microscopic Examination. In a few virus diseases the discovery of typical inclusion bodies in infected tissues may aid in diagnosis. Electron microscope identification of virus particles in infected materials is not practicable at present.

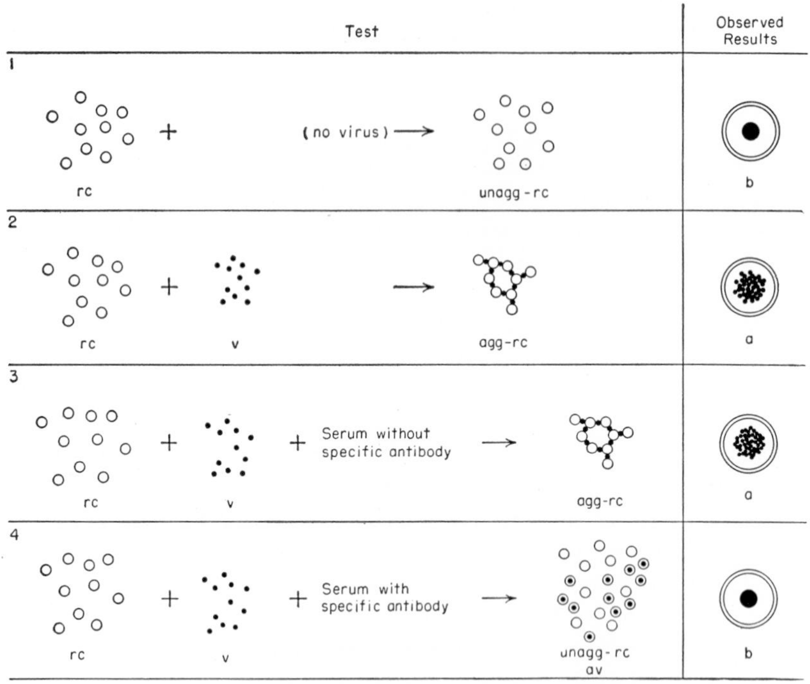

FIG. 33·8 Hemagglutination by viruses. 1 and 2 represent simple hemagglutination tests; 3 and 4 represent hemagglutination inhibition tests. 1. Red cells (*rc*) when added to material without virus are not agglutinated (*unagg-rc*). A button (*b*) is formed in the bottom of the test tube by the sedimented red cells. 2. Red cells (*rc*) when added to material containing virus (*v*) are agglutinated (*agg-rc*). An irregular pattern is seen in the bottom of the test tube as the agglutinated cells stick to the glass (*a*). 3. When red cells are added to virus plus serum that does not contain specific antibodies, they are agglutinated (*agg-rc*). Irregular pattern results on bottom of test tube (*a*). 4. When red cells are added to virus plus serum that contains antibodies specific against that virus, the antibody is adsorbed to the virus (*av*) and the virus then cannot agglutinate the red cells (*unagg-rc*). A button of sedimented red cells forms in bottom of test tube (*b*).

Cultivation. Cultivation of the infecting virus is attempted only in special laboratories. The procedure is expensive and requires special equipment and skilled technicians. Virus cultivation is often required for the identification of the causative organism in an epidemic or in an atypical individual infection. Inoculated animals may develop characteristic symptoms or show characteristic lesions or inclusion bodies at autopsy. Many viruses are readily cultivated in the fertile egg. Recognizable lesions may develop in the embryo

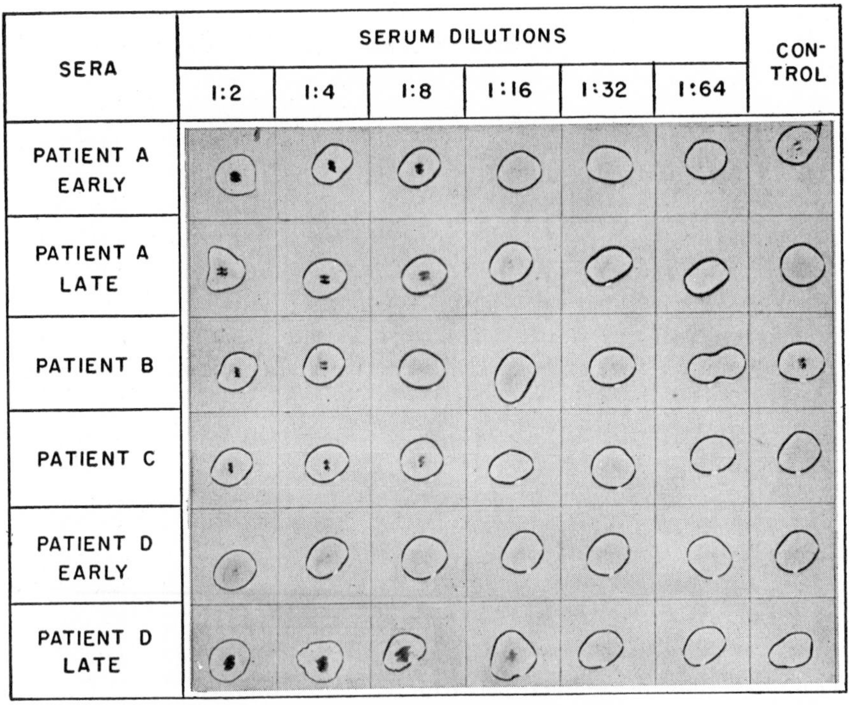

SERA	SERUM DILUTIONS						CON-TROL
	1:2	1:4	1:8	1:16	1:32	1:64	
PATIENT A EARLY							
PATIENT A LATE							
PATIENT B							
PATIENT C							
PATIENT D EARLY							
PATIENT D LATE							

FIG. 33·9   Plate complement-fixation test for herpes simplex. A positive result (patient's serum contains antibody) is indicated by distinct button of unhemolyzed red cells as seen in 1:64 column. A negative result (patient's serum has no complement-fixing antibody) is indicated by completely hemolyzed red cells as seen in top right corner. *Patient A* has herpes infection that is not acute. There is no rise in titer of antibody in his serum; *Patient B's* serum control is positive so results with his serum are inconclusive; *Patient C* has herpes antibody from either new or long-standing infection; *Patient D* has acute herpes infection. There is a distinct rise in antibody titer in his serum.

or its membranes. Hemagglutination tests or serologic tests may be needed to show the presence of virus in the chick embryo material. Certain viruses, notably those of poliomyelitis, are most readily cultivated in tissue cultures.

Serodiagnosis. Virus infections are most often diagnosed in the laboratory by the demonstration of a distinct increase in specific antibodies in the patient's serum. Two specimens (paired specimens) of the patient's blood must be sent to the laboratory. The first is collected as soon as the disease is suspected, the second 2 to 4 weeks later. The increase in antibody is detected by complement-fixation tests, neutralization tests, or by the increasing ability of the serum to inhibit hemagglutination. A complement-fixation test is shown in Fig. 33·9.

Chemotherapy. The true viruses are not affected by the common antibiotics. However where secondary bacterial infections might complicate virus disease, antibiotics are used. The intracellular multiplication of viruses and the physiologic inertness of the extracellular phase presumably protect them against chemotherapeutic substances. Research laboratories are investigating the possibly vulnerable points in the life cycle of the virus. The virus might be destroyed or blocked before it can reach the host cell; attachment to the host cell and penetration into the cell might be inhibited; and the processes within the host cell that carry on the synthesis of virus material might be altered. Scrubbing the site of a dogbite with soap solution to destroy the rabies virus is a simple example of the first method of attack. A number of compounds have been shown to prevent the influenza virus from being adsorbed to red blood cells. Several bacterial products, notably an enzyme-containing filtrate from *Vibrio cholerae* cultures, can not only prevent the combination of virus and red cells but can also remove virus that has recently become attached to the erythrocytes. These substances are known as *RDE compounds* (receptor-destroying enzymes). Another bacterial product, a polysaccharide of *Klebsiella pneumoniae,* prevents the reproduction of the mumps virus and the pneumonia virus of mice (*PVM*) in cells already infected. This action is very specific, for the polysaccharide does not inhibit the multiplication of the influenza virus. A single small dose of the substance given 3 days after a lethal dose of PVM saves two-thirds of the infected mice from death. An antimetabolite (6-methyltryptophan) has been shown to protect mice and monkeys against one strain of poliomyelitis virus. The compound presumably interferes with the use of the essential amino acid tryptophan in the synthesis of the virus protein.

Control of Virus Disease. Viruses are spread by all known means of transmission, including biologic transfer by arthropods. Because of their resistance to drying, air-borne infection is always a possibility. Since so many viruses spread to man from animal reservoirs, the control or elimination of animal hosts is important. As with bacterial diseases, detailed knowledge of the possible sources and modes of infection for each disease is needed as the basis of any rational program for its control.

CLASSIFICATION OF VIRUSES AND VIRUS DISEASES

The editors of the 6th edition of *Bergey's Manual of Determinative Bacteriology* have tentatively included all the known viruses in the order *Virales*. This order is divided into three suborders: (1) the viruses infecting bacteria; (2) the viruses infecting higher plants; and (3) the viruses infecting animals. This classification is outlined in Appendix B, Section 3, page 587.

The viruses attacking man are placed in four families. The first consists of those causing lesions in the skin, the *dermatotropic* viruses; the second, the *neurotropic* group, is made up of viruses that invade the nerve tissues; and the third, the *viscerotropic* group, of the viruses that attack the internal organs, or viscera. The mumps virus is the sole human pathogen in the fourth family, which is made up of viruses invading the salivary glands. The *pneumotropic* viruses, those that invade the respiratory tract, are not considered as a separate group in this classification. The measles virus is included in the dermatotropic group and the influenza and common cold viruses in the viscerotropic group.

The scientific names assigned to the viruses are not in common use at the present time. In the next two chapters the scientific names are given once in parentheses after the first reference to the virus, e.g., the virus of smallpox (*Borreliota variolae*), the mumps virus (*Rabula inflans*). Thereafter the nonscientific name is used.

THE BACTERIAL VIRUSES

The viruses that infect bacteria are placed in the genus *Phagus* and are frequently referred to as *bacteriophages* or simply *phages*. The most obvious effect of these viruses, the transmissible lysis of bacteria, was first described by Twort in 1915 and independently by d'Herelle in 1917. Viruses have been found that infect enterobacteria, vibrios, streptococci, micrococci, lactobacilli, and actinomycetes. A group of phages, designated as T1, T2, etc., that invade *Escherichia coli* strain B have been most extensively studied and provide a large part of the information on which our present ideas about the bacterial viruses are based.

Properties of Bacterial Viruses. Each bacterial virus has a definite morphology. The typical particle has a head and a tail. Electron micrographs show that the head may be round, oval, or polyhedral. The tail is slender and may be long or short. The heads of the T viruses vary from 50 to 95 mμ, while their tails may be as long as 170 mμ, though only 10 mμ in width. Some have tails so short as to be scarcely distinguishable. Four distinctly different chemical compounds are located in definite parts of the virus. The inner portion of the head contains the nucleic acids; the covering of the tail and most of the head is made of protein; the end of the tail is the site of special chemical groups by which it becomes adsorbed to the wall of the host bacterium; and in this region there is also a substance which dissolves away the bacterial wall. Figures 33·10 and 33·11 show the bacterial virus as it is seen in electron micrographs.

Phages become attached to the host cell wall by their tails. Only the nucleic acid of the head enters the host cell, possibly through a tube in the tail. The empty head is left outside. Within the cell the nucleic acid molecules

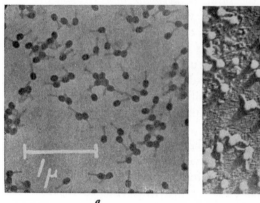

a b

FIG. 33·10 Bacteriophage of *Escherichia coli*. Electron micrographs. (*a*) Phage treated with calcium chloride, ×20,000; (*b*) phage chromium-shadowed, ×15,000. (*SAB print 139, courtesy of Dr. D. G. Sharp.*)

cause the bacterial cell to produce provirus (*prophage*). After a definite time the provirus is converted into mature virus. Then the host cell swells rapidly and bursts, liberating, in the case of the T viruses, from 100 to 300 new virus particles. The action of phage is shown in Fig. 33·12. Many strains of phages remain latent within host cells in the provirus, noninfectious stage. Such phages are said to be *temperate* or *lysogenic*. A phage which is lysogenic for one type of bacterium may be detected by its ability to lyse a related bacterium.

Mutations and genetic recombinations occur in phages. Phage-infected bacteria also mutate, giving rise to strains resistant to phage.

Laboratory Study. When a small amount of specific phage is added to a young broth culture of the host bacterium, the cloudiness of the culture disappears within a few hours. Subcultures show that few if any of the bacteria are still alive. Under the microscope only bits of disintegrated bacteria can be seen. Even more striking is the appearance of infected growth on solid media. A suspension of the bacterium heavy enough to produce confluent growth is spread over an agar plate. A diluted suspension of virus is added. Each infective virus particle initiates an area of bacterial lysis on the plate, so that after incubation the growth seems to be full of holes (*plaques*). This technique can be used to count infectious units of the bac-

FIG. 33·11 Broken phage particle. Electron micrograph, ×90,000. The tail and empty head are at the bottom of the picture. The fine threads that have escaped from the head are desoxyribonucleic acid (DNA), the infectious material of the virus. (*Courtesy of Dr. R. C. Williams.*)

terial virus. The appearance of such a plate is similar to the one shown in Fig. 33·6.

Practical Importance. D'Herelle believed that phage is the determining factor in recovery from and immunity to many bacterial diseases, and he thought that phage should be used for treatment. Unfortunately phage action is definitely inhibited by the presence of blood, pus, and tissue fluids. Bacterio-phage therapy is now very seldom attempted.

Bacterial viruses are usually present in polluted waters and soils and in decaying plant and animal matter. They may be important in altering the bacterial populations in these environments. Unwanted phages interfere with at least two microbial processes important to man. The action of phage on

Streptomyces griseus may interrupt the production of streptomycin; and phages attacking lactobacilli are responsible for the failure of milk-souring processes in the production of cheese.

Bacteriophage typing of typhoid strains, salmonella and shigella cultures, staphylococci, and streptococci is important in tracing the spread of epidemics of infections caused by these bacteria. By skillful laboratory methods strains

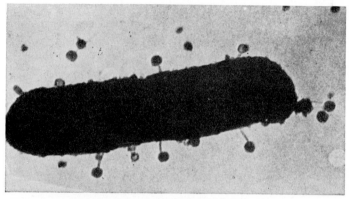

a

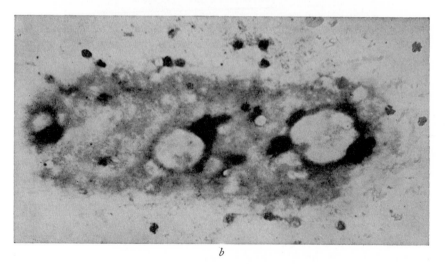

b

FIG. 33·12   Bacteriophage action of cells of *Escherichia coli.* ×2,500. (*a*) Phage particles adsorbed to a bacterium by their tails. Some heads are empty because the contents have passed through the tails into the bacterium. (*Courtesy of Dr. T. F. Anderson, from Cold Spring Harbor Symposium, Vol. XVIII.*) (*b*) Invasion and disintegration of bacterium after 25 minutes' exposure to phage. (*Courtesy of Dr. S. E. Luria, from J. Bact. 46:57.*)

of phage can be isolated that are specific for each of many different strains of a single species of bacterium. The technique used in the laboratory to determine the phage strain of a typhoid bacterium is illustrated in Fig. 33·13.

Study of bacterial viruses is one of the most important forms of present-day biologic research. Many of these investigations have no immediate appli-

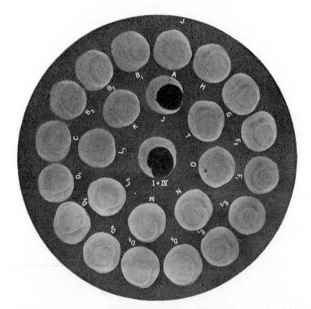

FIG. 33·13 Bacteriophage typing of *Salmonella typhosa*. Each spot on the agar plate is the growth from a loopful of a culture of *S. typhosa*. A loopful of a different phage was placed on each colony. Lysis has resulted from the growth of unadapted phages I and IV, showing that this is a lysable strain. Lysis by the specific phage *J* shows that the bacterium is phage type *J*. (*Courtesy of Dr. P. R. Edwards, Communicable Disease Center*.)

cation to medicine and little immediate practicality. They are, however, giving us new understanding of the nature of those activities, which are the essential life processes of living matter, and greater comprehension of the mechanisms by which cells pass on inherited characteristics.

STUDY SUGGESTIONS

What evidence would indicate that a disease is caused by a virus? What are the three possible ways of cultivating an animal virus? What are the advantages and disadvantages of each method? What methods does the virologist use to detect and measure virus growth? Review the electron microscope as discussed in Chap. 5. How do you explain the "sunlit, three-dimensional" aspect of viruses in electron-microscope, metal-shadowed preparations?

Describe laboratory experiments that might prove that a specific dilution of a chemical was the highest dilution that would affect the growth of a virus in tissue culture but that it had no protective effect against infection in a susceptible species of animal. Discuss disinfection and chemotherapy in virus diseases.

Compare the animal viruses with bacteria, rickettsiae, and large viruses as to size, structure, parasitism, susceptibility to antibiotics, methods of laboratory study, etc. Can you describe or diagram the present concept of the life cycle and growth of an animal virus? Is the virus a cell? Is it alive?

The general methods of laboratory diagnosis of virus disease are the same as the methods used in bacteriology. What are they? However, laboratory diagnosis of a virus disease is generally a much more expensive, exacting, and time-consuming procedure. Why? Explain fully, giving examples.

Answer these questions in as much detail as possible. How could a neutralization test prove that you had a subclinical infection with poliomyelitis in your childhood? How might the hemagglutination test be used to measure the amount of a virus in amniotic fluid from a chick embryo culture? Would this test show that the virus was of a specific strain? If not, how could the hemagglutination test be modified to show that the virus concerned was influenza virus, Type A?

Define bacterial virus. Trace the life cycle of a bacterial virus. How is the presence of active bacterial virus detected? How can the number of virus particles be estimated? Explain the practical importance of the bacteriophages.

SUGGESTED READING

General References

BURNETT, F. M.: "Viruses and Man." Penguin Books, London, 1953.

COLD SPRING HARBOR SYMPOSIUM ON QUANTITATIVE BIOLOGY: "Viruses." Vol. XVIII, Biological Laboratory, Cold Spring Harbor, N.Y., 1953.

DELBRUCK, M.: "Viruses, 1950." California Institute of Technology Bookstore, Pasadena, 1950.

LURIA, S. E.: "General Virology." Wiley, New York, 1953.

RHODES, A. J., and C. E. VAN ROOYEN: "Textbook of Virology." 2d ed., Williams & Wilkins, Baltimore, 1953.

RIVERS, T. M.: "Viral and Rickettsial Infections of Man." 2d ed., Lippincott, Philadelphia, 1952.

SMITH, K. M.: "Recent Advances in the Study of Plant Viruses." Churchill, London, 1951.

How Viruses Are Studied

COX, H. R.: Growth of viruses and rickettsiae in the developing chick embryo. *Ann. New York. Acad. Sc.* **55**:236 (1952).

ENDERS, J. F.: Propagation of Viruses and Rickettsiae in Tissue Cultures, in Rivers's "Viral and Rickettsial Infections of Man." 2d ed., Lippincott, Philadelphia, 1952.

GRAY, B. W.: The ultracentrifuge. *Scient. Am.* **42:**184 (1951).

WARREN, J.: Progress in the purification of viruses. *Bact. Rev.* **14:**200 (1950).

WYCKOFF, R. W. G.: Electron microscope study of viruses. *J.A.M.A.* **136:**1081 (1948).

Nature of Viruses

ANDREWES, C. H.: Adventures among viruses. I. Some properties of viruses. *New England J. Med.* **242:**161 (1950).

————: Classification and Nomenclature of Viruses, in "Annual Review of Microbiology." Vol. 6, Annual Reviews, Inc., Stanford, 1952.

BEARD, J. W.: Physical and Chemical Characteristics of Viruses, in "Annual Review of Microbiology." Vol. 5, Annual Reviews, Inc., Stanford, 1951.

BURNETT, F. M.: "Virus as Organism." Harvard University Press, Cambridge, Mass., 1945.

GOTTSCHALK, E., *et al.:* Mechanisms of Virus and Rickettsial Infections, in "The Dynamics of Virus and Rickettsial Infections." Blakiston, New York, 1954. Chaps. 1–12.

"Viruses as Causative Agents in Cancer." *Ann. New York Acad. Sc.* (1952).

Laboratory Diagnosis

AMERICAN PUBLIC HEALTH ASSOCIATION: "Diagnostic Procedures for Virus and Rickettsial Diseases." New York, 1948.

LENNETTE, E. H.: An Evaluation of Diagnostic Procedures for Virus and Rickettsial Diseases, in "The Dynamics of Virus and Rickettsial Infections." Blakiston, New York, 1954.

MILZER, A.: Routine laboratory diagnosis of virus and rickettsial diseases. *J.A.M.A.* **143:**219 (1950).

WELLER, T.: The Diagnosis of Virus Infections Employing Tissue Culture Methods, in "The Dynamics of Virus and Rickettsial Infections." Blakiston, New York, 1954.

Treatment and Control

HORSFALL, F. L.: Approaches to the control of viral diseases. *Bact. Rev.* **14:**219 (1950).

KOPROWSKI, H.: Practical Application of Living Virus Vaccines, in "The Dynamics of Virus and Rickettsial Infections." Blakiston, New York, 1954.

LENNETTE, E. H.: Interference between Animal Viruses, in "Annual Review of Microbiology." Vol. 5, Annual Reviews, Inc., Stanford, 1951.

McLean, I. W.: Chemotherapy trials in the chick embryo. *Ann. New York Acad. Sc.* **55**:2 (1952).

Bacterial Viruses (See also reference to articles on phage typing on page 380.)

Frease, D., and R. C. Williams: Details of frozen-dried T3 and T7 bacteriophages as shown by the electron microscope. *J. Bact.* **65**:167 (1953).

Hersey, A. D., and J. Bronfenbrenner: Bacterial Viruses: Bacteriophages, in Rivers's "Viral and Rickettsial Infections of Man." 2d ed., Lippincott, Philadelphia, 1952.

Luria, S. E.: Bacteriophage: an essay on virus reproduction. *Science* **111**:507 (1950).

Whitehead, H. R.: Bacteriophage in cheese manufacture. *Bact. Rev.* **17**:109 (1953).

Woodruff, H. B., T. D. Nunheimer, and S. B. Lee: A bacterial virus for *Actinomyces griseus. J. Bact.* **54**:5 (1947).

CHAPTER 34

The Dermatotropic and Viscerotropic Viruses

This chapter considers in some detail the characteristics of the dermatotropic viruses and the viscerotropic viruses. The virus infections of the nervous system will be considered in Chap. 35.

THE VIRUSES OF SMALLPOX AND VACCINIA

The viruses of smallpox, vaccinia, and cowpox, the virus of chickenpox, and several viruses that infect animals but not man are similar in structure and size. They all cause *pocks* (*pox*) in the skin. The smallpox, vaccinia, and cowpox viruses are closely related varieties of a single species, *Borreliota variolae*. Two of the pox viruses are shown in Fig. 34·1.

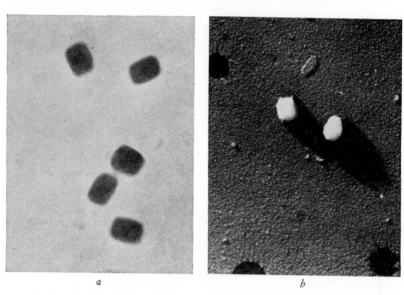

a   b

FIG. 34·1 Electron micrographs of pox viruses. ×30,000. (*a*) Vaccinia virus (vaccine); (*b*) variola virus (smallpox). (*SAB print 45 from Green et al., J. Exper. Med. 75:656, and SAB print 216, Rake et al., J. Bact. 56:293.*)

Characteristics of the Viruses. These viruses are short, stubby rods with denser central areas. They are so large—225 mμ in length—that they can be distinguished in stained smears of infected tissue (Fig. 34·2). They are found in large numbers as elementary bodies within the typical cell inclusions (*Guarnieri bodies*) in infected areas of the skin. They are readily killed by heat but can survive prolonged drying. They can be cultivated in the chorioallantoic membrane of the developing chick embryo and in tissue cultures. Their growth can be recognized and measured quantitatively by the pocks formed in the cultures (Fig. 33·5).

There are many variants within this species of viruses. At least two forms of the smallpox virus exist, one causing the severe form of smallpox (*variola major*), and the other causing a much milder infection (*variola minor, alastrim*). Both viruses cause a generalized eruption and infect man and monkeys but not cows and rabbits. The virus of cowpox causes a single pustule at the site of inoculation in cattle, rabbits, man, and monkeys. The virus of *vaccinia* is the laboratory-grown variant that is used to immunize man against smallpox. Vaccinia infection in man is similar to cowpox infection, but the virus is not identical with that of naturally occurring cowpox. It is not certain whether vaccinia virus was derived from cowpox virus or from smallpox virus.

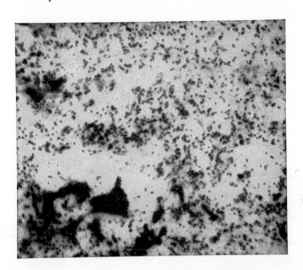

FIG. 34·2   Elementary bodies of variola virus in smear from the base of a smallpox vesicle, as seen with the light microscope. ×1,400. (*Courtesy of Dr. F. O. MacCallum, from "Dynamics of Virus and Rickettsial Infections," McGraw-Hill, Blakiston Division.*)

Smallpox Disease. The classic case of smallpox has an incubation period of about twelve days. The onset is marked by fever and mucous membrane ulcerations. These precede the development of typical skin lesions by several days. The severe eruption lasts for 2 weeks or longer (Fig. 34·3). Before the introduction of vaccination, smallpox was a childhood disease with high fatality. Now, in privileged areas of the world where vaccination and public health measures are thoroughly carried out, there are only occasional cases. These are usually in adults who have a partial immunity because of previous vaccination. The resulting mild form of the disease is called *varioloid*. Variola major still is an important epidemic disease with high fatality in many parts of the world.

Vaccination. The only truly effective means of controlling smallpox is by universal active immunization by vaccination.

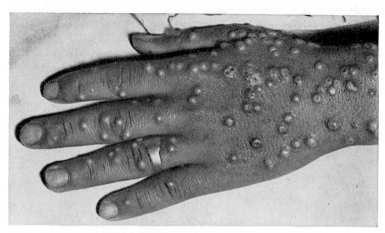

FIG. 34·3   Lesions of smallpox in late vesicle and pustule stages. (*Armed Forces Institute of Pathology print OA 44-271E.*)

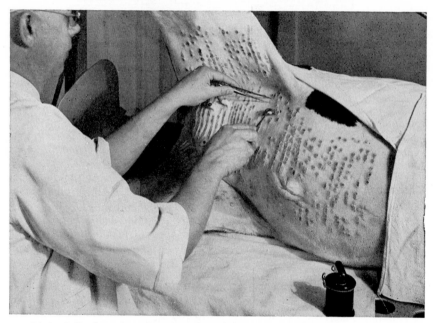

FIG. 34·4   Collection of vaccine virus from lesions on calf. (*Eli Lilly and Company.*)

Preparation of the Vaccine Virus. Stock virus that has been cultivated in the rabbit's skin is inoculated by many parallel scratches on the skin of the belly and thighs of a healthy calf. After 5 days the virus is harvested by cureting the vesicles (Fig. 34·4). This material is called vaccine *lymph.* It is thoroughly mixed with glycerin and kept at low temperature for a month. During this period of "ripening" most of the bacteria die. White mice are inoculated to detect possible presence of tetanus spores. The potency

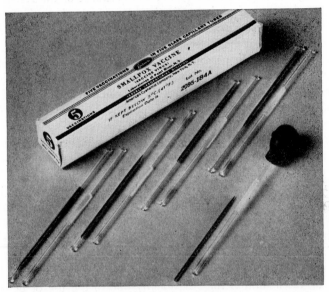

Fig. 34·5 Smallpox vaccine (vaccine virus). Calf-lymph virus and sterile needles in capillary tubes. (*Lederle Laboratories Division, American Cyanamid Company.*)

of the vaccine is tested on rabbits and by actual use in public clinics. The vaccine is distributed in capillary tubes, except in the tropics where a dried vaccine is used because it remains active for a longer time.

Vaccines made from chick embryo culture and distributed in dried form have many advantages. Experiments and practical use have shown them to be as effective as calf lymph. It is likely that the *CE* (chick embryo) *vaccine* will replace the calf-lymph form as the standard antismallpox biological.

The Technique of Vaccination. In the United States the accepted method of vaccination is by the *multiple pressure method* on the skin of the arm at the site of the insertion of the deltoid muscle. The skin is cleaned with acetone and the contents of a single capillary tube of vaccine virus dropped on the area (Fig. 34·5). A sterile needle, held parallel to the skin, is repeatedly pressed through the drop so that it just catches in the superficial epidermis. No bleeding should result. Excess virus is wiped off with sterile gauze. The vaccination should not be covered by a dressing. If an impervious covering is used, healing is delayed and infection encouraged. Some physicians still prefer to make a single scratch or two parallel scratches in the skin.

The vaccine virus deteriorates rapidly at any temperature above freezing. It must always be kept in the freezing compartment of the refrigerator. It should never be used after the expiration date stamped on the package.

Reactions Following Vaccination. The three types of reaction resulting from vaccination are

1. *Primary reaction.* In persons who have never before been vaccinated, a papule appears on the third day which enlarges to a vesicle by the fifth day. By the ninth day the lesion is a pustule surrounded by a halo of inflammation. After the eleventh day the pustule dries. When the scab falls off. a pitted scar is left.

2. *Vaccinoid reaction* (*accelerated reaction, modified reaction*). In persons who have some remaining immunity from previous vaccination, the lesion develops more rapidly and reaches its maximum in 3 to 7 days.

3. *Immediate reaction.* Frequently the only response to vaccination is a small papule developing within 3 days. This may be due to true immunity resulting from frequent or recent vaccination. However it is not safe to assume this since the reaction may also be due to allergy to nonliving vaccine or to skin injury. Therefore it is now recommended in these cases that vaccination be repeated on another area of skin.

Failure of vaccination is most frequently due to the use of deteriorated vaccine. It may also be due to poor technique of vaccination, use of strong disinfectants on the skin immediately before or after vaccination, or exposure of the area to bright sunshine after vaccination. Vaccination properly done with potent vaccine will result in a "take."

Immunity Resulting from Vaccination. Vaccination results in absolute immunity of several years' duration to both smallpox and cowpox infections. Every child should be vaccinated in early infancy and revaccinated before entering school. Revaccination every 5 years or oftener is desirable where smallpox is endemic. Every individual entering the armed services, planning to travel, or working in hospitals or clinics should be vaccinated. The entire population of a community is vaccinated when an epidemic threatens.

Treatment and Nursing Care. No specific remedy is known for smallpox, but antibiotics may be used to lessen the danger of secondary bacterial infections.

Nursing care of smallpox must include the effective disinfection of all materials from the patient, since both respiratory and skin discharges are infectious. It should be noted that in this respect the disease differs from scarlet fever, in which the skin lesions do not contain the organism. The nurse who is to care for a case of smallpox is always revaccinated. Close contact with a case of smallpox may lead to a contact-carrier state. The nurse's hands and clothing are certain to become contaminated with infectious material. For these reasons special precautions are necessary and the nurse may be quarantined with the patient.

Laboratory Diagnosis. Most cases during epidemics can be readily diagnosed by the clinical picture. Cases early in an epidemic, sporadic cases, and atypical cases can be definitely diagnosed by the aid of laboratory tests. It is often very important to distinguish mild smallpox from chickenpox.

Any one or more of four tests are used. (1) The elementary bodies may be found in stained smears of material scraped from the base of early lesions. (2) The virus can be cultivated from blood or from vesicles early in the disease by inoculation on the chorioallantoic membrane. The appearance of the plaques differentiates the variola virus from the virus of vaccinia and herpes (Fig. 33·5). (3) The presence of the virus in scrapings and blood early in the disease and in crusts later on can be tested by using these materials as antigens in complement-fixation tests with specific rabbit anti-sera. (4) Late in the disease a retrospective diagnosis can be made by complement-fixation testing to detect antibody in the patient's blood. Suspensions of known viruses are used as the antigens.

THE VIRUS OF CHICKENPOX

The virus of chickenpox (*Briareus varicellae*) is similar in size and shape to the pox viruses. However the inclusion bodies are within the nuclei, the free virus is very much harder to find, and there is less destruction of the host cells. Animals cannot be infected with the chickenpox virus. It has only recently been cultivated in cultures of human tissues. (See Fig. 34·6.)

Chickenpox (*varicella*) is a mild communicable disease and no method of active immunization seems to be needed. It is believed that gamma globulin can prevent the development of the infection. Correct diagnosis is important, for sometimes mild cases of smallpox are mistaken for chicken-pox. Laboratory diagnostic methods are used which will identify variola but which will have negative results if the disease is varicella.

The virus of chickenpox is practically indistinguishable from the organism that causes another quite different clinical condition known as *herpes zoster,* or *shingles*. This disease is usually found in adults. The vesicular eruption is distributed along the course of cranial and other peripheral nerves. The characteristic lesions are found not in the skin but in one or more spinal ganglia. There is some epidemiologic and some experimental evidence that children acquire chickenpox from adults with herpes zoster and that adults develop herpes when in contact with cases of chickenpox.

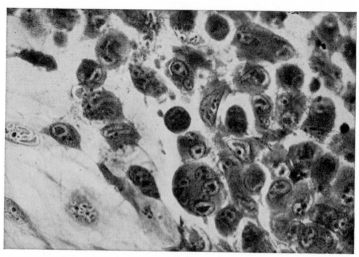

FIG. 34·6 Intranuclear inclusions of chickenpox virus in tissue culture of human embryonic skin. ×550. The inclusions are the darker bodies within the cell nuclei. *(Courtesy of Dr. T. H. Weller, from Proc. Soc. Exper. Biol. & Med. 83:340.)*

THE VIRUS OF HERPES SIMPLEX (SCELUS RECURRENS)

The best-known form of herpes simplex infection is the common cold sore or fever blister. It is believed that the original infection in infants and children is usually an acute *stomatitis* (inflammation of the mouth). Research indicates that this virus remains latent in the tissues of an infected person throughout the rest of his life. At intervals it is activated by the occurrence of other infections, giving rise to the typical vesicles on lips or face. Recurrent but superficial corneal ulcerations (*dendritic keratoconjunctivitis*), herpetic infections of areas of the skin already injured by trauma or eczema, and rare cases of encephalitis and meningitis are also caused by the herpes virus. A number of cases of herpetic infection have been successfully treated with Aureomycin.

The nurse should note and report any stomatitis or other herpetic infection in infants in order to prevent the spread of infection. Persons with cold sores should avoid contact with infants or small children. Nurses with cold sores should be barred from duty on infants' or children's wards.

THE VIRUSES OF MEASLES

Three common contagious exanthemata of children—measles, German measles, and roseola—are caused by viruses. The scientific name of measles is *rubeola*. The scientific name of German measles is *rubella*.

Roseola is a very mild exanthem of infants. The causative virus has not been studied in the laboratory.

The Rubeola Virus (Briareus morbillorum). The virus nature of the cause of measles is indicated by the transfer of the disease to monkeys and man by filtrates of blood and respiratory secretions from recognized cases. The virus has been grown in the chick embryo and in tissue culture. Inclusion bodies have not been described. It is believed that the virus is very small.

The Disease. Every susceptible person who is exposed to rubeola develops a recognizable case of the disease. After 10 days' incubation there is a prodromal period of 3 or 4 days when the patient shows symptoms of acute respiratory infection. An eruption, *Koplik's spots,* develops in the mouth. Then the characteristic measles rash appears.

This is one of the most important of the common epidemic diseases. Although uncomplicated measles is uniformly mild, in children under three years of age secondary bronchopneumonias are often fatal.

No method of serum therapy is considered valuable. Chemotherapy is not effective against the measles virus but may be useful in prevention or treatment of complicating bacterial infections. Diagnosis is entirely on the basis of clinical symptoms.

Control. No method of active immunization against measles is known. Public health measures directed against its spread are quite ineffectual. Control of measles is therefore aimed toward preventing the disease in children under three years of age and in children suffering from chronic disease, toward modifying the disease in healthy children, and toward preventing bronchopneumonias and other serious complications in measles cases

1. *Passive Prophylactic Immunization of Infants.* Antibodies are present in the blood of persons who have recovered from measles. These antibodies are part of the gamma globulin fraction of human serum (Fig. 34·7). Immune globulin preparation should be given to all children under three years of age who are exposed to measles. It must be given within 5 days of exposure. Such passive immunization is not recommended for older healthy children.

2. *Modification of Measles.* Healthy children three years of age and over are given immune globulin preparation 6 to 10 days after exposure. This does not prevent the development of measles but does modify the severity of the attack. In this way the children gain permanent active immunity to the disease.

3. *Prevention of Bacterial Complications.* Masks should be worn by doctors, nurses, and visitors to measles patients. This is done not to protect the healthy individual but to keep his potentially dangerous respiratory bacteria from reaching the patient. Each patient should be protected by respiratory precautions to avoid the spread of dangerous bacteria from patient to patient. Ultraviolet light or aerosol vaporizers should also prove useful in preventing such cross infection. All patients who develop complications are removed to separate units. When measles is prevalent in the community all newly

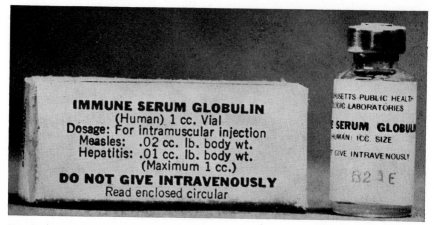

FIG. 34·7   Immune serum globulin. Gamma globulin from pooled human blood. Used for passive immunization against measles, infectious hepatitis, and poliomyelitis. (*Institute of Laboratories, Massachusetts State Department of Health.*)

admitted children should be kept separate from others and no visitors should be allowed on infants' wards. Low incidence of complications among measles patients indicates careful nursing.

The Virus of Rubella. German measles can be transferred by filtered washings from the nose and throat. It is not readily cultivated. It is a much milder infection than measles, with little tendency to develop complications. No immunization is practiced. Community control measures are not considered worthwhile. Hospital control measures are the same as for measles. Infection of women in the first months of pregnancy is to be avoided because there is evidence that it results in development of congenital deformities in the fetus.

OTHER DERMATOTROPIC VIRUSES

The virus of foot-and-mouth disease (*Hostis pecoris*), one of the smallest of all known viruses, causes a serious infection of cattle and other farm animals. It can be transmitted to man. Slaughter of infected animals and careful disposal of the carcasses has been the most successful method of control. Recently a vaccine for immunization of cattle has been prepared from growth in tissue cultures of beef tongue.

There are a number of other dermatotropic viruses of animals that are sometimes transferred to man. Among them are the virus of *pustular dermatitis* of sheep and goats, and the virus of *vesicular exanthem,* a disease that has recently caused widespread epidemics on American hog farms.

THE VIRUSES OF YELLOW FEVER, DENGUE FEVER, AND SAND-FLY FEVER

These viruses are spread by insects.

The Virus of Yellow Fever (Charon evagatus).

The Virus. The yellow fever virus is spherical and very small, averaging less than 25 mμ. It is present in high concentrations in the blood during the first 4 days of fever. The virus multiplies in the bodies of aëdes and other mosquitoes. It can be transmitted to rhesus monkeys. In the laboratory it is grown in mice, in tissue cultures, and in the fertile egg. In all cultures it tends to develop variants. Although the virus resists drying and freezing, it deteriorates very rapidly in liquid suspensions.

The Disease. Although all human forms of the virus seem to be alike, the disease varies greatly in severity. Among the natives of endemic areas it is commonly a mild disease of childhood. When it attacks nonnatives or spreads to other areas the infection is severe and there is a high death rate. The *urban* (city) form of the disease was a horrible plague of the Caribbean area until it was brought under control by the researches of the U.S. Army Commission in Cuba and the sanitary measures first enforced by General Gorgas in Panama (see Chap. 21). In the 1930s the *jungle* type of the disease was recognized in Africa and South America. This type is spread by forest mosquitoes from forest animals to human beings. It is now believed that this is the primitive form of the disease and that the urban type arises when the jungle infection comes into a community where there are many *Aëdes aegypti* mosquitoes and a population of susceptible humans.

The sources of infection are early cases in the cities and infected animals in areas where the jungle type occurs. Under natural conditions the disease is entirely mosquito-borne. The *A. aegypti,* a mosquito that breeds in small artificial bodies of water around dwellings, spreads the urban type. The forest species breed in small collections of water in jungle plants. The mosquito does not become infectious until about twelve days after her meal of infected blood.

Control. The urban type of yellow fever was entirely eliminated from infected areas early in this century by sanitary measures destroying the breeding places of *A. aegypti*. The jungle type cannot be handled in this fashion, for the breeding places of the mosquitoes are inaccessible. Spread of the vectors from infected regions to other areas is prevented by inspection and spraying of airplanes.

Vaccination. The *17D* strain of yellow fever virus is used for the vaccine. This strain has lost its pathogenicity for man and monkeys as the result of over 150 transfers in tissue cultures of mouse embryo and chick embryo. The virus is cultivated in the fertile egg and is distributed in a dried form. The dried powder is resuspended in salt solution and inoculated subcutaneously.

Laboratory Diagnosis. A rise in neutralizing antibodies in paired specimens of blood is the usual method of laboratory diagnosis of suspected cases. In endemic areas it is customary to remove a small piece of liver tissue from persons who have died from unexplained causes. Examination of stained sections will disclose the cellular degeneration typical of yellow fever.

The Viruses of Dengue Fever and Sand-fly Fever. There are two other viscerotropic viruses that are insect-borne. Aëdes mosquitoes carry the virus of dengue (pronounced *denghee*) fever, an acute, nonfatal infection occurring in epidemics in tropical and semitropical areas. Sand flies spread another nonfatal fever of the Mediterranean regions and southern Asia. Sand-fly fever is more correctly called *phlebotomus fever*.

THE VIRUSES OF VIRAL HEPATITIDES

Hepatitis (inflammation of the liver) may be due to a variety of causes. The epidemic type caused by a spirochete was described in Chap. 31, page 429. Two forms are caused by viruses, virus IH causing *infectious hepatitis*, and virus SH causing *homologous serum hepatitis*. Jaundice is a frequent but by no means invariable symptom of these infections, but the diseases may be called *infectious jaundice* and *serum jaundice*. Little is known of the exact nature of the causative microorganisms. Cases are diagnosed from their histories and from the results of liver-function tests. The diseases are seldom fatal, but chronic hepatitis may develop in older persons.

The Virus of Infectious Hepatitis. The IH virus is found in the stools of infected persons and is spread by water and food. The incubation period is from 15 to 40 days. IH virus can also be spread by the methods described below for serum hepatitis. There is some evidence that infectious hepatitis may be a very mild disease in infants. In one American orphanage it was found to be continuously spread among the young children over a period of 8 years. Some children excreted the virus for as long as 1 year. Although the infections were subclinical in the infants, over a third of newly exposed nursing students developed clinical infection. It was found that they could be protected by stricter attention to hand-washing and similar techniques and also by the use of gamma globulin. Very small doses of gamma globulin have been effective in preventing the spread of hepatitis in family groups and in institutions.

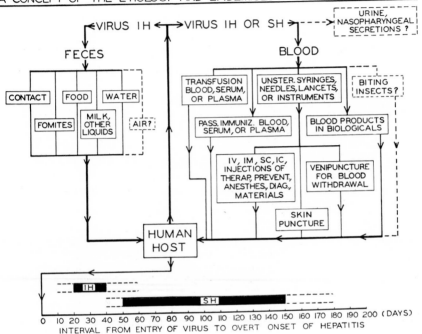

A CONCEPT OF THE ETIOLOGY AND EPIDEMIOLOGY OF VIRAL HEPATITIS

Fig. 34·8 The spread of viral hepatitis. (*Courtesy of Dr. J. R. Neefe, from New England J. Med. 240:445.*)

The Virus of Serum Hepatitis. The SH virus is spread, as far as we know, only by blood. Its transmission is the result of some medical procedure. Spread by insects is a possibility but has not been indicated by epidemiologic evidence. The various procedures believed to be incriminated are shown in Fig. 34·8. The incubation period for the SH virus is from 50 to 150 days. Cases due to the improper sterilization of needles and syringes and to poor techniques of blood transfusions, parenteral therapy, etc., can be prevented by the substitution of good techniques. Rejection of donors having histories of recent jaundice or of exposure to epidemics of the infections does not entirely eliminate the danger, because the virus is present during the incubation period and in many atypical, undiagnosed cases. Sera and serum products produced by biological supply houses, antitoxin laboratories, and blood banks may transmit the viruses. However there is no evidence that hepatitis viruses are spread by such blood fractions as gamma globulin or albumin. It has been the practice to treat plasma by ultraviolet irradiation to inactivate any virus that may be present. This has not proved entirely satisfactory. Holding the plasma at 37°C. for 3 to 12 months is believed by some to be a better method.

THE VIRUSES OF INFLUENZA

Characteristics of the Viruses. The influenza virus particle is spherical and averages slightly less than 100 mμ in size (Fig. 34·9). A smaller, soluble

a　　　　　　　　　　　　　　　　*b*

FIG. 34·9　Electron micrographs of influenza virus. (*a*) Virus air-dried and therefore flattened. ×50,000. (*b*) Frozen-dried virus showing true dimensions. ×50,000. (*Courtesy of Dr. R. C. Williams, from Cold Spring Harbor Symposium, 18:190.*)

particle which may be found in cultures is antigenic but not infectious. It may be provirus that has been released with the virus. The influenza virus grows well in the chick embryo and in tissue cultures. Ferrets are susceptible to the virus. Mice and hamsters can be infected with virus from ferrets and eggs. Its ability to agglutinate red blood cells has already been noted.

Types of Influenza Virus. Epidemics of influenza are usually caused by viruses belonging to the groups designated as *A* (*Tarpeia alpha*) or *A prime* (*A'*). In interepidemic periods viruses of group *B* (*Tarpeia beta*) are more often encountered. A third group, *C*, has been found in a few epidemics. Within each group there are many strains. The A-prime viruses are similar antigenetically to the A strains, but there are no common antigens between the A and B strains.

The influenza viruses of the A groups show extraordinary ability to develop variants. This can be readily demonstrated in the laboratory. Study by laboratories affiliated with WHO indicate that such variation is constantly taking place in the viruses as they exist in the infected human population.

The Disease. Sporadic cases of influenza are usually mild and often not definitely diagnosed. Epidemics occur when a variant appears in a population that contains many persons susceptible to the new strain. The viruses attack the epithelial tissues lining respiratory passages. The cells undergo rapid destruction over limited areas and then quickly regenerate. Pneumonic complications are sometimes caused by the direct effect of the virus on lung tissue. Micrococci, pneumococci, hemolytic streptococci, and *Hemophilus influenzae* are frequent secondary invaders in the pneumonias associated with severe influenza.

Several times in the last century pandemics of influenza have swept over the world. The latest pandemic, in 1918–1919, is estimated to have totaled over 600 million cases and 20 million deaths. At that time methods were not available for the study of the virus. It is believed that an unusually virulent form of the influenza virus arose in the fighting area of western France in April, 1918. Three epidemic waves spread the infection as far as India and New Zealand. Only a few isolated island communities escaped.

Control. Influenza control must include methods of preventing the spread of the usual forms of the disease and also long-range plans for dealing with any threatened pandemic. Public health measures such as isolation and quarantine are not effective. Present methods of vaccination are useful but not entirely satisfactory. Careful nursing procedures may help to protect contacts.

Vaccination. Egg-cultured virus killed by formalin is used. In order to provide protection against a wide range of influenza viruses, the vaccine is made up of several strains of A and A-prime viruses and a strain of B type. The inoculation is given subcutaneously. Immunity lasts only a few months. The vaccine may fail to immunize against a new strain of virus of markedly different antigenic composition. It is believed that the duration of immunity may be prolonged by adding an adjuvant to the vaccine. A search is also being made for strains of A and A-prime viruses that will give a wider protection against all the antigenic components of these groups.

Strains of viruses isolated from cases all over the world are now sent to England to the central influenza laboratory of WHO. Here the strains are typed and a study is made of the reported attack rates and death rates. If a virulent variant should be found associated with an epidemic of severe influenza somewhere in the world, other countries would be alerted. They would be advised to incorporate the new strain in their vaccines and to be on the watch for the possible spread of the epidemic.

Nursing Techniques. When influenza epidemics occur, hospital personnel must be protected against acquiring the infection from patients, and patients must be protected against acquiring dangerous secondary bacterial infections from other patients. Face masks, if properly worn, help protect nurses, doctors, and bedside visitors. The virus is susceptible to the action of aerosols and ultraviolet light, and these should be used in the wards. Careful nursing technique will prevent spread of secondary infections. Cases of influenza pneumonia should be separated from uncomplicated cases. Beds in influenza wards should be "spaced out" to prevent cross infection by air.

Laboratory Diagnosis. Most cases of influenza are diagnosed solely on the basis of the clinical picture. Laboratory diagnosis may be needed in sporadic cases. The isolation and typing of the virus is a very essential part of the study of an epidemic.

Isolation of the Virus. Throat washings are collected from the patient. Penicillin and streptomycin are added to inhibit the growth of bacterial contaminants, and the material is inoculated into several fertile eggs. After 38 to 48 hours virus can be detected in the egg fluids by hemagglutination tests.

Identification of the Virus. The hemagglutination-inhibition technique is used to determine the type of influenza virus or to differentiate it from the mumps virus. If the virus is type A, it will not agglutinate the red cells when type A antiserum is added, but its red-cell-agglutinating ability will not be affected by the addition of type B antiserum or mumps antiserum. (See Fig. 33·8.)

Serologic Diagnosis. Two specimens of the patient's serum are sent to the laboratory. One is collected as early in the disease as possible, the other 2 weeks later. A rise in complement-fixation titer or in hemagglutination-inhibition titer indicates influenza infection.

THE VIRUS OF THE COMMON COLD

So-called *common colds* include a variety of relatively mild upper respiratory infections. Three types probably due to viruses have been described in a very thorough study of infections produced experimentally in volunteers. These are (1) the common cold which has a one- or two-day incubation period and little fever; (2) an undifferentiated respiratory infection which has an incubation period of 5 days and is usually accompanied by sore throat and fever; (3) the mild case of primary atypical pneumonia (see page 450), which has a longer incubation period, some degree of pneumonitis, and is successfully treated by antibiotics. In addition many nonepidemic cases of influenza may be misdiagnosed as severe colds.

Although uncomplicated colds are mild infections of limited duration, they cause the majority of absences from school, offices, and factories. Colds predispose to chronic infections such as sinusitis and to acute respiratory infections such as bronchial pneumonia. Persons with colds spread, by their coughing and sneezing, not only the cold virus but also dangerous strains of pneumococci, streptococci, and other respiratory pathogens.

The Viruses. Filtrates of nose and throat washings from persons with typical colds will cause similar infections in about fifty per cent of persons inoculated. Chimpanzees are also susceptible, but no other animals. Filtration experiments indicate that the virus is of relatively small size. Some investigators have been able to cultivate cold virus in the chick embryo; others have reported repeated failures. It is possible that they were working with different viruses.

Prevention of Colds. The sources of colds are persons with clinical cases of the disease, persons in unrecognized early stages of the disease, and possibly carriers. The spread is by droplets, droplet nuclei, etc. Ideally every person with a cold should be kept in bed for 2 or 3 days beginning with the first appearance of symptoms. The nurse who feels herself "coming down with a cold" should report it immediately and be relieved from duty. Limitation of visitors to sick children and to persons suffering from certain diseases such as rheumatic fever is advisable during seasons when colds are prevalent.

Cold Vaccines. The preparations that have been known as cold vaccines are not antigenic preparations of the viruses, but rather mixtures of bacteria common in the complications of colds. Streptococci, pneumococci, and micrococci have usually been included. There is no evidence that they prevent colds and little evidence that they make the infections less severe.

Carefully controlled studies have failed to support the alleged effectiveness of antihistaminic drugs in the treatment of colds. Antibiotics have no effect on colds. In fact no known method of drug therapy can be shown to alter the course of a cold. Two or more days of rest in bed protects contacts against the patient's microorganisms and the patient against secondary infections.

VIRUSES ATTACKING LYMPH NODES AND GLANDS

Viruses that have a predilection for lymphoid and glandular tissue include those of mumps, infectious mononucleosis, and inclusion disease.

The Virus of Mumps (Rabula inflans). The virus of mumps is comparatively large, 150 to 200 mμ. No animals can be infected except certain monkeys. The virus can be grown in the chick embryo. It is readily destroyed by heat and by formalin.

The Disease. Since the virus usually causes acute inflammation of the parotid glands, the disease is also called *infectious parotitis.* Some degree of inflammation of the testis (*orchitis*) is common in adolescent and adult males. Inflammation of the ovaries is less common. Mumps meningoencephalitis is the most common complication. In some cases orchitis, or meningo-encephalitis, may occur without any signs of salivary gland infection.

The disease is transmitted by infected saliva. Missed cases and early cases are the usual sources of infection. While infants should be protected against the disease, it is generally considered desirable that school children be exposed in order to protect them from more severe infections in adolescence.

Immunity. Vaccination with chick embryo virus inactivated by formalin or irradiation or with egg-passage attenuated virus has been shown to be effective. However no vaccine is in common use. Convalescent serum is sometimes used for passive immunization or therapy. Its effectiveness is doubtful. A skin test can be done to distinguish those who have had the disease (positive reaction) and those who have not been infected (negative reaction). It is of no help in diagnosis.

The Virus of Infectious Mononucleosis. Little is known of the agent causing this infectious disease of children and younger adults. The disease is characterized by sore throat, enlarged lymph nodes, and sometimes by a rash. The blood contains an excessive number of lymphocytes and they are abnormal in appearance. An unusual antibody that agglutinates sheep erythrocytes (*heterophil antibody*) is present. The disease has not been readily transferred experimentally and its natural modes of spread are not known.

The Virus of Inclusion Disease. Many rodents are susceptible to viruses that cause subclinical infections resulting in intranuclear inclusions in cells of the salivary gland and other tissues. Similar bodies have been found in the cells of children with fatal liver disease. The virus may be latent in adults, since the inclusions have been found in stillborn infants.

THE COXSACKIE VIRUSES

In 1948 Dalldorf and Sickel of the New York State Laboratories reported the discovery of a new type of virus from the feces of two children of the village of Coxsackie, New York. Since then viruses of this group have been shown to cause several acute, nonfatal infections including *pleurodynia, herpangina,* and *3-day fever.* These viruses are also known as the *C viruses.*

Characteristics of the Viruses. The sizes of various types of C virus have been reported as from 15 to 35 mμ. They are resistant to the action of phenol, ether, alcohol, Lysol, and Roccal but are inactivated by weak acid and by formaldehyde. They have been found in sewage and in flies, as well as in feces and in throat swabbings. Monkeys can be infected. Newborn (suckling) mice are very susceptible to the infection but become resistant by the time they are a week or two old. The viruses also grow well in the chick embryo and in tissue cultures.

Groups and Types. Twelve or more serologic types have been placed in Group A. The viruses of this group cause a rapid degeneration of striated muscle in the infected suckling mice. A smaller number of types make up Group B. They affect the pancreas, heart muscle, and other internal organs, as well as the skeletal muscle. The types are determined by serologic tests. The virus (antigen) is usually a suspension of infected brain tissue from the suckling mouse. Specific antiserum (antibody) is obtained from adult mice immunized by several doses of type-specific virus. Complement-fixation tests and neutralization tests on groups of suckling mice are both useful. It is also possible to type a virus by inoculating it into litters of suckling mice born of mothers immunized to specific types.

Infections Due to C Viruses. *Herpangina.* The illness is a brief fever associated with herpeslike lesions in the throat and back of the mouth. It may occur in epidemics among children. The viruses belong to Group A. Similar short fevers in which no throat lesions are noted are also associated with Group A viruses.

Epidemic Pleurodynia. In Europe this disease has been called *Bornholm disease.* It is also called *epidemic myalgia* because muscle pain is the most important symptom. The pain may be in the chest wall, abdominal wall, or back. Appendicitis or some other condition needing surgical treatment may be suspected. There is also headache and fever.

Other Coxsackie Infections. Epidemics of *summer grippe* (a brief influenzalike infection) have been shown to be due to a Coxsackie virus. Several outbreaks of *aseptic meningitis* have also been caused by these viruses. Cases diagnosed as nonparalytic or mild poliomyelitis have been found on laboratory investigation to be Coxsackie infections.

Epidemiology of C Viruses. There are many subclinical infections with C viruses. Infected persons may continue to excrete the virus in feces for over a month. The virus may also be present in the mouth. Infections and positive specimens are more common during the summer months. There is evidence that the infections are spread from person to person by contact in family groups. Protective antibodies against C virus strains have been found in adult sera and in gamma globulin preparations from many parts of the world. It is probable that most people acquire immunity to the various types by chance mild or inapparent infections in childhood.

STUDY SUGGESTIONS

Summarize the chief facts about smallpox, measles, yellow fever, influenza, and the common cold. Use the following headings: *Character of disease, Character of virus, Methods of spread, Methods of immunization, Nursing techniques.*

What other viruses belong to the dermatotropic group? to the viscerotropic group? What are their characteristics?

Several topics in this chapter need extra study and thought. Are you clear about the materials, methods, and results of vaccination against smallpox? What has been your personal vaccination history?

Discuss immunization against influenza, measles, the common cold, yellow fever.

What is the modern conception of cold sore infection?

Virus hepatitis is a perfect example of a "newly discovered" infection. What reasons do we have for thinking there are at least two forms of this disease? If a person develops symptoms of infectious hepatitis, why does the doctor ask if he has had any recent blood transfusions? If a considerable number of dormitory students come down with hepatitis, what would be the most likely sources and modes of infection?

What lines of research are needed to solve the problems of the Coxsackie viruses? influenza? the common cold?

SUGGESTED READING

General References (See also medical texts listed on page 572 and general references on page 476.)

AMERICAN PUBLIC HEALTH ASSOCIATION: "Diagnostic Procedures for Virus and Rickettsial Diseases." New York, 1948.

The Viruses of Smallpox and Vaccinia

BERENSON, A. S.: Immediate (so-called "immune") reaction to smallpox vaccination. *J.A.M.A.* **143**:1238 (1950).

CABASSO, V. J., *et al.*: Primary response of children to glycerinated or dried vaccines of calf lymph or chick embryo origin. *Am. J. Pub. Health* **44**:194 (1954).

DOWNIE, A. W.: Infection and immunity in smallpox. *Lancet* **1**:419 (1951).

GAYLORD, W. H., JR., and J. L. MELNICK: Intracellular forms of pox viruses as shown by the electron microscope. *J. Exper. Med.* **98**:157 (1953).

MACCALLUM, F. O.: Early Diagnosis of Smallpox, in "Dynamics of Virus and Rickettsial Infections." Blakiston, New York, 1954.

SMADEL, J. E., and C. L. HOAGLAND: Elementary bodies of vaccinia. *Bact. Rev.* **6**:79 (1942).

WEINSTEIN, L.: An outbreak of smallpox in New York City. *Am. J. Pub. Health* **37**:1376 (1947).

The Virus of Chickenpox

BLANK, H., *et al.*: Cytologic smears in diagnosis of herpes simplex, herpes zoster, and varicella. *J.A.M.A.* **146**:1410 (1951).

RAKE, G., *et al.:* The relationship of varicella and herpes zoster: electron microscope studies. *J. Bact.* **56:**293 (1948).

WELLER, T. H., and A. H. COONS: Fluorescent antibody studies with agent of varicella and herpes simplex propagated in vitro. *Proc. Soc. Exper. Biol. & Med.* **84:**789 (1954).

The Virus of Herpes Simplex

BURNET, F. M.: "Virus as Organism." Harvard University Press, Cambridge, Mass., 1945. Chap. IV.

SCOTT, T. F. M., A. J. STEIGMAN, and J. CONVEY: Acute infectious gingivostomatitis. *J.A.M.A.* **117:**999 (1941).

The Viruses of Measles

JANEWAY, C. S.: Clinical use of products of human plasma fractionation: (1) gammaglobulin in measles. *J.A.M.A.* **126:**678 (1944).

TOWSLEY, H. A.: Measles. *Am. J. Nursing* **47:**278 (1947).

WESSELHOEFT, C.: Medical progress: Rubella (German measles) and congenital deformities. *New England J. Med.* **240:**258 (1949).

The Virus of Yellow Fever and Dengue

DICK, G. W. A., and K. C. SMITHBURN: Immunity to yellow fever six years after vaccination. *Am. J. Trop. Med.* **29:**57 (1949).

ELTON, N. W.: Public health aspects of the campaign against yellow fever. *Am. J. Pub. Health* **42:**170 (1952).

HAVENS, W. P.: Hepatitis, Yellow Fever and Dengue, in "Annual Review of Microbiology." Vol. 8, Annual Reviews, Inc., Stanford, 1954.

SABIN, A. B.: The dengue group of viruses and its family relationships. *Bact. Rev.* **14:**225 (1950).

STRODE, G. K.: "Yellow Fever." McGraw-Hill, New York, 1951.

WORLD HEALTH ORGANIZATION: "Yellow Fever: Report of First Session." WHO Tech. Rep. No. 19, 1950.

The Viruses of Hepatitis

ALLEN, J. G., *et al.:* Homologous serum jaundice and its relation to methods of plasma storage. *J.A.M.A.* **144:**1069 (1950).

CAPPS, R. B., and J. STOKES, JR.: Epidemiology of infectious hepatitis and problems of prevention and control. *J.A.M.A.* **149:**557 (1952).

HENLE, W., *et al.:* Studies on the agent of infectious hepatitis. I. Propagation of the agent in tissue culture and in the embryonated hen's egg. *J. Exper. Med.* **92:**271 (1950).

KUH, C., and W. E. WARD: Occupational virus hepatitis; an apparent hazard for medical personnel. *J.A.M.A.* **143:**631 (1950).

NEEFE, J. R.: Viral hepatitis. *New England J. Med.* **240**:445 (1949).

ROSENTHAL, N., *et al.:* Probable transmission of viral hepatitis by ultra-violet-irradiated plasma. *J.A.M.A.* **144**:224 (1950). First of three articles on irradiated plasma.

STOKES, J., JR., *et al.:* Infectious hepatitis: length of protection by immune serum globulin (gamma globulin) during epidemics. *J.A.M.A.* **147**:714 (1951).

The Viruses of Influenza

ANDREWES, C. H.: Adventures among viruses. II. Epidemic influenza. *New England J. Med.* **242**:197 (1950).

BRIODY, B. A.: Variation in influenza viruses. *Bact. Rev.* **14**:65 (1950).

COMMISSION ON ACUTE RESPIRATORY DISEASES (U.S. Army): Studies on the 1943 epidemic of influenza A. *Am. J. Hyg.* **48**:253 (1948). First of a series of articles.
————: Endemic influenza. *Am. J. Hyg.* **47**:290 (1948).

CULBERTSON, J. T.: Plans for United States cooperation with the WHO in the international influenza study program. *Am. J. Pub. Health* **39**:37 (1949).

FRANCIS, T., JR., J. J. QUILLIGAN, and E. MINUSE: Identification of another epidemic respiratory disease. *Science* **112**:495 (1950).

JORDAN, W. S.: Acute upper respiratory tract infections. *Am. J. Nursing* **50**:39 (1950).

REIMANN, H. A.: Viral infections of the respiratory tract. *J.A.M.A.* **132**:487 (1947).

SALK, J. E.: Use of adjuvants in studies on influenza immunization. *J.A.M.A.* **151**:1169 (1953).

TAYLOR, R. M.: Studies on survival of influenza virus between epidemics and antigenic variants of the virus. *Am. J. Pub. Health* **39**:171 (1949).

The Virus of the Common Cold

ANDREWES, C. H.: Adventures among the viruses. III. The puzzle of the common cold. *New England J. Med.* **242**:235 (1950).

COMMISSION ON ACUTE RESPIRATORY DISEASES (U.S. Army): Experimental transmission of minor respiratory illness to human volunteers by filter-passing agents. *J. Clin. Investigation* **26**:957, 974 (1947).

COUNCIL ON PHARMACY AND CHEMISTRY (American Medical Association): Status report on antihistaminic agents in the prophylaxis and treatment of the common cold. *J.A.M.A.* **142**:566 (1950).

WARD, T. G., and D. F. PROCTOR: Isolation of a common cold virus in chick embryos and the clinical manifestations it produces in human volunteers. *Am. J. Hyg.* **52**:91 (1950).

Viruses Attacking Lymph Nodes and Glands

BOLTON, W.: Rival of the common cold. *Hygeia* **28**:52 (1950). Mononucleosis.

HABEL, K.: Vaccination of human beings against mumps; vaccine administered at the start of an epidemic. *Am. J. Hyg.* **54:**295, 312 (1951).

HENLE, G., *et al.*: Isolation of mumps virus from human beings with induced apparent or inapparent infections. *J. Exper. Med.* **88:**223 (1948).

RAMBAR, A. C.: Mumps. *Am. J. Nursing* **48:**86 (1948).

WESSELHOEFT, C.: Mumps. *New England J. Med.* **226:**530 (1942).

The Coxsackie Viruses

BRIEFS, A., *et al.*: Physical properties of two groups of A Coxsackie viruses when propagated in eggs and mice as determined by ultracentrifugation and electron microscopy. *J. Bact.* **64:**237 (1952).

CONTRERAS, G., V. H. BARNETT, and J. L. MELNICK: Identification of Coxsackie viruses by immunological methods and their classification into 16 antigenically distinct types. *J. Immunol.* **69:**395 (1952).

DALLDORF, G., and R. GIFFORD: Clinical and epidemiologic observations of Coxsackie virus infections. *New England J. Med.* **244:**868 (1951).

HUEBNER, R. J., *et al.*: The importance of Coxsackie viruses in human disease, particularly herpangina and epidemic pleurodynia. *New England J. Med.* **247:**249, 285 (1952).

The Neurotropic Viruses

The viruses that attack the nervous system are considered in this chapter.

THE VIRUS OF RABIES

Rabies is a fatal brain infection that can attack all kinds of mammals and birds.

The Virus. The virus of rabies (*Formido inexorabilis*) is 100 to 150 mμ in size. Characteristic cell inclusions known as *Negri bodies* are found in the infected brain. The virus also multiplies in the salivary glands. Dogs, rabbits, and white mice are generally used in the laboratory study of the virus. The virus has also been grown in tissue cultures and in the chick embryo.

Rabies virus is resistant to the action of ether, phenol, and many other chemicals. It is quickly inactivated by ultraviolet irradiation and slowly inactivated by drying.

Like all viruses the rabies virus is capable of variation. There are three important types of the virus. (1) The *street virus* is the form which is found in naturally infected dogs and other animals. This is the form which man acquires from rabid animals. (2) The *fixed virus* was first produced by Pasteur, who passed street virus serially in rabbits by intracerebral inoculation of brain tissue. Eventually a stabilized virus was produced that is relatively less virulent for man. (3) *Avianized virus* is the name given to strains that have been adapted to growth in the yolk sac of the chick embryo. The *Flury strain* is the one most used.

The Disease. Man is infected by the bite of a rabid animal. The virus spreads from the wound to the central nervous system. It is believed that the virus reaches the brain by passing along peripheral nerves. Spread through the blood is also a possibility. The incubation period is from 15 days to 5 months. It is shortest in persons bitten on the face. Large amounts of virus inoculated by the bite shorten the incubation period. After 2 or 3 days of prodromal symptoms, encephalitis develops, accompanied by paralysis, delirium, and convulsions. Death occurs within 10 days.

Sources of Infection. The rabid dog is the usual source of rabies in man. Some people in this country have been infected by skunks, cats, or squirrels. Epizootics of rabies occur in many wild animals that may or may not bite man. The disease is present in foxes in several parts of this country and from them is spread to cattle and dogs. The only known animal that does not die from rabies infection is the vampire bat. It is possible that this animal is the natural host of rabies and the reservoir from which the disease spreads to other animal hosts.

Control. The two methods of rabies control are the elimination of the disease from the animal population and the immediate treatment of persons known to be exposed to rabies.

Protection of the Exposed Person. Local Treatment. The wound and surrounding skin should be immediately scrubbed thoroughly with 20 per cent tincture of green soap. This removes the virus.

Vaccination. The long incubation period of rabies permits immunization after exposure to the disease. The vaccine used in the *Pasteur treatment* was a preparation of the spinal cords of rabbits infected with fixed virus. The cord material was dried to reduce its virulence. Phenolized preparations from infected brain tissue (*Semple vaccine*) have been widely used. Other chemicals and ultraviolet light have also been used to completely or partially inactivate the fixed virus preparations. The *UV vaccine* is irradiated fixed virus preserved with merthiolate. Avianized virus grown in tissue culture is the newest vaccine. The virus is not inactivated. Daily injections of vaccine are given by subcutaneous inoculation for a period of 2 to 3 weeks.

Passive Immunization. Antirabies serum is prepared by immunization of sheep. Extensive laboratory tests have shown that it is very effective in preventing rabies in laboratory animals and in man. One large dose is given intramuscularly as soon as possible (Fig. 35·1). Active immunization with vaccine is begun 24 hours later.

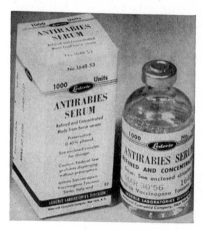

FIG. 35·1 Antirabies serum for immediate passive immunization. (*Lederle Laboratories Division, American Cyanamid Company.*)

Indications for Immunization. It is not considered desirable to vaccinate every person who has had contact with a rabid animal. Vaccination is an expensive and disagreeable experience. Various forms of paralysis, sometimes fatal, occasionally result from vaccination. Only 5 to 15 per cent of bites by rabid dogs result in rabies infection. There may be no virus in the saliva or too little to initiate infection. Bites through clothing seldom result in infection. Immunization should always be done if the victim is bitten by a dog that has clinical rabies or by an uncaptured dog if rabies is endemic in the locality. It should be started on persons severely bitten in the face or hands even if the dog appears normal. The dog must be quarantined. If the animal shows no signs of illness within 7 to 10 days, the treatment can be stopped. The Expert Committee on Rabies of the WHO has recently outlined standard criteria for vaccination (see reference at end of this chapter). Now that rabies antiserum is available commercially, the single dose of antiserum is increasingly used for protection in borderline cases—for example when abraded skin has been licked by a possibly rabid dog.

Control of Rabies in Animals. Muzzling dogs or keeping them on leashes may be required by laws or local ordinances, but such measures are very hard to enforce. Yearly vaccination of dogs is a much more effective measure. A single dose of active avianized vaccine is used (Fig. 35·2). Elimination of the disease in wild animals is much more difficult. It has been accomplished in limited areas, by shooting, trapping, and poisoning.

Nursing Care. Although the spread of rabies from person to person is practically unknown, it is possible. The patient's saliva may be infected. He should not be allowed to kiss anyone. Any saliva that gets on the skin of an attendant should be immediately washed off with strong soap solution.

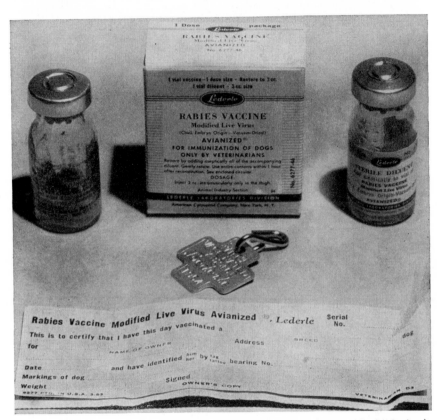

FIG. 35·2 Rabies vaccine for active immunization of dogs (living avianized virus). Tag is placed on dog's collar after vaccination. (*Lederle Laboratories Division, American Cyanamid Company.*)

Laboratory Diagnosis. Laboratory diagnosis is directed primarily at detecting the disease in animals that have bitten human beings. The animal's head is sent to the laboratory. Bits of tissue from definite areas of the brain are smeared on slides and stained by *Seller's method.* They are examined for the presence of Negri bodies. (See Fig. 35·3.) Emulsified brain tissue is inoculated into the cerebrum of several white mice. If the rabies virus is present, the mice die within 5 to 10 days and Negri bodies are abundant in their brain tissue. This mouse inoculation test discloses the virus in many

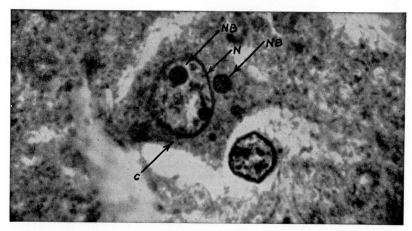

FIG. 35·3 Negri bodies. ×1,500. The large nerve cell (*C*) from a human brain contains Negri bodies (*NB*) in its cytoplasm and in its nucleus (*N*). (*From Burrows, "Textbook of Microbiology," Saunders.*)

dog brains where the Negri bodies cannot be found. The diagnosis of the disease in man is confirmed by similar examination of the brain after death.

THE VIRUSES OF POLIOMYELITIS

Poliomyelitis means inflammation of the gray matter of the spinal cord. The disease is also called *infantile paralysis*. Both names are misleading. The brain stem, as well as the spinal cord, is infected. The infection is by no means limited to infants, nor is paralysis always present.

The Viruses. The viruses of poliomyelitis (*Legio debilitans*) are spherical particles of about 25 mμ in diameter (Fig. 35·4).

Types and Strains. There are three distinct types of poliomyelitis viruses. Each type includes a number of strains. The types are known by numbers or by the name of the first strain described. Type I, the *Brunhilde* type, is the one that has been most frequently found in American epidemics. Type II, called the *Lansing* type, is seldom found in epidemics. Type III, the *Leon* type, has been found in epidemics in some parts of the country. The strains of the Lansing type can be adapted to rodents. Types I and III infect only man, monkeys, and chimpanzees. Neutralization tests indicate that the types are antigenically different.

Cultivation. For many years experimental and diagnostic laboratory studies on infantile paralysis were done entirely on monkeys, for no other method of cultivation was known. For the last 10 years much experimental work has been done using the Lansing viruses in rats. In 1949 Dr. John Enders of Boston announced that the virus could be cultivated in tissue cultures of human origin. The techniques by which all poliomyelitis viruses are grown in such tissue cultures were described in Chap. 33 (page 458). Tissue culture techniques have been widely adopted and are used for practically all recent research as well as for laboratory diagnosis and the preparation and testing of the new vaccines.

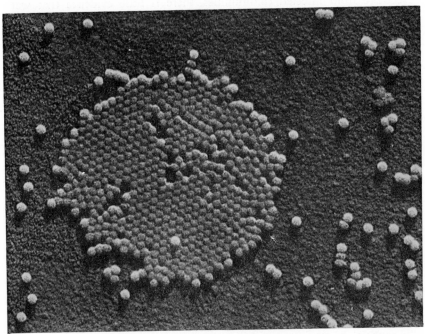

Fig. 35·4 Virus of poliomyelitis. Electron micrograph. ×85,000. (*Courtesy of Dr. R. C. Williams, from Proc. Soc. Exper. Biol. & Med. 86:310.*)

Resistance to Chemical and Physical Agents. Surface-active agents such as Zephiran do not inactivate the virus. It is resistant to alcohol and ether. Iodine (2 per cent) is quickly virucidal. The concentration of chlorine used in disinfection of water is sufficient to inactivate the virus. Prolonged exposure to formalin is used to destroy the virus in vaccine preparations. Ultraviolet radiation has been used for the same purpose. Mercury compounds are also effective. The virus is destroyed by 3 minutes' exposure to 50°C.

Infection with Poliomyelitis Virus. The virus is discharged from the nasopharynx early in the infection. The feces of patients contain the virus from the time of onset until a month or so later. Recognized cases are less important as sources of infection than missed cases and contact carriers. Epidemiologic evidence points to personal contact within the family group as the chief mode of infection. Flies can be infected by feeding on feces in the laboratory. The virus has been recovered from flies caught in epidemic areas. The fact that the height of the fly season coincides with the season of maximum incidence of the disease has led some authorities to believe that the insects are important factors in the spread of the disease. Although the virus is present in sewage from infected communities, there is little evidence that water is important in the spread of the disease.

Clinical Varieties of Infection. Infection with the virus results in subclinical infection, nonparalytic disease, or paralytic disease.

Subclinical infection (abortive infection) is a short minor illness with fever and headache. Ninety-nine of every 100 infections are of this sort. The virus does not reach the central nervous system. Immunity is developed which protects against future infection with the same strain of virus.

Nonparalytic disease is an aseptic meningitis. The central nervous system is involved and the patient is often drowsy and has a stiff neck and back. This is the usual form of the disease when the infection spreads to the nervous system. There is no residual paralysis. Immunity is gained by the infection.

Paralytic poliomyelitis develops in an occasional case of poliomyelitis infection. There is flaccid paralysis of one or more muscle groups. The development of paralysis comes after a 1- to 2-week period of incubation and often follows stages resembling the subclinical infection and nonparalytic infection. The paralysis is due to the injury to the cell bodies of the motor neurones, the cells that have the final direction of all skeletal muscle. The paralysis varies in distribution and in severity. It persists after the acute infection is over.

Spread of the Virus in the Body. The virus probably enters the body by being ingested. There are two principal theories as to how it reaches the brain and spinal cord. One theory pictures the virus as invading the nerve endings in the nose, pharynx, and intestine, and then traveling via the nerves to the central nervous system. Recent laboratory and epidemiologic studies give greater support to a second theory. The virus is believed to multiply first in the mucous membranes of the pharynx and intestine. Then it spreads to the blood and finally may reach the nervous system. In abortive cases it is thought that antibodies develop rapidly in the blood and prevent the virus from spreading to the nervous system.

Factors Predisposing to Paralytic Disease. A number of factors seem to increase the possibility that the virus will reach the nervous system and cause paralysis. One is age. Paralysis is usually mild or absent in infants and small children. The second is exertion. Fatigue and muscular exercise after the infection has begun seem to increase the chance of severe paralysis. Other factors that have been shown to predispose to paralytic disease are operations such as tooth extractions and tonsillectomies, diphtheria and tetanus vaccinations, trauma as from a fall, and pregnancy.

Treatment and Nursing Care. There is no evidence that any serum or antibiotic influences the course of poliomyelitis.

No other acute communicable disease needs more exacting nursing care than the acute stage of poliomyelitis. In addition to orthopedic techniques and psychotherapy which cannot be discussed here, the nurse must practice complete precautions against both respiratory and enteric spread of the virus. Patients should have separate cubicles if possible. No patient with a doubtful diagnosis should be placed in a ward with known cases of poliomyelitis.

The nurse herself may not be immune to the strain infecting her patients. It may be advisable to protect young nursing students against infection by the use of gamma globulin. It can probably be assumed that more experienced nurses already possess protective antibodies. As soon as satisfactory vaccines are available, all nursing students will presumably be immunized at the start of their training.

After-care cases of poliomyelitis such as the nurse meets in orthopedic work are no longer infectious.

Control. Recognized cases should be isolated for 1 week from onset, or for the duration of any fever that may persist longer than 1 week. Quarantine of contacts has not proved useful. Exposed children should avoid overexertion and should not have tonsillectomies, vaccinations, etc.

Immunity. It is probable that most people become immune to all three types of poliomyelitis virus as the result of subclinical infections in childhood. Protective antibodies can be detected in the blood of most adults.

Passive Immunization. Gamma globulin from pooled human serum contains poliomyelitis antibodies. If given to monkeys before the viremia stage of the infection, it prevents the virus from reaching the central nervous system. There is considerable experimental and clinical evidence that it similarly prevents paralytic poliomyelitis in man. Special lots of human gamma globulin that have been tested for the presence of poliomyelitis antibodies are available for the passive immunization of children and pregnant women who have been intimately exposed to the infection. The resulting immunity is, of course, of short duration. Large scale use of gamma globulin for mass immunization before expected epidemics has been tried with some success. This measure has, however, been supplanted by active immunization with vaccine.

Active Immunization. In the past a number of antipoliomyelitis vaccines have been tested on monkeys and a few on children. None have proved both effective and safe. The tissue culture method of cultivation has opened the way for better methods of producing and testing poliomyelitis antigens.

By 1952 Dr. Jonas Salk of Pittsburgh had produced a vaccine that he found to be safe in trials on monkeys and man. The vaccine contains three strains of the virus, one of each type, grown in monkey kidney tissue cultures and inactivated by formalin. Tests show that this vaccine causes appreciable rises in antibody in vaccinated monkeys and people. In 1954 several hundred thousand primary school children were given the vaccine. Comparable groups of unvaccinated children served as controls.

In spring 1955 a committee of experts, after studying the incidence of clinical infection, paralysis, and deaths among these children, concluded that the vaccination was 60 per cent effective in preventing the clinical infection and 90 per cent effective in preventing paralytic disease. A widespread immunization program began immediately.

At this time (fall of 1955) it is impossible to state definitely what the results have been on the incidence of the disease during the summer of 1955. The late start and inconsistencies of the program in many communities have meant that many children were not truly immunized by the start of the epidemic season. The discovery of incompletely inactivated virus in a few batches of the vaccine alarmed both the public and the medical professions. The more consistent program in Canada has apparently resulted in definite reduction of clinical disease and paralysis among the vaccinated children there.

No one believes that the present vaccine is the best one possible. Dr. Salk reports that vaccine with added adjuvant will produce a more durable immunity. Ultraviolet irradiated vaccine is being tested. Many competent virologists believe that the most effective vaccine must be one made from active viruses and are working to produce antigenic but avirulent varieties of all three types.

Laboratory Diagnosis. There are no simple in vitro tests for the laboratory diagnosis of poliomyelitis. For many years the only test for the virus was the inoculation of monkeys; the only method for the detection of specific antibody in the patient's serum was its ability to protect a monkey against infection. Now tissue cultures are used instead of monkeys.

Fecal specimens are examined for the presence of the virus. Antibiotics are added to the fluid from a centrifugalized suspension of the feces to destroy bacteria present. Tissue cultures are then inoculated and later observed for typical cytopathic changes. The virus is then typed by transfer to cultures protected by type-specific antisera. Paired specimens of serum are examined for increase in specific antibody. This is done by protection tests that measure the amount of the patient's serum that will prevent infection in tissue cultures inoculated with definite amounts of each type of virus. The titer of neutralizing antibody in the "convalescent" specimen should be several times that found in the acute-stage specimen. Complement-fixing antibody in the patient's serum specimens can be measured by tests using tissue-culture-grown virus as the antigen.

At present laboratory diagnosis of poliomyelitis is limited to special reference laboratories usually located in research institutions. Simpler tissue culture methods may soon make them possible in hospital and public health laboratories. This is very desirable. Without accurate, widely used laboratory methods the individual nonparalytic or abortive case cannot be identified. Moreover our understanding of the epidemiology of poliomyelitis depends on the identification of these cases.

THE VIRUSES OF THE ENCEPHALITIDES

Encephalitis (pl. *encephalitides*) is any inflammation of the brain. Since the spinal cord is often involved, the name *encephalomyelitis* is also used. The epidemic virus encephalitides are spread by arthropod vectors from birds and animals to man.

The Important Forms of Virus Encephalitides. Three varieties of these infections are recognized in this country.

St. Louis Encephalitis. Since 1933, when an epidemic of over 1,000 cases occurred in and around St. Louis, this form has been endemic in the region, and cases have been identified from other parts of the United States.

Western Equine Encephalitis. The virus of this disease was first discovered in infected horses in California in 1930. Cases in animals and man have been reported throughout the United States west of the Appalachian Mountains.

Eastern Equine Encephalitis. A type of equine disease more severe in its effects on man occurs east of the Appalachians. Human cases were first identified in 1938.

The Viruses. The virus of eastern equine encephalitis (*Erro equinus*) is approximately 20 to 30 mμ in diameter. It is spherical and sometimes shows internal round or oblong bodies (Fig. 35·5). It is destroyed by heat and formalin but is resistant to the action of cold, glycerol, phenol, and many other chemicals. The western equine virus and the St. Louis virus (*Erro scelestus*) are very similar. All these viruses can be grown in laboratory animals, in the fertile egg, and in tissue cultures.

Epidemic Encephalitis Disease. An almost endless list of birds, rodents, and wild and domestic animals, large and small, have been found infected in nature or shown to be infectible. The over-all picture is rather confusing, but it is probable that the natural hosts are mites and ticks that parasitize birds. The viruses can be passed on transovarially in these arthropods. Infected birds are bitten by various species of mosquitoes, which then spread the disease to animals and man. Epidemics of human disease occur when the disease is prevalent in birds or animals and some mosquito that feeds on both the animal host and on man is abundant in the community. There is no evidence of person-to-person spread.

As in poliomyelitis, epidemics seem to include many abortive cases as well as those that are clinically recognized. The severe case is characterized by headache, fever, mental confusion, and other signs of cerebral involvement. Sequelae such as mental retardation, spastic paralysis, muscular tremors, etc., may persist, particularly after attacks of the equine type. No specific treatment is known.

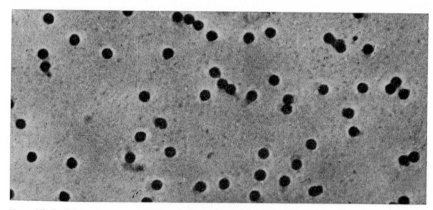

FIG. 35·5 The virus of equine encephalomyelitis. Electron micrograph. ×100,000. (*SAB print 140, courtesy of Dr. A. R. Taylor.*)

Laboratory Diagnosis. The Public Health Service provides special services to communities when epidemics occur. Diagnosis of cases is by the demonstration of a rise in mouse-protection antibodies against challenge doses of the specific viruses. The virus is seldom found until after death, when it can be recovered from brain specimens. However it may sometimes be found during the epidemic in mosquitoes or animals.

Control. The animal reservoirs are so numerous and elusive that their control is impossible. Elimination of known mosquito vectors is the best way of protecting the human population.

Vaccines have been used on a large scale to protect horses against the equine infections. They have been used experimentally on man, particularly on laboratory workers. The vaccines are formalinized preparations of chick embryo cultures.

Other Arthropod-borne Encephalitides. Diseases of this sort are found all over the world. Many varieties have been recognized, but few have been extensively studied. One type that has received considerable attention is *Japanese B encephalitis*. Epidemics of this mosquito-borne type have occurred in American forces and civilian populations in Okinawa and South Korea since the Second World War. At least two forms of encephalitis are spread to man by ticks rather than by mosquitoes. *Russian spring-summer* encephalitis is spread by ticks from forest birds and mammals to persons who work in woodlands. *Louping ill* is a serious tick-borne infection of sheep which sometimes attacks man.

Encephalitis Lethargica (von Ecomomo's Disease). This infection has also been called sleeping sickness but it must not be confused with African sleeping sickness which is due to a protozoan (see page 545). There were many cases and deaths from encephalitis lethargica in Europe and North America in the years 1917 to 1925. Few cases have been reported since. Its etiology and sources and modes of infection are unknown.

Postinfection and Postvaccination Encephalitides. Neurologic involvement is often noted in cases of other viral infections. They are particularly common in mumps, measles, chickenpox, and smallpox. Encephalitis has followed smallpox vaccination in a small number of older children. No virus can be found in the central nervous system in cases of postinfection or postvaccination encephalitis. The most generally accepted explanation is that the symptoms and lesions result from an allergic response of nerve tissue to the virus infection.

THE VIRUSES OF LYMPHOCYTIC CHORIOMENINGITIS AND ENCEPHALOMYOCARDITIS

Certain viruses of animals have been considered to be related to the viruses of poliomyelitis. There is little evidence that they are actually so related, but the diseases they cause are similar in some respects. The usual laboratory diagnostic methods distinguish these infections.

The Virus of Lymphocytic Choriomeningitis. The *LCM virus* (*Legio erebea*) causes an inapparent infection of wild and laboratory mice that is transmitted to the suckling mice from their mothers. In man it produces varied symptoms resembling meningitis and influenza. Many cases in man are not diagnosed. Man is infected by ingesting or inhaling organisms from mouse feces and urine. There is little evidence of spread from man to man, but since the virus is present in the patient's excretions, they should be carefully handled and properly disposed of.

Other Neurotropic Viruses. Several viruses of rodents including the *MM virus,* the *SK viruses,* the *EMC* (*encephalomyocarditis*) *virus,* and the *Mengo virus* are responsible for occasional acute infections in man.

Two viruses causing epidemics that in some ways resemble poliomyelitis are the Theiler virus of mice and the Teschen virus of pigs. There is no evidence that they can infect man.

Many research laboratories are isolating the causative viruses from nonparalytic cases of suspected poliomyelitis and atypical cases of meningitis by tissue culture methods. Every once in a while they discover new and as yet unidentified viruses. These viruses have been found not only in specimens from patients ill with these infections but also from tissues of monkeys and man that have been used to make the cultures.

STUDY SUGGESTIONS

Which disease is more preventable, rabies or poliomyelitis? Explain your answer fully. In which disease is laboratory diagnosis more satisfactory? Why? Has either of these diseases appeared in your community? What measures of control were taken?

What types of encephalitis might occur in your community? (Don't forget the para-infection and postinfection types.) Compare these infections with poliomyelitis. In what respects are they similar? In what respects are they different?

From what other forms of meningitis would lymphocytic choriomeningitis have to be distinguished? Review the meningitides and note the laboratory findings that would lead to a diagnosis of each type.

Our leading virologists are increasingly impressed by the relationship of human viral infections to those in animals. They are also impressed by the increasing number of virus diseases that have been shown to have insect vectors. Give as many examples as you can of facts that support these impressions.

SUGGESTED READING

The Virus of Rabies

BERNSTEIN, J.: Portrait of a vampire. *Natural History* **61**:83 (1952).

BLATT, N. H., and M. H. LEPPER: Reactions following antirabies prophylaxis. *Am. J. Dis. Child.* **86**:395 (1953).

KOPROWSKI, H., and H. R. COX: Recent developments in the prophylaxis of rabies. *Am. J. Pub. Health* **41**:1483 (1951).

KORNS, R. F., and A. ZEISSIG: Dog, fox, and cattle rabies in New York State—evaluation of vaccination in dogs. *Am. J. Pub. Health* **38**:97 (1948).

PAIT, C. F., and H. E. PEARSON: Rabies vaccine encephalomyelitis in relation to the incidence of animal rabies in Los Angeles. *Am. J. Pub. Health* **38**:51 (1948).

VENTERS, H. D., *et al.*: Rabies in bats in Florida. *Am. J. Pub. Health* **44**:183 (1954). See also article following this one.

WORLD HEALTH ORGANIZATION, Expert Committee on Rabies: "Report of First Session." WHO Tech. Rep. No. 28, 1950.

The Virus of Poliomyelitis

BACHRACH, H. L., and C. E. SCHWERDT: Purification studies on Lansing poliomyelitis virus. *J. Immunol.* **72**:30 (1954).

BODIAN, D.: Pathogenesis of poliomyelitis. *Am. J. Pub. Health* **42**:1388 (1952).

CASEY, A. E.: Clinical manifestations of infection with poliomyelitis virus. *J.A.M.A.* **138**:865 (1948).

CORALITA, SISTER M., F. BOLES, and M. JACOBSEN: Meeting a poliomyelitis epidemic. *Am. J. Nursing* **63**:935 (1953).

EDITORIAL: Vaccination against poliomyelitis. *New England J. Med.* **253**:155 (1955).

FABER, H. K., and L. DONG: Virucidal activities of some common surface antiseptics with special reference to poliomyelitis. *Am. J. Dis. Child.* **86**:469 (1953).

GREENBERG, M., et al.: The relation between recent injections and paralytic poliomyelitis in children. *Am. J. Pub. Health* **42**:142 (1952).

HORSTMANN, D. M.: Acute poliomyelitis: relation of physical activity at the time of onset to the course of the disease. *J.A.M.A.* **142**:236 (1950).

MELNICK, J. L.: Isolation of poliomyelitis virus from single species of flies collected during an urban epidemic. *Am. J. Hyg.* **49**:8 (1949).

————: Poliomyelitis and Poliomyelitis-like Viruses of Man and Animals, in "Annual Review of Microbiology." Vol. 5, Annual Reviews, Inc., Stanford, 1951.

MILZER, A., et al.: Immunization studies in human subjects of trivalent tissue culture vaccine inactivated by ultraviolet irradiation. *Am. J. Pub. Health* **44**:26 (1954).

NATIONAL FOUNDATION FOR INFANTILE PARALYSIS: "Isolation Techniques and Nursing Care in Poliomyelitis." New York (no date).

SABIN, A. B.: Present status and future possibility of a vaccine for the control of poliomyelitis. *Am. J. Dis. Child.* **86**:301 (1953).

SALK, J. E.: Studies on human subjects on active immunization against poliomyelitis. II. A practical means for inducing and maintaining antibody formation. *Am. J. Pub. Health* **44**:994 (1954).

WELLER, T. H.: Medical progress: the application of tissue-culture methods to the study of poliomyelitis. *New England J. Med.* **249**:186 (1953).

The Viruses of Encephalitis

HALVERSEN, W. L., W. A. LONGSHORE, and R. F. PETERS: The 1952 encephalitis outbreak in California. *Pub. Health Rep.* **68**:369 (1953).

HAMMON, W. M.: The arthropod-borne encephalitides. *Am. J. Trop. Med.* **28**:515 (1948).

OLITSKY, P. K., and J. CASALS: Neutralization tests for diagnosis of human encephalitides. *J.A.M.A.* **134**:1224 (1947).

PEERS, J. H.: Allergic encephalitis and its possible relationship to human disease. *Am. J. Clin. Pathol.* **20**:503 (1950).

REEVES, W. C.: The encephalitis problem in the United States. *Am. J. Pub. Health* **41**:678 (1951).

The Viruses of Lymphocytic Choriomeningitis, Encephalomyocarditis, etc.

DALLDORF, G., C. W. JUNGEBLUT, and M. D. UMPHLET: Multiple cases of chorio-meningitis in an apartment harboring infected mice. *J.A.M.A.* **131**:25 (1946).

DICK, G. W.: The relationship of Mengo encephalomyelitis, encephalomyocarditis, Columbia-Sk and M. M. viruses. *J. Immunol.* **62**:375 (1949). See also the next article in the same issue.

ROBBINS, F. C., *et al.:* Studies on the cultivation of the poliomyelitis virus in tissue culture. V. The direct isolation and serologic identification of virus strains in tissue culture from patients with non-paralytic and paralytic poliomyelitis. *Am. J. Hyg.* **54**:286 (1951).

SMADEL, J. E., and M. J. WALL: Identification of the virus of lymphocytic chorio-meningitis. *J. Bact.* **41**:421 (1944).

———, and J. WARREN: The virus of encephalomyocarditis and its apparent causation of disease in man. *J. Clin. Investigation* **26**:1197 (1947).

The Pathogenic Actinomycetes and Fungi

The term *mycosis,* meaning fungous disease (pl. *mycoses*), is given to diseases caused by yeastlike and moldlike fungi. Because the infections caused by the moldlike bacteria, the actinomycetes, are clinically similar to those caused by the true fungi, the pathogenic members of that group are ordinarily included in the discussion of pathogenic fungi.

IMPORTANCE AND CLINICAL CHARACTERISTICS

Mycotic diseases are usually divided into two groups, (1) the cutaneous mycoses that cause lesions in the skin, hair, and nails, and (2) the systemic mycoses in which the organisms invade deeper tissues. These infections are more common in warm climates but are found in all parts of the world. Their importance is sometimes not appreciated. In some areas of the South Pacific three-quarters of the service men reporting for sick call were suffering from mycotic infections. The authors of a recent treatise on these diseases (Conant *et al., Manual of Clinical Mycology,* 1954), speaking of their experience at the clinics of Duke University Hospital in North Carolina, say, "Fungous infections are of such common occurrence that we have found it necessary to consider mycotic diseases in the differential diagnosis of practically every obscure infection."

Some mycoses seem capable of causing disease in persons in normal health. But most of them, particularly the commoner skin and mucous membrane infections, attack those who are undernourished and localize in tissues injured by constant uncleanliness. On the whole, mycoses are diseases of low-income groups living in unsanitary surroundings.

Intensive use of the common antibiotics, particularly penicillin, depresses the normal bacterial population of various tissues. Under these conditions fungi normally present in small numbers increase and fungous infections develop (see page 132). Persons who have fungous infections may become hypersensitive to substances present in antibiotics of fungal origin.

Most mycotic infections develop insidiously and tend to become chronic. Even in the fatal forms, illness is often very prolonged. Although antibodies are formed, absolute immunity does not develop, and the disease may recur after apparent cure. Tissue inflammation is not marked in mycoses, and extensive lesions may give rise to few if any symptoms, unless some vital center is attacked. In addition to local lesions in which the causative fungus is growing, sterile lesions due to allergy may develop on other parts of the body. These allergic lesions are called *ids*.

LABORATORY DIAGNOSIS

The presence of the fungus in hair, sputum, pus, or bits of infected tissue can usually be demonstrated by direct microscopic examination. The material is treated with strong alkali to clear it (make the body tissue transparent). Fungi in sections of tissues are best seen when stained by the periodic acid-Schiff stain. Hyphal or spore elements or both may be found. Such a demonstration is sufficient to show that the infection is mycotic but usually does not identify the specific fungus. To do that, cultures are required. They are made on acidic, sugar-containing media such as Sabouraud's agar or corn meal agar. The growth characteristics, and the morphology of the fungus as seen in lactophenol mounts, identify the genus and species.

Animal inoculation sometimes allows the discovery of fungi that fail to grow on culture media. Serologic tests, particularly complement-fixation tests, are sometimes useful. Skin tests with extracts of specific fungi aid in diagnosis and also help assess allergic factors in known cases.

CONTROL AND TREATMENT

The sources of mycotic infection are varied. Some of the cutaneous infections, such as ringworm of the feet, are spread from person to person and tend to become epidemic. Some ringworm infections and other mycoses may come from animals. In others, as far as can be determined, the fungi are normal inhabitants of the human skin or passageways, gaining entrance and becoming virulent under some unusual circumstance. Others, particularly those that cause systemic infection, are apparently present in the environment as organisms of plants or soil. However, it should be emphasized that the saprophytic food-spoilage types and the plant pathogens are not associated with human disease. Most systemic mycoses do not spread from person to person.

The spread of mycotic infections is facilitated by the resistance of spores to drying and exposure. The lesions of the cutaneous mycoses are often so extensive that it is inevitable that they spread the organisms to clothing, towels, bedding, and furniture. Entrance of the organisms through the injured skin or mucous membranes is most common. Pulmonary infection, the commonest form of internal infection, probably arises from the inhalation of the fungus. With one or two possible exceptions, entrance through the alimentary canal is uncommon. No biologic transfer by insect vectors is known. Mechanical transfer of skin infections by insects is possible but not important.

Cleanliness and good nutrition help to prevent the development of the commoner types of mycoses. Where mycotic infections are prevalent in the tropics and in certain occupations, chemicals in the form of powder may be used prophylactically on the skin.

Treatment of mycotic infections is quite unsatisfactory. Iodides and dyes such as gentian violet and potassium permanganate are drugs that have been used for many years. During the Second World War certain fatty acids such as undecylenic acid were found effective against superficial mycoses and are now incorporated in many ointments and dusting powders. The actinomyces infections are treated with penicillin, but no satisfactory antibiotics against other mycoses are in use, though considerable research on this problem is being done. The hunt for drugs effective against specific systemic mycoses has already produced one effective chemotherapeutic agent, stilbamidine, which cures the American form of blastomycosis.

All mycoses must be regarded as possibly communicable. Nursing techniques must be carried out in such fashion that no living pathogen from the patient reaches any other person. The nurse must be on the alert to note any abnormal condition of the skin of her patients that might indicate a

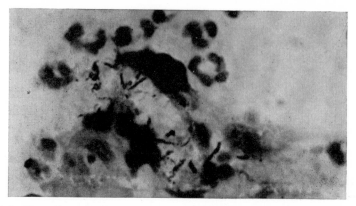

FIG. 36·1 *Nocardia asteroides.* ×1,000. Branching filamentous organisms in crushed granule from sputum. (*Courtesy of Dr. N. F. Conant.*)

fungous infection. Prompt reporting will ensure immediate diagnosis and treatment and prevent possible spread to other patients. The nurse's carelessness in bathing her patients, in powdering or oiling infants, and in caring for the mouths of helpless patients may provide opportunities for the start of fungous infections.

PATHOGENIC ACTINOMYCETES

The pathogenic actinomycetes belong to the anaerobic genus *Actinomyces* and to the aerobic genus *Nocardia* (Appendix B, page 584).

Actinomyces bovis, the Cause of Actinomycosis. The filamentous, branching bacteria are found in the mouth and tonsils. In abscesses in the tissues they grow in yellowish masses, called "sulfur granules." The filamentous bacteria can be seen in crushed granules. They can be grown in deep tubes of infusion broth or agar.

Actinomycosis is usually a chronic destructive infection of the face, neck, and jaw. Inhaled organisms give rise to abscesses of the lungs, and ingested organisms cause lesions in the lower abdomen that may be mistaken for appendicitis. Pulmonary and abdominal lesions spread to the vertebrae and through the abdominal wall. All forms of actinomycosis are treated by antibiotics.

Nocardia asteroides, the Cause of Nocardiosis. These aerobic bacteria have their source in the soil. The branching cells closely resemble the actinomycetes (Fig. 36·1), but the nocardia grow readily on the surface of agar. Systemic nocardiosis begins as a lung infection resembling tuberculosis. Later lesions develop in the brain, liver, spleen, etc.

Nocardias also cause *mycetoma,* a slow but severe infection of the soft tissue and bones of the foot, and *erythrasma,* a chronic, benign, pigmented infection of the skin.

Sulfadiazine is effective in the treatment of nocardiosis.

THE PATHOGENIC FUNGI CAUSING CUTANEOUS INFECTIONS

The Dermatophyte Fungi, the Causes of the Dermatomycoses. The *dermatomycoses* are fungous infections of the skin, hair, and nails caused by three closely related genera of fungi called the *dermatophyte fungi.*

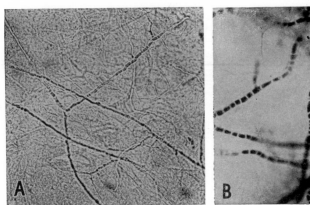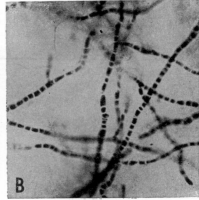

FIG. 36·2 Hyphae of dermatophyte fungi as seen in direct microscopic examination of infected skin. (*A*) ×200; (*B*) ×450. (*From Conant et al., "Manual of Clinical Mycology," Saunders.*)

The dermatophyte fungi include a number of species belonging to the genera *Epidermophyton, Trichophyton,* and *Microsporum.* Direct microscopic examination of hairs and scrapings from lesions reveal branching hyphae and sometimes masses or chains of spores (Fig. 36·2). Further morphologic characteristics are seen in slides made from cultures. Representative species are described below.

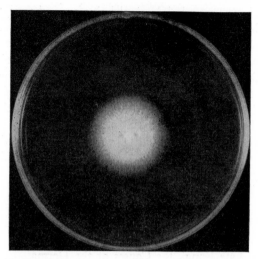

FIG. 36·3 *Epidermophyton floccosum* colony. (*Courtesy of Dr. N. F. Conant.*)

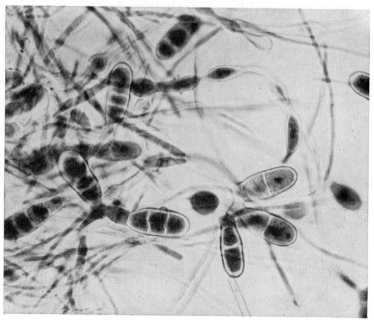

FIG. 36·4 *Epidermophyton floccosum* spores and mycelium. ×700. (*From Conant et al., "Manual of Clinical Mycology," Saunders.*)

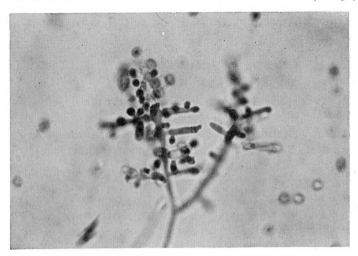

Fig. 36·5 *Trichophyton schoenleini* from a culture. ×550. (*From Conant et al., "Manual of Clinical Mycology," Saunders.*)

1. *Epidermophyton floccosum* is the commonest of all dermatophytes in cutaneous infections not involving the hair. A typical colony is shown in Fig. 36·3. The large club-shaped spores shown in Fig. 36·4 are characteristic of this genus.

2. *Trichophyton schoenleini* is the principal cause of favus (see following section) and is one of many species of this genus. It attacks hair as well as skin. The colonies are more cottony than those of *Epidermophyton* and are often colored. Figure 36·5 illustrates the morphology of the trichophyton group.

3. *Microsporum audouini* is the cause of the epidemic form of ringworm of the scalp. It can attack skin and hair but not nails. The colonies are woolly and have a

Fig. 36·6 Fruiting body of *Microsporum audouini* from a culture. ×400. (*Courtesy of Dr. N. F. Conant.*)

brownish hue. Slides made from the colonies show large, spindle-shaped sporing bodies (Fig. 36·6).

Clinical Forms of the Dermatomycoses. These infections attack all parts of the outside of the body. Many names are given to the various types of infection. The term *tinea* seems to be most acceptable. The popular term is *ringworm*.

Tinea pedis (ringworm of the feet, athlete's foot, etc.) is the infection of the skin between the toes and of the sole of the foot, and sometimes of similar areas on the hands. The most common lesion is the chronic "soft corn" between the fourth and fifth toes. Severe acute and chronic types occur in persons with abnormal circulation.

Tinea unguium (ringworm of the nails) attacks the fingernails and toenails.

Tinea cruris (ringworm of the groin) involves the skin but not the hair of the groin. It is more common in men than women. It is spread by infected towels and borrowed clothing. Tinea pedis, tinea unguium, and tinea cruris are usually caused by *Epidermophyton floccosum.*

Tinea corporis (ringworm of the smooth skin) appears as annular (ringlike) lesions on the smooth skin. It is more common in children than in adults. It is often acquired from pet dogs and cats, or from farm animals ("barn itch").

Tinea capitis (ringworm of the scalp) is common in boys of school age. The usual chronic form due to *Microsporum audouini* is of human origin and epidemic. A serious form caused by *Trichophyton tonsurans* is now common in the South and in New York City. Sporadic cases due to other epidermophyte fungi are acquired from infected animals. *Wood's light,* a special form of ultraviolet radiation, is helpful in indicating the type and extent of the infection. Infected hairs have a colored glow under the lamp.

Tinea favosa (honeycomb ringworm) is also known as *favus.* The organisms, *Trichophyton schoenleini* or closely related species, attack both hair and skin and often injure the hair follicles, causing permanent areas of baldness. The infection may also be found on the smooth skin. The lesions are yellow cup-shaped crusts. Favus is uncommon in this country. It is often epidemic in children in concentration and refugee camps.

Tinea barbae (ringworm of the beard) is a chronic infection of the bearded area on men's faces. It is also known as *barbers' itch* because it is spread by imperfectly disinfected shaving equipment.

Other Fungi Causing Cutaneous Mycoses. *Malassezia furfur* is a fungus that grows only in the outer layers of the epidermis, never invading deeper tissues. It causes a brownish, scaly discoloration of the skin known as *pityriasis versicolor* or *tinea versicolor.*

The dermatophytic fungi and a number of other species may cause fungous infection of the outer ear, *otomycosis.* It sometimes develops in persons whose ear canals are repeatedly exposed to moisture.

FUNGI CAUSING SYSTEMIC MYCOSES

The systemic mycoses are less common than the cutaneous infections but more serious and disabling. Each of these diseases is caused by a definite species of fungus. Satisfactory methods of treatment have not been found for most of these diseases. Four mycoses common in the United States are described below in detail. Other less important types are listed briefly.

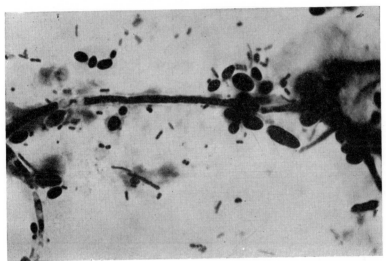

Fɪɢ. 36·7   *Candida albicans* in sputum. ×1,500. (*From Conant et al., "Manual of Clinical Mycology," Saunders.*)

Candida albicans, the Cause of Moniliasis. *C. albicans* (previously named *Monilia albicans*) grows in both tissues and cultures as thin-walled, oval, yeastlike cells and short hyphae (Fig. 36·7). It is found on the skin and in the mouth and feces of normal people. The many clinical forms of moniliasis (more correctly called *candidiasis*) develop in tissues injured by malnutrition or kept abnormally moist. The few candida cells normally present on the skin and mucous membranes may increase rapidly and cause trouble when the normal bacteria are reduced by the use of antibiotics. The most common clinical forms of candidiasis are those involving (1) the skin, (2) the mucous membranes of the body openings, and (3) the respiratory or digestive tract.

Moniliasis of the Skin. Ringwormlike lesions due to *C. albicans* occur on the hands of housewives and others whose hands are often immersed in water and imperfectly dried. The fungus frequently grows in *intertriginous* areas (where two skin surfaces are in constant contact with each other) as a complication of "chafing." Such sites include the neck folds in small babies, the skin under the breasts of nursing mothers, and the folds in the groin.

Moniliasis of the Mucous Membranes. The oral infection, *thrush,* is a disease of poorly nourished, ill-cared-for infants and of elderly persons with chronic disabling illnesses. In the past it was often epidemic in orphan asylums and infant wards. Since it can be prevented by good nutrition and

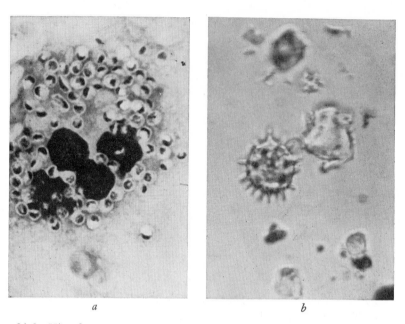

a *b*

FIG. 36·8 *Histoplasma capsulatum.* (*a*) Yeastlike cells in tissue smear. ×1,500. (*b*) Tuberculate spore found in dust. ×600. (*From Communicable Disease Center and Dr. Roland Rooks.*)

nursing care, its occurrence in a modern hospital is considered a disgrace. Endogenous mouth infections have been reported in persons receiving intensive antibiotic therapy. Moniliasis of the vagina is common in persons with diabetes and in pregnant women.

Moniliasis of the Respiratory and Digestive Tracts. C. albicans can cause a chronic nonfatal bronchitis as well as a more severe pneumonitis. Large numbers of candida are found in the diarrheal feces of persons with pernicious anemia, of persons with *sprue* (an intestinal disease of the tropics), and of persons who have received excessive amounts of antibiotics by mouth.

Histoplasma capsulatum, the Cause of Histoplasmosis. *H. capsulatum* grows within the cells of infected persons as small, yeastlike bodies (Fig. 36·8). Hyphae and large characteristic spores are found in cultures. The spores have also been found in water and air and in the soil of farm buildings. Animal sources such as rodents and pigeons are suspected. The organisms are not spread from man to man.

Histoplasmosis is most common in the Ohio and middle Mississippi Valley states. For many years only the rare, fatal form of the disease was recognized. It is now known that mild or asymptomatic pulmonary infections are very common, especially in childhood. Reinfection cases resemble pulmonary tuberculosis. A small portion of infected persons develop progressive disease involving many internal organs.

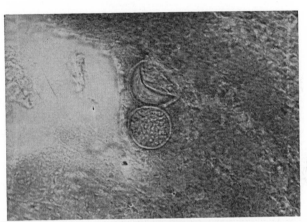

FIG. 36·9   *Coccidioides immitis* in pus. ×800. Spherical cells filled with smaller cells. (*From Conant et al., "Manual of Clinical Mycology," Saunders.*)

The slowly developing calcified nodules that result from infection with the mild form of the disease may later be mistaken for healed lesions of tuberculosis. Differential diagnosis can be made by tuberculin and *histoplasmin* skin tests.

Coccidioides immitis, the Cause of Coccidioidomycosis. In preparations from infected tissues, *C. immitis* is in the form of heavy-walled spherules filled with small endospores (Fig. 36·9). In cultures the fungus develops hyphae and many small spores.

Coccidioidomycosis is endemic in southern California, Arizona, New Mexico, and Texas. It also occurs in many regions outside the United States. The fungus is present in soil and is spread by dust-borne spores. Rats and other animals may harbor the fungi. In the past the only recognized cases were chronic malignant infections that were almost invariably fatal. Now it is certain that acute respiratory attacks, two-thirds of them so mild as to be missed, are the common form of the disease. Primary skin lesions may also occur. Disseminated generalized coccidiomycosis is very rare, though somewhat commoner in Negroes, Indians, and Mexicans than in our general population. The healed lung lesions of coccidioidomycosis, like those of histoplasmosis, may be confused with calcified nodules of tuberculosis. *Coccidioidin,* like histoplasmin, can be used for diagnostic skin tests.

Blastomyces dermatitidis, the Cause of North American Blastomycosis (Gilchrist's Disease). *B. dermatitidis* grows in the form of a budding spherical yeast in the tissues and in young cultures incubated at body temperature.

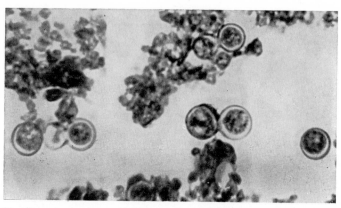

Fɪɢ. 36·10   *Blastomyces dermatitidis* in tissue, showing budding cells and refractile cell walls. ✕800. (*Communicable Disease Center, Public Health Service.*)

Room temperature cultures develop branching hyphae with many small spores. Both forms are shown in Fig. 36·10.

The cutaneous form of the disease is characterized by chronic suppurating lesions on the face or extremities. Generalized blastomycosis starts as a pulmonary infection and spreads to other internal organs, the bones, and the central nervous system. Infection with *B. dermatitidis* is found only in the United States and Canada. It is believed that the fungus must come from some environmental source.

North American blastomycosis is one of the fungus diseases for which specific chemotherapy has been developed within the last few years. Stilbamidine, an aromatic diamidine, and its derivative 2-hydroxystilbamidine are effective.

A somewhat similar disease, *South American blastomycosis,* is caused by *Blastomyces brasiliensis.* This infection is successfully treated by sulfonamides. The tropical skin disease known as *chromoblastomycosis* is characterized by spreading, warty growths. It is not, however, caused by a characteristic blastomycete, but by a variety of pigmented soil molds.

Other Fungi Causing Systemic Mycoses.

Cryptococcus neoformans, the Cause of Cryptococcosis. The yeastlike cells of this organism are heavily encapsulated. The smooth, brownish colonies do not develop hyphae. The fungus has been found in the soil and in normal skin and feces. When it enters the body through the skin or lungs it may invade a variety of tissues. In some cases it spreads to the central nervous system, causing so-called torula meningitis. Diagnosis depends on finding the encapsulated cells in the spinal fluid.

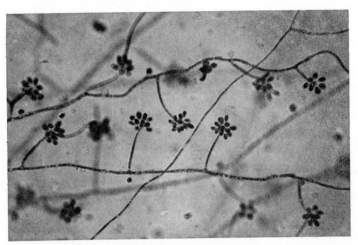

Fig. 36·11   *Sporotrichum schenckii* from a culture. ×650. (*From Conant et al., "Manual of Clinical Mycology," Saunders.*)

The Fungi of Maduromycosis (Madura Foot, Mycetoma). In tropical climates, following injury of the skin of the foot, severe suppurative lesions of the soft tissues and bones may develop. Several species of molds and nocardia are responsible for these chronic infections.

Sporotrichum schenckii, the Cause of Sporotrichosis. This fungus is difficult to find by microscopic examination of infected tissues, but it grows well in culture media. It is a moldlike organism readily identified by whorls of elongated spores on short hyphal branches (Fig. 36·11). It is known to grow saprophytically in plant material. Most infected persons in this country give a history of an initial injury such as a scratch from a barberry thorn. The primary ulcerating nodule is often on the hand, with secondary nodules on the arm along the course of the lymphatics. Generalized sporotrichosis is also sometimes encountered.

HOW THE NURSE CAN AVOID MYCOTIC INFECTION

Ringworm of the feet is so common among nurses that it may be considered an occupational disease. The nurse must use every precaution to avoid it. She must wear slippers at all times in public bathrooms. Tinea pedis attacks feet that are unclean, continually sweaty, and cramped by improperly fitted shoes. The nurse must wear shoes that fit perfectly. They should not be made of types of materials impervious to air, such as patent leather. Stockings must be changed daily or oftener. Shoes may be disinfected by fumigation for 24 hours with formaldehyde gas. The feet should be thoroughly washed and dried at least once a day. Antimycotic powders may be used. During the Second World War the Navy developed very effective preparations containing undecylenic acid and zinc undecylenate. Propionic and caprylic acid preparations are also used. Any scaling, blistering, or soft corns should be immediately reported and treated.

Nurses repeatedly expose their hands to water that may contain irritating soaps, disinfectants, or other materials. It is not surprising that they frequently develop tinea and monilia infections of the hands and nails. The nurse should always rinse her hands thoroughly in clear water after they have been exposed to other liquids. Then she should dry them completely. She should use the skin lotion provided in the hospital and should procure a recommended lotion or cream for use when she is off duty.

STUDY SUGGESTIONS

Be sure to review the text and illustrations concerning the fungi and actinomycetes in the first four chapters.

Read this whole chapter carefully to gain a general view of the subject. Study the sections dealing with general aspects of the mycotic infections.

Study intensively the sections dealing with the three kinds of mycoses most important in the United States—(1) the actinomycetes and actinomycosis, page 520, (2) the dermatophytic fungi, page 521, tinea capitis and tinea pedis, page 524, and (3), *Candida albicans* and moniliasis, page 525.

Read over again the sections on other pathogenic fungi. Group these infections with the three typical examples that you have studied intensively.

In studying this chapter read, spell, and pronounce aloud each scientific term as you meet it so that it becomes familiar to you.

What mycotic infections have you met in your personal and hospital experience? What prophylactic measures have you observed in schools, bathing beaches, swimming pools, and gymnasiums?

What measures are used in your hospital to prevent and control tinea pedis among nurses? What routine ward practices have you learned or observed that aid in controlling cutaneous mycoses in your patients? What precautions are practiced when it is discovered that a patient is suffering from one of these infections?

SUGGESTED READING

General References

Christian, I. B., and N. F. Conant: Antifungal action of some aromatic diamidines. *J. Lab. & Clin. Med.* **42**:638 (1953).

Conant, N. F., et al.: "Manual of Clinical Mycology." 2d ed., Saunders, Philadelphia, 1954.

Jillson, O. F.: Medical progress—Mycology. *New England J. Med.* **249**:523, 561 (1953).

Skinner, C. E., C. W. Emmons, and H. M. Tsuchiya: "Henrici's Molds, Yeasts, and Actinomycetes." 3d ed., Wiley, New York, 1947.

Smith, D. T., and N. F. Conant: "Zinsser's Textbook of Bacteriology." 10th ed., Appleton-Century-Crofts, New York, 1952.

Laboratory Diagnosis

Ajella, L.: Collecting specimens for the laboratory diagnosis and isolation of fungi. *J.A.M.A.* **146**:1581 (1951).

Conant, N. F.: Pathogenic Fungi, in "Diagnostic Procedures and Reagents." 3d ed., American Public Health Association, New York, 1950.

Gordon, M. A.: A key to the human mycoses. *J. Bact.* **63**:385 (1952).

Actinomycetes

Lane, S. L., A. H. Kutscher, and R. Chaves: Oxytetracycline in the treatment of orocervical facial actinomycosis. *J.A.M.A.* **151**:986 (1953).

Slack, J.: The source of infection in actinomycosis. *J. Bact.* **43**:193 (1942).

Dermatophyte Fungi

Georg, L. K.: *Trichophyton tonsurans*—a new public health problem. *Pub. Health Rep.* **67**:53 (1952).

Jillson, O. F., and W. R. Buckley: Fungous diseases in man acquired from cattle and horses. *New England J. Med.* **246**:996 (1952).

Lee, R. K. C.: Epidemic tinea capitis. *Pub. Health Rep.* **63**:261 (1948).

Morehead, M. A.: Epidemic ringworm of the scalp. *Pub. Health Nursing* **40**:186 (1948).

Schwartz, L., et al.: Control of ringworm of the scalp among school children. *J.A.M.A.* **132**:58 (1946).

Candida albicans

McGovern, J. J., et al.: The effect of aureomycin on the fungal and bacterial flora of children. *New England J. Med.* **248**:397 (1953).

WOOD, J. W., I. H. MANNING, JR., and C. N. PATTERSON: Monilial infections complicating the therapeutic use of antibiotics. *J.A.M.A.* **145**:207 (1951).

Histoplasma capsulatum

FURCOLOW, M. L.: Further observations on histoplasmosis: mycology and bacteriology. *Pub. Health Rep.* **65**:965 (1953).

GRAYSTON, T. F., and M. L. FURCOLOW: The occurrence of histoplasmosis in epidemics. *Am. J. Pub. Health* **43**:665 (1953).

LOOSLI, C. G., *et al.:* Epidemiological studies of pulmonary histoplasmosis in a farm family. *Am. J. Hyg.* **55**:392 (1952).

ZEIDBERG, L. D., *et al.:* Isolation of *Histoplasma capsulatum* from soil. *Am. J. Pub. Health* **42**:930 (1952).

Coccidioides immitis

SILVERMAN, M.: The mystery of the deadly dust. *Sat. Eve. Post* (Dec. 17, 1949).

SMITH, C. E., and R. R. BEARD: Varieties of coccidioidal infection in relation to the epidemiology and control of the disease. *Am. J. Pub. Health* **36**:1394 (1946).

SMITH, C. E., *et al.:* Effect of season and dust control on coccidioidomycosis. *J.A.M.A.* **132**:833 (1946).

Blastomyces dermatitidis

FINK, J. C., D. E. VANDER PLOEG, and M. P. MOURSAND: "Stilbamidine" in the treatment of cutaneous blastomycosis. *J.A.M.A.* **151**:1395 (1953).

SCHOENBACH, E. B., *et al.:* Systemic blastomycosis treated with stilbamidine. *J.A.M.A.* **146**:1317 (1951).

The Pathogenic Protozoa

The important morphologic and physiologic characteristics of the protozoa were described in Chaps. 1 and 3. The four pathogenic types most important in North America are considered in some detail in this chapter and the facts about others summarized. The occurrence of protozoal diseases is often limited to specific areas by the distribution of the insect vectors involved. Up to the present time no methods of active or passive immunization against these diseases have been discovered. However, effective specific drugs are available for treatment. The identification of the insect vectors and animal reservoirs has led to effective methods of control.

ENDAMOEBA HISTOLYTICA, THE CAUSE OF AMEBIASIS

It is better to call this disease *amebiasis* than to use the older name, *amebic dysentery,* since many cases do not show intestinal symptoms.

The Organism and the Disease. The vegetative form, or *trophozoite,* of *E. histolytica* is motile and uninucleate (Fig. 37·1). It multiplies by fission and is able to invade the mucosa of the large intestine, where it causes

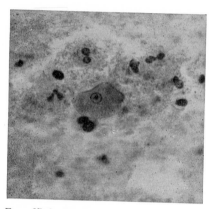

ulcerations. It may be carried to the liver, lung, or brain and cause abscesses in those organs. In the intestine the motile form may develop into the four-nucleated *cyst.* Ninety per cent of infected people are not obviously ill and are often referred to as "carriers," or as *cyst passers.* Only about 10 per cent of the cases have active dysentery. These dysenteric cases discharge trophozoites. Since these motile cells die rapidly outside the body and are killed by gastric juice and bile if they are ingested, the dysenteric cases are not important as sources of infection. The cysts, however, are able to survive for some time outside the body and can pass uninjured through the alimentary canal to the ileum. Here the amebae excyst, each cyst giving rise to eight small infective trophozoites.

FIG. 37·1 Motile form of *Endamoeba histolytica* in a fecal smear. ×500. (*Armed Forces Institute of Pathology print 41196; courtesy of Prof. F. G. Haughwant.*)

The cyst passers are therefore the dangerous sources of infection. Food contaminated by them is undoubtedly the most important means of spread. Polluted water supplies are responsible for explosive epidemics. In concentration camps, prisons, and in homes where sanitation and personal hygiene are bad, direct transfer and flies spread the disease.

Treatment. *Emetine hydrochloride* (ipecac) is the traditional drug. Quinoline drugs, particularly chloroquine, are now used. The broad-range antibiotics, particularly oxytetracycline, are effective against the trophozoites in the intestine. A new antibiotic, *fumagillin* (Fumadil), acts directly on the motile amebae. Combined therapy is usually employed. Chronic cyst passers are particularly resistant to treatment.

Laboratory Diagnosis. Motile forms or cysts may be found in stained slides or moist smears of feces or scrapings from rectal ulcerations. Fresh, dysenteric stool specimens are mixed with a colorless plastic, polyvinyl alcohol, to prevent the disintegration of trophozoites during transportation to the laboratory. Cultivation is possible on special media. The laboratory worker must be an expert to avoid confusing *E. histolytica* with harmless amebae which often are present in the intestine.

Distribution. Although amebiasis is often considered a tropical disease, there are occasional epidemics of acute cases in the temperate zone accompanied by high fatality. The cyst-passer state is common in all parts of the world. Surveys show that ten per cent of Americans are carriers. The incidence is highest in areas where sanitation is defective.

PLASMODIUM VIVAX, THE CAUSE OF VIVAX MALARIA
PLASMODIUM MALARIAE, THE CAUSE OF QUARTAN MALARIA
PLASMODIUM FALCIPARUM, THE CAUSE OF FALCIPARUM MALARIA

Vivax malaria is sometimes called *benign tertian malaria.* Falciparum malaria is also known as *malignant tertian malaria.* The term *tertian* refers to the "3-day" cycle of the types of malaria in which chills and fever recur at approximately 48-hour intervals. The term *quartan* refers to the "4-day" cycle of malaria due to *P. malariae,* in which chills and fever recur approximately every 72 hours. A fourth species, *P. ovale,* is the cause of a less common mild form of tertian malaria.

Plasmodia are members of the class *Sporozoa* because they form sporelike bodies at one stage of the life cycle. The plasmodia of malaria are always spread by female anopheles mosquitoes (Fig. 37·2). Both in the human and in the mosquito host, the parasites pass through complicated stages. Figure 37·3 illustrates this life cycle diagrammatically. Each form that the parasite assumes has a scientific name. These names are given in parentheses in the discussion that follows.

Life Cycle of Malaria Parasite. When an infected female mosquito bites a human, she injects the parasite (*sporozoite*). The sporozoite is believed to pass several generations in lymphoid and endothelial cells. After this *tissue (pre-erythrocytic) stage* the parasites invade red blood cells, where they grow into ameboid forms (*trophozoites*). Each parasite nucleus divides into 6 or more new nuclei, and this nuclear division is followed by division of the cytoplasm (*schizont stage*). Soon the red cell ruptures, liberating the 6 to 24 new cells (*merozoites*). At the time of the destruction of the erythrocytes the patient experiences an attack of chills and fever. Each new parasite repeats the process of red cell invasion, reproduction, and cell rupture. The resulting destruction of red cells produces a marked anemia, and spontaneous agglutination of parasitized cells in small blood vessels may cause injury to brain, spleen, liver, heart, and other organs. In vivax and quartan malaria there

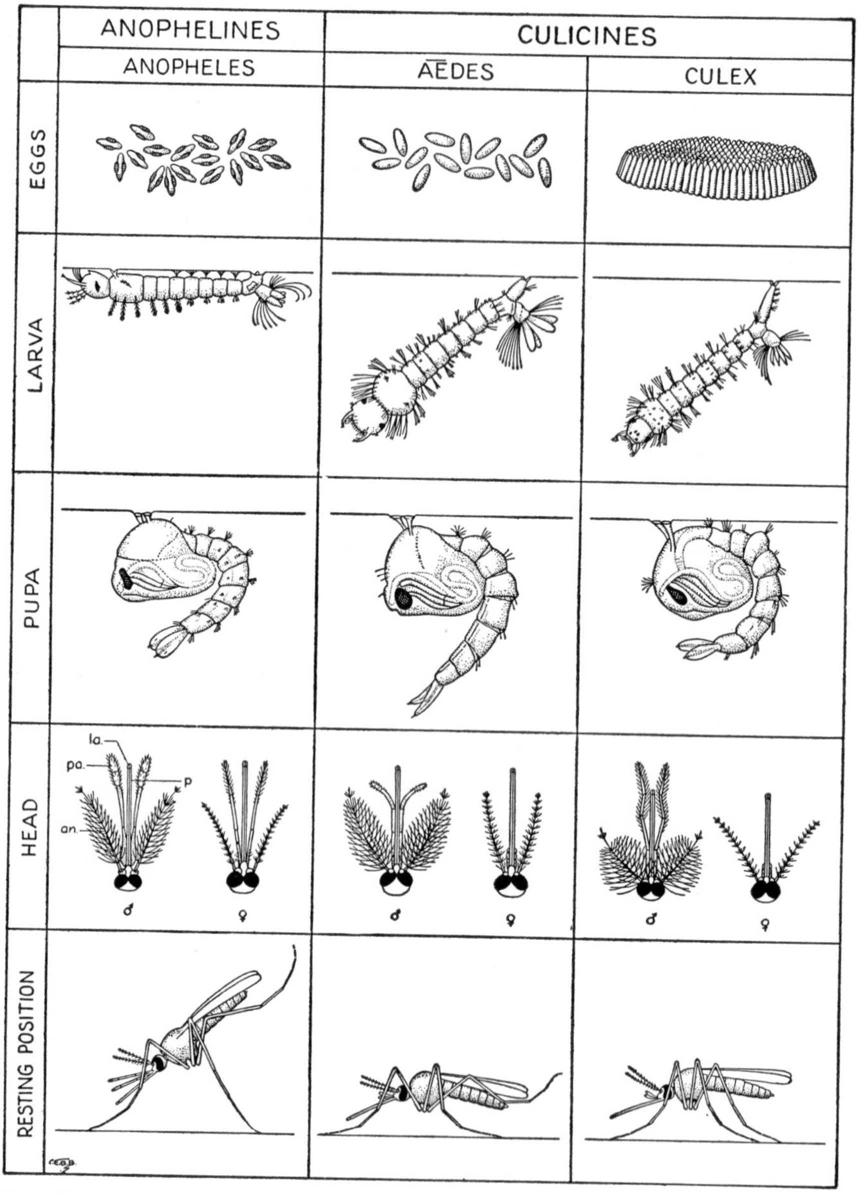

	ANOPHELINES	CULICINES	
	ANOPHELES	AĒDES	CULEX
EGGS			
LARVA			
PUPA			
HEAD			
RESTING POSITION			

FIG. 37·2 Stages and morphology of important mosquitoes. (*From Belding, "Textbook of Clinical Parasitology," Appleton-Century-Crofts.*)

is continuing invasion of tissue cells. These *exo-erythrocytic* parasites are resistant to drug therapy and cause the relapses of vivax malaria and the persisting infections of the quartan-type disease.

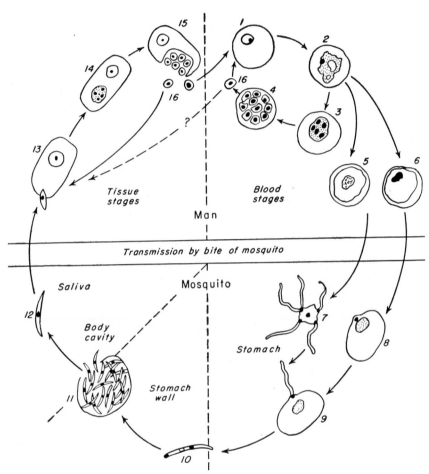

FIG. 37·3 Life cycle of malaria parasite. (1) Young trophozoite (ring stage); (2) trophozoite; (3) schizont; (4) mature schizont; (5) microgametocyte; (6) macro-gametocyte; (7) exflagellation of the microgamete; (8) macrogamete; (9) zygote; (10) oökinete; (11) mature oöcyst discharging sporozoites; (12) sporozoite; (13) (14) (15) extra-erythrocytic stages; (16) merozoites.

After a few such cycles in the human host, some of the parasites develop into specialized forms (*microgametocytes* and *macrogametocytes*) that are capable of producing sex cells. When blood containing these cells is taken into the stomach of the mosquito, the gametocytes develop into the male and female cells (called, respectively, *microgametes* and *macrogametes*). The two fuse, forming a motile cell (*oökinete*), which embeds itself on the outside of the stomach wall. There it grows into a large round cyst (*oöcyst*) (Fig. 37·4) containing hundreds of tiny motile cells (*sporozoites*). These migrate throughout the mosquito's body, and many reach the salivary glands. When this mosquito next bites a human, these cells are injected with her saliva. These processes in the mosquito take from 1 to 3 weeks or more.

Treatment. Quinine derived from the bark of the chinchona tree was

FIG. 37·4 Oöcyst stage of the malarial parasite on the outer wall of the mosquito's stomach. ×400. (*Armed Forces Institute of Pathology print 43040.*)

introduced into Europe from South America in 1640 as a cure for fever and was the standard antimalarial drug for 300 years. During the Second World War, when the quinine supply of the world was cut off by the Japanese conquest of the East Indies, the synthetic drug *atabrine* (*quinacrine*) was found to be generally superior to quinine. During and since the war other synthetic drugs have been developed which have many advantages. The most important of these is *chloroquine*. Other drugs now being extensively used are *pyrimethamine* and *Amodiaquin*. By the careful selection of drugs and proper dosage it is now possible to prevent the development of malaria in persons exposed to the disease (*suppressive treatment*), to treat effectively all types of malaria, and to cure falciparum malaria. Prevention of relapses of vivax malaria is the most difficult therapeutic problem. *Primaquine,* the drug most effective against the exo-erythrocytic stages, is quite toxic.

Laboratory Diagnosis. Malaria is diagnosed by thin or thick blood smears stained with Giemsa's or Wright's stains (Figs. 37·5 and 37·6). Experts can differentiate the three types of malaria by the morphologic differences of the intracellular stages (Table 37·1).

Table 37·1

Morphologic Characteristics of the Malaria Parasites as Seen in Human Blood

Stage	Plasmodium vivax	Plasmodium malariae	Plasmodium falciparum
Young trophozoite	Unpigmented ring, ⅓ size of red blood cell	Thicker, smaller pigmented ring	One or more very thin rings
Trophozoite..	Ameboid, irregular	Band form with coarse granules	Small, compact *
Schizont......	Ameboid, irregular	Band form with coarse granules	Small, compact, with small granules *
Merozoites...	12 to 24 (average 16); irregularly arranged	6 to 12 (average 8); in rosette	8 to 36 (average 20); irregularly arranged *
Parasitized red blood cells	Young reticulocytes, enlarged; Schuffner's stippling †	Old erythrocytes; not enlarged; no granules †	Erythrocytes of all ages; not enlarged; no granules †
Microgametocyte	Large, round; with central chromatin	Small, round; with central chromatin	Sausage-shaped; scattered chromatin
Macrogametocyte	Very large; chromatin at edges	Medium size; chromatin deeply stained at edges	Sickel-shaped; compact chromatin in center

* Not found in peripheral blood.
† Refers to granules outside parasite but in cytoplasm of erythrocyte.

Distribution. In the past malaria has been the most widespread and serious of all transmissible diseases, but the picture has changed radically in the last 25 years. In the United States the disease has been practically eradicated. The only cases are those returning from endemic areas overseas and secondary cases resulting from their infection of local mosquitoes. Since the war the campaigns against malaria waged in Greece, Sardinia, southern Italy, Ceylon, and many other parts of the world, by WHO and other agencies, have freed whole populations from the disease. But there are still areas where millions are ill and thousands die every year from the disease. Where quartan and vivax malaria are endemic, natives have constant, recurring, mild attacks which confer partial immunity; but newcomers to the area develop severe cases. Falciparum malaria causes explosive outbreaks of acute and frequently fatal malaria. One of the fatal complications of falciparum infection is called *blackwater fever* because it is characterized by an unexplained hemolysis resulting in the passage of dark urine.

Transfer of Malaria by Blood Transfusion. Persons with quartan malaria may remain without symptoms for years. If one of these people is used as a donor of whole blood, the blood recipient will develop the disease. For this reason adults whose early life was spent in areas around the Mediterranean where this form is most common and service personnel from that theater of war should not be used as blood donors.

Control and Eradication. The most effective control of malaria is accomplished by the eradication of the mosquito vectors. Ideally this is done by

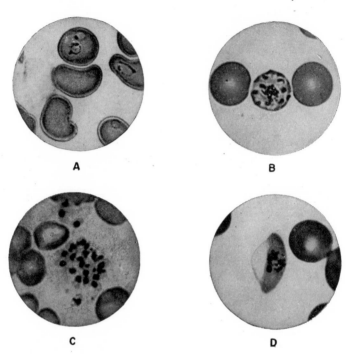

A

B

C

D

FIG. 37·5 Plasmodia in red blood cells. ×2,000. (*A*) Ring forms of *Plasmodium falciparum;* (*B*) schizont of *P. malariae;* (*C*) merozoites of *P. vivax;* (*D*) macrogametocyte of *P. falciparum.* (*Armed Forces Institute of Pathology print 30843.*)

the destruction of their breeding places. Screening helps, and so does the poisoning of the larvae in swamps and other places. The inexpensive method of using DDT or other residual insecticide sprays once or twice a year in homes and other buildings to kill the adult mosquitoes is used in the extensive antimalarial campaigns carried out in undeveloped countries.

TRICHOMONAS VAGINALIS, THE CAUSE OF TRICHOMONAS VAGINITIS

Investigators have found this small flagellate in the vagina of over 20 per cent of women. Its morphology is shown in Figs. 37·7 and 1·2. It may

MALARIAL PARASITES

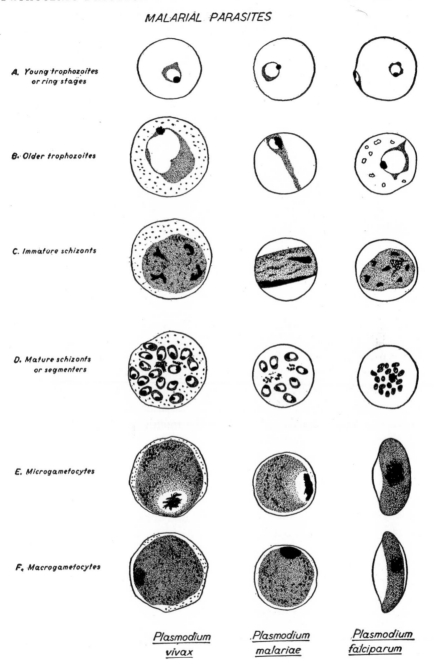

FIG. 37·6 Stages of malarial parasites in red blood cells. × approximately 3,000. (*From R. M. Cable, "Manual of Parasitology," Burgess.*)

cause very few symptoms, but frequently there is a frothy, white, very irritating discharge and considerable superficial inflammation and itching of the vagina and labia. It is not certain whether this protozoan is a true pathogen or an opportunist that becomes established if conditions in the vagina are abnormal. Trichomonas infections also occur in the urethra and prostate

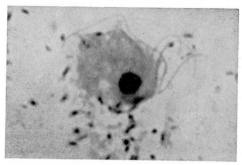

FIG. 37·7 *Trichomonas hominis.* ×2,000. A species similar to *T. vaginalis.* The small rods are bacteria on which the trichomonad is feeding. (*"Medichrome,"* Clay-Adams Co., Inc., Dr. H. E. Meleney.)

gland of the male. Sexual intercourse may be a method of spread, but it is believed that chance infection from towels and other objects is very common. The nurse should remember the prevalence and communicability of this infection and realize that she may spread it from patient to patient by careless techniques. She must always report labial inflammation or abnormal vaginal discharge observed in any female patient. (See also Chap. 31, page 428.)

Harmless trichomonads are found in the mouth and in the intestine.

TOXOPLASMA GONDII, THE CAUSE OF TOXOPLASMOSIS

The sporozoan *Toxoplasma gondii* is a small, crescent-shaped, intracellular parasite infectious for man, rodents, and many other animals. It can be grown in susceptible rodents, in the fertile egg, and in tissue culture. (See Fig. 37·8.) It invades many tissues, but its most devastating effects are on the nervous system.

Acute cases resembling rickettsial infections occur in adults, but symptomless infections are believed to be more common. Infected pregnant women pass the organism on to their infants, who develop encephalomyelitis and chorioretinitis during the first months of life with resulting mental deterioration and injured vision. Cultural and serologic tests aid in diagnosis. A toxoplasmin skin test gives useful information in mass surveys. Sulfadiazine and the pyrimethamine drugs are being tried for treatment. No methods of immunization or public health control are known.

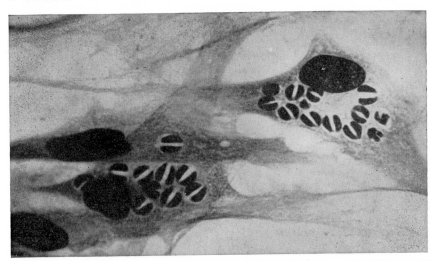

FIG. 37·8 *Toxoplasma gondii* in tissue culture. ×4,000. (*Courtesy of Dr. Thomas H. Weller, from Chernin and Weller, Proc. Soc. Exper. Biol. & Med. 85:68.*)

OTHER PATHOGENIC PROTOZOA

Intestinal Parasites. *Endamoeba gingivalis, the Ameba of the Gums.* This is found in the mouth of at least 50 per cent of Americans. It is most plentiful around the roots of badly decayed teeth and is much more common in dirty mouths. It feeds on leukocytes and on bits of disintegrating tissue. Most parasitologists consider it a harmless scavenger, but some believe that it is definitely harmful. It does not form cysts and must be spread directly from person to person.

Giardia lamblia. This is a flagellate that lives in the duodenum. Each protozoan adheres to the free surface of a columnar epithelial cell and presumably lives on the mucus that the cell secretes. When millions are present as a layer covering the duodenal epithelium, they interfere with fat absorption and other processes of digestion. As a result the patient may show signs of dietary deficiency. The cysts are found in large numbers in the feces and are the means by which the disease is spread.

Balantidium coli. This is the only ciliate that is important as a parasite of man (Figs. 37·9 and 1·2). This very large protozoan may cause severe ulcerations of the large intestine, though in many cases a mild diarrhea is the only symptom. Cysts and motile forms may be found in the feces. Pigs, which commonly harbor this parasite, may be the source of the infection for man.

The Hemoflagellates. The *hemoflagellates* are the flagellated protozoa that live chiefly in the blood stream. They belong to two groups, the *leishmanias* and the *trypanosomes*. All are spread by insects.

In the human the trypanosomes usually occur as motile cells in the blood and lymph. The leishmanias occur as rounded, nonmotile, intracellular forms in the human, but in the insect hosts they assume a trypanosomelike form

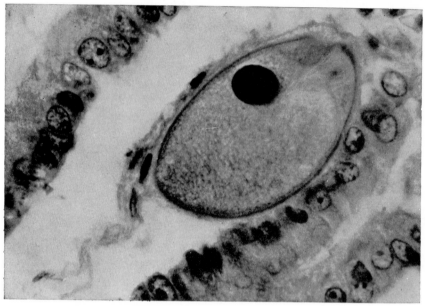

FIG. 37·9   *Balantidium coli* in a villus of the intestine. ×1,700. (*Armed Forces Institute of Pathology print 39165, courtesy of Prof. F. G. Haughwant.*)

(Fig. 37·10). The term *trypanosomiasis* can be used for any disease caused by a trypanosome and the term *leishmaniasis* for any caused by a leishmania. However, these diseases are called by a bewildering variety of local names in the countries where they occur. All these diseases are treated with special drugs and controlled by methods that eliminate the insect vectors or keep them away from man. The cause, vector, geographic distribution, and general character of these infections are summarized below.

Leishmania donovani, the Cause of Kala-azar. This is a disease of scattered regions of Asia, Africa, and Mediterranean Europe. Both visceral and skin lesions are evident, and the disease is frequently fatal. Dogs are an important animal reservoir, and sand flies are the vectors (Fig. 16·1, page 196).

Leishmania tropica, the Cause of Oriental Sore. This ulcerating skin lesion is most common in native children and in newcomers to the endemic regions. The vectors are sand flies. Wild rodents are believed to be the sources of infection. The disease is found around the Mediterranean and in Asia Minor, India, and central Asia.

Leishmania braziliensis, the Cause of Mucocutaneous Leishmaniasis. This disease is the New World type of leishmania infection and is commonest in

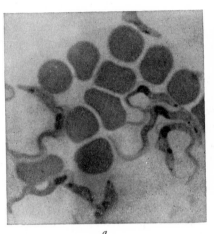
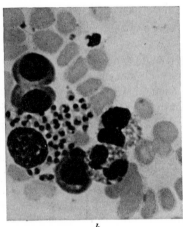

a   b

Fig. 37·10 Hemoflagellates. (*a*) *Trypanosome* sp. in blood. ×1,200. (*b*) *Leishmania donovani* in bone marrow. ×1,000. (*Armed Forces Institute of Pathology prints 40564 and AC218689-2.*)

central South America. Cases occur as far north as Mexico. Among the native names for this disease are *uta* and *espundia*. As in Oriental sore, the lesions are cutaneous, but they are on the face and spread into the nose, pharynx, and mouth. The vectors are sand flies. This disease is spread from person to person.

Trypanosoma gambiense and Trypanosoma rhodesiense, the Causes of West African and East African Trypanosomiasis. These diseases are also referred to as *African sleeping sickness.* They are spread by tsetse flies (Fig. 37·11). Man is the most important source of infection, but game animals and pigs may be animal reservoirs. A week or two after being bitten by an infected fly, the patient develops a prolonged recurrent fever. He may recover

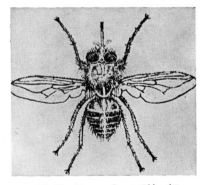

Fig. 37·11 Tsetse fly. ×2½. (*From Belding, "Textbook of Clinical Parasitology," Appleton-Century-Crofts.*)

entirely, or the disease may progress to an infection of the nervous system, the "sleeping" phase of the disease. This stage is always fatal if untreated. The Gambian type is found in west central Africa and is milder than the Rhodesian type, which is prevalent in southeast central Africa.

Trypanosoma cruzi, the Cause of Chagas' Disease. This disease is the Western hemisphere form of trypanosomiasis and occurs in South and Central America. Animal reservoirs include armadillos, dogs, cats, and rodents. The insect vectors are large reduviid bugs (Fig. 16·2, page 198). Chagas' disease is mainly a disease of children. It is characterized by swollen lymph nodes, fever, and anemia. Cases may be acute and quickly fatal or milder and chronic.

Laboratory diagnosis in all the diseases caused by hemoflagellates depends on the detection of the specific organism in blood, lymph, spinal fluid, or scrapings from superficial lesions. Animal inoculations and cultivation in artificial media may help to confirm diagnoses.

STUDY SUGGESTIONS

Be sure to review the morphology and physiology of the protozoa.

After reading this chapter once, go over it again carefully and at the same time fill out a table with the following headings: *Disease, Cause* (include name and morphology), *Mode of spread, Methods of control, Specific chemotherapy, Geographic distribution.* Use this table to check your knowledge. Close the text, cover up all save the headings and the first column of the table, then see if you can fill in the essential facts.

Certain protozoa studied in this chapter are harbored by people in North America. Which are they? In many infected persons the presence of these parasites is not known. Many nurses are inevitably possible sources of these infections. Many patients are unsuspected protozoa carriers. List some techniques of personal hygiene and nursing that help to prevent the spread of these undetected but dangerous organisms. (Example—disinfection of enema tubes. Why?)

In studying the morphology of the organisms, do not neglect the illustrations. See also the diagrams in Chap. 1. If these pathogens are not seen and drawn in the laboratory, it will help you to remember their appearance if you make a copy of each diagram.

The life cycles of the organisms of amebiasis and malaria are very important. An understanding of the processes involved is more essential than the rote memorizing of the scientific terms used. If the diagrams in this chapter are not clear to you, ask your instructor for help.

SUGGESTED READING

General References

BELDING, D. L.: "Textbook of Clinical Parasitology." 2d ed., Appleton-Century-Crofts, New York, 1952.

BROWN, H. W.: Laboratory Diagnosis of Helminthes and Protozoa, in "Diagnostic Procedures and Reagents." 3d ed., American Public Health Association, New York, 1950.

CHANDLER, A. C.: "Introduction to Parasitology." 9th ed., Wiley, New York, 1955.

MACKIE, T. T., G. W. HUNTER, and C. B. WORTH: "Manual of Tropical Medicine." 2d ed., Saunders, Philadelphia, 1954.

Endamoeba histolytica and Amebiasis

McHARDY, J., and W. W. FRYE: Antibiotics in the management of amebiasis. *J.A.M.A.* **154**:646 (1954).

PORTER, R. J.: Amebiasis, in "Annual Review of Microbiology." Vol. 7, Annual Reviews, Inc., Stanford, 1953.

SMITH, G.: The Case of the Plumber's Patchwork, in "Plague on Us." Commonwealth Fund, New York, 1941.

The Plasmodia and Malaria

ANDREWS, J. M., G. E. GRIFFITHS, and A. D. LANGMUIR: Malaria eradication in the United States. *Am. J. Pub. Health* **40**:1405 (1950).

COVELL, G.: Current research toward a global control of malaria. *New England J. Med.* **125**:31 (1953).

HUFF, C. G.: Life cycle of malaria parasite, in "Annual Review of Microbiology." Vol. 2, Annual Reviews, Inc., Stanford, 1947.

RUSSELL, P.: The eradication of malaria. *Scient. Am.* **186**:22 (1952).

WILCOX, A.: The Malaria Parasites of Man, in "Diagnostic Procedures and Reagents." 3d ed., American Public Health Association, New York, 1950.

Toxoplasma gondii and Toxoplasmosis

SABIN, A. B., *et al.*: Symposium on toxoplasmosis. *Am. J. Trop. Med. & Hyg.* **2**:360 (1953).

WEINMAN, D.: Toxoplasma and Toxoplasmosis, in "Annual Review of Microbiology." Vol. 6, Annual Reviews, Inc., Stanford, 1952.

CHAPTER 38

The Pathogenic Worms

The morphologic and physiologic characteristics of the parasitic worms were outlined in Chaps. 1 and 3. Three groups of worms (*helminths*) are parasites in man—the roundworms (*nematodes*), the flukes (*trematodes*), and the tapeworms (*cestodes*). Two helminthic diseases, trichinosis and pinworm infection, are common in all parts of this country. Several others—hookworm, strongyloidiasis, ascariasis, and dwarf tapeworm infection—are prevalent in the South. Three diseases caused by arthropods are also described in this chapter.

THE LIFE CYCLES OF THE HELMINTHS

Invasion of the human body by a worm parasite is very different from a bacterial or virus infection. In the human body the virus or bacterium multiplies almost indefinitely, but generally speaking, worm parasites do not multiply in the human host. Each one passes through some stage in the human host; then its other stages must take place in one or more other animal hosts or in soil or water. Some parasitologists do not speak of helminthic infections but of *infestations*. Many persons harbor so few worm parasites that their infestations are subclinical and symptomless. Not until repeated exposure has resulted in massive infestation does the illness become apparent.

The life cycles of the parasitic worms are so varied that it is impossible to give a single example that will serve for all. Five basic cycles are discussed here and illustrated by diagrams.

1. The simplest type is illustrated in Fig. 38·1. The adult pinworms in the human intestine produce ova which are discharged at the anus. The ova contaminate clothing and bedding and may even survive in dust for some time. Eventually the ovum may be ingested by another human and develop into a new adult in the intestine. Life cycles of the other intestinal roundworms are similar but are complicated by migration of the larval forms through various tissues and the development of larval forms in soil or water.

2. The life cycle of the trichina worm involves *alternate hosts*. This nematode can pass through the same stages in a human, a pig, or a rat. In any one of these animals the adults develop in the intestine. The larvae migrate to muscle tissue, where they encyst. If the muscle tissue is ingested by another of these animals, the encysted larva excysts and becomes a mature adult. (Fig. 38·2.)

3. The filariae and related nematodes that live in the tissues produce well-developed young in the blood or tissues. These larval forms are ingested by bloodsucking insect vectors. The larvae continue to develop in the insect intestine and then migrate to the mouth parts, where they are ready to invade the next human that is bitten. (Fig. 38·3.)

4. The flukes have the most amazing life cycles of all. The adult flukes

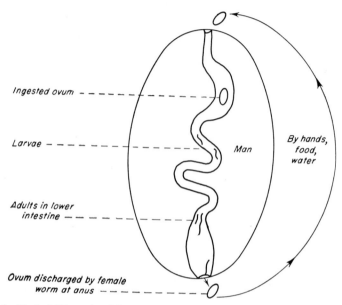

FIG. 38·1 Typical life cycle of intestinal roundworm (*Enterobius vermicularis*). Note that no alternate or intermediate host or insect vector is involved.

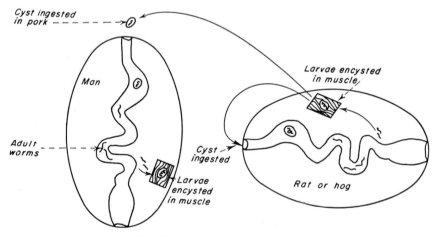

FIG. 38·2 Life cycle of trichina.

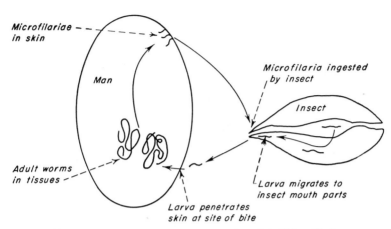

Fig. 38·3   Life cycle of insect-borne tissue-inhabiting filariae.

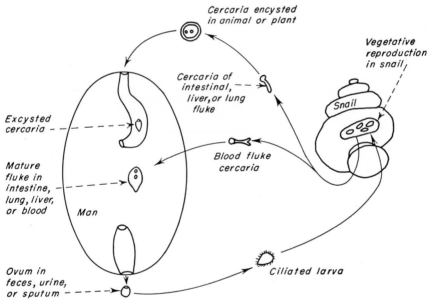

Fig. 38·4   Life cycle of flukes. Note that blood fluke larvae penetrate skin; other fluke larvae encyst on or in objects used for food by man.

develop in the body of man or certain alternate hosts. Ova are discharged in various ways, and motile larval forms hatch from them when they reach water. These motile forms must find and penetrate a suitable species of snail. In the snail they undergo further development for several weeks. New motile forms are produced and liberated from the snail. These either penetrate the skin of man to infect him or encyst on fish, crabs, or water plants which are ingested by man. (Fig. 38·4.)

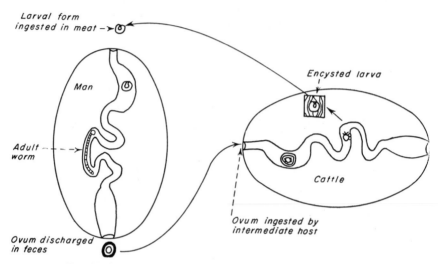

FIG. 38·5   Life cycle of a typical tapeworm (*Taenia saginata*).

5. Each tapeworm has a *definitive host,* the animal in which the adult cestode lives and produces its ova, and an *intermediate host,* another animal in which certain immature stages are passed. In most of the tapeworm diseases of man, man is the definitive host. An adult worm in the human intestine produces thousands of ova, which are discharged in the feces. They are ingested by some other animal. In the intestine of this intermediate host the ovum hatches into a larval form, which invades and encysts in the tissues. When this flesh is eaten by man, the larvae reach maturity in his intestinal tract. (Fig. 38·5.)

THE CONTROL AND TREATMENT OF HELMINTHIC DISEASES

An exact knowledge of each worm parasite and its life cycle is necessary for its adequate control. When the parasites are spread by feces, the most important measure is proper disposal of human excreta. If intermediate or alternate hosts are valuable animals, they must be protected from infection.

If they are valueless animals, such as rats, they are destroyed. Diseases spread by insect vectors are controlled by destruction of the insects. The detection of both clinical and subclinical cases and their effective treatment remove the sources of infection from the community.

Immunity to helminthic diseases never becomes absolute. Antibodies are produced in the infected person but do not confer complete immunity. Active and passive immunization are not effective in these diseases. Treatment is by chemotherapy. Accurate diagnosis must precede the choice of drugs, since they are somewhat specific in their action. Many of the drugs are quite toxic to human tissues and must be used with great care. The old-fashioned term *vermifuge* (literally worm chaser) is used for those that are given by mouth to eliminate intestinal parasites. The drugs used against the tissue-invading parasites are often given parenterally.

LABORATORY DIAGNOSIS OF HELMINTHIC DISEASES

These animal forms are always distinguishable by their morphologic characteristics, and laboratory diagnosis is almost invariably by direct microscopic examination. The commonest of all tests is the examination of fecal smears for the worm ova. Each species of intestinal worm produces a characteristic type of ovum, and these are readily recognized by experienced technicians (Fig. 38·6). Feces may also be examined for the larval or adult stages of worms. In worm infestations involving other parts of the body, urine, blood, sputum, and even bits of excised tissue (*biopsy specimens*) may be examined. In a few of these diseases, skin tests employing extracts of the parasites may give positive reactions in infected individuals.

THE PARASITIC ROUNDWORMS: INTESTINAL TYPES

The adult stages of several roundworms parasitize the intestinal tract of man. These nematodes all have relatively simple life cycles of the type illustrated in Fig. 38·1.

Ancylostoma duodenale and Necator americanus, the Causes of Hookworm Disease. Hookworm is prevalent in practically all tropical and semitropical parts of the world, including the southern United States. *Ancylostoma duodenale,* the Old World hookworm, is rare in the Western hemisphere. *Necator americanus,* the New World or American hookworm, is common in the Western hemisphere, in Asia, and in the Pacific regions. The two infestations may be called *ancylostomiasis* and *necatoriasis,* respectively. Since the two species and the resulting infections are very similar, no attempt is made to distinguish them further in this discussion.

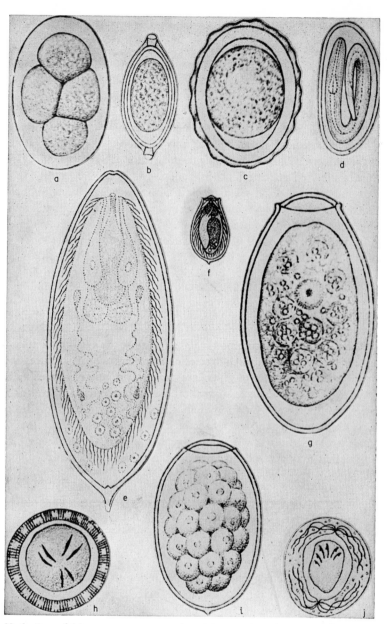

Fig. 38·6 Ova of important worm parasites. × approximately 800. Top row—round-worms. (*a*) *Ancylostoma duodenale;* (*b*) *Trichuris trichiura;* (*c*) *Ascaris lumbricoides;* (*d*) *Enterobius vermicularis.* Middle row—flukes. (*e*) *Schistosoma haematobium;* (*f*) *Clonorchis sinensis;* (*g*) *Paragonimus westermani.* Bottom row—tapeworms. (*h*) *Taenia solium;* (*i*) *Diphyllobothrium latum;* (*j*) *Hymenolepis nana. (From Belding, "Textbook of Clinical Parasitology," Appleton-Century-Crofts.*)

The Parasite and Its Life Cycle. Each hookworm is a little round worm about one-half the size of an "invisible" hairpin (Fig. 38·7). It has a toothed mouth by which it attaches itself to the lining of the small intestine. The female produces microscopic ova, which leave the body in the fecal material. If the ovum reaches warm, moist soil it develops within a day or two into a larval form. The larva is capable of penetrating human skin, particularly the soft skin between the toes of barefoot persons. As it bores its way through, it causes a local irritation called "ground itch." The larva is carried by the blood stream to the lungs. There it penetrates the alveolar wall into the air spaces and travels up the bronchi and trachea to the pharynx, whence it is swallowed and passes down the esophagus through the stomach to the intestine. Infection from larvae ingested with water or food is possible but much less common. Figure 38·7 illustrates very graphically the epidemiology of hookworm.

Hookworm Infection and Hookworm Disease. Each hookworm may suck 0.5 ml. or more of blood per day from its host. If only a few worms are present, the infection may be entirely symptomless. When one to two hundred or more worms are present, symptoms of severe anemia and intoxication develop and the person can be said to have hookworm disease. The effects are most severe in growing children, who are retarded mentally and physically, and in persons who also have vitamin deficiencies or concurrent infections. Heavy infestations occur only in those who are repeatedly exposed over considerable periods, since each adult worm in the intestines must enter the body as an individual larval form.

Laboratory Diagnosis. The typical ova are found by microscopic examination of feces. Often some method of preliminary treatment by separating the relatively light ova from the heavier masses of fecal material is used. The *Stoll count* is a quantitative method, a microscopic count of the number of ova in a measured amount of feces. The number of ova indicates roughly the number of worms harbored by the individual.

Treatment. Many drugs are effective in the chemotherapy of hookworm disease, but most of them are toxic. A single dose of the relatively nontoxic tetrachlorethylene, preceded and followed by a saline purge, reduces the infestation by 90 per cent.

Creeping Eruption. Several species of hookworm that normally parasitize dogs and cats may cause skin irritation called *creeping eruption* in human beings. The animal hosts pollute the soil of beaches, children's sand piles, and similar places. The hookworm larvae enter the skin but are unable to penetrate beyond the lower layers of the epidermis. A red papule forms at the site of entrance, and from it a twisting "burrow" leads for several inches immediately under the outer layer of epidermis. The itching is intense. This infection is endemic in the southern United States.

FIG. 38·7 Epidemiology of hookworm disease. (*From Mackie, Hunter, and Worth, "Manual of Tropical Medicine," Saunders.*)

Strongyloides stercoralis, the Cause of Strongyloidiasis. The worm *Strongyloides stercoralis* and the disease strongyloidiasis are very similar to hookworm and hookworm infestation. Motile larvae rather than ova are discharged by the female worm and found in human feces, and the worms are able to multiply in the soil as well as in the host's intestine. Otherwise the life cycle is like that of the hookworms.

Trichuris trichiura, the Cause of Trichuriasis. This parasite is popularly known as the *whipworm* because of its shape. It is slightly larger than the hookworm. The ova, which are discharged in enormous numbers in the feces, require several weeks for development in the soil. Then they are ready to reinfect human beings. They enter through the mouth in contaminated food and water. Heavy infestations in young children produce relatively mild symptoms. In adults most infestations are symptomless.

Ascaris lumbricoides, the Cause of Ascariasis. Ascaris is the largest roundworm, 8 to 12 inches in length. Ova are produced in the intestine. They pass several weeks in the soil before they reach an infective larval stage. When swallowed, the larvae penetrate the intestinal wall and are carried through the blood stream to the lungs. They penetrate the alveoli, work their way up the air passages to the epiglottis, and then are reswallowed. When they again reach the intestine they grow into adult worms. The serious symptoms of ascaris infection are due to the wanderings of the larval forms rather than to the adult worms. When a considerable number of larvae are ingested at one time, high fever and pneumonitis develop. Fatal bacterial pneumonia may follow. Sometimes larvae pass through the lungs to the general circulation and reach the brain, spinal cord, or kidneys, causing serious local lesions.

Enterobius vermicularis, the Cause of Enterobiasis. The popular names *pinworm* and *seat worm* are given to these nematodes. They are about the size of hookworms (Fig. 38·8). The adults live in the ileum. The females migrate through the anus and deposit thousands of ova on the skin of the perianal region. The ova do not leave in the feces. Pinworm ova are immediately infective but are very resistant to drying and may remain alive in dust and dirt for many days. The ingested ova develop into larvae and then into adults entirely within the intestine. The chief symptoms of pinworm infestation are due to the intense *pruritus* (itching) around the anal region. This results in restlessness and insomnia in children and sometimes in skin infections of the region due to constant scratching. Laboratory diagnosis is done by the microscopic examination of anal swabs. Pinworm infestation in children is extremely common but often unsuspected.

The Control of the Intestinal Nematodes. Infections with these five worms are primarily dooryard and household infections. The cartoonist who drew Fig. 38·8 gives a graphic and realistically unpleasant picture of home conditions where these diseases flourish. The principal control methods are

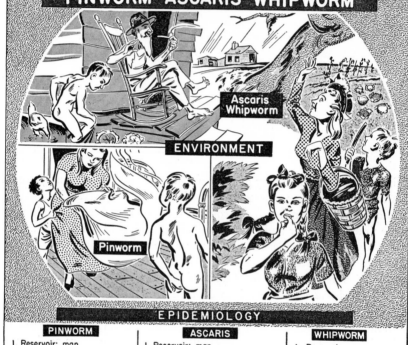

Fig. 38·8　Epidemiology of pinworm, whipworm, and ascaris infections. (*From Mackie, Hunter, and Worth, "Manual of Tropical Medicine," Saunders.*)

eradication of the infection in those who are the sources of the parasites, provision of sanitary privies, and training of people in sanitary personal habits.

THE PARASITIC ROUNDWORMS: TISSUE-INHABITING TYPES

One tissue-inhabiting nematode, *Trichinella spiralis,* has a unique life cycle (Fig. 38·2). The others are insect-borne (Fig. 38·3).

Trichinella spiralis, the Cause of Trichinosis. Trichinosis is the only serious worm infestation that is common in all parts of the United States.

The Parasite and Its Life Cycle. Adult trichina worms are just barely visible to the naked eye. They live in the duodenum. The female worm penetrates the intestinal wall and deposits tiny larvae in the mucosa. These larvae are carried by the blood stream to all parts of the body. Those that reach striated muscle tissue grow and become surrounded with capsules. The resulting cysts are gradually calcified, but the larvae inside them remain alive for months. No further development of the larvae is possible unless the muscle tissue is ingested by some animal host of trichina. When that happens, the larvae are released in the intestine by the digestion of the surrounding muscle and capsule. They then mature and the cycle begins again. It is important to note that although both adults and larvae develop in a single animal, each trichina must pass its larval stages in one host animal and its adult life in another.

Trichinella spiralis can parasitize many flesh-eating animals. Hogs and rats are the most important as sources of infection for man (Fig. 38·9). Both hogs and rats feed on garbage and other refuse that may contain infected hog flesh. Man acquires the infection when he eats imperfectly cooked pork and pork products.

Diagnosis and Treatment of Trichinosis. Trichinosis occurs sporadically in small epidemics. The victims are usually members of a family group who have eaten undercooked pork from a home-slaughtered animal. The severity of the attack depends on the number of living larval forms consumed. Intestinal discomfort due to the invasion of the mucosa by the female trichinae is followed by fever as the larvae invade the blood stream and then by rheumatic pains as they encyst in muscle tissue. Death results from bronchopneumonia or heart failure.

Diagnosis of trichinosis in the laboratory is difficult because at no time do the parasites leave the host's body. Fecal examination is useless. Bits of tissue from arm or leg muscle may be excised and examined under the microscope. The muscle may be digested by enzyme action and the liberated larvae found in the sediment. The same techniques are used to demonstrate the presence of the parasite in meat (Fig. 38·10). A positive skin reaction to

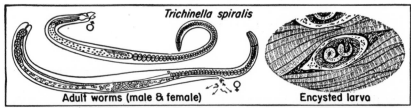

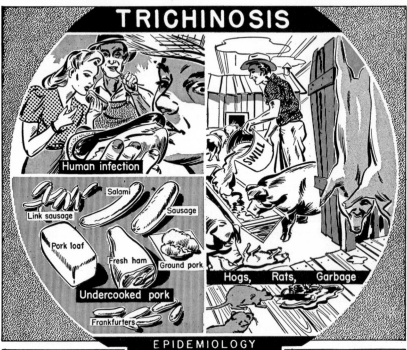

Fɪɢ. 38·9 Epidemiology of trichinosis. (*From Mackie, Hunter, and Worth, "Manual of Tropical Medicine," Saunders.*)

an antigen prepared from dried powdered trichinae develops in the later stages of the infection and persists for several years. Clinical diagnosis of trichinosis is very difficult because the disease has no clear-cut syndrome but resembles a variety of other diseases. Most mild cases go undiagnosed.

No specific drug or serum has been discovered that is useful in the treatment of this disease.

Control of Trichinosis. All effective measures against trichinosis are directed at elimination of the disease in hogs and destruction of the parasite in infected meat. Public health laws should require the cooking of all garbage

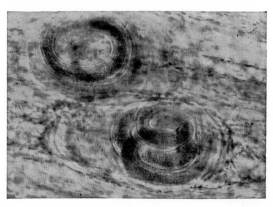

FIG. 38·10 Trichina larvae encysted in striated muscle. ×100. (*Ward's Natural Science Establishment, Inc.*)

fed to hogs. All pork and pork products should be held in cold storage for a period long enough to ensure the death of the larvae. All pork and pork products should be thoroughly cooked before serving. Government inspection of meat cannot protect the public from this disease, for it is impossible to detect milder forms of the infection in the routine examination at slaughterhouses.

Wuchereria bancrofti and Wuchereria malayi, the Causes of Filariasis. These filaria worms cause an acute inflammatory reaction, which often is most marked in the male reproductive organs. In some cases in which allergic reactions are aggravated by reinfections, extraordinary permanent swelling of legs, scrotum, or breasts develops. This condition is known as *elephantiasis.*

The life cycle of the filariae is shown in Fig. 38·3. The adult female produces larval forms known as *microfilariae* (Fig. 38·11). They are present in the peripheral blood and may be ingested by and develop in several genera of mosquitoes. After about two weeks in the mosquito they are infective and migrate to the mouth parts of the insect to wait there until she bites another human being.

Bancroft's type of filariasis originated in Africa and is still common there. It was imported to the New World with the African slaves. The Malayan type occurs only in the islands of the South Pacific. It was an important and troublesome cause of disability among our troops in that area during the Second World War.

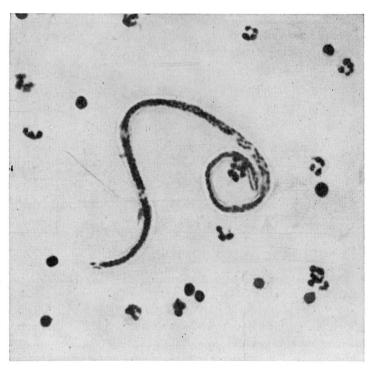

FIG. 38·11   Microfilaria in a thick blood smear. ×125. The small objects are nuclei of leukocytes. (*Armed Forces Institute of Pathology print 78176.*)

Other Tissue-inhabiting Nematodes. *Onchocerca volvulus, the Cause of Onchocerciasis.* The microfilariae of this worm are spread by black flies. The adult worms live in the subcutaneous tissue and cause the development of nodules, particularly in the region of the face and neck. The most serious complication is blindness, which may result from infection in the orbit. This disease has spread from Africa to Guatemala and southern Mexico. Since the Pan-American highway passes through infected regions, there is a possibility that it may spread to our Southern states, where there are black flies to act as vectors.

Loa Loa, the Cause of African Eyeworm Disease. This disease is also called *loiasis.* It is spread by a fly.

Dracunculus medinensis. This worm is also known as the *guinea worm.* Its scientific name means "little dragon of Medina." The adult female migrates to the skin of the legs and discharges larvae when the part is in contact with water. The further development of the larvae depends on their ingestion by water arthropods known as *copepods.* After 10 days the copepod becomes infective, and the parasite reaches the human host when it is swallowed in drinking water.

THE PATHOGENIC FLUKES (TREMATODES)

The typical life cycle of the fluke has already been outlined (Fig. 38·4). The flukes are customarily divided into those that live in the blood, in the liver, in the intestine, and in the lungs. Human trematode diseases are

FIG. 38·12 Adult blood flukes. ×8. The anterior and posterior ends of the long female fluke are partially enfolded by the shorter and fatter male fluke. (*"Medichrome,"* *Clay-Adams Co., Inc., Dr. H. E. Meleney.*)

uncommon in the United States but are very important in other parts of the world. American farm animals, particularly sheep, suffer from fluke diseases, but these are not normally infectious for man.

Blood Flukes. *The Schistosomes.* Three species of blood flukes named *Schistosoma haematobium, Schistosoma mansoni,* and *Schistosoma japonicum* cause schistosomiasis in man. Chronic illness in millions of people in Africa and Asia is due to this disease. *S. mansoni* infection is endemic in the

Caribbean area and in northern South America. The adult worms are much narrower and more elongated than other flukes. During fertilization the female remains within the folds of the male worm (Fig. 38·12). When the ova are mature the female forces her way into the capillaries of the lower intestinal or bladder wall, where she discharges the ova. The passage of the ova through the tissues into the lumen of the intestine or into the bladder (in the case of *S. haematobium* only) causes the inflammatory reactions that produce the chief symptoms of the disease. After the larval forms have emerged from the snail host they do not encyst, as do the other flukes, but remain motile until they penetrate the skin of the new human host.

Swimmer's itch. This is a troublesome skin irritation acquired by persons bathing in warm shallow waters. It is due to the penetration of the skin by the larval forms of certain blood flukes that are natural parasites of birds and wild rodents. Since these larvae cannot survive in human tissue, the infection does not go beyond this brief skin inflammation.

Intestinal Flukes. *Fasciolopsis buski* is the most important intestinal fluke. The adult fluke, which contains both male and female reproductive systems, lives in the upper small intestine. The infection is acquired by eating un-cooked water plants such as water chestnuts on which the fluke has encysted.

Liver Flukes. The Oriental liver fluke, *Clonorchis sinensis,* causes a disease that is very prevalent throughout eastern Asia. The fluke lives in the bile passages (Fig. 38·13). The larval forms encyst on fresh-water fish. Man is

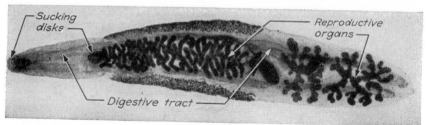

FIG. 38·13 *Clonorchis sinensis.* ×7. (*Ward's Natural Science Establishment, Inc.*)

infected when he eats such fish without adequate cooking. Both intestinal and liver fluke diseases are particularly severe in people who also suffer from inadequate nutrition.

Lung Flukes. Fluke infection of the lungs is caused by *Paragonimus westermani.* The adult fluke lives in the lung tissue. The ova may be coughed out in sputum or discharged in the feces if the sputum is swallowed. When the larval forms leave the snail they invade the tissues of crayfish and fresh-water crabs. Humans become infected when they eat these infected crustaceans raw. The larval forms pass from the intestine into the abdominal cavity, through the diaphragm to the thoracic cavity, and then into the lung tissue. Typical cases suffer from a chronic bronchitis. Parasites that wander from their usual path may cause lesions in the brain.

Control and Treatment of Fluke Diseases. The most practical measure for the control of intestinal, liver, and lung infestations by flukes is the proper cooking of the foods involved. Sanitary disposal of sewage and elimination of snail hosts are also effective but seldom attainable in the backward regions where these diseases flourish. Specific chemotherapy is the only effective method of treatment.

THE TAPEWORMS (CESTODES)

Figure 38·5 illustrates the typical life cycle of the tapeworms. Figure 38·14 shows the principal parts of the three large tapeworms. Figure 1·1, page 6, shows a diagram of a complete cestode.

Taenia solium and Taenia saginata, the Causes of Large Tapeworm Infection. *Taenia solium* is also known as the pork tapeworm, and *Taenia saginata* as the beef tapeworm, since these animals are the parasites' usual intermediate

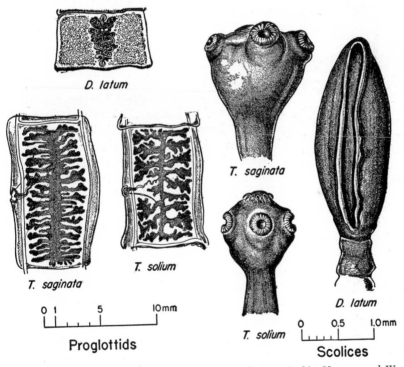

Fig. 38·14 Scolices and proglottids of tapeworms. (*From Mackie, Hunter, and Worth, "Manual of Tropical Medicine," Saunders.*)

hosts. They are often 10 to 20 feet in length. A single taenia is sufficient to cause toxic and nutritional symptoms.

Infection with these cestodes is uncommon in the United States, since cattle and hogs for the American market are generally raised on land uncontaminated by human feces. The government meat inspection eliminates any infected meat that reaches slaughterhouses.

FIG. 38·15   Dwarf tapeworm attached to the intestinal mucosa. ×30. (*Armed Forces Institute of Pathology* print *81770.*)

Diphyllobothrium latum, the Cause of Broad Tapeworm Infection. This is also a giant-sized tapeworm. Each *proglottid* (segment) is much broader than it is long (Fig. 38·14). Dogs, cats, and bears as well as man are definitive hosts of these worms. The ova must reach water. There ciliated embryos are released and ingested by the first intermediate host, a copepod. In these water arthropods the parasite develops for 2 to 3 weeks. Then if the copepod is swallowed by a fish the parasite continues its development in the muscle tissue of the fish. If the fish is eaten in a raw or undercooked state by man or one of the other definitive hosts, the parasite develops into the adult tapeworm.

Broad tapeworm infection is common in northern Europe. Immigrants from that region brought the disease to the United States. Cases are common in Michigan and Minnesota, where the fresh-water pike are heavily infested. Obviously these fish should never be eaten unless thoroughly cooked.

Hymenolepis nana, the Cause of Dwarf Tapeworm Infection. This is the commonest of all human tapeworms in the United States (Fig. 38·15). It is found in about one per cent of all persons in the South and is even more frequent in children. Each worm is so small that it appears like a thin strand of mucus averaging an inch or so in length, but infected individuals may harbor dozens of worms. This multiple infestation with *Hymenolepis* is the result of the parasite's unusual life cycle. This tapeworm does not require an intermediate host. Ova of the adult worm may remain in the intestine, develop into larval form in the intestinal villi, and then break out again into the intestine to become mature worms. In other words, this cestode can actually reproduce indefinitely in one host. Spread of this infection is probably direct from person to person by fecal contamination of food and hands. Some parasitologists believe that the infection can also be acquired from mice and rats.

Echinococcus granulosus, the Cause of Hydatid Cyst. The adult stage of this worm lives in the intestine of dogs. Ova in the dog's feces are ingested by the intermediate hosts, which are usually sheep, hogs, or cattle. In these animals the larval stage develops in the liver. The parasite again reaches the dog when the latter feeds on killed or slaughtered animals that are infected. Occasionally a human being may contaminate his hands or food with dog feces and so ingest the ova. The larval form penetrates the liver or other organs and develops into a lesion known as a *hydatid cyst.* This is a bladder-like growth which may continue to enlarge for years. The cyst may cause symptoms because of pressure on surrounding tissues. It may spread, much like a malignant tumor. Human infection is most common in sheep-raising countries.

ARTHROPODS THAT INFEST MAN

Several arthropods are actual parasites of man causing specific diseases.

Sarcoptes scabiei, the Cause of Scabies. The cause of scabies is an eight-legged mite, *Sarcoptes scabiei* (Fig. 38·16), which passes its whole existence in tiny burrows in human skin. The disease is commonly called *the itch.* Initial infestation causes little irritation. Later the person becomes hypersensitive to the parasite and more severe reactions develop. Scratching of the lesions may result in secondary bacterial infection. Transfer is always by close personal contact rather than by clothing or bedding. Since lesions on the hands are common, handshaking and hand holding are often the mode of spread. Two chemicals, sulfur and benzyl benzoate, in the form of ointments, are effective in destroying the mite. Although mange of animals is caused by closely related species, man does not contract the disease from them.

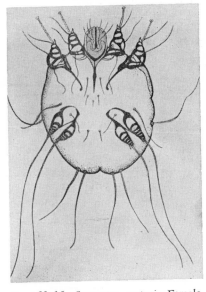

Fig. 38·16 *Sarcoptes scabiei.* Female, ventral view. ×100. (*From Belding, "Textbook of Clinical Parasitology," Appleton-Century-Crofts.*)

Lice, the Causes of Pediculosis. Three types of lice (sing. louse) cause three types of *pediculosis* (lousiness). These types are the body louse (*Pediculus humanus* var. *corporis*), the head louse (*Pediculus humanus* var. *capitis*), and the pubic or crab louse (*Phthirus pubis*). The eggs (nits) and adults of the body louse are found in the clothing; those of the head louse and crab louse are found in the hair of the head and pubis, respectively. Sensitization plays an important part in the development of severe itching. Secondary infection after scratching is common. Pediculosis is common wherever cleanliness is impossible or neglected. The lice are spread by personal contact and by contact with clothing, headgear, and bedding. Pediculosis of the scalp of school children is the most common form of the infestation in this country. Body lice are vectors of bacterial and rickettsial disease. The body louse is pictured in Fig. 16·2, page 198.

Flies, the Causes of Myiases. Immature forms of some flies are obligate parasites of the skin of animals and man. The most common of these are the botflies. Others develop in putrid material anywhere and may be attracted to wounds by purulent discharges or to the eyes, vagina, or nasal passages. The larvae of screwworm flies and flesh flies develop in these sites. Larvae of other flies, including the common housefly, may reach the stomach in ingested food. Still others invade the anal and urethral openings. All these infestations are *myiases* (sing. *myiasis*). Many myiases are common in domestic animals. Control of the infestations in host animals, all measures of insect eradication, and cleanliness are the chief factors in their prevention.

STUDY SUGGESTIONS

Review the discussions of worms in Chaps. 1 and 3 and do not neglect the diagrams.

Your instructor may wish to consider parts of this chapter as reference material. She will tell you which portions may be omitted from concentrated study at this time.

If you follow the study procedure outlined below, it will help you to clarify and memorize the details about these parasites.

1. Read the whole chapter and examine the diagrams and other plates. Reread and study pages 549 to 552, which give you a general picture of this group of organisms.

2. Study each of the groups of organisms indicated in the table below.

Group	Type	Typical organism	Other similar organisms
1	Intestinal nematode (Fig. 38·1)	Hookworm (p. 553)	Strongyloides, whipworm, ascaris, pinworm
2	Trichina (Fig. 38·2)	Trichina (p. 559)	None
3	Filaria (Fig. 38·3)	Wuchereria (p. 561)	Onchocerca, loa, dracunculus
4	Fluke (Fig. 38·4)	Clonorchis (p. 564)	All other flukes
5	Tapeworm (Fig. 38·5)	Taenia (p. 565)	All other tapeworms

a. Study the life-cycle diagram.

b. Study the typical organism by learning the facts in the text and studying the illustrations.

c. Study the other organisms belonging to the group, noting particularly the ways in which they differ from the typical organism.

Why should dogs and cats be kept out of rooms and sand piles where small children play?

Name two American foods that should always be thoroughly cooked in order to prevent the spread of two different worm parasites.

Why should hogs and cattle on farms be kept away from outdoor privies? What precautions should be taken about feed for pigs?

What observations by the nurse might aid in detecting pinworm infections? When a case of pinworm is recognized on the wards, what precautions must be taken?

What helminthic diseases did military authorities have in mind when they forbade our forces in certain areas to eat native foods? to bathe or wade in fresh-water ponds or rivers?

Are insects the cause or the vectors of myiasis, scabies, and pediculosis? Have you had any personal experience with these infestations?

SUGGESTED READING

General References (See also general references, page 547.)

CHAPMAN, M. L.: Have you met the parasite family? *Pub. Health Nursing* **44**:16 (1952).

FAUST, E. C.: "Human Helminthology." 3d ed., Lea & Febiger, Philadelphia, 1949.

Intestinal Nematodes

ANDREWS, J.: New methods of hookworm diagnosis, investigation, and control. *Am. J. Pub. Health* **32**:382 (1942).

BUMBALO, T. S., *et al.*: Pinworm infestation (enterobiasis) in children. *Am. J. Dis. Child.* **86**:592 (1953).

Trichinosis

GOULD, S. E.: Control of trichinosis by gamma irradiation of pork. *J.A.M.A.* **154**:653 (1954).

ROUECHÉ, B.: A Pig from Jersey, in "Eleven Blue Men." Little, Brown, Boston, 1954.

Filaria

AUGUSTINE, D. L.: Filariasis in tropical Asia. *J. Trop. Med. & Hyg.* **56**:75 (1953).

OTTO, G. F., and T. H. MAREN: Studies on chemotherapy of filariasis. *Am. J. Hyg.* **51**:353 (1950).

Schistosomes

CORT, W. W.: Studies on schistosome dermatitis. XI. *Am. J. Hyg.* **52:**251 (1950).
MAGATH, T. B., and D. B. MATHIESEN: Important factors in the epidemiology of schistosomiasis in Leyte. *Am. J. Hyg.* **43:**152 (1946).

Sarcoptes scabiei

CANNON, A. B., and M. E. McRAE: Treatment of scabies. *J.A.M.A.* **138:**557 (1948).

Lice

WEISS, M.: Who said lice? *Am. J. Nursing* **46:**225 (1946).

Appendix A

The Literature of Microbiology

No matter how carefully it is prepared, an elementary text such as this can cover only the minimum basic facts of its subject. For further information the teacher and the student must turn to the literature of microbiology and related subjects. This literature, as is inevitable in a growing science, is not well organized, and the inexperienced student often does not know how to proceed. The chapter bibliographies and this section of the appendix have been included in this text to make the task somewhat easier.

THE CHAPTER BIBLIOGRAPHIES

The references listed at the end of each chapter have been selected for one or more of the following reasons:

1. To present a more complete discussion of some subject than was possible in the chapter. (*Example:* reference at the end of the chapter on the rickettsiae to the symposium volume, *Rickettsial Diseases of Man.*)

2. To present recent and often controversial material. (*Example:* references to recent reports on the nature and mode of action of the newer antibiotics.)

3. To bring to the reader's attention articles of popular or professional interest relative to the subject matter. (*Example:* articles on the protection of hospital personnel from tuberculosis infection.)

Reference to general texts have usually been omitted from the chapter bibliographies to save space and avoid constant repetition of titles. But it is assumed that the texts listed below will be consulted in addition to the chapter references.

BOOKS FOR MICROBIOLOGY

The books listed below include those that the author has found most directly and constantly useful for nursing microbiology. Many books on special phases of microbiology and related subjects are listed in the chapter bibliographies.

Elementary Texts (of college and nursing school level)

Buchanan, R. E., and E. D. Buchanan: "Bacteriology." 5th ed., Macmillan, New York, 1951.

Burdon, K. L.: "Textbook of Microbiology." 3d ed., Macmillan, New York, 1947.

Clifton, C. E.: "Introduction to the Bacteria." McGraw-Hill, New York, 1950.

Frobisher, M., Jr.: "Fundamentals of Microbiology." 5th ed., Saunders, Philadelphia, 1953.

Grant, M. P.: "Microbiology and Human Progress." Rinehart, New York, 1953.

Henrici, A. T. (rev. by E. J. Ordal): "The Biology of Bacteria." 3d ed., Heath, Boston, 1949.

Hilliard, C. M.: "Bacteriology and Its Applications." Rev. ed., Ginn, Boston, 1945.

Kelly, F. C., and K. E. Hite: "Microbiology." 2d ed., Appleton-Century-Crofts, New York, 1955.

Kreuger, W. W.: "Principles of Microbiology." Saunders, Philadelphia, 1953.

Morse, M. E., M. Frobisher, Jr., and L. Sommermeyer: "Microbiology for Nurses." 8th ed., Saunders, Philadelphia, 1951.

Salle, A. J.: "Fundamental Principles of Bacteriology." 4th ed., McGraw-Hill, New York, 1954.

Sarles, W. B., *et al.:* "Microbiology—General and Applied." Harper, New York, 1951.

Thomas, S., and T. H. Grainger: "Bacteria." Blakiston, New York, 1952.

Thompson, LaV. R.: "Introduction to Microorganisms," 3d ed., Saunders, Philadelphia, 1954.

Wedberg, S. E.: "Microbes and You." Macmillan, New York, 1954.

Advanced Texts (of graduate school and medical school level)

Belding, D. L.: "Textbook of Clinical Parasitology." 2d ed., Appleton-Century-Crofts, New York, 1952.

Burrows, W.: "Textbook of Microbiology." 16th ed., Saunders, Philadelphia, 1954.

Conant, N. F., *et al.:* "Manual of Clinical Mycology." 2d ed., Saunders, Philadelphia, 1954.

Dubos, R. J.: "Bacterial and Mycotic Infections of Man." 2d ed., Lippincott, Philadelphia, 1952.

Mackie, T. T., G. W. Hunter, and C. B. Worth: "Manual of Tropical Medicine." 2d ed., Saunders, Philadelphia, 1954.

RHODES, A. J., and C. E. VAN ROOYEN: "Textbook of Virology." 2d ed., Williams & Wilkins, Baltimore, 1954.

RIVERS, T. M.: "Viral and Rickettsial Infections of Man." 2d ed., Lippincott, Philadelphia, 1952.

SMITH, D. T., and N. F. CONANT: "Zinsser's Textbook of Bacteriology." 10th ed., Appleton-Century-Crofts, New York, 1952.

WILSON, G. S., and A. A. MILES: "Topley and Wilson's Principles of Bacteriology and Immunity." 3d ed., Williams & Wilkins, Baltimore, 1946.

Other Useful Books

ALEXOPOULOS, C. J.: "Introductory Mycology." Wiley, New York, 1952.

AMERICAN ACADEMY OF PEDIATRICS: "Report of the Committee on Immunization and Therapeutic Procedures for Acute Infectious Diseases." Evanston, 1955.*

AMERICAN ASSOCIATION FOR THE ADVANCEMENT OF SCIENCE: "Rickettsial Diseases of Man." Washington, D.C., 1948.

AMERICAN PUBLIC HEALTH ASSOCIATION: "The Control of Communicable Disease." 8th ed., New York, 1955.*

———: "Diagnostic Procedures and Reagents." 4th ed., New York, 1955.

———: "Diagnostic Procedures for Virus and Rickettsial Diseases." New York, 1948.

———: "Standard Methods for the Examination of Dairy Products." 10th ed., New York, 1954.

———: "Standard Methods for the Examination of Water and Sewage." 10th ed., New York, 1955.

AMERICAN STERILIZER COMPANY: "Principles and Methods of Sterilization." Erie, Pa., 1953.*

"Annual Review of Microbiology." Annual Reviews, Inc., Stanford (published yearly since 1947).

BREED, R. S., *et al.:* "Bergey's Manual of Determinative Bacteriology." 6th ed., Williams & Wilkins, Baltimore, 1948. Condensed version available from Biotech, Geneva, N.Y.

BURNET, F. M.: "Natural History of Infectious Disease." Cambridge, New York, 1953.

CHRISTENSEN, C. M.: "The Molds and Man." University of Minnesota Press, Minneapolis, 1951.

DIFCO LABORATORIES, INC.: "Difco Manual of Dehydrated Culture Media and Reagents." 9th ed., Detroit, 1953.

DUBOS, R. J.: "The Bacterial Cell." Harvard University Press, Cambridge, Mass., 1945.

* The cost of this booklet is low, and it is desirable for each student to have her own copy.

Hopkins, E. S., and F. B. Elder: "The Practice of Sanitation." Williams & Wilkins, Baltimore, 1951.

Jahn, T. L., and F. F. Jahn: "How To Know the Protozoa." Brown, Dubuque, 1949.

Knaysi, G.: "Elements of Bacterial Cytology." 2d ed., Comstock, Ithaca, N.Y., 1951.

Lammana, C., and M. F. Mallette: "Basic Bacteriology." Williams & Wilkins, Baltimore, 1953.

Maxcy, K. F.: "Rosenau's Preventive Medicine and Hygiene." 7th ed., Appleton-Century-Crofts, New York, 1951.

McCulloch, E. C.: "Disinfection and Sterilization." 2d ed., Lea & Febiger, Philadelphia, 1945.

Raffel, S.: "Immunity." Appleton-Century-Crofts, New York, 1953.

Rahn, O.: "Microbes of Merit." Ronald, New York, 1945.

Skinner, C. E., C. W. Emmons, and H. M. Tsuchiya: "Henrici's Molds, Yeasts, and Actinomycetes." 3d ed., Wiley, New York, 1947.

Society of American Bacteriologists: "Manual of Methods for the Pure Culture Study of Bacteria." Biotech, Geneva, N.Y., various dates.

Stitt, E. H., *et al.:* "Practical Bacteriology, Hematology, and Parasitology." 10th ed., rev., Blakiston, New York, 1952.

Underwood, A. B., and J. J. Perkins: "Textbook of Sterilization." 2d ed., Charles C Thomas, Springfield, Ill., 1955.

Wadsworth, A. B.: "Standard Methods." 3d ed., Williams & Wilkins, Baltimore, 1947.

Walter, C. W.: "Aseptic Treatment of Wounds." Macmillan, New York, 1948.

JOURNALS FOR MICROBIOLOGY

Scientific journals publish the material from which scientific books are written. No book on microbiology contains the latest information, for it is commonly a year and sometimes longer from the time the author finishes writing a book until it reaches the reader. So every teacher of microbiology and every nurse must read the current journals to keep up to date.

The abbreviations given on the right are those used in the *Quarterly Cumulative Index Medicus*. They are used in the chapter bibliographies in this text.

Journals Most Essential in Microbiology

American Journal of Hygiene	*Am. J. Hyg.*
American Journal of Nursing	*Am. J. Nursing*
American Journal of Public Health	*Am. J. Pub. Health*
Bacteriological Reviews	*Bact. Rev.*
Journal of the American Medical Association	*J.A.M.A.*

Journal of Bacteriology	*J. Bact.*
Journal of Experimental Medicine	*J. Exper. Med.*
Journal of Infectious Disease	*J. Infect. Dis.*

Abstract and Bibliographic Journals

Biological Abstracts—Section C	
Bulletin of Hygiene	*Bull. Hyg.*
Quarterly Cumulative Index Medicus	
Tropical Disease Bulletin	*Tr. Dis. Bull.*

Other Useful Journals

Bulletin of the World Health Organization	*Bull. WHO*
Canadian Journal of Public Health	*Canad. J. Pub. Health*
Hygeia	*Hygeia*
Lancet	*Lancet*
Modern Hospital	*Mod. Hosp.*
New England Journal of Medicine	*New England J. Med.*
Physiological Reviews	*Physiol. Rev.*
Public Health Reports	*Pub. Health Rep.*
Virology	*Virol.*

HOW TO USE THE LITERATURE

Suppose you want to find out more about some particular subject—for teaching purposes, for a class assignment, or for your own information. Here are the steps that will lead you most quickly to what you need to know. You may pursue them relentlessly until you have exhaustive information on the subject; or if your time or interest is limited, you may be satisfied with a limited review of the subject.

1. Read what your text and one or more other elementary texts (page 572) have to say on the subject. Consult one or more advanced texts, preferably those of the most recent date. Remember that all good texts have subject indexes. The chapters may have bibliographies which will yield useful suggestions for further reading.

2. Consult the chapter bibliographies in this text. If there is an authoritative monograph or review article listed on the subject, read it. Then read the other references listed. The volumes of the *Annual Review of Microbiology* (see page 573) should also be checked.

3. Consult the index numbers of appropriate journals for the last 2 years (see list of journals on page 574). List and read the articles that are appropriate to your topic. Consult the tables of contents of the issues of these magazines for the current year (i.e., since the latest index issue).

4. Consult the last 2 years of *Biological Abstracts—Section C* or the *Bulletin of Hygiene*. List and read the abstracts that pertain to your subject. If the article seems important to you, and if it is available and in a language that you can read, you may wish to study the original. In many cases the abstract will provide all the material you need.

5. Rearrange your notes and your knowledge under suitable headings. Digest the information you have collected and make it part of your working knowledge.

Appendix B

Classification of Medically Important Schizomycetes

All data in the following tables are from *Bergey's Manual of Determinative Bacteriology,* 6th edition, 1948.

All medically important groups and species of the class *Schizomycetes* are included. In order to simplify the classification all family and tribe designations are omitted. Instead the important orders and suborders are divided into groups. The classifications of the members of the tentative orders, *Rickettsiales* and *Virales,* are also included.

The numbers in parentheses immediately following the names of orders, suborders, and genera refer to the pages on which these forms are described in the 6th edition of *Bergey's Manual.*

SECTION 1

Classification of Bacteria—Class Schizomycetes

Orders and suborders	Groups	Genera	Important species
Order I. *Eubacteriales* (66)—rigid single cells, not acid-fast, not filamentous or branching Suborder I. *Eubacterineae* (67)—no photosynthetic pigment, no free sulfur, not attached by stalk	Group 1—autotrophic bacteria, can grow in inorganic media	Genus *Nitrosomonas* (70)—oxidize ammonia to nitrite	
		Genus *Nitrobacter* (74)—oxidize nitrite to nitrate	
		Genus *Thiobacillus* (78)—oxidize sulfur and sulfur compounds	
	Group 2—rods, gram-negative, free-living or plant pathogens	Genus *Azotobacter* (219)—large rods and cocci that fix free nitrogen while growing in the soil	
		Genus *Rhizobium* (223)—small rods that fix free nitrogen while growing in root nodules of legumes	
		Genus *Alcaligenes* (412)—no pigment, no acid from carbohydrates	
		Genus *Achromobacter* (417)—no pigment, produce acid from carbohydrates	

	Genus *Pseudomonas* (82)—soluble blue-green or yellow-green pigment	*Pseudomonas aeruginosa*—the organism of blue-green pus
	Genus *Flavobacterium* (427)—nonsoluble yellow pigment	
	Genus *Chromobacterium* (231)—nonsoluble violet pigment	
	Genus *Serratia* (479)—nonsoluble red pigment	*Serratia marcescens*—used as "tracer" organism in experiments
	Genus *Xanthomonas* (150)—plant pathogen, yellow pigment	
	Genus *Erwinia* (463)—plant pathogen, ferments many sugars	
	Genus *Acetobacter* (179)—the vinegar bacteria, oxidize alcohol to acetic acid	
Group 3—rods, gram-negative, usually motile, usually parasites of man or animals, not excessively small	Genus *Proteus* (486)—often free-living, utilize urea, spreading colonies on agar	*Proteus vulgaris*—may cause infant dysentery; found in wounds; used in Weil-Felix test; *Proteus morganii*—may cause infant dysentery
	Genus *Aerobacter* (453)—usually free-living, active fermenter	*Aerobacter aerogenes*—nonfecal member of coliform group
	Genus *Escherichia* (444)—intestinal, active fermenter	*Escherichia coli*—common fecal organism, indicator organism in sanitary bacteriology; *Escherichia freundii*—coliform intermediate

SECTION 1 (Continued)

Classification of Bacteria—Class Schizomycetes

Orders and suborders	Groups	Genera	Important species
Order I. Eubacteriales (*Continued*) Suborder I. Eubacteriineae (*Continued*)	Group 3 (*Continued*)	Genus *Klebsiella* (457)—heavily capsulated	*Klebsiella pneumoniae*—cause of some cases of pneumonia
		Genus *Salmonella* (492)—usually pathogenic for man and animals; limited fermentation of sugars	*Salmonella typhosa*—the cause of typhoid fever *Salmonella paratyphi*—cause of paratyphoid A fever *Salmonella schottmuelleri*—cause of paratyphoid B fever *Salmonella enteritidis* *Salmonella typhimurium* } causes of salmonella *Salmonella choleraesuis* } food poisoning *Salmonella anatis*
		Genus *Shigella* (535)—pathogenic, non-motile, little fermentation of sugars	*Shigella dysenteriae*—cause of Shiga-type dysentery *Shigella paradysenteriae*—cause of Flexner-type dysentery *Shigella sonnei*—cause of Sonné-type dysentery
	Group 4—rods, very small, gram-negative, parasitic, usually pathogenic for man and animals	Genus *Pasteurella* (546)—bipolar granules, ferment carbohydrates	*Pasteurella pestis*—cause of plague *Pasteurella tularensis*—cause of tularemia
		Genus *Malleomyces* (554)—bipolar granules, may form chains, little fermentation of sugars	*Malleomyces mallei*—cause of glanders *Malleomyces pseudomallei*—cause of melioidosis

Genus *Brucella* (560)—no granules, do not ferment sugars	*Brucella melitensis*—cause of brucellosis from goats *Brucella abortus*—cause of brucellosis from cattle *Brucella suis*—cause of brucellosis from pigs and cattle
Genus *Bacteroides* (464)—anaerobic, rounded ends	
Genus *Fusobacterium* (581)—anaerobic, pointed ends	*Fusobacterium plauti-vincenti*—associated with fusospirochetal infections
Genus *Hemophilus* (584)—small single rods, require body fluids for growth	*Hemophilus influenzae*—cause of influenzal meningitis *Hemophilus pertussis*—cause of whooping cough *Hemophilus ducreyi*—cause of chancroid
Genus *Moraxella* (590)—small paired rods, require body fluids for growth, associated with eye infections	

Group 5—gram-positive, non-sporing rods

Genus *Lactobacillus* (349)—microaerophilic rods, produce acid from sugars, nonmotile	*Lactobacillus acidophilus*—bacterium of lactic acid milks *Lactobacillus bifidus*—chief organism of feces of infants
Genus *Corynebacterium* (381)—pleomorphic, granular, nonmotile rods	*Corynebacterium diphtheriae*—cause of diphtheria *Corynebacterium pseudodiphtheriticum*—the commonest diphtheroid *Corynebacterium acnes*—associated with acne

SECTION 1 (Continued)

Classification of Bacteria—Class Schizomycetes

Orders and suborders	Groups	Genera	Important species
Order I. *Eubacteriales* (*Continued*) Suborder I. *Eubacterineae* (*Continued*)	Group 5 (*Continued*)	Genus *Listeria* (408)—small motile rods	
		Genus *Erysipelothrix* (410)—microaerophilic, nonmotile rods, in filaments	*Erysipelothrix rhusiopathiae*—the cause of erysipeloid
	Group 6—sporing rods, gram-positive	Genus *Bacillus* (705)—aerobes and facultative anaerobes	*Bacillus anthracis*—cause of anthrax *Bacillus subtilis*—common contaminant
		Genus *Clostridium* (763)—obligate anaerobes or microaerophils	*Clostridium botulinum*—cause of botulism *Clostridium tetani*—cause of tetanus *Clostridium perfringens* *Clostridium septicum* } organisms of gas *Clostridium novyi* gangrene *Clostridium histolyticum* *Clostridium sporogenes*
	Group 7—spiral rods	Genus *Vibrio* (192)—short bent rods with single flagellum	*Vibrio comma*—cause of Asiatic cholera
		Genus *Spirillum* (212)—long spiral rods with more than one flagellum	*Spirillum minus*—cause of ratbite fever
	Group 8—spherical bacteria	Genus *Neisseria* (295)—cocci, gram-negative, paired, bean-shaped	*Neisseria meningitidis*—cause of epidemic meningitis *Neisseria gonorrhoeae*—cause of gonorrhea *Neisseria catarrhalis*—common inhabitant of upper respiratory tract *Neisseria flavescens*—occasional cause of meningitis

Genus *Diplococcus* (305)—gram-positive, paired, lance-shaped cocci	*Diplococcus pneumoniae*—cause of lobar pneumonia
Genus *Streptococcus* (312)—gram-positive cocci in chains	*Streptococcus pyogenes*—cause of most acute streptococcal infections of man *Streptococcus agalactiae*—cause of bovine mastitis *Streptococcus equi*—cause of strangles in horses *Streptococcus salivarious*—cause of less acute streptococcal infections of man *Streptococcus lactis*—lactic acid producer in milk and milk products *Streptococcus faecalis*—inhabitant of alimentary canal
Genus *Micrococcus* (235)—gram-positive cocci in plates or irregular bunches	*Micrococcus pyogenes* var. *albus* } causes of most staphylococcal infections *Micrococcus pyogenes* var. *aureus*
Genus *Gaffkya* (283)—gram-positive cocci in tetrads	*Gaffkya tetragena*—common inhabitant of upper respiratory tract
Genus *Sarcina* (285)—gram-positive cocci in regular packets	*Sarcina lutea*—common contaminant of cultures

Suborder II. *Caulobacteriineae* (828)—attached to substrate by stalks, not pathogenic

SECTION 1 (Continued)

Classification of Bacteria—Class Schizomycetes

Orders and suborders	Groups	Genera	Important species
Order I. *Eubacteriales (Continued)* Suborder III. *Rhodobacteriineae* (838)—have photosynthetic pigment, may have sulfur granules, not pathogenic			
Order II. *Actinomycetales* (875)—elongated nonmotile cells, often branching and mold-like; some are acid-fast		Genus *Mycobacterium* (876)—seldom branch, always acid-fast, irregular slender rods	*Mycobacterium tuberculosis* var. *hominis*—cause of tuberculosis in man *Mycobacterium tuberculosis* var. *bovis*—cause of tuberculosis in cattle and man *Mycobacterium leprae*—cause of leprosy
		Genus *Nocardia* (892)—aerobic, branching, segment to bacillary forms, sometimes acid-fast	*Nocardia asteroides*—cause of nocardiosis in man
		Genus *Actinomyces* (925)—anaerobic, branching, segment to bacillary forms, not acid-fast	*Actinomyces bovis*—cause of actinomycosis in cattle and man
		Genus *Streptomyces* (929)—branching mycelium with terminal chains of conidia, not acid-fast	*Streptomyces griseus*—source of streptomycin *Streptomyces aureofaciens*—source of chlorotetracycline *Streptomyces rimosus*—source of oxytetracycline
		Genus *Micromonospora* (978)—branched mycelium with single terminal spores, not acid-fast	

Order III. *Chlamydobacteriales* (981)—large, algaelike filaments, often sheathed, not pathogenic			
Order IV. *Myxobacteriales* (1005)—flexuous, elongated cells, move by gliding in secreted slime, not pathogenic			
Order V. *Spirochaetales* (1051)—flexuous, spiral, motile by flexion	Group 1—large spirals with definite protoplasmic structures, not pathogens		
	Group 2—small, tightly coiled spirals without visible protoplasmic structures	Genus *Borrelia* (1058)—stain readily with usual stains, loosely spiraled	*Borrelia recurrentis*—cause of louse-borne relapsing fever *Borrelia duttonii* } causes of tick-borne relapsing fever *Borrelia novyi* } *Borrelia vincentii*—associated with fusospirochetal infections
		Genus *Treponema* (1071)—anaerobic, stain with difficulty, small tight spirals	*Treponema pallidum*—cause of syphilis *Treponema pertenue*—cause of yaws *Treponema carateum*—cause of pinta
		Genus *Leptospira* (1076)—aerobic, finely coiled, one or both ends hooked, stain with difficulty	*Leptospira icterohaemorrhagiae*—cause of infectious jaundice *Leptospira canicola*—cause of spirochetosis of dogs and man

SECTION 2

Classification of Rickettsiae

Order	Groups	Genera	Important species
Order *Rickettsiales* (1083)—very small but not ultramicroscopic, rarely filtrable, obligate parasites	Group 1—typical rickettsiae, growth in or associated with cells, arthropod vectors	Genus *Rickettsia* (1084)—nonfiltrable	*Rickettsia prowazekii*—cause of classic typhus *Rickettsia typhi*—cause of murine typhus *Rickettsia rickettsii*—cause of American spotted fever *Rickettsia tsutsugamushi*—cause of tsutsugamushi fever *Rickettsia conorii*—cause of boutonneuse fever *Rickettsia akari*—cause of rickettsialpox
		Genus *Coxiella* (1092)—filtrable	*Coxiella burnetii*—cause of Q fever
	Group 2—growth in or associated with erythrocytes, arthropod vectors	Genus *Bartonella* (1100)—pathogenic for man	*Bartonella bacilliformis*—cause of Oroya fever and verruga peruana
	Group 3—intracellular growth with sheathed cell inclusions, no arthropod vectors	Genus *Chlamydozoon* (1114)—no growth in chick embryo	*Chlamydozoon trachomatis*—cause of trachoma *Chlamydozoon oculogenitale*—cause of inclusion blennorrhea and mild genitourinary infection
		Genus *Miyagawanella* (1115)—grow in chick embryo	*Miyagawanella lymphogranulomatis*—cause of lymphogranuloma venereum *Miyagawanella psittaci*—cause of psittacosis *Miyagawanella ornithosis*—cause of ornithosis *Miyagawanella pneumoniae*—cause of atypical pneumonia

SECTION 3

Classification of Viruses

Orders and suborders	Group	Genera	Important species
Order *Virales* (1128)—very small, filtrable, intracellular agents of disease			
Suborder I. *Phagineae*—parasitic on bacteria		Genus *Phagus*—all bacteriophages	
Suborder II. *Phytophagineae*—parasitic on higher plants			
Suborder III. *Zoophagineae*—parasitic on animals	Group 1—the pox group, characterized by skin pustules, dermatotropic	Genus *Borreliota* (1229)—typical pox disease group	*Borreliota variolae*—cause of smallpox and cowpox
		Genus *Briareus* (1233)—varicella group	*Briareus varicellae*—cause of chickenpox and herpes zoster; *Briareus morbillorum*—cause of measles
		Genus *Scelus* (1234)—herpes group	*Scelus recurrens*—cause of herpetic infections
		Genus *Hostis* (1239)—foot-and-mouth disease group	*Hostis pecoris*—cause of foot-and-mouth disease
		Genus *Molitor* (1241)—wart disease group	*Molitor verrucae*—cause of common warts; *Molitor hominis*—cause of molluscum contagiosum

SECTION 3 (Continued)

Classification of Viruses

Orders and suborders	Groups	Genera	Important species
Order *Virales* (1128) (*Continued*) Suborder III (*Continued*)	Group 2—the encephalitis group, neurotropic	Genus *Erro* (1248)—typical encephalitis group	*Erro japonicus*—cause of Japanese B encephalitis *Erro scelestus*—cause of St. Louis encephalitis *Erro equinus*—cause of equine encephalitides
		Genus *Legio* (1257)—poliomyelitis group	*Legio debilitans*—cause of infantile paralysis *Legio erebea*—cause of lymphocytic chorio-meningitis
		Genus *Formido* (1263)—rabies group	*Formido inexorabilis*—cause of rabies
	Group 3—yellow fever group, viscerotropic	Genus *Charon* (1265)—yellow fever group	*Charon evagatus*—cause of yellow fever
		Genus *Tarpeia* (1268)—influenza group	*Tarpeia alpha*—cause of type A influenza *Tarpeia beta*—cause of type B influenza *Tarpeia premens*—cause of common cold
	Group 4—mumps group, infections of salivary glands	Genus *Rabula* (1284)—salivary gland viruses	*Rabula inflans*—cause of mumps

Index

Figures in boldface refer to pages containing most important entries.